MW00426297

Concurrent Design of Products and Processes

Concurrent Design of Products and Processes

A Strategy for the Next Generation in Manufacturing

By

James L. Nevins and Daniel E. Whitney, *Editors*

and

Thomas L. De Fazio
Alexander C. Edsall
Richard E. Gustavson
Richard W. Metzinger

Charles Stark Draper Laboratory, Inc.

and

William A. Dvorak

Ingersoll Engineers

McGraw-Hill Publishing Company

New York St. Louis San Francisco Auckland Bogotá
Caracas Hamburg Lisbon London Madrid Mexico
Milan Montreal New Delhi Oklahoma City
Paris San Juan São Paulo Singapore
Sydney Tokyo Toronto

Library of Congress Cataloging-in-Publication Data

Concurrent design of products and processes : a strategy for the next generation in manufacturing / by James L. Nevins, Daniel E. Whitney, editors ; and Thomas L. De Fazio . . . [et al.].
p. cm.
Includes bibliographies and index.
ISBN 0-07-046341-7
1. Design, Industrial. 2. Production engineering. 3. Manufacturing processes. I. Nevins, James L. II. Whitney, Daniel E. III. De Fazio, Thomas L.
TS171.C655 1989
670.42—dc19 88-36451
CIP

1234567890 DOC/DOC 895432109

ISBN 0-07-046341-7

The editors for this book were Robert W. Hauserman and Nancy Young, the designer was Naomi Auerbach, and the production supervisor was Dianne L. Walber. This book was set in Century Schoolbook. It was composed by the McGraw-Hill Publishing Company Professional & Reference Division composition unit.

Printed and bound by R. R. Donnelley and Sons Company.

Contents

Preface

Motivation

During the last 15 to 30 years, the United States has lost its lead in manufacturing. This loss is expressed in declining trade balances and lower quality, but it has deeper roots. Manufacturing is often not considered to be a suitable intellectual activity in universities or a fruitful career path in industry. According to Skinner (1986), manufacturing is regarded by managers as a sort of dirty business that must be done so that the "real" activities of business, such as marketing and finance, will have meaning.

Naturally, no single effort, book, or other campaign can succeed alone in reversing this trend, which will require changing the methods, ambitions, and attitudes of thousands of people. The authors hope to multiply the effect of this book by giving readers an approach to manufacturing that is scientific, yet accesible. Several principles underlie this approach:

1. Manufacturing is one of the most complex human group activities. It comprises hundreds or thousands of simultaneous and serial subactions, some of which occur in fractions of a second, while others take hours, months, or even years to have full effect. These actions may be material, technical, informational, social, or economic.
2. *Competitive* manufacturing is an intensely scientific enterprise. It involves careful study of potential markets, customers' needs, behavior of materials, organization and planning of activities, design of products, understanding of the processes of fabrication and assembly, and rational mustering of people and machines.
3. *Noncompetitive* manufacturing suffers by comparison because it relies too heavily on slogans, outworn experience, empiricism, and lack of basic knowledge. The data needed for rational decisions are missing. When processes fail to perform as expected, no one knows why, or how to improve them.
4. Processes *can* be understood. Too often, they are put into use under the extreme time pressure associated with introducing a new product. No one has time to understand them, but somehow they must be made to work. It is the task of research and development engineers to identify these knowledge gaps, form theories and models to explain them, verify these theories experimentally, and convey the results to suppliers who can convert them into products.
5. While manufacturing researchers are familiar with the tasks of formulating and verifying theories, they have less skill in the other activities—identifying the gaps and conveying the results. They may imagine or romanticize manufacturing and spend their effort analyz-

ing problems that do not exist. People engaged in manufacturing also have difficulty identifying knowledge gaps, although this may seem paradoxical. A major purpose of this book is to sensitize manufacturing managers, engineers, and researchers to the need to communicate and collaborate.

6. By itself, advanced technology such as robots or artificial intelligence will not solve the problems of manufacturing (National Academy of Engineering, 1986). Machines cannot, for example, decide if a product's design sufficiently considers the needs of customers or repair people. Second, machines cannot be designed to perform processes that are not understood. Third, a well-understood process might be performed well, even optimally, by simple devices that could not have been designed without benefit of that understanding. Complex technology may signify a poorly understood process. The least understood processes are those traditionally done by people.

7. The fact that people "do" a task does not mean that they do it well. People are poor machines, and it is a mistake to pattern the actions of machines after the actions of people doing a similar job. Airplanes do not flap their wings, cars do not have legs, and home dishwashers do not use brushes to scrub dishes clean. In the sections on process modeling, we emphasize the need to formulate the requirements for machines by using models of the underlying processes that are to be mechanized.

8. Manufacturing consists of more than processes. It also includes systems—that is, coordinated sets of machines, processes, products, and people. The sections of the book concerned with systems deal with rational decision methods for designing fabrication and assembly systems.

9. Effective manufacturing systems form a true marriage of the products and the processes that comprise them. This book repeatedly points out this synergy. A flexible manufacturing system cannot be both totally flexible and totally efficient but will achieve a good mix of these conflicting attributes if it is designed to process a congenial and carefully designed set of workpieces. An assembly robot should not be enhanced with sensors and artificial intelligence so that it can assemble parts that are presented to it in disarray. Instead, an integrated analysis will determine what parts of the enterprise need change most urgently and can best benefit from it.

In sum, we are trying to help the reader understand manufacturing and the applicable technology in order to make rational choices. This understanding will help a manager identify a product whose design is inconsistent with competitive manufacturing. It will help engineers decide when they must push for better understanding of a process. It will help researchers to make valid assumptions when formulating research problems. It will help them all to decide where to seek change in the matrix of processes, products, and people that comprise manufacturing.

Approach

The steps and processes of Manufacturing can be summarized as:

- Product design
- Manufacturing system design
- Manufacturing system operation, comprising
  - Fabrication of parts
  - Assembly and inspection of products

Our focus is design, because design decisions completely determine the costs, constraints, and options for operating a manufacturing enterprise. We are particularly concerned with coordinated design of products and processes so that effective and efficient manufacturing will be possible. The term "concurrent design" is used in this book to refer to this process. Traditional product design techniques separate design aimed at performance from design of manufacturing systems and many other considerations related to the product's life cycle. Concurrent design seeks to combine the concerns of marketing, production, field service, and performance-oriented design into one *integrated* procedure.

This book uses assembly as the focus for approaching concurrent design because assembly is inherently integrative. This emphasis necessarily reduces the space devoted to part fabrication and day-to-day factory operation. For similar reasons, the creative aspects of design are also omitted. These crucial topics are the subjects of many available books.

About the Authors

The authors have worked together for up to 20 years in the allied fields of system engineering, information science, robotics, and automation. We are simultaneously researchers and practitioners attempting to use our research results. This is an intense two-way process: On the one hand, we have engaged in research to develop basic knowledge and techniques applicable to automation and product design. On the other hand, we have worked with many industrial firms and government agencies, applying our knowledge to real problems, such as determining whether a process is mature enough to be scaled up for manufacturing or whether a product is suitable for automated assembly. Applying the knowledge tests its validity and reveals generic problems that are in need of systematic investigation. Thus are new research problems recognized.

Two types of results have flowed from this experience. The first is a collection of new knowledge, analytical techniques, computer programs, experimental methods and instruments, and commercial products. The second is a methodology for approaching problems in manufacturing science and practice. The aim of this book is to present these results.

Our approach is grounded in our background as information, control, design, and system engineers. Such engineers are taught to focus on the connections between ideas, things, organizations, and elements of a design. This attitude is well suited to understanding manufacturing in its broadest sense.

Historical Development

Our interest in this area began in the late 1960s with research in robotics and remote manipulators. We developed some new control techniques and sensors to improve these devices. However, applying these new ideas was more difficult than we had anticipated. Any such technique must be focused on an application. Without this focus, the technique remains largely unformed.

So we looked for applications in the fields of nuclear equipment repair and industrial assembly, seeking specifications of the requirements of typical tasks, such as sizes, weights, distances, forces and torques, accuracies, speeds, and costs. We found, however, that such specifications did not exist. There was only a collection of "test tasks" for remote manipulators, performed on an array of knobs and handles that are usually operated by bare-handed people. There was no way to determine the conditions under which a manipulation or assembly task would succeed, based on geometry, relative errors between part positions, and other considerations. That is, the field of assembly lacked "process models."

Recognizing this gap, we spent much of the period from 1974 to 1980 formulating the theory of part mating, which describes the conditions for successful assembly of mechanical parts. We also applied these new models to robot assembly of real products, demonstrating complete robot assembly of an automobile alternator in 1977 (Scientific American, 1978). With the help of a team of industrial advisors and funding from the National Science Foundation, we began to formulate an approach to advanced automation. The elements of this approach were:

- Understanding the basic processes and determining their requirements—the technical side of the problem
- Understanding how to link processes into systems that accomplish a series of process steps—the economic side of the problem

Since 1980, we have sought to apply this knowledge to industrial problems. Again, we have found the task more difficult than we had anticipated. As others have discovered, it is not easy to apply new technology to a well-developed field like manufacturing. Not only are there many difficult choices to make among alternative methods, but there are also many institutional barriers.

The most formidable barrier is the traditional method of designing products and the large body of existing products and factories designed by old methods. New technologies have requirements of their own, with broad implications for product design, factory operation, and treatment of people. We have therefore added two additional elements to our approach:

- Understanding how to design products and systems together
- Establishing the necessary relationships among groups involved in the process: product and manufacturing engineers, customers, purchasing agents, vendors, repair personnel, and so on

This is a *requirements-driven* approach. It denies that any one technique or technology can solve the problems of manufacturing. Instead, the product and process requirements will indicate what techniques are feasible or what their characteristics must be, how products should be designed, or how factories should be laid out and operated.

The requirements-driven approach separates our work from typical research and applications in "robotics." The latter tends to be driven too much by anthropomorphism—that is, the desire to re-create the methods of people in machines. The distinction is a crucial one (Whitney, 1986) because there is no reason why the methods of people are more suitable than any other methods. They are merely the ones used by people, who until now have performed the majority of assembly tasks. People pick parts from jumbled masses in bins, discard damaged parts, try several times when a badly made part will not assemble properly, deal with anomalies, and otherwise cope with poorly structured situations.

To many observers, the ability of people to cope with this environment is a source of pride and an impetus to research that will create machines with similar capabilities. We view this situation with alarm, since efficient factories cannot exist under such circumstances. Understanding that today's factories and products are poor models for future factories and products is a necessary first step. Providing a scientific basis for new products, technologies, and methods is the second. This scientific base will also guide, and be enriched by, advanced research. This book will help build that base.

Intended Readers

The intended readers of this book are engineers and managers, students and teachers, and anyone who wishes to better understand the system nature of manufacturing, as well as how he or she can contribute to its improvement. Some of the material is technical, some narrative, as the topic dictates. Readers may skip the mathematics as long as they understand the assumptions that precede and the conclusions that follow.

Organization of this Book

The book is organized as follows (see Fig. 1).

Part 1 provides a frame for the chapters that follow. It presents the current state of manufacturing, the changes coursing through it, and an outline of an integrated approach to design of products and processes. A history of manufacturing and examples of good and bad manufacturing practice conclude Part 1.

Part 2 treats the processes of manufacturing, starting with a

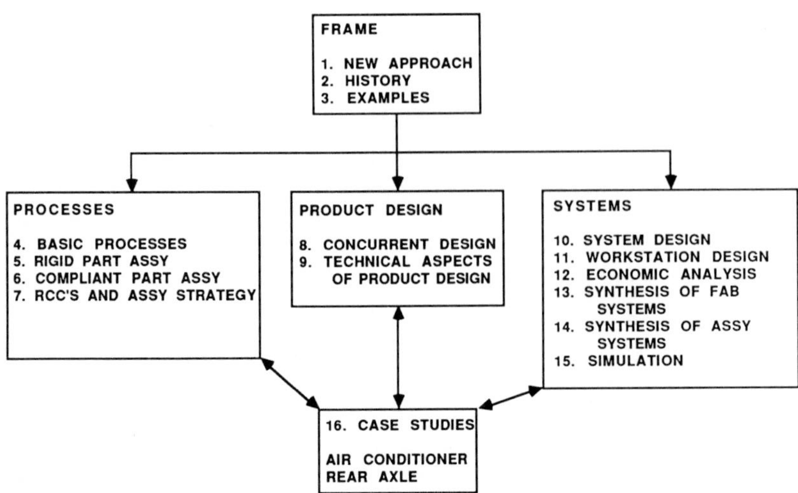

Fig. 1. A diagram of the organization of the book.

discussion of the importance of process models as the foundation of all that follows. The remaining chapters present process models of manufacturing tasks and assembly operations and conclude with a description of how to perform reliable assembly operations with compliant tooling.

Part 3 is about product design. Its two chapters describe, first in nontechnical terms, then mathematically, methods of designing products so that both their function and producibility are considered.

Part 4 extends the methods of Part 3 to design of fabrication and assembly systems and workstations and the economic evaluation of these designs.

Part 5 contains case studies that show product and process designs in detail.

As this book goes to press we find increasing awareness of the importance of manufacturing among the public, government, academia, and the media. Manufacturing is critical to the nation's economic health and standard of living.

This is our first book in a series intended to address manufacturing and design. It describes a process that can be applied now, using currently available techniques. Later books will address specific parts of the problem, including fully documented case studies and the application of knowledge-based or artificial intelligence techniques which are still topics of research.

References and additional reading

National Academy of Engineering: *Toward a New Era in U.S. Manufacturing: The Need for a National Vision*, National Academy Press, Washington D.C., 1986.

Nevins, J. L., and D. E. Whitney: "Computer-Controlled Assembly," *Scientific American*, vol. 238, no. 2, Feb., 1978, pp 64–72.

Skinner, W.: *Manufacturing, The Formidable Competitive Weapon*, John Wiley, New York, 1986.

Whitney, D. E.: "Real Robots Do Need Jigs," *Harvard Business Review*, May–June 1986, pp 110–116.

Acknowledgments

The authors owe thanks to many people and organizations for their support for, or contributions to, the material in this book. First, thanks go to our many colleagues, present and past. Their publications are mentioned many times in the text. Second, we want to thank all the students who have done their thesis research in our laboratory and enriched our work with their technical results and enthusiasm.

The authors also would like to thank the following organizations for their guidance, support, and insight.

National Science Foundation

Defense Advanced Research Projects Administration

Office of Naval Research

Massachusetts Institute of Technology, Mechanical Engineering Department and Sloan School of Management

The National Science Foundation deserves special thanks. It is unique in having supported our work continuously for the past 17 years. Under NSF support we created many of the theories, methods, and computer tools described in this book. NSF also supported the work of over 50 students.

MIT contributed these students as well as the intellectual support of its faculty.

The following companies supported specific product design and system design projects where the theories were tested. These projects also provided new insights, helped identify new research goals, and verified that our methods had technical merit and economic benefits.

AMP, Inc.

Bendix Corp.

BMW A G

Colt Industries

Digital Equipment Corp.

Ford Motor Co.

General Dynamics Corp.

General Electric Co.

General Motors Corp.

Regie Nationale des Usines Renault

Rockwell International Corp.

Singer Corp.

Texas Instruments, Inc.

Todd Pacific Shipyards, Inc.

Unimation, Inc.

Westinghouse Electric Corp.

Finally, the authors thank the professional and academic readers who offered suggestions and editing, including Mr. Charles J. Klein of GM and Dr. Joel Orr of Orr Associates, Inc. Our appreciation, too, to the editors, Mr. Robert Hauserman, Ms. Betty Sun, and Mr. Harold Crawford for their encouragement and support.

Chapter

1

A New Approach to Manufacturing

What's Changing in Manufacturing

Manufacturing comprises the technical and economic processes that convert raw materials, energy, and purchased items into components for sale to other manufacturers or into end products for sale to the public. It includes product and manufacturing system design as well as factory operation. It is also an essential part of the U.S. economy, contributing about 20 percent of the GNP, employing about 19 percent of the work force in high-paying jobs, and accounting for about 40 percent of our exports.

The first generation of advanced manufacturing technology is already firmly in place. It is called flexible manufacturing systems (FMSs), consisting of groups of computer-controlled metal-cutting machines with a common control and material-handling system.[1] The impact of FMSs has been great. Particularly important is the manner in which product design, carried out with computer-aided design (CAD) systems, is connected directly to these new manufacturing systems. Automatic inventory control, tool operations, inspection, and quality control are now or can be closely coupled operations.

However, the impact of FMSs on the way in which companies operate is minimal. Designers give too little consideration to important *product life cycle issues* such as product assembly, test, repair, and modification. This is true even though designers are increasingly

[1] The word "manufacturing" in the context of the FMS is used very narrowly to describe the fabrication of single parts, usually by traditional metal cutting. "Manufacturing" as used in this book refers very broadly to all the activities required to create and produce products.

aware of the need to design product parts so that they can be fabricated economically and still meet performance requirements. While "design for manufacturing" has increased productivity, it is not an integrated approach and thus misses most of the opportunities for productivity enhancement.

When companies consider the second generation of advanced manufacturing, namely automated flexible assembly, they find that matters cannot be treated on a part-by-part basis. Assembly is coupled not only to manufacturing but also to design, vendor control, quality control, and the customer.

Moreover, assembly can be used as the focusing issue for integration. Assembly is the first point in the process at which parts are put together. Before assembly they are designed, made, handled, and inspected separately. During and after assembly, they are joined, handled, tested, and must work together. Thus assembly is *inherently integrative*. It focuses attention on pairs, then groups, of parts. It is therefore a natural platform from which to launch an integrated attack on all the phases of a product from conception and fabrication to quality and life cycle. Decisions that affect assembly affect nearly every other aspect of production and use of a product.

It is crucial to achieve this integration during the product design process because about 70 percent of the life cycle cost of a product is determined when it is designed (see Fig. 1.1). Design choices determine materials, fabrication methods, assembly methods, and to a lesser degree material-handling options, inspection techniques, and other aspects of the production system. Manufacturing engineers and factory workers have very few choices and can affect only a small part of the overall cost if they are presented with a finished design that does not reflect their concerns.

When companies recognize the potential for an integrative approach, the result is a new activity which could be called the strategic approach to product design (SAPD). The rewards can be spectacular. This approach allows the entire system to be rationalized. Further, it helps identify the need for computerized design tools to support this tightly integrated activity and give it a scientific base in the future. Today this activity can be accomplished only with teams of highly trained people.

This book bases its approach on assembly because of the leverage and integrative focus it provides. The realization that assembly is an important phase in the product's life cycle is not new, however. It has spurred interest in design for assembly which, like design for manufacturing, helps a designer simplify products and design single parts so that they will be easier to assemble. However, other phases of a product's life cycle are important, too. They last longer than assembly

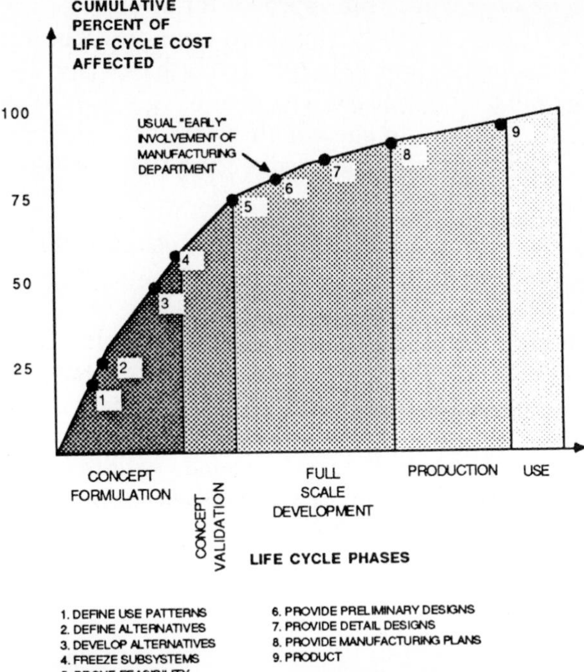

Fig. 1.1 How the life cycle cost of a product is determined during various phases of design. Life cycle cost includes cost of materials, manufacture, use, repair, and disposal of a product. The curve does not show how much money is spent in each phase toward creating the product. Rather, it shows how much influence on final cost each phase has. Thus, concept formulation determines about 60 percent of the cost, and all activities up to the start of full-scale development determine about 75 percent. This means that the design decisions made early in the process determine most of the cost, and later decisions make only minor changes to the ultimate total. (*Sources: Internal company studies at Westinghouse, General Motors Detroit Diesel Allison Division, Ford, and Rolls Royce, among others.*)

and cost more. To make a product easier to assemble might make its parts cost too much, for example. Thus design for assembly can no more be done in isolation than can design for fabrication because there are too many interactions and trade-offs. To determine which of many conflicting goals and rules to apply, we need an overall strategy for the product. SAPD provides the opportunity to formulate the strategy and deal with these trade-offs at the best time, when the product is being designed.

While many companies recognize the advantages of an integrated approach, the Japanese are the most proficient, since the best

Japanese companies have been using this approach for 20 or 30 years. Advanced U.S. companies have recently embraced the approach, but in both the United States and Japan it is intuitively based and depends on the skills of groups of engineers. The goal of this book is to describe this process in detail and to show both where the scientific base is firm and where there are still knowledge gaps that are filled intuitively.

Manufacturing in the Context of a Single Company

In the U.S. economy, a manufacturing company occupies a place in a long chain of suppliers, fabricators, producers, transporters, wholesalers, and retailers. Raw material is converted into standard stock. Stock materials are made into standard components, such as bearings and fasteners. Materials and standard parts are made into products that are sold to wholesalers and retailers. Figure 1.2 depicts this chain schematically.

The management of a company seeks to operate within this chain by determining market demands, designing products, scheduling pro-

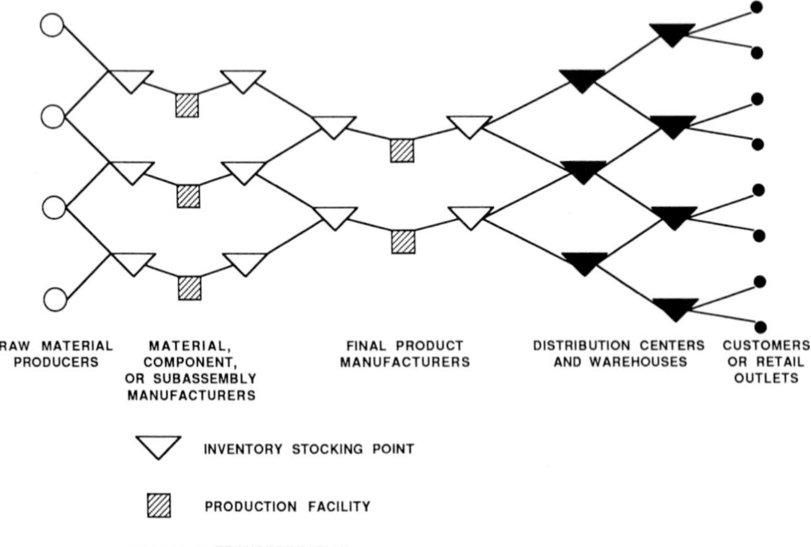

Fig. 1.2 The supplier-manufacturer-seller chain. Over the economy as a whole, production is distributed geographically and functionally, with different sectors contributing different steps in the chain. Inventory stocking points may be companies whose business is to wholesale items and resell them, or they may be warehouses owned by manufacturing companies. Within each company, there are more such stocking points, containing material referred to as incoming, work-in-process, and finished goods inventories. [*Adapted from Cohen and Lee* (1988).]

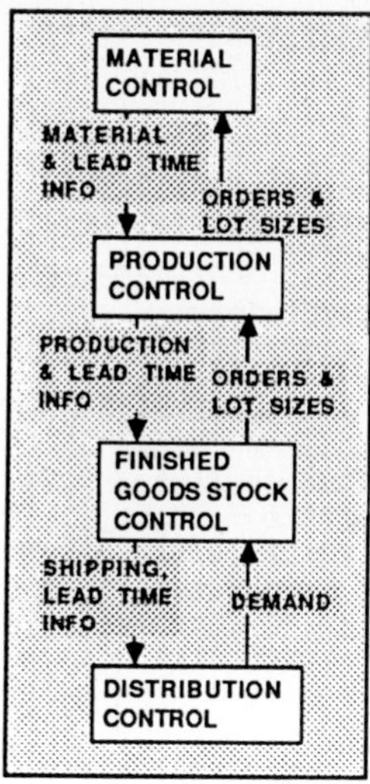

Fig. 1.3 A manufacturing company's operational decisions and their relationships.

duction, predicting sales, and deciding upon materials orders. The decisions are difficult because of uncertainties surrounding material availability and price as well as market demand and the prices consumers will be willing to pay. Material orders must be timed and must be of the correct quantity. Figure 1.3 isolates the operating decisions into groups comprising material, production, finished goods, and distribution control. Solid mathematical models for and theories about operating such a system are only now emerging (Cohen and Lee, 1988).

Goals of Product and System Design

Whatever approach management takes toward operating this system, four major parts of the company must be prepared to respond: the marketing, finance, product design, and manufacturing departments.

Figure 1.4 diagrams some of the functions of a marketing department. Its job is to determine the characteristics and features of a potential product and how big its market might be at a certain price. Using a model of production cost and possible market share, the marketing department estimates whether a product might be made in the right quantity for the right price.

The product design department (see Fig. 1.5) seeks to design a product that will meet the market's needs or stimulate a market. Design must be responsive to price: A recently used strategy for high-technology consumer products is to open the market with a luxury

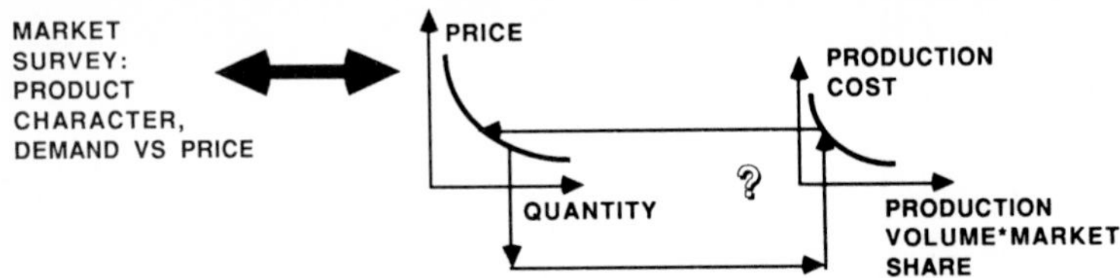

Fig. 1.4 The marketing department's view. Left: A lower price will encourage a larger market to develop. A lower production cost will allow a lower price to be charged profitably. Right: A larger market and larger share will permit a larger production volume, permitting lower-cost production methods to be used. These interlocking issues are illustrated by the loop enclosing the question mark. As shown in the figure, it does not work out satisfactorily: At the anticipated market share, production cost will dictate a selling price too high to support even the hoped-for market size. Possible remedies are to abandon the product, redesign it, change marketing strategy, or seek more efficient production methods.

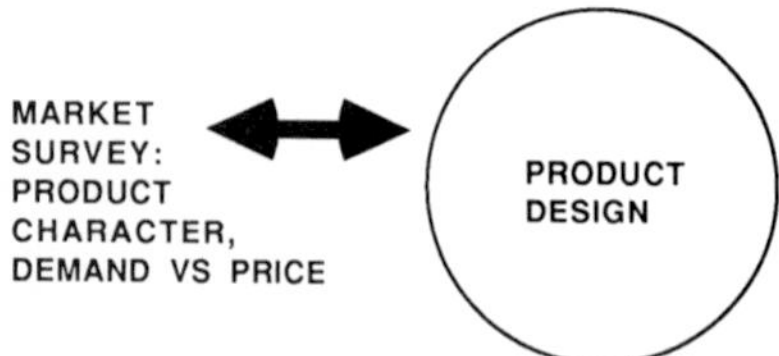

Fig. 1.5 The product design department's view. Based on the findings of market surveys or stimulated by product research and development, the design department seeks to design a product with a target price that will meet the market's needs or create a new market.

model that will recover some of the development cost and start a market trend, following up later with less expensive models. More of these might be sold, improving production volume, lowering costs, and maintaining profit.

The manufacturing department (see Fig. 1.6) must be able to make the product as designed and as it is planned to be sold. Here lies the company's ability to accomplish the goals set by marketing and design. Some general guidelines have been given in the past (see Figs. 1.8 and 1.9) for how manufacturing might be organized in response to the kind of product and market environment, but they are rather vague and must be replaced in practice with detailed and rationalized designs. Techniques for rational system design are described in this book.

The finance department (see Fig. 1.7) must determine if the manufacturing department's plans make sense economically. Not only must the overall estimated investment be compared to the market and prospective revenue from selling the product, but the investment must

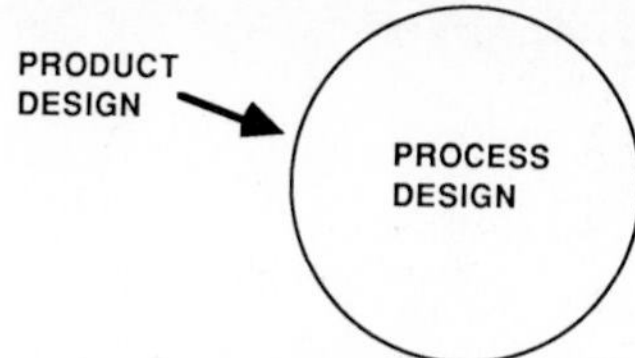

Fig. 1.6 The manufacturing department's view. A manufacturing process must be designed to create the product as designed. This process must comprise a strategy for meeting the anticipated marketing method, including what models will be made, how production will grow, and so on.

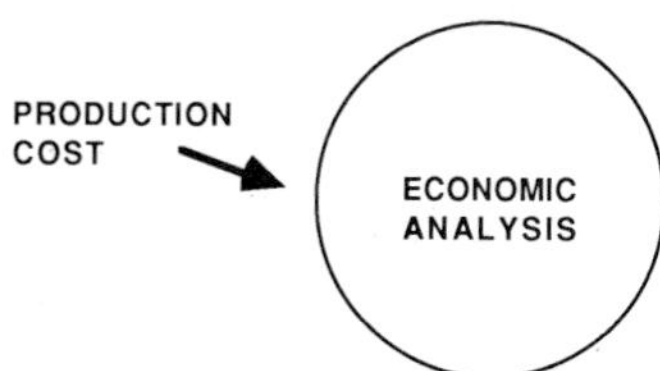

Fig. 1.7 The finance department's view. Based on the production department's cost estimates, the finance department must decide if production will be economically rewarding.

also be compared against alternate investments to determine if the return is adequate. The company's prosperity often hangs on these decisions. [A history of these decisions inside the Ford Motor Company makes fascinating reading (Halberstam, 1986).] In this book, we present methods by which product and manufacturing designers can evaluate the economics of their own designs.

Drivers of Change in Manufacturing

The following are some of the converging forces that will demand new approaches:

1. The complexity of new products and the disappearance of the learning curve
2. The disappearance of manual assembly as an option
3. The complexity of modern worldwide production and the changing nature of competition
4. The changing basis of economic analysis

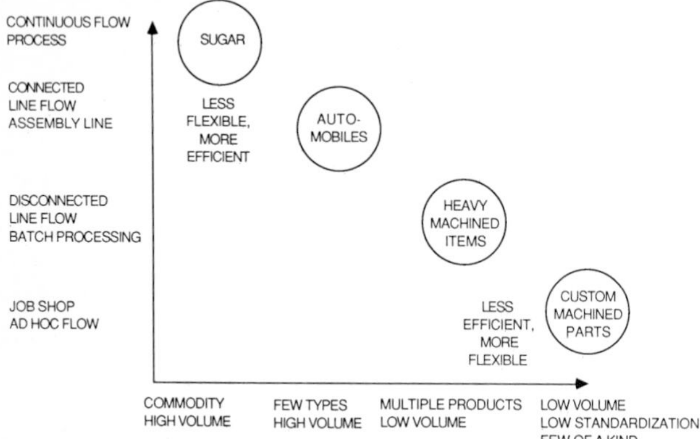

Fig. 1.8 The product-process matrix. This shows in a general way the main choices available to the manufacturing system designer. The circles contain example products suitable to common combinations of volume and model mix (horizontal axis) and production arrangement (vertical axis). The upper left represents methods with low flexibility but high efficiency in comparison to methods in the lower right. The lower left consists of inappropriate low-flexibility–low-efficiency choices, while the upper right is the nirvana of high efficiency and high flexibility. One is not always free to choose a place in this matrix. Existing production technology or competition may force a choice. On the other hand, the size of the potential market might force a choice along the horizontal axis by determining what the maximum volume for a product will be. Or the marketing department might determine that a high volume could be created if a particular selling price could be established for the product. The job of the product and manufacturing system designers in this case would be to create a system which can achieve such a manufacturing cost that the product can be sold profitably at the target price. (*Modified and reprinted by permission of the Harvard Business Review. An exhibit from "The Dynamics of Process-Product Life Cycles" by Robert H. Hayes and Steven C. Wheelwright, March/April 1979. ©1979 by the President and Fellows of Harvard College; All rights reserved.)*

Complexity of products and the disappearance of the learning curve

Modern products can contain thousands of parts and many technologies. A new automobile can take 5 years from initial specifications to first production item (see Fig. 1.10). Many skills and disciplines from psychology and marketing to composite materials and inventory control contribute. A new surface combat ship can take 7 to 10 years to cover the same process and is probably the most complex item built today. Modern products are characterized by combinations of energy and information storage and transformation, sometimes called "mechatronics." Such products contain a true integration of mechanical and electronic functions and thus require more broadly educated

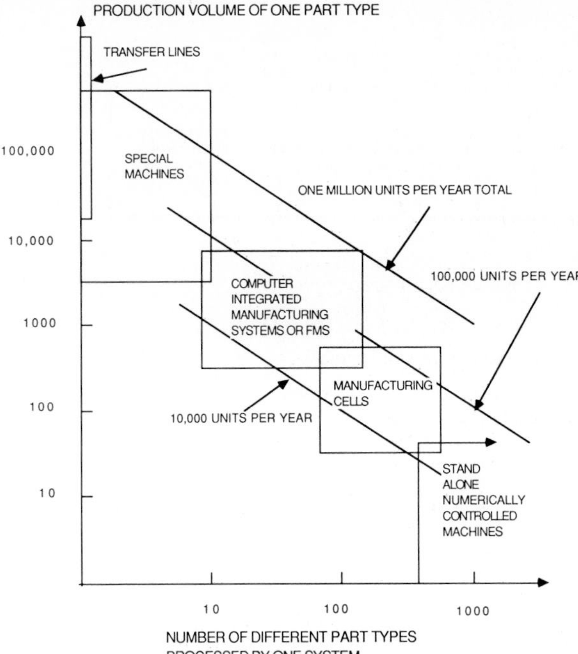

Fig. 1.9 The volume-variety matrix. This figure shows a particular example of a product-process matrix. The themes emphasized here are production method and production volume for machined parts. This matrix originated in the early 1970s (Haas, 1973) and was used to indicate where in the spectrum of part manufacturing the new technology of computer-integrated manufacturing systems (FMSs) would lie. Whereas in Fig. 1.8 the cases are broadly defined and permit only qualitative choices, Fig. 1.9 is so specific that the choices can often be resolved by economic and operations analysis. Yet even here we must be careful. A manufacturer takes a chance when predicting how large or diverse a market will be. If a diverse and specialized market emerges, a manufacturer with an efficient, focused plant may be too inflexible to meet the varying demand. If a large but homogeneous market develops, a manufacturer with a flexible system may find production costs too high and the dearly purchased flexibility unexploitable. Recent data from Japan indicate that some manufacturers have built FMSs that can economically make 300,000 automobile engine blocks per year.

product and process designers. An example is the *precision product* typified by computer disk drives. They may be made of materials that, unlike past ones, are not merely transformed from mined ores or feedstocks but are specially created anew from the atoms up to serve the needs of the product (Scientific American, 1986). New products are tailored to market niches; therefore, production volumes may be small

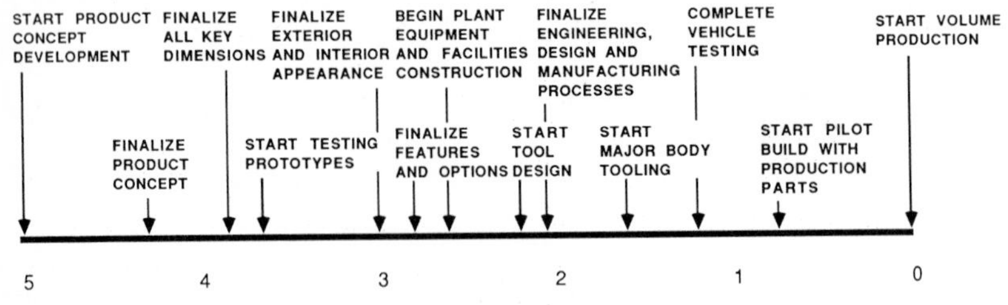

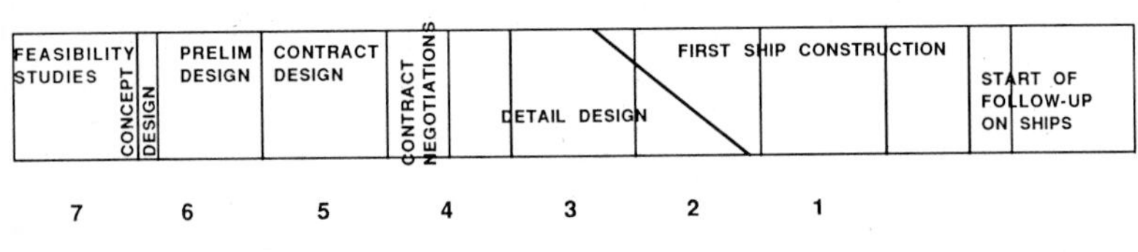

Fig. 1.10. Product development cycles for automobiles and warships [Jurgen (1987), Bosworth (1985)]. *(Above © 1987 IEEE. Below © 1985 MIT. Both reprinted by permission.)*

and product lives short. Thus there is a need for rapid advances in a product line, fast design updating, and quick changes in production schedules. The learning curve that allowed design errors or production glitches to be worked out over time is compressed.

To overcome time compression, manufacturers must be able to use lessons from previous design activities to aid the current one. That is, the learning may still take longer than the time available to design one new product or system, but it can be systematized. Its basis is the recognition of generic or repeating elements in the product, the processes, or the design steps themselves. Japanese shipbuilding, discussed in some detail in Chap. 3, is an excellent example.

Two responses to the disappearance of the learning curve can be identified. First, manufacturers must do things faster. Products and systems need to be designed more rapidly so that there will be time to find the mistakes and eliminate them. Better planning and more effective computer tools are recognized ways of attaining speed. Better planning means organizing the design process so that more factors are taken into account early, reducing the chance of damaging surprises later during manufacturing or product launch. Planning also involves identifying a good sequence in which to make design decisions so that iteration is avoided. Better computer tools allow calculations to be made more rapidly and to cover more cases. These advantages, too, increase the speed with which designs can be created. Well-known efforts in computer-aided design, computer-aided engineering, and computer-aided manufacturing are examples of this approach to the challenge of time compression.

Second, a less well-known method emphasized in this book is to involve all departments of a company in the product design process from the beginning so that decisions can be made sooner and with better information, avoiding delay and mistakes, and compressing the design process.

To exploit these ideas in design, we need a systematic approach which asks the same kinds of questions and requires the same kinds of analyses again and again. As we perform these design steps repeatedly, we get better at recognizing the similarities, even though each product or system is outwardly different. As the steps become clearer to us, we develop computer tools for carrying them out. The formulation of these steps and their organization into a coherent approach constitute the intellectual challenge of manufacturing.

Disappearance of the manual assembly option

Until recently it was thought that manual assembly was always an option, and for many products it still is. Manual metal removal was never an option, so metal removal machinery developed early in the industrial revolution. Thus metal removal processes were among the first to be well understood. Manual assembly is rapidly disappearing as an option in high-technology products because people have too much difficulty providing the required quality, uniformity, care, documentation, and cleanliness. This is not to say that remarkable human performance is impossible. Consider that in Japan it is usual for a person to make only one assembly error (wrong, missing, or broken part) in 25,000, 100,000, or even 250,000 operations (Sata, 1986). And this is considered not good enough! The Japanese use these numbers to justify automation, such is their conviction that modern products demand even higher quality.

Yet we already know that direct substitution of robots for people will not solve the problem. Such technology requires a carefully designed environment comprising a properly designed product, well-trained operators, well-scheduled operations, and so on—exactly the same kind of requirements that FMSs need. A full-scale strategic change is needed in the way products and manufacturing systems are designed. Neither is it enough to make these changes in one company. Since a company will purchase many of its parts and subassemblies, the same kinds of problems must be solved by its vendors.

All this means that we have to understand assembly as deeply as we now understand metal cutting. Indeed, all the processes in manufacturing—material handling, stocking, transport, inspection, judgment of suitability, and granting of "exceptions"—which are now routinely handled by people in an intuitive and often undocumented way—will have to be brought to a higher level of understanding, even if they are not executed by machines. Otherwise there is no way to overcome the complexity of manufacturing.

Complexity of processes and the changing nature of competition

The production process is becoming more complex. Timing is more critical, processes require more care and attention, more data are needed to determine how a manufacturing system is performing. New production technology requires new skills and attitudes from workers and managers. It is more difficult to decide on the correct kind of technology, and the right mix of technology and people, to suit the product and its market.

Product and process complexity arise from the appearance of new kinds of products, mostly those characterized as mechatronics. These items depend on careful design, precise tolerances, extreme cleanliness, fine timing and balance, and the skill and attention of dedicated people. The technologies involved include mechanics, electronics, optics, signal processing, plastic materials, and so on.

The success of such products depends in turn on new kinds of competition. In mature industries, products differ little in technology, and the basis of competition is usually price, which is governed by production efficiency. Managers in such industries focus on asset management and make most of their decisions based on economic criteria. The finance department may dominate.

In newer industries (and in many older ones faced with new competitors), the bases of competition are more likely to be product innovation, advanced technology, and quality. Newer products may command a price premium based on quality or novelty. Manufacturing decisions in such industries are therefore less likely to be dominated by economics and more by the ability of the product and factory designs to support the competitive strategy behind the product, such as the ability to evolve rapidly or be responsive to a changing market without reducing quality. All company departments must cooperate in order for such methods to succeed. The competitive strategies of

Japanese companies, including deliberately narrow product lines, aggressive pricing, efficient production facilities, and rapid product change allowed by a shorter product design process, are described vividly in *Kaisha, The Japanese Corporation* (Abegglen and Stalk, 1985).

The changing basis of economic analysis

Because of the changing basis for competition, the decision-making processes now accomplished with routine economic analyses must be supplanted by more sophisticated criteria, computer tools, assumptions, and priorities. Traditional manufacturers use economic analysis to decide on a case-by-case basis whether replacing a person with a piece of machinery, such as a robot, will save money. The replacement calculation is based on the assumption that the candidate substitute is equivalent to the current method in every way except cost.

However, each candidate is different in its ability to deliver quality, its reliability, its tolerance of noise and vibration, its speed of changeover, and so on. We must reflect these factors in the analysis. Failure rates, repair costs, and testing methods, for example, must be considered. These in turn are affected by product design. In high-technology products, materials cost much more than time or labor, so the ability of an assembly-test system to deliver a good yield is crucial to maintaining production volume and profit. Thus economically justifiable manufacturing systems can contain both machines and people if they can deliver superior quality or can otherwise make the company competitive.

The success of any analytical method, technical or economic, depends on the availability of good data. It is surprising how little good economic and cost data exist in many factories. A good example is rework, the process of correcting a mistake. If mistakes are considered normal, the time to fix them will be counted as part of the standard time to do the work, and no separate data on percentage of rework will be kept. Thus the ability to analyze the rework-saving potential of redesign or automation will be lost.

The terms of competition have changed. Strategically designed products and manufacturing systems have the ability to compete on new grounds. A major part of that ground is dominated by new assembly systems and new product design methods integrated by assembly considerations. A company may thus have to alter its methods and invest in new ones strictly because its competitors are doing so. The incremental decisions made on criteria internal to the company must be replaced by strategic decisions keyed to what is happening outside the company.

Concurrent Design of Products and Systems

The preceding sections of this chapter posed several issues:

- The problems facing manufacturing (the challenge of competitiveness, the need for better quality, more flexibility and efficiency, and difficulty attaining these with manual labor in complex products)
- The fact that these problems are of long standing
- The great complexity of manufacturing as an enterprise
- The fact that only a mix of technological and institutional advances will be effective

The most sophisticated companies realize that a new approach to manufacturing is needed. There is a growing awareness that manufacturing can have a strategic impact on how a company operates. Management must decide what business it is in and how to design and manufacture its products so as to be competitive in that business. Manufacturing managers and engineers must understand their role in this strategy and learn the tools and methods for implementing it.

An integrated approach to manufacturing comprises five interrelated elements; they are:

- Careful analysis and understanding of fabrication and assembly processes to permit their operation with consistency and quality
- Strategic product design, conceived to support a specific strategy for making and selling the product
- Rationalized manufacturing system design coordinated with product design
- Economic analysis of design and manufacturing alternatives to permit rational choices
- Product and system designs that are characterized by robustness and structure.

These elements must be present in the correct balance and executed in an integrated way.

We will describe briefly here and in more detail throughout the book a coordinated and integrated approach to achieving these goals which we call the "strategic approach to product design." This approach includes how the product is designed and marketed as well as how it is made. All the entities described in prior sections of this chapter and illustrated in Figs. 1.3 through 1.7 must be welded into a coherent team that makes its decisions simultaneously. Figure 1.11 seeks to represent this by combining the separate entities in those fig-

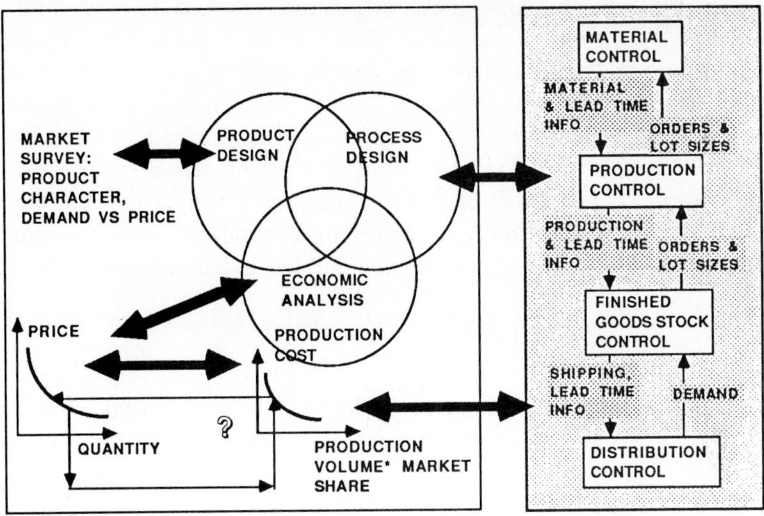

Fig. 1.11 All of the departments in a company must work together to define a product, determine how to design it so that it can be made and sold profitably, and decide how the factory can be operated to support the logic of the design and production-marketing strategy.

ures into one. In this broader view, operation is no longer separate from design; product design is no longer separate from marketing or process design. Product and process design are no longer separate from finance. The key to this approach is integration.

By integration we do not mean to imply any particular implementation or technology. The correct role of computers and "computer integration" is unclear at this point. The same may be said of robots, expert systems, and other new developments. The importance of human relations and interactions, and organizational and institutional arrangements, is only dimly perceived, although many observers are convinced that these issues far outweigh technology in forming an effectively integrated approach. Yet the demands of complex products and processes strongly indicate that technology will be needed. The issue is to design, choose technology, and operate human-machine systems wisely.

The procedure described below must be recognized as our view of an ideal that has not yet been achieved and is not yet fully formed or understood. More experience and effort will undoubtedly modify and improve it. Since the method is new, it is severely short of computer aids and analytical methods. The state of the art is the multidiscipline team that is formed at the beginning of the design process and stays together until the product is well into production.

Assuming the above restrictions, we can describe the integrated approach starting from the completion of product concept design as follows (see Fig. 1.12). Once a product idea has been formulated, estimates are made of the quantity that can be sold at what price. The task of the design team is to create a design for both the product and the manufacturing processes that can yield the desired production quantity at a price that allows the company to sell the product for a profit. The team keeps modifying the designs until it appears that the goals can be met. At this point, a decision to proceed results in the construction and operation of the manufacturing system. Both product

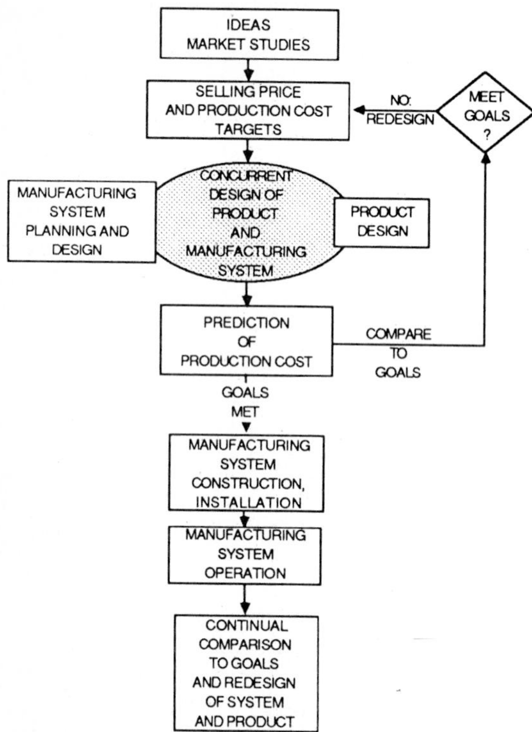

Fig. 1.12 Integrated design of product and manufacturing system. This diagram represents the ideal of the concurrent process of designing products and manufacturing systems. It shows that selling price, product design, and system design must all be worked out together so that the final product can be produced for a price that the market will bear at the hoped-for production volumes. Production costs and methods are both very sensitive to product design. Higher production volumes allow use of more efficient production methods, lowering production costs further. Thus the main design-decision loop must be closed through marketing and product and system design. Once this main constraint appears to be satisfied, integrated detailed design of the product and the manufacturing and assembly processes goes ahead.

and processes are continually monitored, both to ensure that they meet the price, quantity, and quality goals and, more importantly, to improve all of them. Some companies may turn the improvement into larger profits, while others may lower the price, thereby gaining market share.

Product Design

Within the above procedure are several steps of interest to us. The first, product design (see Fig. 1.13), begins with a concept which specifies the capabilities and performance requirements and sets goals for production cost and annual volume. Next, the technical concepts for the product's function are established. Major decisions regarding configuration, materials, energy, size, and so on, are made at least tentatively. The bulk of the design effort in this phase and the next is devoted to ensuring that the product will function as desired, together with intense study to anticipate and avoid ways the product might fail to function.

Following the initial specification, designers break the design into parts and subassemblies. Competitive advantages can be designed in by, for example:

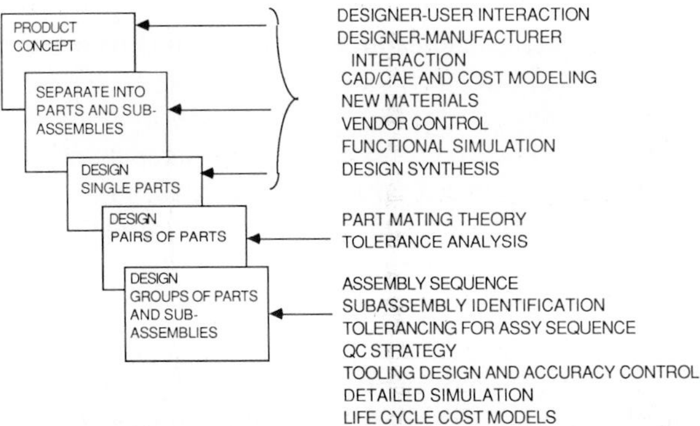

Fig. 1.13 Activities and main issues in product design via the strategic approach. Product design proceeds from the whole to the parts and back to the whole. The concept design is broken down into major modules and subassemblies, then into single parts. Both product function and producibility factors influence this breakdown. Pairs of parts are designed to ensure proper function and reliable assembly. Groups of parts are designed to support a suitable assembly sequence, whose effect on assembly system design and testing strategies must also be evaluated. Because many parts and subassemblies are purchased, the strategic approach must extend to vendors.

- Supporting model mix flexibility through commonality of parts or by identifying subassemblies that express the model differences
- Permitting rapid response to market changes by concentrating model differences in only a few parts that are added at the end of the assembly sequence or by making long lead time parts (hard to buy or hard to make) common to all models
- Designing for assembly sequences that permit the product to be made in modules or subassemblies, thereby supporting model mix production and thorough testing at the subassembly level

This is an iterative process, inasmuch as the identities of single parts depend strongly on how they are to be made. Modern techniques make increasingly complex items from one piece of material, whereas in the past such items would have been agglomerations of many parts fastened together by fasteners or adhesives. The definition of subassemblies is accompanied by decisions on what to buy versus what to make. Division into subassemblies also coincides with decisions on what items belong in what model variations, since it is convenient to have model boundaries coincide with the boundaries of major subunits of the product. Thus when the production system is designed, the switch from one model to another will coincide with the switch from one subassembly to another.

The next step is to design single parts. The main consideration here is performance of the product, and the designer considers such matters as materials, strength, weight, fabrication technique, and tolerances on the dimensions of functional surfaces. A major concern is to predict the part's possible failure modes.

It is at this point that the design has traditionally been passed to the manufacturing department, which must then figure out how to make it. However, in the integrated design process, design continues, with increasing attention to manufacturing issues. The design process goes more quickly and a better design results because of faster and more relevant communication and avoidance of errors.

The first consideration beyond single parts is pairs of parts. That is, parts that are to be mated to each other must be designed so that this is not only possible but easy and certain to succeed. Matters of importance include tolerances and clearances between parts, chamfers on rims of holes, and attention to how the parts will be fed and presented to assembly stations. There is a growing literature on this stage of the design. Part pairs are examined to determine ease of assembly or feeding, and those that present problems are identified. Several types of redesign are available, including adding chamfers, changing part shape slightly to permit easier feeding, or changing insertion path from "push-twist" to "push" or some other simplification (Boothroyd et al., 1982; Hitachi). Condensations and rationalizations are also possible, such as combining parts to reduce their number or designing parts so that in different combinations they can be made into different models of the product.

It is not enough, however, to consider just pairs of parts. One must then consider groups of parts, up to and including complete subassemblies, to ensure that a good assembly sequence has been obtained. Choice of assembly sequence is pivotal because it influences many other design decisions such as:

- The recognition of jigging and gripping surfaces and specification of their tolerances
- Identification of subassemblies and definition of sequences that create the subassemblies
- Definition of testing strategies, based on the sequence in which potential failures become detectable as assembly proceeds
- Correlation of sequence with fabrication and assembly equipment choice, grouping of adjacent operations in the sequence on one machine, and related floor layout opportunities

Fabrication and Assembly System Design

Corresponding to product design is the design of fabrication and assembly systems. Here the major issues are to produce the required quantities of parts and products having the required tolerances and quality, all at the target cost. Specific ways these systems can contribute to the product's strategy are:

- Designing the system to achieve the product's quality goals
- Defining the system to contain the right mix of fixed and flexible machines geared to the common and variable parts that support model mix
- Arranging the system to permit fast changeover from one model to another or to a new design

Fabrication system and assembly system design have certain parallels, since both may be described in stages running from specification of single workstations up to complete systems with transportation and sets of tools (see Fig. 1.14). All the factors determined during design, such as part tolerances, assembly sequence, testing strategy, and model mix, must be provided by single stations or groups of stations.

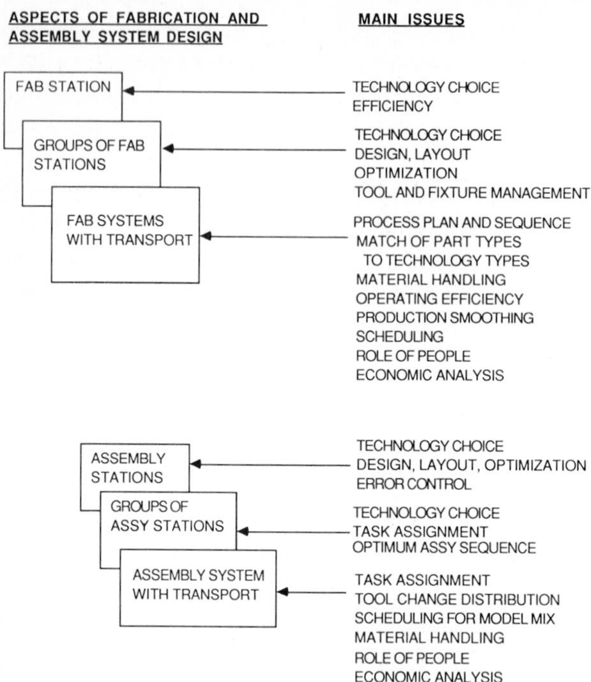

Fig. 1.14 Design of fabrication and assembly systems via the strategic approach. Fabrication and assembly system design follow similar patterns and must consider similar constraints. The main decisions are choice of method or technology and assignment of operations or tasks. In assembly, the assembly sequence is especially important to these choices, as is the definition of subassemblies. Both can affect feasible technology, floor layout, equipment grouping, and ability to respond flexibly.

In both fabrication and assembly system design, the stations must be selected and then grouped. Station selection is often done on a task-by-task basis, but there is an advantage to selecting groups of stations at once if it is possible to put more than one task on a station. With the availability of numerically controlled (NC) machine tools and robots, this possibility is increasingly common in both fabrication and assembly. The suitability of a machine or person for a task depends on its cost, speed, and quality of work. These can be affected by product design and detailed task design, as we shall see in later chapters.

Especially in assembly, different schemes for accomplishing a task may have different likelihoods of success, depending on what mechanical accuracy or force levels are involved, how much care or cleanliness is required, or how sensitive the technique is to small errors in how the parts were made. To the extent that the different capabilities of stations can be quantified, we can use computer algorithms to select groups of machines and people suitable for performing groups of fabrication or assembly tasks, meeting production quantity requirements on multiple models of a product and minimizing unit production cost. These algorithms are discussed in Chap. 14. They permit much more rational equipment choice, task assignment, and economic justification than the traditional method of first designing a manual system and then considering possible automation of each station individually. The latter method too often ignores the savings of combining work from many stations or the ability to implement a strategy.

Designing Production Systems for Robustness and Structure

"Robust" describes systems that work even in the face of disturbances, "structure" is a property that gives them robustness, and the designer's job is to figure out how to create structure. This topic applies to both product and process designs—to ensure that they will work successfully.

What do we mean by structure? Structure means predictability, order, alignment, prearrangement, planning. Its opposites (enemies, in fact) are randomness, disorder, jumbles, surprise, improvisation (see Table 1.1). Structure is what makes factories work. It does not occur by itself but is the result of deliberate design.

Let us compare fully structured, partially structured, and unstructured situations (see Table 1.2). Each situation requires different methods and technologies so that tasks will be successful. Serious errors can result if one assumes structure when none has been provided,

TABLE 1.1 Examples of Structure and Lack of Structure.
At McDonald's, employees are taught a 19-step process for making and bagging French fries (*Business Week*, 1986). McDonald's is so structured that it has achieved the remarkable status of a multibillion dollar company run almost entirely by children.

What is structure?	
Structured	Unstructured
A row	A pile
A parade	A mob
McDonald's	Children making cookies
Parts in pallets, trays, carrier strips, tapes, rows ...	Parts in bins, boxes, piles ...
"Pick up the part at $(X + I, Y + J)$"	"Where is it?"

TABLE 1.2 Environments with Different Inherent Amounts of Structure

Three degrees of structure		
Situation	Amount of structure	Characteristics
Factory	Structured (or should be)	Parts lined up Detailed work instructions Division of labor Need for discipline, high quality, cost control 99.5 percent success typical
Equipment repair	Partially structured	Equipment "deformed" from original state but recognizable Detailed work instructions usually can be followed in a predetermined order 90 percent success maximum?
Fire fighting Exploring Mars	Unstructured	May not know what to expect Work instructions can't be followed very far Emergencies occur often 10 percent success maximum?

as in lack of planning, or if one ignores structure that is easily available, as in overuse of technology.

Consider Fig. 1.15, which shows "before" and "after" in an automobile plant in 1984. Because of the impetus toward just in time manufacturing (JIT), the company had recently invested in plastic tote bins for the parts. Each part is held in a good location and orientation and is protected from damage. One of this book's authors toured the same plant in 1974 and was shown the jumbled parts on the right. "Robots must deal with this or else we won't use robots," he was told. When he asked why the parts could not be put in plastic tote bins, he was told that it would "cost too much."

How times change. In 1974 manufacturers wanted robots to be able to do what people do—in essence, to deal with disorder. Robots still cannot pick up the jumbled parts, but the company has found another reason to invest in structure. Now, a simple robot can pick up the parts in the bin. The company's change of heart reflects its recognition of additional costs implicit in the lack of structure, and it has taken steps to reduce those costs. It is just as well that money and time were not invested in creating robots that could access the jumble, allowing wasteful lack of structure to persist. The example also shows that advanced technology is not the only way to solve a problem.

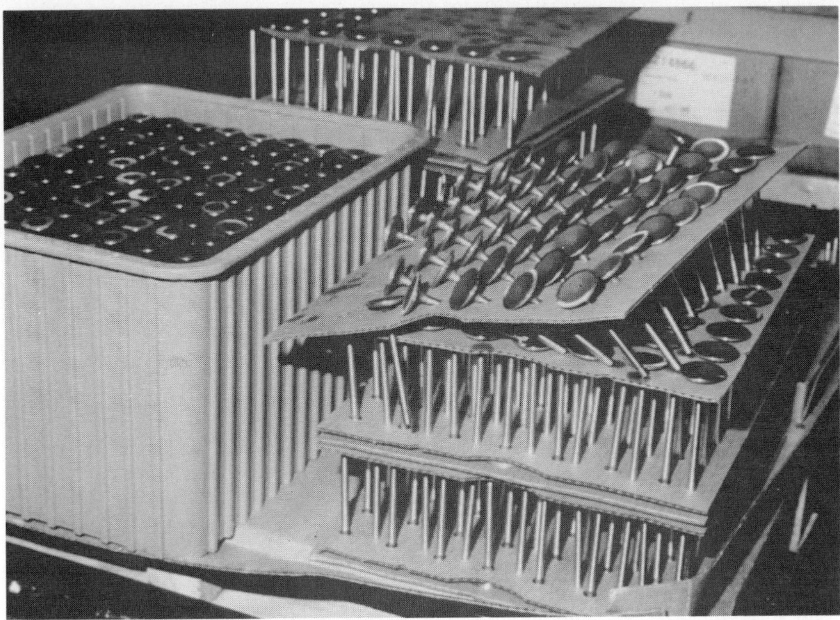

Fig. 1.15 Engine valves delivered to the assembly line by the old method (right) and the new method (left). (*Courtesy of Society of Manufacturing Engineers. Reprinted by permission.*)

Summary

This chapter described the challenges to, and main missions of, manufacturing, and it outlined the main tasks in concurrent product and manufacturing system design.

The concurrent design process was described within the context of meeting a target market in terms of a profitable selling price and sales volume. Thus the strategic approach involves all areas of the company. Since many parts are purchased, vendor costs and design and manufacturing methods must follow a similar approach.

It is important to note that the strategic approach is an ideal rather than an accomplished fact. Many of the required design tools and algorithms do not yet exist or are emerging from research laboratories now. In some companies, the institutional atmosphere is not yet sufficiently supportive.

The main theme is that successful manufacturing requires integration of many previously compartmentalized activities, plus new knowledge and greater understanding of manufacturing processes, product design methods, and manufacturing system design methods.

References

Abegglen, J. C., and G. Stalk, Jr.: *Kaisha, The Japanese Corporation,* Basic Books, New York, 1985.

"Bag Those Fries, Squirt That Ketchup, Fry That Fish," *Business Week*, Oct. 13, 1986, p. 86.

Boothroyd, G., C. Poli, and L. E. Murch: *Automatic Assembly,* Marcel Dekker, New York, 1982.

Bosworth, M. L.: "Producibility as a Design Factor in Naval Combatants," S M Thesis, MIT Ocean Engineering Department, 1985, p. 53.

Cohen, M. A., and H. L. Lee: "Strategic Analysis of Integrated Production-Distribution Systems: Models and Methods," *Operations Research,* vol. 36, no. 2, Mar.-Apr. 1988, pp. 216–228.

Haas, P. R.: "Flexible Manufacturing Systems: A Solution for the Mid-Volume, Mid-Variety Parts Manufacturer," *SME Technical Conference,* Detroit, Apr. 1973.

Halberstam, D.: *The Reckoning,* Avon Press, New York, 1986.

Hayes, R. H., and S. C. Wheelwright: "The Dynamics of Product-Process Life Cycles," *Harvard Business Review,* Mar.-Apr. 1979

Hitachi Assembleability Method, a proprietary product which may be licensed from the Hitachi Production Engineering Research Laboratory, Yokohama, Japan.

Jurgen, R. K.: "Survival Strategy: Go Global," *IEEE Spectrum,* Oct. 1987, p. 38.

"Materials for Economic Growth," *Scientific American,* vol. 255, no. 4, Oct. 1986.

National Academy of Engineering: *Toward a New Era in U.S. Manufacturing,* National Academy Press, Washington, D.C., 1986.

Sata, T.: "Development of Flexible Manufacturing Systems in Japan," *Proceedings of the First Japan-USA Symposium on Flexible Automation,* Japan Association of Automatic Control Engineers, Osaka, Japan, 1986.

Chapter

2

History and Macroeconomics of Manufacturing

Introduction

This chapter describes manufacturing in three contexts: its history, generic problems, and economics. The history of manufacturing reveals that many of the problems facing industry today are similar to those of prior decades and thus may be considered generic: the search for efficiency and flexibility, the need to use more advanced technology, and institutional problems such as labor-management relations. The economics of manufacturing reveal cost patterns and operating conditions that help managers and engineers understand what constrains their decisions.

A Brief History of Manufacturing Technology

Today's manufacturing technology did not spring into existence overnight; neither did its current problems. Careful study of the history of manufacturing shows that many of its key ideas stem from the early 1800s. The development has been evolutionary, each step solving some problems and creating others. A great deal of intellectual effort has gone into this development. As we contemplate improving today's methods, it is well to be aware of and to appreciate what has come before and to understand why. Historical analysis provides this perspective, helps eliminate many myths, and allows us to appreciate that alternatives exist, that *what is* has resulted from many circumstances, and that *what will be* need not follow directly from *what was*.

TABLE 2.1 Five Different Types of Manufacturing Organizations (Cusumano, 1987)

TYPE 1: JOB-SHOP OR CRAFT ORGANIZATIONS

FOCUS ON CUSTOMIZED PRODUCTS, GENERAL PURPOSE EQUIPMENT AND HIGHLY SKILLED LABOR, TO MAXIMIZE FLEXIBILITY IN DESIGN; FULL BUT UNSYSTEMATIC INTEGRATION OF DESIGN AND PRODUCTION; HIGH PROFITS FROM UNIQUE DESIGNS MAKE COST CONTROL A LOWER PRIORITY. EXAMPLE: HAND ILLUMINATED BOOKS.

TYPE 2: BATCH OPERATIONS

FOCUS ON LOW-VOLUME MULTIPLE PRODUCTS, BUT STILL MUCH CUSTOMIZING AND HIGH PROFITS. EXAMPLE: BOOKS PRINTED VIA MOVEABLE TYPE.

TYPE 3: RIGID MASS PRODUCTION AND ENGINEERING

FOCUS ON HIGHER VOLUMES AND FEW PRODUCTS; STANDARDIZED PRODUCT TECHNOLOGY MAKES SIMPLE FIXED AUTOMATION AND DIVISION OF DE-SKILLED LABOR HIGHLY ECONOMICAL; SPECIALIZATION CAN LEAD TO SEPARATION OF DESIGN FROM MANUFACTURING. EXAMPLE: FORD MODEL T CAR.

TYPE 4: LOW AUTOMATION FLEXIBLE MASS PRODUCTION

FOCUS ON PROCESS AND COMPONENTS STANDARDIZATION AND MEDIUM TO HIGH BUT CONTROLLED VOLUMES, LESS RIGID AUTOMATION AND RAPID SETUPS, LESS SPECIALIZED WORKERS; SMALL LOT PRODUCTION COMBINES BENEFITS OF PRODUCT VARIETY OF BATCH OPERATIONS WITH COST AND QUALITY CONTROLS OF MASS PRODUCTION. EXAMPLE: TOYOTA CAR.

TYPE 5: HIGH LEVEL AUTOMATION, FLEXIBLE PRODUCTION

FOCUS ON DESIGN OF A SYSTEM CAPABLE OF FULLY INTEGRATING AND AUTOMATING PRODUCT AND MANUFACTURING ENGINEERING FUNCTIONS, SO THAT HIGH VOLUME AND STABLE PRODUCT DESIGNS ARE NOT AS IMPORTANT; CAPTURES BENEFITS OF BOTH JOB-SHOP FLEXIBILITY AND PRODUCT CUSTOMIZATION WITH PRODUCTIVITY, PRECISION, AND STANDARDIZED HIGH QUALITY OF MASS PRODUCTION TYPE AUTOMATION. EXAMPLE: INTEGRATED CAD/CAM PRODUCTION OF AIRCRAFT PARTS.

Cusumano (1987) summarizes five basic types of manufacturing organizations, as shown in Table 2.1. These are in approximate historical sequence.[1] In a variety of industries, countries, and time periods, production technology for goods such as books, textiles, guns, paper, and automobiles has tended to standardize, at least temporarily. As production volumes increased, many companies shifted their focus from product development to process innovation to evolve from craft-like job shops or batch operations into large-scale design and production for mass markets.

Once firms made this transition, the strategic issues faced by shop managers shifted toward increasing the volume, lowering the unit costs, reducing product variety, increasing standardization, specializing labor activities, and lowering labor skills. Perfected by Ford in the early 1910s, this method helped make sophisticated goods like automobiles available to a mass market. These benefits appeared to offset

[1] The following few paragraphs are adapted freely from Cusumano (1987).

the advantages of higher quality, ability to customize products, and flexibility of workers' tasks attributable to batch or craft operations.

Recently, a new type of organization has appeared in Japan. Pioneered most effectively by Toyota, this strategy combines many of the benefits of mass production with the flexibility of batch operations. This approach relies on even stricter process control and component standardization than Ford used, but it broadens workers' job specifications, uses automation much more selectively, and adds an interrelated set of production strategies such as rapid setups, low inventories, and self-inspection of work by workers. Analysis of Toyota's success shows convincingly that technology alone was not sufficient; the most important contributions appear to lie in the management policy area: process analysis, standardization, and worker discipline and cooperation.

The flexible manufacturing system (FMS) represents another recent organizational model. Presently only applied to metal-cutting methods but applicable to others, this technique appears able to produce a variety of products quickly and with little economic penalty for low volumes. In these systems, a larger amount of time and money than in other production methods is devoted to product engineering and development of manufacturing systems capable of automating a large number of operations.

Early History of Manufacturing in America

A recent book (Hounshell, 1984) gives a thorough history of the development of "mass production" in America in the period from 1800 to 1932. This history treats two themes in parallel: the development of physical *processes* or machines and the development of *methods,* techniques, and ideas. In this section we will give a summary of this early history. (The reader may refer to Fig. 2.1 while reading this section.) For the complete story, the reader should consult Hounshell and other similar books. The next section summarizes later developments leading to the present time, most of which have occurred too recently to have been subjected to rigorous historical analysis.

The desire for interchangeable parts is the root of a long development of *manufacturing methods.* In the early history of manufacturing, the role and needs of governments and armies played a decisive role. As early as 1765, the French army recognized the desirability of making guns from interchangeable parts so that repairs could be made on the field of battle. The ideal of interchangeable parts comprises the ability to take any randomly selected set of the necessary parts and assemble a working gun from them. Cost of manufacture was not a factor; neither would it ever be dominant in later military

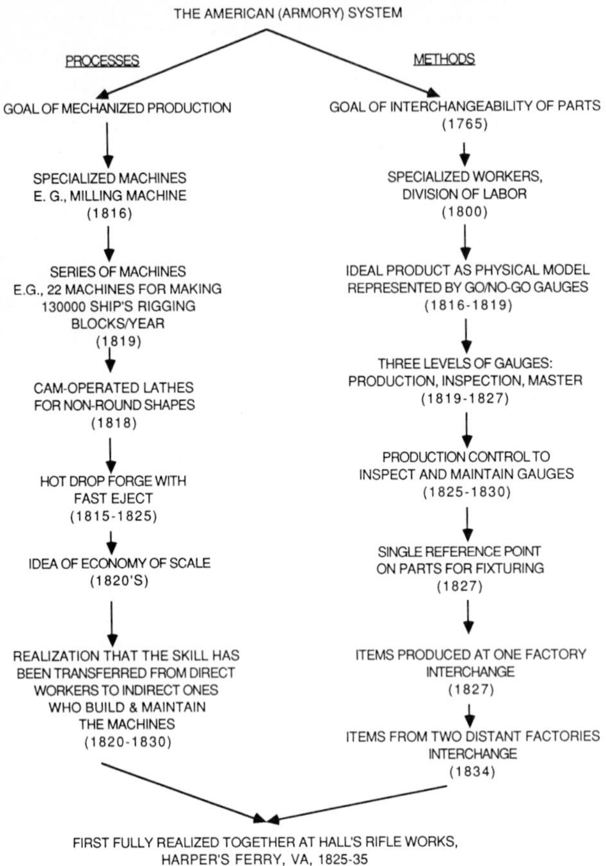

Fig. 2.1 Development of the armory system of manufacture.

efforts to achieve interchangeable parts. Instead, the goal of these efforts is distinctly a life cycle concern, namely to enhance the usefulness of the product after manufacture. In fact, there is little evidence that interchangeable parts manufacture by itself ever resulted in lower production costs. Since early manufacturing focused on making guns, the resulting methods have been named "the armory system" by Hounshell.

Parallel to the desire for interchangeable parts but largely independent of it in the early days was the desire for mechanized manufacturing, a desire which forms the root of a chain of *process developments*. Mechanized production stemmed from a desire to reduce production costs and increase production capacity. Its earliest applications were to the production of single parts that were used singly, requiring no assembly to other parts, or to production of products whose operating tolerances were large. Interchangeability was not an issue and the lack of it did not matter. Typical of such parts are ships' pulleys (called blocks) that were made in large quantities in the early 1800s by a sequence of specialized machines conceived according to the relatively new concept of division of labor. As new kinds of machines were developed to do different tasks formerly done by craftsmen, it was realized that production skill could be transferred to machines and that the valued skills of people were now the ability to create, build, and maintain these machines.

These machines did not necessarily produce parts so uniform that they could be assembled interchangeably. To achieve the latter goal required much thought and development of methods of measurement and management rather than invention of machines. The basic problem is that the output of a machine is fundamentally variable, because of variations in itself, its surrounding conditions, how it is operated, and the condition of the materials it works on. Interchangeability requires that the machines' output be uniform enough, though it need not be perfect. Perfection lies in the conceptual "ideal product," toward which each actual unit should strive.

By the late 1810s it was realized that gauges could be used to decide if a part was the correct size and shape. Such gauges were made from an example of the final product that was known to function properly. The example product's parts passed the gauges, and it was assumed that subsequent parts which passed would not only function but would interchange and still function. The example product therefore stood as the "ideal."

To make this concept work in practice required imposing a lot of discipline on manufacturing activities, including requiring workers to actually use the gauges, maintaining a second set of gauges to ensure that the workers' gauges had not worn out, and maintaining yet a third set of gauges as "masters." Additionally, it was realized that if each part had to visit a series of specialized machines, to maintain accuracy the machines would each have to grip the part the same way in the same place. Thus was born the idea of the jigging surface. Not until the mid-1820s was full interchangeability achieved in the manufacture of muskets. Another 10 years were needed to establish two distant factories whose muskets could be interchanged with each other.

In 1853 at the Springfield Armory, 10 rifles were taken from inventory, one each from production years 1844–1853, taken apart, the parts jumbled, and successfully reassembled randomly and successfully test fired. To this day, the "interchange" test is applied to each batch of 1000 guns bought by the U.S. Army. Ten guns must interchange successfully or else the whole batch is refused until the reason is found and corrected. It is a tense time for the manufacturer.

Interchangeability and mechanization were applied after 1850 to commercial products, for which the goal was lower production cost. Although good success was achieved with some products in the period from 1850 to 1900 (such as watches, pistols, and bicycles), great difficulty was experienced with others, notably Singer sewing machines and McCormick reapers. The difficulty was manifested in the need to file the parts to fit, and thus assembly was an extended activity of "fitting" that required large numbers of skilled workers.

The reasons for the difficulty are unclear but probably stemmed from several interrelated factors. First, while pistols are similar in complexity to muskets, sewing machines and reapers may have been much more complex and required closer tolerances than available machines could deliver. Especially important was the distortion of steel parts during hardening. Parts that fit before heat treatment had to be filed again afterward. The most successful sewing machine from the point of view of interchangeability was the Willcox and Gibbs machine, made by the Brown and Sharpe Company. It employed the simple one-thread chain stitch rather than the complex two-thread Singer method; it is likely that the chain stitch machine can operate with looser tolerances, making interchange easier.

It is interesting to note that Brown and Sharpe had to develop machines and measuring instruments in order to make the Willcox and Gibbs sewing machine. It found sewing machines less interesting but continued to make them until 1950 just to have an in-house factory in which to test its mainline machine and measuring products.

Significantly, the inability to interchange sewing machine or reaper parts did not inhibit the products' popularity or profitability. Demand exceeded supply, and buyers could finance their purchases. Both products were made in quantities of 200,000 to 500,000 per year by the 1880s. While the historical record is incomplete, it appears that limited interchangeability was achieved in these two industries after 1880.

To support such large production volumes, much progress was needed in industrial organization. Plants were laid out with the machines or processes in the sequence that the product needed them so that work flowed smoothly from machine to machine. This is called a "flow line" or "flow shop" arrangement.[2] Accompanying better physical organization was the beginning of industrial engineering, comprising process sheets to describe each operation and industrial commerce in the form of contracts to permit subcontractors to make some of the parts.

Some of these contractors set up shop within the walls of the main factory and were called inside contractors. In the Singer sewing ma-

[2] Different shop arrangements are described in Chap. 4.

chine factory, there were a large number of these inside contractors, who hired and paid their own workers. They tended to drive their workers hard and used authoritarian methods to control them. Coordinating the activities of these contractors was difficult. The main manufacturers gradually bought them out, and the contractors were converted to foremen. It is likely that some patterns of authoritarian production line management originated with this practice. The opposite practice, often called "participatory management," has been taking root in the United States only in the last few years.

Sewing machines and bicycles, another important industry of that period, required two additional operations to ensure their quality and customer acceptance, namely painting and inspection. The Pope Bicycle Company, the biggest, had separate inspection and quality control departments whose activities included testing to destruction to determine how to reduce the bicycle's weight. Bicycle makers also introduced two techniques essential to the automobile industry: ball bearings and press forming of metal parts. Press forming, as an alternative to casting and machining, yielded much lighter parts much more quickly. In recognition of the importance of this process, Ford bought a press manufacturer in the early 1900s.

Throughout the 1800s, progress was achieved by brilliant but largely uneducated individuals. These people knew how the product was to function and often contributed to its design. Then they designed the production machines and laid out the factories. Industries or companies that had the most success with interchangeable parts benefited from the experience of people who had worked in the pistol or musket industries first. Certain generic machine types such as lathes and milling machines evolved, and new companies were formed to manufacture them. Even at this date, there was an unresolved debate over whether to use such generic machines or to build strictly special and dedicated machines for each process step on each part.

Recent History of Manufacturing

The reader may refer to Fig. 2.2 while reading this section.

By the early 1900s the challenge of manufacturing lay in automobiles. Henry Ford saw the opportunity to create a true mass market entailing production volumes of 2 million or more per year. To achieve such volumes he knew he could not permit any time-consuming "fitting" during assembly. ("In mass production there are no fitters," he said.) Interchangeability therefore became the route to rapid assembly, while retaining such life cycle advantages as simplicity of field repair. By 1910 he had achieved sufficient simplicity of design and quality of machines that interchangeability was no longer a prob-

Fig. 2.2 Recent developments in manufacturing.

lem. His factories were laid out as flow shops. They operated by what is today called just in time (JIT) production with such small inventories that raw iron ore was converted into a car in 10 days. His model for this kind of manufacturing came from tin can making, the canned food industry, and the meat packing industry. (The latter was also a model of poor working conditions.)

But, assembly was still a bottleneck. Assembly was done by teams of workers who built an entire car. However, they spent too much time moving from job to job. Ford solved this in 1913 with the development of the moving assembly line. Workers each did one small assembly job and the conveyor brought the work to them. Productivity increases

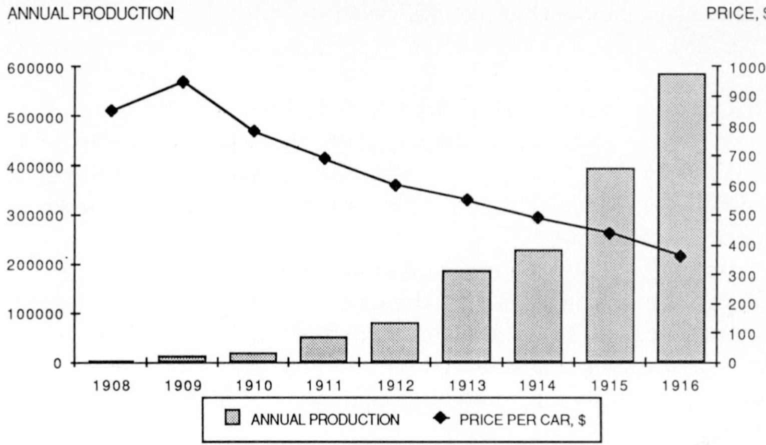

Fig. 2.3 Annual production volume (left axis) and retail price (right axis) for Ford Model T's. The assembly line was introduced in 1913 and most of the factory was operating by assembly line methods by 1914.

were typically between 3 and 5 to 1. The final block to huge production volumes was thus removed.

The assembly line idea was first tested on subassemblies such as magnetos and transmission covers, later on engines, chassis, and front axles, and finally on final car assembly itself. By the old bench assembly method, 29 workers made 35 to 40 magnetos each per 9-hour (hr) day, or about 1 every 13 minutes (min). A year later, 14 men on an assembly line made 1335 in an 8-hr day, or 1 every 5 min. A chassis that used to take 750 min was produced by assembly line in 93 min.

It appears that the time study method developed by Taylor (1911) did not play a large role in these reductions. This method relied on analyzing an existing assembly process and optimizing it by selecting the best people for each task, dividing up the tasks to get similar total work times for each worker, and establishing standard times for each task. The Ford approach differed in that it examined each job to see if it could be improved or eliminated *before* any attempt to optimize it was made. The time standard for each job was set by the capacity and output rate of neighboring machines rather than by using an abstract standard, forcing people to work at the pace of the machines. Pacing people to machines is one of the most distasteful aspects of factory work, and it has been eliminated or greatly reduced in recent years. In some countries, it is illegal.

Figure 2.3 shows the results of Ford's development of mass production in terms of number of Model T's made and their retail price.

This method also destroyed the last vestige of craftsmanship in high-volume manufacturing and helped lead to numerous labor-management problems that are still with us. Ford doubled his wages to $5 per day to keep employees from quitting after a few months of work.

Ford's product design philosophy was to build one basic design year after year with a few add-on options. The supporting manufacturing strategy was to design and build specialized production machines of great efficiency. Model change would have forced the scrapping of most of these machines.[3]

Even up to the 1920s the main method of ensuring interchangeability was the use of gauges. Until the early 1900s there were no measurement standards, so the master parts and master gauges were the standards. To convert to a nongauge method required changing the form of the ideal product. Instead of a physical ideal, a symbolic ideal in the form of a drawing was needed. Drawings could represent the parts and product in a standard way and, with the advent of precision metal gauge blocks, could contain dimensions stated in a standard length measure such as inches. Anyone could interpret such dimensions accurately by using the gauge blocks to calibrate measuring instruments. The United States established the National Bureau of Standards in 1901 and the engineering societies set up the American National Standards Institute (ANSI) in 1917. By 1923 Ford had bought the American rights to the famous Johannsen gauge blocks, which are still widely used.

Drawings with dimensions were common by the 1920s, but drawings with tolerances were not. Tolerances contain the vital data concerning how far a part can deviate from the ideal and still both function and interchange. Determining appropriate tolerances for parts is a challenging design task. Errors in many assembled parts interact to produce the final state of assembly and operation. Tolerances that are too loose risk failure of the assembly while tolerances that are too tight unnecessarily increase manufacturing costs.

The science of tolerances is still in development, as is the science of how to state tolerances on drawings. A major problem is that drawings are two dimensional while parts are three dimensional. Many past tolerancing methods allowed manufacturers alternate interpretations of the same drawing. Only in the 1940s in England was the currently used method of "true position tolerancing" developed. The ability to interpret drawings unambiguously is a great benefit in a modern industrial economy because it permits interchangeability,

[3] When Ford finally did change over to the Model A in 1927, 16,000 machines were scrapped, 16,000 were rebuilt, and 4500 new ones were bought (Hounshell, 1984).

subcontracting, manufacture, and sale of standard-size parts by catalog, multiple suppliers for the same kind of part, and so on.

Generic Problems in High-Volume Manufacturing

Ford's philosophy of uniform mass production of one model by dedicated machines fell apart in the mid-1920s when supply finally exceeded demand. General Motors had recognized the potential for selling cars that were *more* expensive than Model T's. GM designed and sold several models in various price ranges. Smaller markets were envisioned for each model, and sales were stimulated by annual model changes. GM organized its design and manufacturing operations to support annual changeovers, which typically took several weeks to implement after several years of design. GM made great use of more generic machines that were designed to accept new workheads each model year. Chevrolet production was 280,000 in 1924, 1,000,000 in 1928, and 1,500,000 in 1929. Annual changeover took 3 weeks, about as long as it takes today.

The same Ford engineers who brilliantly conceived the Model T and its production methods had such trouble designing its successor and implementing production that the company was nearly ruined. The total changeover cost, including lost profits, amounted to about $250 million. The year of the change, 1926, saw Ford lose the U.S. market share lead to GM; it has not yet recovered it.

The differences in approach adopted by these two companies illustrate a basic conflict in high-volume production, namely how to attain flexibility without sacrificing efficiency. As we shall see later in the book, this problem remains an important one. Much of the effort in robotics and FMSs is directed at this problem, with varying degrees of success.

GM also made heavy use of certain principles of economics and accounting. The company's success has contributed to the spread of these techniques. The basic idea, as practiced today, is that each capital expenditure by the company should be looked upon as an investment that is expected to earn a return, expressed as an interest rate. Since the company could as well put its money safely in a bank, each investment had to be analyzed to see if it would return more than a bank account would. This is a very systematic procedure that rationalized investments by holding them to a common standard.

The focus of economic analysis fell on labor replacement, perhaps because of the influence of labor efficiency experts like Taylor. Taylor made a science out of division of labor and provided experimental techniques for determining which tiny slice of work should be done by each worker. The amount of time required for a job became the paramount measure, and since workers were paid by the hour, the cost of labor became the center of accounting principles in manufacturing. This in turn has contributed to poor labor-management relations, in as much as management saw labor replacement as the main cost-saving method while labor saw job preservation as its highest priority.

Another problem is that of dealing with the costs of support or overhead. These items include energy and taxes, plus purchasing, material handling, supervision, maintenance, and so on, which are necessary but cannot be attributed individually to identifiable product units. Such costs are arbitrarily allocated to the production process, usually by adding an amount to each production worker's salary to arrive at a synthetic hourly rate. This method seems to have been adopted decades ago as a simple means of determining the cost of inventory (Worthy, 1987) and seriously clouds attempts to determine the true costs of manufacturing. In particular, it often deludes management into thinking that reducing the number of production workers will save money.

A critical historical eye is now being turned on traditional economic analysis methods (Kaplan and Johnson, 1987). According to this study, the method of return on investment, as originally conceived, was never intended to be used to evaluate individual investments in machines or processes. Instead, it was supposed to be a guide to top management seeking to allocate available capital to diverse divisions of a large company. The intention was that division managers would decide how to use this capital budget. The duPont Company invented this method between 1890 and 1910 to manage its diverse operations in chemicals and munitions. They later applied it to rescue their investment in foundering General Motors in the 1920s. GM's success caused the method to be widely adopted without its original intent being understood. It is now used to judge every individual investment, giving it the power to form company strategy piecemeal without this power ever having been delegated consciously and without judging whether the strategy thus evolved was good for the company. It has also made it difficult to justify investments whose return could not be expressed in pure financial terms. Such sources of return include the firm's reputation for quality or fast delivery, possibly intangible but of great influence on the firm's profitability.

Today, as we show later in this chapter, labor is a small part of the cost of any one factory's total. Good product design plus wise management of materials, machines, and people are the most effective cost-control techniques. Yet the old accounting methods remain, and their ability to stifle large strategy considerations can still cause companies problems as they try to modernize. The tension between finance-oriented and manufacturing-oriented people in the Ford and Nissan auto companies in the 1950s–1970s is well documented by Halberstam (1986).

Generic Problems in Low-Volume Manufacturing

In the many companies whose annual volumes are well below the millions typical of autos, the challenge is a mirror image of that of the large-scale manufacturers. Makers of pumps, tractors, and aircraft have long sought to attain flow line efficiencies in spite of the wide variety of their products. Low-volume producers are often organized as job shops in which machines of one type are grouped together since no one product provides a dominant flow around which a flow line can be organized.[4] Each product or model takes a different route through the factory according to its processing requirements. A large fraction of each machine's time is spent setting it up for a new job. To save the impact of setup time on the workpieces, they are grouped into batches with one setup per batch. However, a large portion of each workpiece's time is spent waiting for other pieces in the batch to be processed. The advent of numerically controlled machine tools in the 1950s promised to alleviate these problems, but the reward has been slow in coming.

In the late 1930s, a technique called "group technology" was developed to handle such situations (Opitz, 1970). The idea was to create larger production batches and make setups less frequent by combining similar (i.e., not necessarily identical) parts into one batch. Such groups would share a process route through the factory. The challenge is to select parts wisely for membership in a group. This is accomplished by identifying differences between parts that matter, while ignoring those that do not. Differences that matter will affect the kind of machines needed or the sequence of operations, for example. Each difference (material, length, etc.) is assigned a code class, and variations within a class are given different numbers (Material: steel = 6, brass = 9; Size: over 10-mm diameter = 1, etc.). Individual parts are then assigned code numbers, and those with the same number are processed together or take the same route through the factory.

So far, the most success has been gained with parts of simple geometry, such as shafts. However, the same ideas have been applied successfully in shipbuilding, as discussed more fully in Chap. 3. Group

[4] Job shops are discussed in Chap. 4.

technology has also been used to identify parts that are easy or difficult to feed to assembly machines or that are easy or hard to assemble (Boothroyd et al., 1982).

The FMS can be thought of as a combination of numerical control and group technology. As described in Chap. 3, the key to a successful FMS is careful selection and design of the groups of parts assigned to it.

Economics and Demographics of Manufacturing in the United States

Manufacturing is an essential part of the U.S. economy. For a variety of reasons, it has been declining relative to other components of the economy. Yet its ability to generate domestic and export income is not matched by other components, in spite of their recent growth. Table 2.2 compares manufacturing's contributions to the economy as a whole over several years.

While interpretations can be undependable, we can make a few observations from this table and other sources. First, manufacturing's fraction of employment and contribution to GNP have fallen since 1970 to about the levels they were in the late 1930s. Second, U.S. manufacturing has recently declined slightly as a force in world trade, but it maintains a high position nonetheless. Third, the ability of U.S. manufacturing to contribute to U.S. exports has fallen since 1975. Yet manufacturing is still the largest single industrial sector of the economy, overshadowing trade, finance, and services (Gold). Moreover, ac-

TABLE 2.2 Selected Economic Data on Manufacturing in the United States

	1970	1975	1980	1983	Source*
Manufacturing percent of GNP	25.4	23.1	22.1	20.7	718
U.S. share of world mfr. exports (percent)	21.1	19.1	18.3	19.4	1353
U.S. mfr. exports as percent of U.S. goods & services exports	44.5	45.8	42.5	39.3	1353/715
Mfr. empl. as percent of U.S. employment	26.4	22.7	22.1	19.8	678
Production workers as percent of all mfr. empl.	72	70	67	64	1337
Value added per $ of production wages	$ 3.30	$ 3.65	$ 3.91	$ 4.16†	1337
Materials cost as percent of value of shipments	54.00	57.00	59.00	58.00	1337
Assets per employee ($K)	14	20	27.8	39.1†	1337

*Table numbers from *Statistical Abstract of the U.S., 1985.*
†Table 1303, *Statistical Abstract of the U.S., 1987.*

cording to Cohen and Zysman (1987), if one includes those portions of the service sector that depend on or aid manufacturing, manufacturing accounts for almost half of the GNP. Such services include transportation, engineering consultants, finance and construction of new factories, and so on.

Can a decline of manufacturing be blamed on production workers? According to the data in the table, each production worker has been contributing more and more value added per dollar of wages, in part because more machinery and equipment have been put at workers' disposal. (Hours worked per year per person have been essentially constant at about 2000.) As a result of the increasingly efficient use of production workers, we find that materials costs are a growing percentage of production cost, and a larger percentage of employees are involved in nonproduction work. This last item may reflect "bloated overhead" or the larger numbers of engineers and technicians needed as industry's technological level rises.

One should particularly note the fact that the cost of a manufactured item is primarily devoted to purchased materials, including energy. Currently, this fraction is about 60 percent. Labor is typically about 20 to 30 percent, with production workers being about 70 percent of this. The result is that production labor is really a small part of overall manufacturing cost within any one company. This fact should be kept in mind when listening to discussions of "cheap foreign labor." The latter is a factor, but it is not overwhelming. For example, during the 1960s when Japanese shipbuilders were taking the world shipbuilding market away from Great Britain, they were paying more per ton for steel than British shipyards were (Todd, 1985). Todd ascribes the Japanese success to more efficient hull and engine designs that permitted more profitable cargo hauling over the life of the ship, plus more efficient ship design and shipyard operation.

Two conclusions emerge immediately. First, a great deal of money stands to be made or lost managing materials: purchasing only what is needed, selling quickly what is made, reducing scrap, designing for economical use of materials, avoiding errors in fabrication, transport, and assembly, and so on. Second, even if only a few people remain on the production floor, their contributions will become increasingly important in seeing that expensive materials and equipment are managed correctly.

The above discussion should not be taken to mean that labor costs are not important across the economy as a whole. Recall the supplier-manufacturer chain depicted in Fig. 1.2. The materials flow through several companies along this chain. At each stage, a ratio of material to labor costs similar to the 60 to 30 cited above probably characterizes the activity. Thus, from raw material through final test, there is in

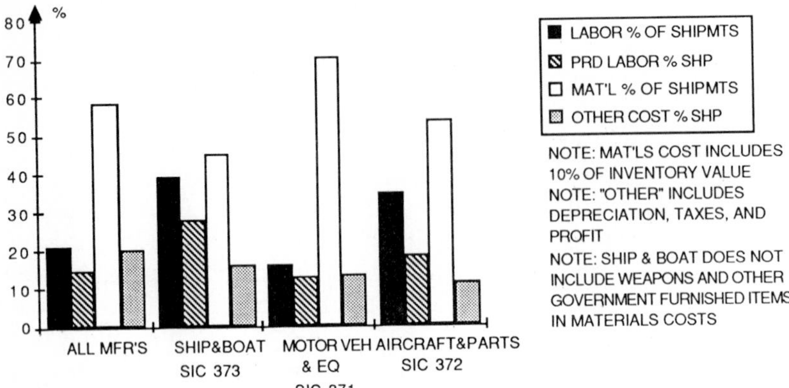

Fig. 2.4 Cost distributions among different factors in manufacturing in different industries. (*Source: U.S. Department of Commerce Annual Survey of Manufactures, 1984.*

fact a great deal of labor, although only a little of it is under the control of one company.[5]

The above conclusions are based on aggregated data for the U.S. economy as a whole. When we look at individual industries, as categorized by the Commerce Department's Standard Industrial Classification (SIC) Code, we see different patterns. Figure 2.4 shows cost distributions in several industries compared to the average of all manufacturers. Ship- and boatbuilders are more like construction firms than manufacturers. For them, labor is a higher percentage of total costs, and materials are correspondingly less. Motor vehicles and parts companies are the prototypical "mass production" firms, and thus it is not surprising that labor is such a small fraction of their total. Aircraft and parts lie somewhere between ships and autos. Also, as befits a high-technology product, the aircraft industry has a lot of nonproduction labor, largely in engineering and other technical areas.

Commerce Department data for these industries reveal similarities and differences. In all three, production workers are 70 percent of all employees, and direct production workers, those who actually add value, are 70 percent of these. However, assemblers (including weld-

[5] For example, suppose an item passes through four production stages, all having 10 percent profit, depreciation, and transport costs. Three stages are in manufacturing with a 60 to 30 ratio of material to labor costs, while the fourth is a raw material creator with a ratio of 80 to 10. Then the final item is overall 60.96 percent labor, 17.28 percent material, and 21.76 profit, depreciation, and transport. Such an item might be a motor containing a bearing made of steel mined from ore.

ers) dominate the auto industry whereas machine operators rank first in aircraft. There are several possible explanations for these differences. First, a high proportion of materials costs indicates that much of what a company produces it buys without changing it very much. Typical of such items are motors and bearings purchased by a company that makes washing machines. Second, different companies and industries will employ different strategies concerning what to make and what to buy. The data indicate that autos are made largely from bought parts, and much labor goes into putting those parts together. Aircraft and ships are made from a larger percentage of raw materials which must be heavily processed, making assemblers a smaller percentage of labor cost than machinists and other material processors.

These data are presented in order to give the reader a feeling for where the cost is in manufactured goods. For example, in the auto industry, labor costs are about 13 percent of the total value of the industry's shipments, and assemblers are about a third of all production workers. Thus magically eliminating all assembly workers would save about 4.4 percent of the total cost. The conclusion to be drawn is that dramatic cost reductions will occur only by attacking *all* the sources of cost, not just labor and not just assembly labor. A more powerful conclusion is that immediate short-term cost reduction is not necessarily the right starting point when assessing options for new manufacturing technology or new product designs. In fact, piecemeal cost reductions may not be the correct strategic framework at all when considering modernizing a manufacturing operation. Instead, the overall cost distribution must be analyzed, and a strategy for making overall cost reductions must be identified. The result may be a total change in how the company operates.

It is clear from Table 2.2 that the United States needs a strong manufacturing sector in order to maintain export income and to provide high-paying jobs. It is also clear that improving the sector will require careful management of increasingly expensive materials and equipment and more highly trained and valuable people. Finally, it will be necessary to ensure that the nonproduction workers are also used efficiently. We may hope that an increasing fraction of these will be well-trained product and manufacturing engineers.

Summary

This chapter provided background for the challenges described in Chap. 1 and the examples and specific technical topics that follow. The history of manufacturing shows that many of today's problems have analogs in the past: the need for uniformity of production, the search for flexibility and efficiency, the conflicts between labor and management, engineers and cost accountants, product designers and manufacturing engineers, supervisors and line workers. A study of the economics indicates that costs are heavily weighted toward materials, both raw materials and purchased assemblies, with labor being much smaller. This weighting should force greater emphasis on better product design and more efficient factory operation.

The next chapter provides several examples of recent products and factories that have been designed to respond creatively to today's challenges.

References

Abegglen, J. C., and G. Stalk, Jr.: *Kaisha, The Japanese Corporation,* Basic Books, New York, 1985.

Boothroyd, G., C. Poli, and L. E. Murch: *Automatic Assembly,* Marcel Dekker, New York, 1982.

Cohen, S. S., and J. Zysman: *Manufacturing Matters: The Myth of the Post-Industrial Economy,* Basic Books, New York, 1987.

Cusumano, M. A.: *The Japanese Automobile Industry: Technology and Management at Nissan and Toyota,* Harvard University Press, Cambridge, MA, 1985.

———: "The 'Software Factory' Reconsidered: An Approach to the Strategic Management of Engineering," MIT Sloan School of Management Working Paper 9-52-87, 1987.

Gold, B.: *Technology and Strategic Management,* Ballinger, Cambridge, MA, not yet published.

Halberstam, D.: *The Reckoning,* Avon Press, New York, 1986.

Hounshell, D.: *From the American System to Mass Production, 1800–1932,* The Johns Hopkins University Press, Baltimore, 1984.

Kaplan, R. S., and T. H. Johnson: *Relevance Lost: The Rise and Fall of Management Accounting,* Harvard Business School Press, Boston, 1987.

Opitz, H.: *A Classification System to Describe Workpieces,* Pergamon, London, 1970.

Taylor, F. W.: *The Principles of Scientific Management,* Harper & Brothers, New York, 1911.

Todd, D.: *The World Shipbuilding Industry,* Croom & Helm, London, 1985).

———: *Statistical Abstract of the U.S.,* 1985.

U.S. Department of Commerce: *Annual Survey of Manufactures,* 1984.

Worthy, F. S.: "Accounting Bores You? Wake Up," *Fortune,* Oct. 12, 1987, pp. 43–50.

Chapter

3

Examples of Recent Advanced Production Systems

This chapter is devoted to descriptions of recent advanced production systems that illustrate many of the points made in the first two chapters. The examples are divided into large-scale and small-scale production and include product design, human relations and management, and integrated design-manufacturing. Most are successes; one is not.

Large-Scale Production

The Toyota production system: A total business strategy

Toyota Motors of Japan has been developing its production system since at least the late 1940s under the leadership of Mr. Taiichi Ohno (Cusumano, 1985). The goal of this system is to achieve the efficiencies of a flow line while producing in small batches. As stated in Sugimori et al. (1977), the method has three basic elements:

- The right material at the right place at the right time
- Continuous learning and improvement
- Respect for the worker

The first of these elements has gained the most publicity under the name just in time (JIT), but one should recognize that JIT is only part of a larger scheme which seeks to make the entire company and its supplier chain operate as much as possible like one big conveyor. To a remarkable degree this has been achieved. An important feature of the system is that it is entirely manual, requiring no computers and little worker training.

Toyota was founded in the 1930s, just as Ford was recovering from its changeover crisis. Toyota was too poor to buy American car designs, machines, or production advice, so it had to make up its own. This painful process took about 10 years, during which it mainly built trucks for the Japanese army. After the war, the company had to start over. To save money it decided to establish a production method that required as little purchased material and in-process inventory as possible. The main thing to avoid was making things that had not already been ordered. Toyota's approach was the "supermarket" method, which it copied from America. In supermarkets, stock is put on shelves only as it is sold, not on the basis of a prior plan. At the same time, a random sequence of orders can be supported as long as the production system is flexible. Not only did the factory not make anything until it was ordered but each workstation followed the same rule, based on taking orders from the station immediately downstream.

Throughout the 1950s Toyota elaborated this method, exporting it to its suppliers in later years. The cooperation of the employees was gained, after a union-breaking strike, by involving them fully in the production process, soliciting their suggestions, and guaranteeing them lifetime employment. The latter was possible because, as with sewing machines in the late 1800s, demand exceeded supply as the Japanese car market grew. Toyota gained the necessary flexibility through cooperation of the workers in establishing rapid changeovers and in the ability to switch workers from one kind of machine or job to another as demand fluctuated. Model variety was restricted so that a measure of efficiency could be maintained.

To attain JIT, Toyota had to develop a production control system that encouraged only needed production and avoided "safety" production. It did this by providing each work center with tickets (*kanbans*) with which it could buy parts from upstream stations as needed. The number of tickets in a package determines the batch size, which is generally 1 to a few hours of production. Thus, within each work center there is an "in-process inventory" of only a few hours work. By contrast, a company not employing JIT might have days or weeks of work in its in-process inventory. Such stock levels may result from (1) poor planning or scheduling, (2) the desire to have extra safety stock on hand in case of breakdowns or shortages, or (3) the belief, possibly encouraged by cost accountants or production schedules based on material requirements programs (MRP), that it is more economical to run the equipment and make parts regardless of whether they are needed or not rather than let the machine stand idle. All such practices are wasteful. Another reason for large inventories may be the inability to utilize JIT because suppliers are too far away.

To implement a production system with little in-process inventory, Toyota had to throw off many widely believed "truths," among them the idea that a certain level of safety stock is good because it provides for continuing work when some machines are broken. Toyota found that one could be safe with much lower stock levels than previously thought possible. Large stocks were instead regarded as flags that pointed to production problems. Work rules were arranged so that line workers could fix breakdowns quickly, avoiding the need for safety stocks to guard against breakdowns.

A second truth that had to be set aside was the idea that a certain level of poor quality was tolerable. Machine breakdowns and stock shortfalls caused by bad parts cannot be tolerated by a JIT system. Valuable personnel cannot be diverted into jobs inspecting incoming parts that vendors should have already inspected. Instead, both parts and machines must perform at very high levels simply to keep the production system going. Parts suppliers, machinery builders, and factory personnel expend great efforts to ensure this.

A third truth set aside was that it takes a long time to change over fixed equipment to make a new batch of parts. This truth forced production runs to be long to reduce the effect of the lost changeover time. To combat this, Toyota trained special changeover teams and redesigned equipment such as stamping presses, with the result that hours of changeover became minutes. The phrase "single minute exchange of die" has become a slogan for efficiency in production (Shingo, 1986).

Like many other Japanese companies, Toyota also limited the number of models it offered, greatly reducing the complexity of operating the factories. Supporting a large range of models requires a great deal of overhead in terms of purchasing agents, parts runners, expediters, stock personnel, and so on, raising costs considerably. Abegglen and Stalk (1985) claim that every doubling in the number of models produced increases overhead costs by 40 percent.

Finally, Toyota had to teach all these new truths to its vendors so that they could respond quickly to JIT, enabling them to ship parts hourly or daily in response to Toyota's orders. (See the discussion of Toyota's supplier, Nippondenso, later in this chapter.)

Toyota thus has been able, by ingenuity and lucky circumstances, to solve several problems that were recognized early in the development of modern manufacturing and to attain:

- High flexibility combined with a large degree of mechanization
- High efficiency without use of strictly dedicated machines

- Good labor-management relations
- Establishment of a cadre of suppliers that can deliver high-quality parts using the same "supermarket" method

These efforts have produced a flexible production system that is able to adapt quickly to changes in the market. When this capability is added to Toyota's ability to create new car designs in less time than its competition, the result is a powerful manufacturing company.

No system of this type can survive without the wholehearted involvement of the production workers. To show the workers how important they were, Toyota gave them the power to stop the production line if they saw a problem they could not fix right away. In this way, Toyota avoided a widespread problem in mass production, namely the tendency to send problems downstream to the next station or department in an effort to maintain the schedule upstream.

Today, JIT is being adopted by many companies. The discipline it forces and the cooperation it fosters have greatly improved efficiency, reduced costly inventories, and raised quality. However, the technique is not completely understood and clearly must be modified to suit conditions different from Toyota's. When suppliers are days away, hourly deliveries are impractical. When a production system consists of complex networks rather than a single line, a simple self-driven unsupervised scheduler will not function well, and the production system may oscillate between models instead of producing a steady mix, or it may fall behind. These points indicate that JIT and other Japanese methods are more than just slogans and require careful study before they can be used successfully. In Chap. 4, the JIT technique is compared to the MRP method for operating a factory.

Other Japanese manufacturers have used different techniques suitable to their products. Complex and high-technology items like compact disk players require much more mechanization and quality control than automobiles. Thus companies like Sony, Hitachi, NEC, and others have made heavy use of computer controls, robots, and statistical quality control to satisfy the exacting needs of their products. By comparison, Toyota is a relatively unmechanized company whose strategy is centered on management.

American auto companies have only recently adopted some of Toyota's methods. In the past, their approach to high-volume model mix manufacture was less disciplined. Long changeover times were considered normal, as were large buffer stocks of parts in the factories. A great deal of "scientific management" study has been devoted to optimally sizing such buffers. Large buffers helped to even out the flow of parts of the various models. At the same time, U.S. companies allowed the number of models they build each year to grow until a great deal of time and attention had to be devoted to keeping track of everything. Now, however, the search for manufacturing efficiency has spurred such companies to reduce the number of models they build and to control their inventories better. They are also designing their products more wisely.

New United Motors Manufacturing, Inc. (NUMMI): Success based on management

NUMMI is the joint venture of General Motors and Toyota Motors which assembles a Toyota-designed small car in a former GM plant in Fremont, California. The main feature of this venture is the high-production efficiency achieved without recourse to advanced automation. This plant uses floor space more efficiently than typical GM plants, though not as efficiently as a typical Toyota plant. Its quality is near the top of GM's divisions, and its productivity in terms of worker-hours per vehicle, while not quite as good as Toyota's, is far better than GM's on similar cars. NUMMI acknowledges the importance of good management to these achievements, but little is known about the effect of the car's original design.

Toyota management brought its production system to the Fremont plant and executed a two-phase program. In the first phase, it identified the causes of the previous plant's low productivity. Then it put in its own management system (Ikebuchi, 1986).

Causes of low productivity included quality problems, low production line efficiency, and excess inventory. The quality problems included suppliers' parts, damage to parts during in-plant transport, and an attitude that repair and rework were normal. Low line efficiency was caused by excess inventory, low utilization of equipment because of poor job design, and excess downtime caused by a centrally controlled repair group and narrow job classifications that prevented line workers from fixing their own machines. Excess inventory wasted floor space, crowded the workers, caused slow response to problems, and generally provided a crutch that kept workers and managers from confronting problems of poor parts quality and low machine uptime.

Toyota's response to these problems is based on the principle of involving the workers in operation and management. Workers are organized into teams of five to seven members, and, based on the union contract, there are only four job classifications in the plant. (Typical unionized U.S. plants have dozens or hundreds of job classifications. Examples are repair, hydraulic; repair, mechanical; repair, electrical; repair, pneumatic; repair, electronic. No one can do work in someone else's classification.) It is a team's responsibility to improve the efficiency of its operations and to reduce wasted time and materials. In this spirit, machines are equipped to stop themselves if quality falls, or people can stop them. Each work operation is standardized by the team, and the standard is used as the basis for improvement. Since few parts are stored near the workstations, people become acutely aware of parts quality. They neither wish to export quality problems to the next station (their "customer") or to be the victims of such problems. Inventory control is by the JIT principle with hourly deliveries within the plant, although suppliers are too far away to permit this technique to be used outside the plant.

The NUMMI approach is a good one in a situation in which manual operations predominate, such as assembly of large objects or products. It corrects a number of problems inherited from the early days of mass production, such as extreme division of labor and authoritative management, and puts responsibility for improving operations in the hands of those who know the operations the best. It is not so obvious that it is the universal answer, especially in small high-technology products where cleanliness, care, attention to detail, and extensive testing are more important than large body movements, the need for space to store large parts, and relatively simple assembly actions typical of automobile assembly. We also probably have an incomplete view of NUMMI in terms of the balance between efficient operations versus good product design and of local optimization of workstation operations versus overall factory planning, layout, and scheduling.

The Sony flexible assembly system: Success based on coordinated product and assembly machine design

In the early 1980s, Sony faced the problem of automating production of its small consumer electronic items, such as the new Walkman. The company found that fewer people wanted to work in factories at a time when its products were growing in popularity, were made of many small parts needing intricate assembly, and had market lifetimes as short as 18 months. An obvious option would be to automate the assembly, but traditional approaches have well-known drawbacks: Typical assembly automation machines have a fixed design that makes them costly to build or to accommodate to rapid product design change.

Sony's approach had two main elements: thorough redesign of the product and creation of a new assembly machine concept (Akiyama, 1981).

The basis of redesign was to create as far as possible a product that could be assembled from one side (see Figs. 3.1 and 3.2). To make au-

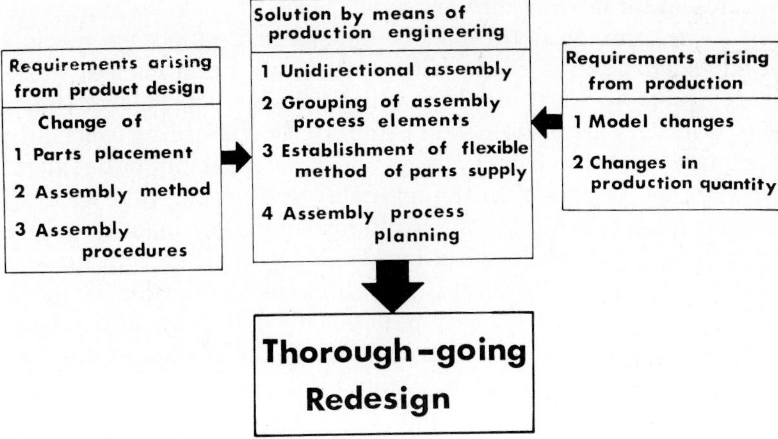

Fig. 3.1 Requirements and measures for flexible automation.

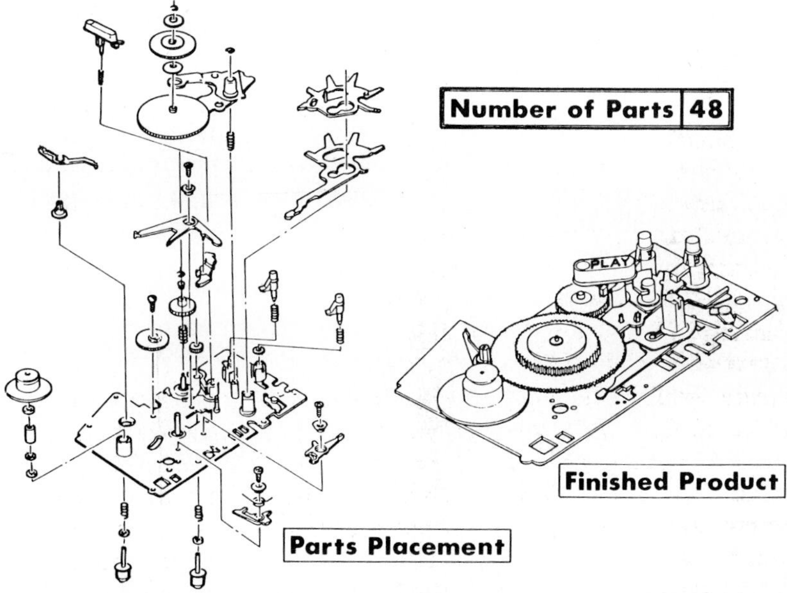

Fig. 3.2 Unidirectional assembly.

tomation easier, the design and assembly sequences were devised so that several operations of the same type—such as lubrication or press fits—occurred together. Flexible part feeding methods were arranged. Among the options are groups of bulk part feeders which are switched on and off as needed for different models and more specialized methods such as pallets.

Sony chose bulk feeding for very small parts like screws that were designed to be common to all models and selected pallets for specialized or odd-shaped parts. Some of the pallets are hand loaded, while others are loaded by vibrating them while parts are poured over them. (These part feeders are described in Chap. 10. Those feeding especially awkward parts contain vision systems which detect empty pallet slots. This information is passed to the assembly system to avoid wasting time reaching for missing parts.) Hand-loaded pallets usually hold a variety of part types while vibrationally loaded pallets contain one kind of part only. Sony also carefully distinguished pallet-loaded parts into two types, small ones on bulk pallets loaded directly onto assembly machines and large ones that traveled with the Walkman itself as it was being assembled. The final design comprised a work-and-parts pallet with space for four assemblies and a stock of the most bulky parts (see Fig. 3.3).

In parallel with product design went assembly machine design. Since all assembly operations were from one side, a rectilinear XY motion system was selected (see Fig. 3.4). This system carries the work pallet from one tool or workhead to another within a 1-meter^2 (m) area. Each tool has a Z- (vertical) motion axis that picks up a part from either a mass feeder or the supply on the work pallet. The pallet is then positioned so that the part's destination is under the tool, which inserts it. A particular objective met by the machine is the ability to perform press fits, which Sony found took people the longest of any type assembly operation. In response to this capability, Sony increased the use of press fits in its products.

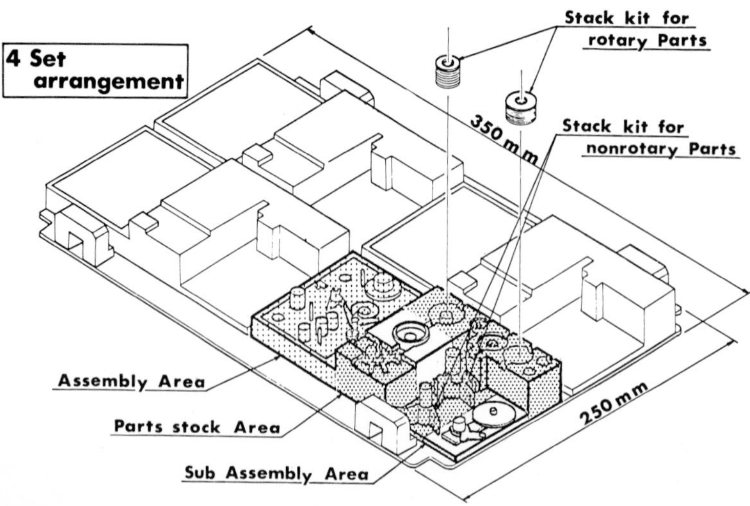

Fig. 3.3 Tray design.

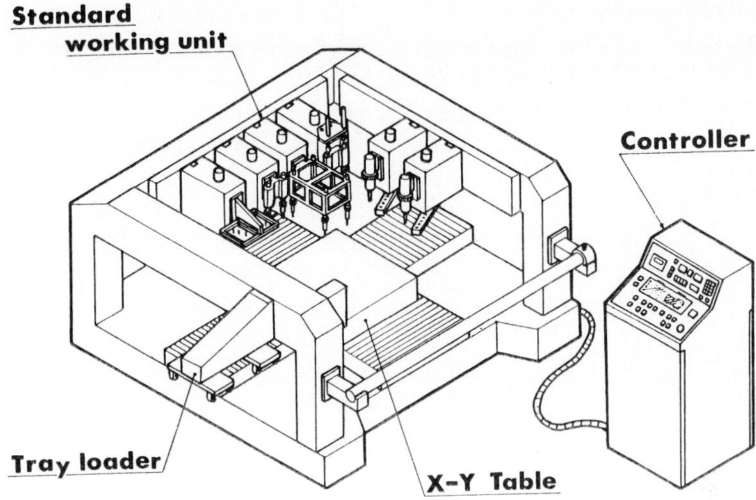

Fig. 3.4 Assembly center.

The final assembly system, installed in 1981, contained six of these standard assembly machine units. The first and second three were identical and each set had a different complement of tools. A pallet visited one of the first set at which 24 parts were installed. The product was then turned over manually and put in a second work pallet, following which it received 24 more parts from a machine in the second set.

The resulting system had high accuracy (about 0.1 mm) and high speed [about 2 seconds (s) per part plus about 4 s to move a pallet out of the machine and put a new one in]. According to Sony, about 80 percent of the investment was recoverable in a change to a new model or new product design. The main elements of model change are a new control program and new tools attached to the machine. The system reflected careful thinking about how to feed different kinds of parts, how to design a product for assembly by a machine with limited degrees of freedom, and how to structure a system that will survive a new product every 18 months.

It should be noted that Sony's approach depends heavily on the product's small size. This in turn results in a relatively small machine with the ability to store and feed large numbers of parts in a small space. Similar approaches to large products, say half a meter or so, immediately run into severe logistical problems.

Sony built three generations of this kind of system between 1980 and 1985, finally concluding that it was too expensive. A major cost contributor was the bulk and bearings required to support force fits. Simultaneous with Sony's work came the SCARA robot (Makino et al.,

1980), which supports the same degrees of freedom and work area size. In recent years, Sony has built its own SCARAs at much lower cost. A recent assembly line contains 20 SCARAs which insert 100 parts into VCR chassis mechanisms at about 2 s per part. There are also two manual assembly stations and one manual inspection station. In this system, the small size of the parts permits the robot to carry five small tools at once on a turret. (A sketch and photos of this turret and a typical workstation appear in Chap. 11.) Between parts, the robot turns the turret. Parts are on pallets of which over half are loaded automatically by the vibration method. Extensive use of sensors in the tools allows the system to tell when a pallet is empty or an insertion attempt has failed. Note that while the Walkman had 24 parts on each of two sides, the VCR chassis has 100 parts all on one side.

Several of the original XYZ assembly systems remain in use doing exclusively press fit operations. However, it appears that Sony's strategy has turned mainly toward SCARAs.

Household appliance: A failure

The ideas in this book are appreciated much more now than they were in the mid-1970s when we witnessed a total corporate product design failure. The company was basing its last hopes on a new version of its complex consumer product. The company had a long history and, like many of our clients, was certain that it knew what it was doing. Yet it made just about all the mistakes possible. The product was designed unwisely so that it had to be mechanically adjusted into operation. Adjustment can be part of a successful strategy, especially when high precision is needed at low cost and expensive high-tolerance parts cannot be used. But in the present case it led to chaos. The product almost never worked the first time, partly because of dictates from the styling department that prevented the product's mechanical foundation from being made to sufficiently high tolerances. In addition, the product was assembled without any subassemblies or intermediate tests.

The result of all this was a long line devoted to assembling the product, followed by another line devoted to taking it apart again to find out why it didn't work. No one in management detected this fatal situation in time to save the company. The breadth of the problem, comprising marketing, product design, and factory design, exceeded the authority of anyone who understood the situation and was beyond the understanding of anyone with enough authority to change it.

Automobile factory: Success based on technology and product redesign

Volkswagen's remarkable Hall 54 was recently opened to the public. In it, Golfs and Jettas are put through final assembly with 25 percent of the steps done by robots or special machines. Five percent was VW's best in the past (see Fig. 3.5).

To appreciate the full impact of the story, one needs to know a bit about conventional product cycles in automobile companies. Many products are proposed and undergo development and prototype testing but only a few are approved. Prior to approval, they compete in an underfunded limbo. Once one is approved, money suddenly appears. At the same time, however, the product introduction date (PID) is set, usually only 24 or 36 months ahead. This date is so near that little time for rationalizing the design is available. Purchase orders for machinery must be negotiated almost right away. The time for "thinking" is past, when in any case there wasn't enough money for it. There is also great reluctance to change the PID unless some major problem arises.

To make Hall 54 a success, VW got approval from its Board of Directors for the momentous decision to delay introducing these cars a year while "every part was examined" (Hartwich, 1985) and several large departures from conventional automotive design practices were made. A major example is the configuration of the front end: At a cost of adding one extra frame part, the front was temporarily left open so

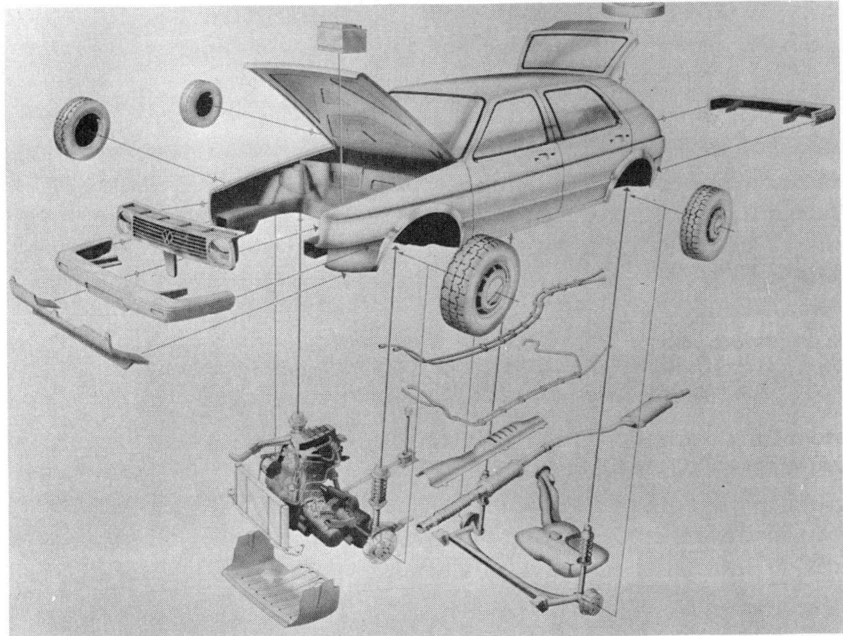

Fig. 3.5 Exploded view of a Volkswagen Golf showing the parts installed by robots or machines. (*Source: Hartwich; courtesy Volkswagen AG. Reprinted by permission.*)

that the engine and shock absorbers could be installed by hydraulic arms in one straight upward push. Normally a 1-min operation or longer, requiring several workers, VW now does it unattended in 26 s. Reducing the time of this bottleneck station permitted all the other stations to be designed for a 26-s cycle time, making the entire line run more efficiently.

Another telling example concerns screws. VW convinced its purchasing department to pay an additional 18 percent for screws having cone-shaped tips so that they would go easily into holes even if the sheet metal or plastic parts were misaligned. This made robot- and machine-insertion of screws practical. In 2 years, so many German companies have adopted cone-point screws that the price has been forced back to that of flat-tip screws. In this instance, everyone from manufacturing to purchasing is happy.

This story contains two interesting lessons. First, a "rule" that one should reduce the number of parts was violated when the extra frame part was introduced. Second, a more expensive fastener was used in order to make robot assembly possible. These examples show that one must analyze each case rather than depend on rules. The basis of the analysis must be a strategy of assembly set up before design begins so that designers and engineers will know how to evaluate the choices.

Radiators and panel meters: Success based on integrated design

Nippondenso (ND) is the Delco of Japan. It builds generators, alternators, voltage regulators, radiators, antiskid brake systems, and so on. Its main customer is Toyota. Over the years, ND has learned to be Toyota's supplier, especially how to live with daily JIT orders for thousands of items in an arbitrary model mix. To meet this challenge, ND has employed several strategies:

1. The combinatoric method of achieving model-mix production
2. In-house development of manufacturing technology
3. Jigless manufacturing methods (where possible)

The combinatoric method is the basis of the strategy. A product is divided into generic parts or subassemblies, and necessary variations of each are identified. The product is designed so that any combination of varieties of these basic parts will go together physically and functionally. If there are 6 basic parts and 3 varieties of each, the company can build 3^6, or 729, different models.

The in-house manufacturing team participates in the design of these parts so that the manufacturing system can handle each part.

The usual technique is to design common jigging features onto them. Then the same machines and grippers can grip each variety of a generic part because the parts are identical at the grip points.

The in-house team also can advise the designers where in the manufacturing process it would be most advantageous to be able to work without jigs. Wherever jigless manufacturing can be used, it has the advantages that setup and changeover time is saved, as well as an inventory of expensive jigs. Thus jigs pose no interference with any arbitrary schedule or sequence of assembling the various models ordered by Toyota. The usual technique here is to design the product so that it snaps together, not requiring any jigs (or fasteners) to keep it together during later manufacturing steps.

Using the in-house manufacturing team also solves three difficult institutional problems. First, there are no proprietary secrecy problems caused by revealing sensitive future product plans or design details to outsiders. Second, equipment can be delivered without paying a vendor's markup, reducing cost and making financial justification easier. Third, over the years this team learns the company's philosophy and knows how to contribute to it.

This strategy was employed in the design and manufacture of radiators and panel meters. Radiators are discussed first (Ohta and Hanai, 1986) (see Fig. 3.6). The basic parts are the core (with its basic parts, the tubes, fins, and headers), two end plates, and two plastic tanks. Hot liquid enters the inlet tank and is distributed in the header to the tubes. The fins, soldered to the tubes, radiate and conduct the heat away. The liquid collects in the outlet header and tank and is pumped away.

An engineer can design a radiator using a CAD program that helps choose tube length, number of tubes, and number of rows of tubes to meet a given heat transfer requirement. Families of headers, end plates, and tanks are available so that a wide variety of radiators may be designed as Toyota's needs change. However, the factory, too, must be designed not only to be able to make these new designs without requiring a lot of new machines but also to make arbitrary batch sizes of each existing design from day to day as Toyota orders them. Several features of the radiator's design make this possible.

Tubes are made at high speed by a machine that rolls them up and seam welds them, then cuts them off in arbitrary lengths. Similarly, fins are made from thin sheet metal. A third machine stacks tubes and fins alternately until the required number have been grouped into a core. (These machines were originally invented in the United States.) Tubes and fins are then pushed into a header, with each tube sticking through a hole in the header. Cores, headers, and end plates are then snapped and crimped together so that they do not need jigs while be-

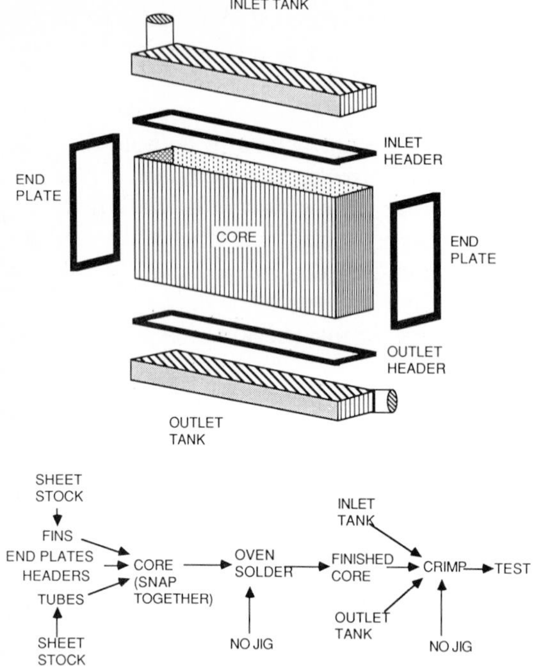

Fig. 3.6 Jigless, batch-size-of-one radiator manufacture.

ing oven-soldered together. Thus any mix of sizes of radiators can be run through the oven without gathering up jigs or making a large batch of the same size radiator.

The tanks are plastic and are crimped on so that prior soldering is not melted. The crimp die can be adjusted between cycles to take any tank size so that radiators can be processed through crimping in any model order in any quantity.

When the chief engineer on this project was asked "How much did this factory cost?" he replied, "Strictly speaking, you have to include the cost of designing the product." His point is that product and factory design cannot be separated—they must be integrated.

The panel meters (see Fig. 3.7) are also designed by the combinatoric method (Aoki, 1980). The figure shows that old panel meter designs were redesigned to establish seven standard kinds of parts. A small variety of each is sufficient to support 288 different models, of which about 40 are currently being made. Each morning the foreman takes Toyota's orders and dials them into a control panel at the head end of the machine. The machine then proceeds to make them one model at a time in solid batches. Each meter travels through

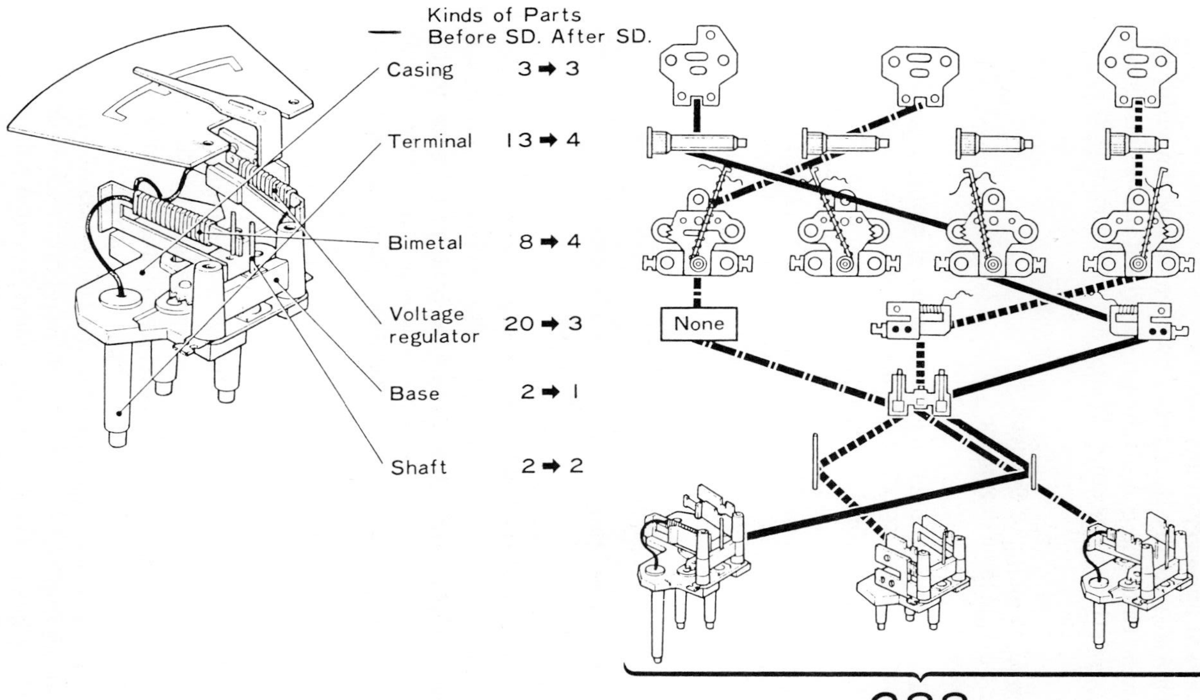

Fig. 3.7 Nippondenso panel meter. This meter actually represents a family designed by the combinatoric method. Production specifications: 22,000/day, cycle time 0.9 s, 150 models/day, 200 orders/day. Each solid or dashed line at the right represents a possible model that the machine can assemble. A total of 288 is theoretically possible. ("SD" means standardization of design) (*Drawing courtesy Nippondenso Co. Ltd. Used by permission.*)

the machine using its casing as the pallet. When the last one in the batch has been launched, a robot at the head end places a dummy casing on the machine that marks the boundary between batches. Then the next batch begins. The machine assembles, calibrates, and adjusts meters at the rate of one every 0.9 s.

These two examples vividly illustrate how a company can tailor its products and factories to the conditions under which it does business. Better examples of strategic product design are difficult to find.

Product redesign to be modular: Success leading to better workplace environment and product quality

We recently redesigned a product so that, instead of being made from 40 parts attached to a base, it is made from five subassemblies of 6 to 8 parts each. Each subassembly is made by a team of people which takes responsibility for the quality of their work. Another team performs final assembly and test. Each team knows if it is doing a good job. In the previous design, workers were each responsible for one part and could not identify their roles in the overall product's quality. A case study of this product appears in Chap. 16.

Small-Scale Batch Production

A robot that assembles precision instruments: Success based on process analysis

At the Draper Laboratory we have built and successfully tested a robot–clean room combination that assembles precision instruments, including gas bearings whose clearances are about 1 micrometer (μm; 40 microinches, or about the wavelength of light) (Rourke and Seltzer, 1985). Prior to the existence of this system, it was widely believed that only skilled technicians could assemble these instruments.

A major cause of the high cost of precision instruments is that they must be taken apart many times because they do not work correctly the first time. An important cause of failures is particulate contamination, while another is inadvertent damage caused by the assemblers. It is well known that the assemblers are the major source of particulates. For example, skin flakes are about 1 μm thick. A few such flakes will ruin one of these instruments, and thousands of flakes fall off a person every few minutes. The conventional approach to contamination control is to build expensive clean rooms provided with filtered air and to dress production workers head to toe in protective clothing.

These precautions are costly in time and energy and are difficult to enforce.

Our process analysis consisted of four elements: developing a basic strategy that integrated a number of mechanized steps that could be totally isolated from people, economic analysis of rework, determination of the sources of particulate contamination, and application of our previously developed understanding of part mating, the basic science of how parts behave during assembly. (This theory is presented in Chap. 5.) The system Draper designed is closed and recirculates the air through filters so many times that a Class 1 environment is maintained. [Class 1 means that in 1 cubic foot (ft^3) of air there will be only one particle larger than 0.5 μm across.] Such recirculation would be impossible if people had to breathe the air. Inside this closed system is a 3-degree-of-freedom robot. The robot's wrist contains patented spring-loaded tooling and measuring instruments that permit a more delicate touch than people are capable of and can monitor the machine for any errors or sticking parts. (The compliant wrist technology is described in Chap. 7.) The result is a reproducible self-documenting process that duplicates or exceeds the care of the best technician. It can also detect incompletely cleaned parts and reject them during assembly even if technicians have previously inspected them, put them through trial assembly, and approved them for final assembly.

To implement this system, we had to convince the designers of these instruments that the design changes we needed and the assembly methods we wanted to use would not impair the instruments' quality. It was shown that the changes needed for mechanized assembly were transparent to the design issues of concern for performance. This required several years of preliminary experiments and long discussions while we learned the fine points of the designs.

The flexible manufacturing system (FMS)

An FMS is a collection of metal-cutting machines and a parts conveying system. The machines are numerically controlled from a central computer. They can change tools automatically and have storage carousels that can hold about 100 tools. The conveyors carry workpieces that are attached to pallets which in turn can be locked accurately into the machines. Transfer of pallets between the conveyor and the machine is done automatically.

The goal of an FMS is to achieve the flexibility of a job shop and the efficiency of a flow line. Flexibility is attained by means of the conveyor, which can carry pieces between any pair of machines, and by the numerical control capability of the machines, which allows almost any cutter path to be generated. Efficiency beyond that of a job shop is attained by only presenting the machines with parts and tools that are ready for immediate cutting. All setup and preliminary measuring are done away from the machines. To further increase the percent of time that machines spend cutting, most systems contain waiting places at each machine where incoming pallets can stand ready to move in at the moment the machine finishes with the previous piece.

While it is estimated that job shop machines may spend only 5 percent of their time actually cutting, the machines in an FMS spend 10 times that or more in productive work. The most productive FMSs operate around the clock, a capability which requires great sophistication in online sensing to detect failures such as broken tools. The most sophisticated systems seek to avoid broken tools by means of adaptive control, a technique by which tool cutting forces are sensed in real time and the machine's controls adjusted for optimum cutting in spite of variations in metal hardness.

The FMS well represents the trade-offs discussed in previous chapters. A numerically controlled machine tool costs more than a conventional machine, because of the extra controls and computers. This capability is used to generate arbitrary cutter paths. But typical NC machines cut with only one spindle at a time, whereas less flexible dedicated machines may have 5 or 10 spindles cutting. Thus much more metal can be removed or more parts can be worked on per unit time. In the early 1970s, Cincinnati Milacron attacked this problem by building NC machines for FMS use that had the ability to automatically change cluster tool heads that carried multiple cutters.

Another problem with current NC machines in FMS use is that storage space for 100 tools is often not enough. Each workpiece type requires many specialized tools to cut its many holes, edges, and surfaces. As the system attempts to deal with more types of parts, more tools are needed. Advanced FMSs with large parts repertoires thus contain a second conveyor system whose job is to bring new tools and take away old ones, either to sharpen them or to allow different types of parts to be worked on.

In response to these problems, sophisticated computerized design tools for FMS have evolved (CSDL FMS Handbook, 1984). These tools developed because production technology alone cannot bear the entire load of providing flexibility. In particular, an important issue is that of choosing what workpiece types should be grouped together for one FMS. If this choice is not made carefully, there will be an imbalance of work for the different machines; some will be working all the time while others will be idle. The result will be a flexible but inefficient system.

Now that these limitations are more fully appreciated, effort is turning toward designing workpieces to be more appropriate for FMS work. Prime targets are simplifying part design and reducing the number of tools needed to make a part. A cascade of advantages results: The system can work on more kinds of parts and can change over from one part to another more easily; systems can be built that contain several of the same kind of machine instead of different specialized machines, perhaps at the cost of some efficiency but permitting much easier scheduling, higher machine utilization, and greater output in the face of machine breakdowns; often a part can be worked completely by one machine, reducing transport requirements and simplifying system operation (Jaikumar, 1986).

In summary, FMSs are effective systems in their domain. One must be prepared for the fact that their flexibility does not come free. To attain reasonable efficiency requires very careful design and operation.

Japanese shipbuilding: Large-scale efficiency in one-of-a-kind products

The Japanese have revolutionized shipbuilding, which is an intensely complex and time-consuming process. The efficiency of shipbuilding is so heavily influenced by planning and organization that the Japanese method makes actual design of the ship a part of the construction planning process: "Design is a subset of production" (Chirillo, 1985; Vogel, 1985). That is, once a ship's functional characteristics have been determined and the outside shape, internal bracing, and propulsion method decided upon, much of the rest of the design is determined by how it will be built. In most products, the reverse is true: How it will be built is determined by its design.

The need for increased ship production efficiency made the new approach necessary, and the welded structure of modern ships made it possible. Since welded joints are just as strong as the surrounding metal, it doesn't matter what shape the pieces are that get welded or where the joints are. In a reverse way, it is like peeling an apple—many different techniques exist, all yielding differently shaped peelings and the same result.

The method described below is an outgrowth of methods introduced during World War II by U.S. builders of both cargo and small warships. Assembly line methods based on building ships in modules were responsible for production rates as fast as a new ship every 72 hr. Before modular methods were used, the customary method of shipbuilding was to lay the keel and then add each plate, beam, pipe, engine, and so on, directly to the growing structure. This method focused all activity in one crowded space exposed to the weather, required construction of massive and dangerous scaffolds, and made every piece and part travel the same long distance from shop to ship. However, since each small piece was individually fitted to the structure, small construction errors in the pieces were easily removed during assembly, albeit with some time penalty.

In the modular method, the first thing to be decided is the size and shape of the largest subassemblies into which the pieces will be built. Then the planners identify and give shape to smaller and smaller subsubassemblies, finally arriving at the design of the individual pieces of hull plate, pipe, and deck. Design includes the precise schedule of ordering raw material, specifying the sequence of joining of parts, determining how and where to measure to ensure that the assemblies will fit together the first time, and so on. Each of these subassemblies is a zone, and all management, scheduling, cost accounting, and supervision are done by tracking these zones through several predetermined stages of production. Zones at a particular stage are grouped into similar areas, where each area constitutes a type of work with similar needs in terms of human skills, machinery, and measuring equipment. The ship is designed so that as many of the zones as possible comprise areas that are easy to make.

This method separates much of the work into sections that can be accomplished in shops under good working conditions, with plenty of space and no exposure to the weather. To make it work, one must be extremely careful about measurements and quality control since there is no way to change the shape of a huge welded structure if it does not fit to its mate. Thus management, based on the zones, is crucial.

We may say that the Japanese choose subassembly and module shapes to exploit efficient group-technology methods for making them. Some examples are shown in Fig. 3.8. This figure indicates some of the levels of planning and production that the Japanese have introduced in parallel with their new designs. Example areas include "flat in large quantity," "special flat in small quantity," "complex curved," and so on. Example stages include cutting, joining, marking, erecting, outfitting, and painting.

In addition to careful design, Japanese shipbuilders also cultivate their vendors, especially steel mills, so that they can order just the shape plates they need, on short notice, and with the necessary uniform quality that permits carefully developed low-distortion welding methods to be used.

Ships are low-volume, high-complexity items, and they belong in the middle to lower right of Fig. 1.8. But that does not prevent group technology from being used to design them so that they can be produced efficiently. In place of assembly lines, one finds "process lanes" in shipyards. The items move very slowly along such lanes compared

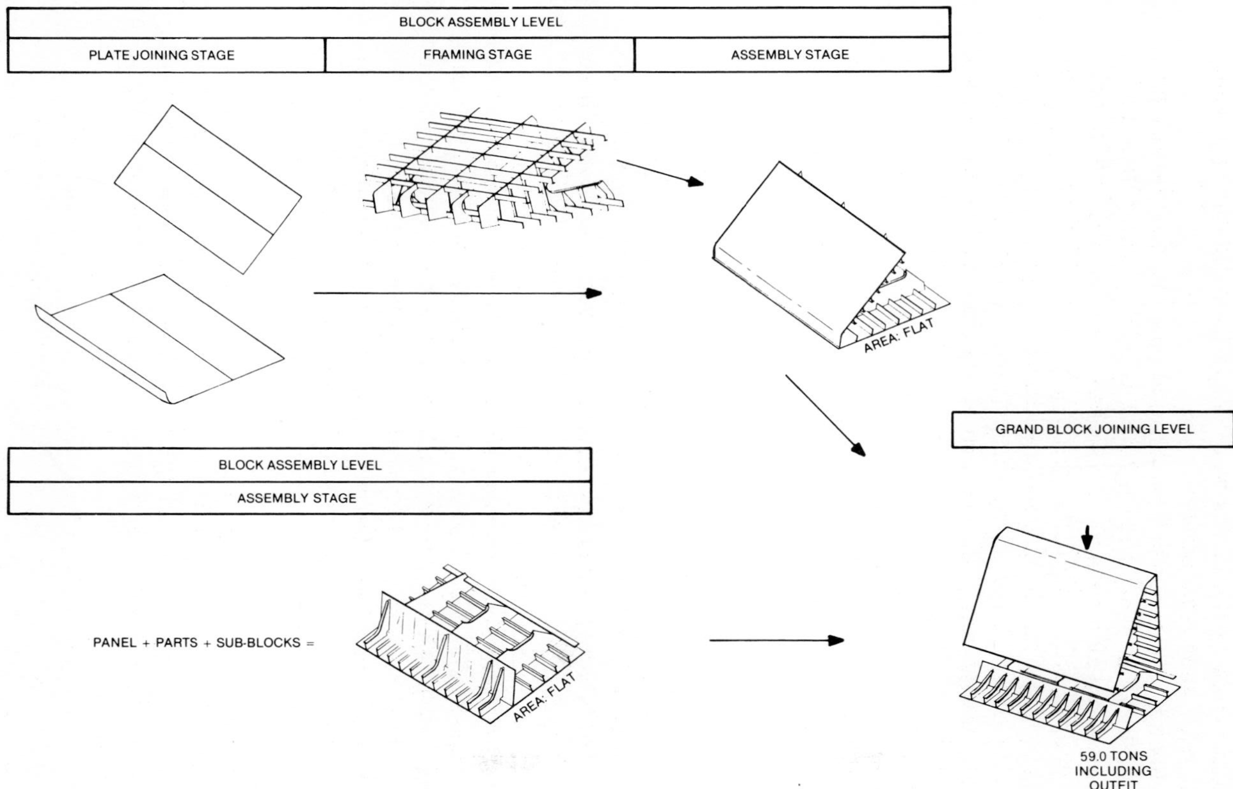

(a)

Fig. 3.8 Examples of Japanese shipbuilding practice. The figure illustrates use of group technology to identify types of structural units that share production requirements by virtue of their shape, work requirements, or production quantity. Also illustrated are several of the stages into which production work is divided. (*Reprinted from Chirillo, 1982 by permission.*)

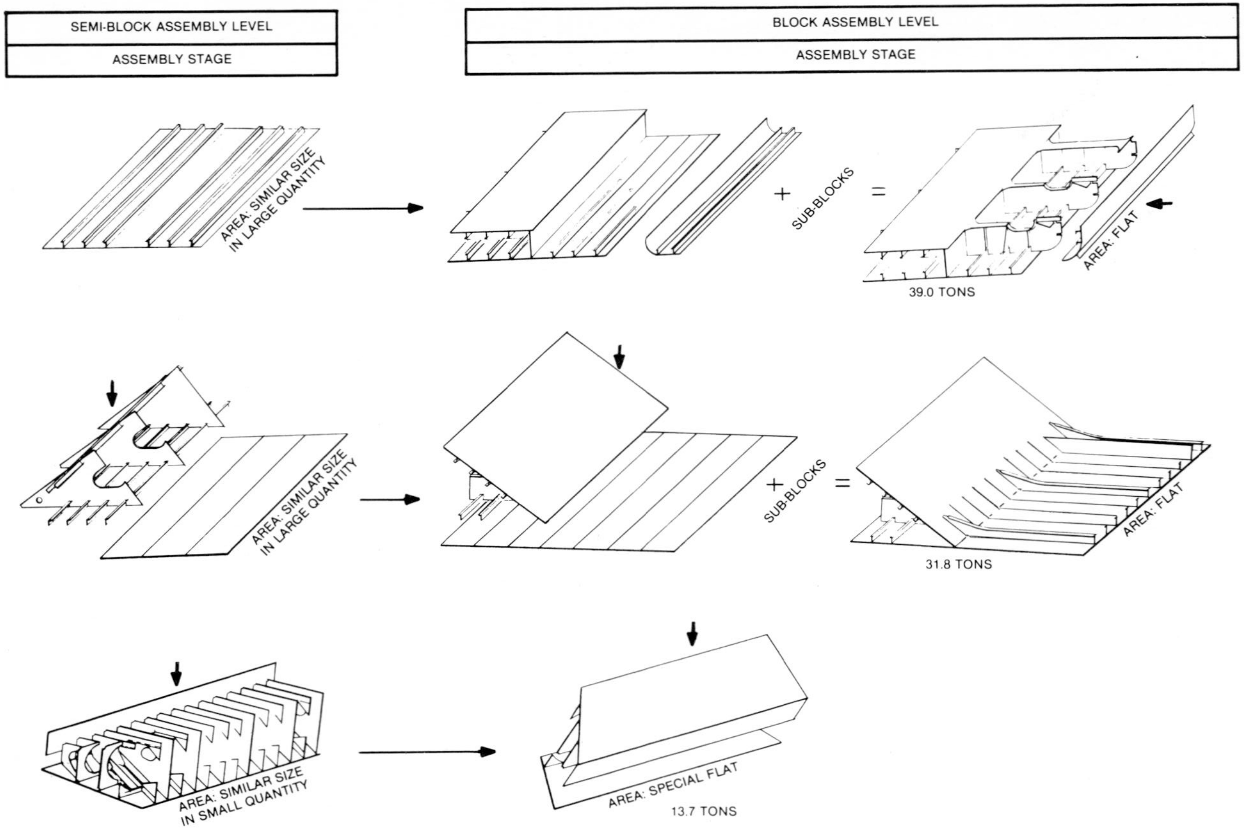

SEMI-BLOCK ASSEMBLY LEVEL	BLOCK ASSEMBLY LEVEL
ASSEMBLY STAGE	ASSEMBLY STAGE

AREA: SIMILAR SIZE
IN LARGE QUANTITY

\+ SUB-BLOCKS =

AREA: FLAT

39.0 TONS

AREA: SIMILAR SIZE
IN LARGE QUANTITY

\+ SUB-BLOCKS =

AREA: FLAT

31.8 TONS

AREA: SIMILAR SIZE
IN SMALL QUANTITY

AREA: SPECIAL FLAT

13.7 TONS

(b)

Fig. 3.8 *(Continued)*

to line speed in a car factory, but the idea is the same: Similar types of work, tools, skills, and equipment can be used on each workpiece because it is designed and selected for a particular lane. The employees see the same kinds of work each day and get used to doing it efficiently, even if the workpieces differ in detail. This "sameness in spite of differences" is the heart of group technology.

While all Japanese shipyards practice similar methods, the father of the technique is acknowledged to be Mr. Hisashi Shinto of IHI Shipbuilding Company, who developed it during the period from 1955 to 1970. Many ships had to be built while this procedure was being worked out. While these ships differ in detail, the process not only emphasizes and takes advantage of the similarities, but it also encourages designers to design a ship using the most useful types of similarities and thus identifies rational ways of improving the producibility of later ships.

Summary

This chapter has presented several examples of advanced manufacturing, covering both large-scale and small-scale batch manufacturing. No one technique dominates these examples, which include innovative product design, management of materials and people, and automation. None of these techniques is yet perfected, and the examples point to evolutions that are occurring even now. The unifying themes are a thorough-going analysis of a problem to determine its requirements and a multidisciplined approach to the solution. It should be noted that many of the techniques discussed in Chaps. 2 and 3 took years or decades to develop.

Both the Toyota Production System and the NUMMI examples show what can be done to improve factory operations without use of high technology. The Sony example illustrates total design of product and a series of assembly machines to meet a comprehensive assembly strategy. Hall 54 contains examples in which "rules" were broken by the designers in pursuit of an overall strategy. Nippondenso's radiators and panel meters illustrate product and process design tuned intimately to a company's total way of doing business with its dominant customer. The precision assembly case shows that analysis of the assembly task can result in a system able to perform tasks previously thought impossible. The discussion of the FMS seeks to emphasize the evolving level of understanding of this new technology. The potential has not yet been reached, and users are still learning to design products suitable for FMS production. Finally, Japanese shipbuilding illustrates the result of totally rethinking the relation between production and design, with the former dominating in this case.

The remainder of this book goes into detail on how such analyses of products and processes are carried out, concentrating on assembly because of its ability to focus designers on the need to integrate their activities.

References

Abegglen, J. C., and G. Stalk, Jr.: *Kaisha, The Japanese Corporation,* Basic Books, New York, 1985.

Akiyama, J.: "Flexible Assembly Center System—FX-1," presentation to C. S. Draper Laboratory Annual Seminar on Robotics and Advanced Assembly Systems, Nov. 1981

Aoki, K.: "High Speed and Flexible Automated Assembly Line—Why Has Automation Successfully Advanced in Japan?" proceedings, *4th Int'l. Conf. on Production Engineering,* Japan Society of Precision Engineering, Tokyo, 1980, pp. 1–6.

Chirillo, L. D.: *Product Work Breakdown Structure,* U.S. Department of Commerce, Maritime Administration, Washington, 1982.

———, and R. D. Chirillo: "The History of Modern Shipbuilding Methods: The U.S. Japanese Interchange," *Journal of Ship Production,* vol. 1, no. 1, 1985, pp. 1–6.

CSDL FMS Handbook, *Flexible Manufacturing Systems Handbook,* Noyes Publications, Park Ridge, NJ, 1984

Cusumano, M. A.: *The Japanese Automobile Industry: Technology and Management at Nissan and Toyota,* Harvard University Press, Cambridge, MA, 1985

Hartwich, E. G.: "Possibilities and Trends for the Application of Automated Handling and Assembly Systems in the Automotive Industry," proceedings, *International Conference on Metalworking and Automation, Hanover Federal Republic of Germany,* VDW (German Society of Machine Tool Builders), Frankfurt, Sept., 1985, pp. 126–131.

Ikebuchi, K.: Unpublished talk given at a conference on the Future Role of Automated Manufacturing, New York University, 1986.

Jaikumar, R.: "Post-Industrial Manufacturing," *Harvard Business Review,* Nov.-Dec. 1986.

Makino, H., et al.: "Research and Development of the SCARA Robot," proceedings, *4th Int'l. Conf. on Production Engineering,* Japan Society of Precision Engineering, Tokyo, 1980, pp. 885–890.

Ohta, K., and M. Hanai: "Flexible Automated Production System for Automotive Radiators," proceedings, *1st Japan-USA Symposium on Flexible Automation, Osake, Japan, 1986,* Japan Assoc. of Automatic Control Engineers, Kyoto, pp. 553–558.

Rourke, J. M., and D. S. Seltzer: "Precision Automated Assembly in a Clean Room Environment," presented at the 9th Contamination Control Working Group Meeting, Oct. 1985.

Shingo: *The SMED (Single Minute Exchange of Die) System,* IFS Publications, Kempston, Bedford, UK, 1986.

Sugimori, Y., et al.: "Toyota Production System and Kanban System—Materialization of Just-In-Time and Respect-For-Human System," proceedings, *4th Int'l. Conf. on Production Research, Tokyo,* Taylor & Francis, London, 1977, pp. 1–12.

Vogel, E.: *Comeback,* Harvard University Press, Cambridge, MA, 1985.

Chapter

4

Basic Process Issues

Introduction

This chapter begins a section of the book that deals with processes and process models. While the emphasis is on assembly processes, this chapter discusses general issues and manufacturing processes other than assembly. The goal is to acquaint the reader with the basic issues: what the basic manufacturing processes are, why we need models of processes, what processes can be modeled, and what features of processes need to be modeled in order that successful manufacturing systems can be designed.

Process Models

The essence of structured, successful manufacturing is the ability to operate the component processes and systems and know what will happen, how they will behave, how long they will take, and how much they will cost to operate. Compared to traditional processes, new ones may be poorly understood in the sense that the outcome may be less predictable: Dimensions may be out of tolerance, surfaces may be too rough, or the parts may jam rather than assemble smoothly. Manufacturing systems may be less efficient than hoped for, or quality may be too low. The predictability of a process is determined by the existence and sophistication of a "process model" which describes how the process behaves in relation to the physical and economic variables that affect it.

The simplest way to model a process is to view it as an input-output device (see Fig. 4.1). Raw materials, energy, time, money, fabricated workpieces, and human effort go in, and something of value comes out, such as a finished workpiece or an assembled product. When processes are viewed this way, we can include whole systems of machines

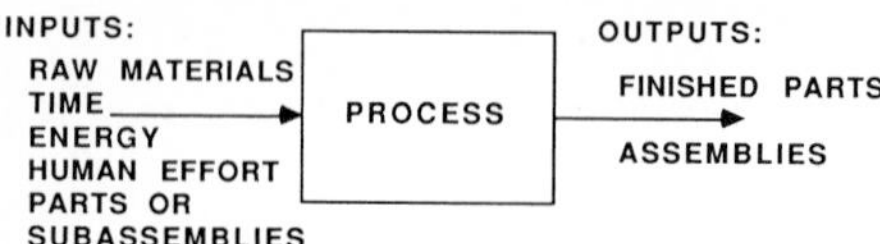

Fig. 4.1 Representation of a process as an input-output device.

and people as processes. Then we are comfortable making models of them, too.

Note particularly that process models involve both familiar physical and economic quantities such as cost and time. Considering either physical or economic quantities in isolation is meaningless.

We will discuss models of fabrication, assembly, inspection and test, and entire systems. Fabrication processes are blessed with very well-developed and detailed models. The other processes listed above have weaker models, and in some areas have no models at all.

Why Process Models Are Important

We need process models for three main reasons. First, we need to *design* processes to do specific jobs. Given the economic nature of manufacturing, we cannot afford to spend too much money, time, energy, or human effort to obtain too little output, at too low quality. Knowing in advance how a process will behave given its physical parameters will permit an intelligent design to be made that will meet the requirements set forth by product designers, cost accountants, and production schedulers. In brief, these requirements are that we make what is needed within tolerances, within budget, and on time.

Second, we need to be able to *operate* these processes after we have installed them. Operation entails making deliberate changes in physical parameters; a metal-cutting machine may be run faster or for a longer time, affecting the dimensions of its products; a flexible machining system may be given a new set of workpieces and its efficiency will be affected. New requirements force us to change the operating state of processes. Models help us predict what new state will meet the new requirement.

Finally, the existence of good process models is a requirement for *automating* the process. In assessing the adequacy of process models for the purpose of automating, it is necessary to look more deeply at Fig. 4.1, which is redrawn in more detail in Fig. 4.2. Here we distinguish types of inputs and outputs and indicate those we have a chance to control or measure versus those we do not. Automation seeks to mechanize or computerize the tasks of measuring, inter-

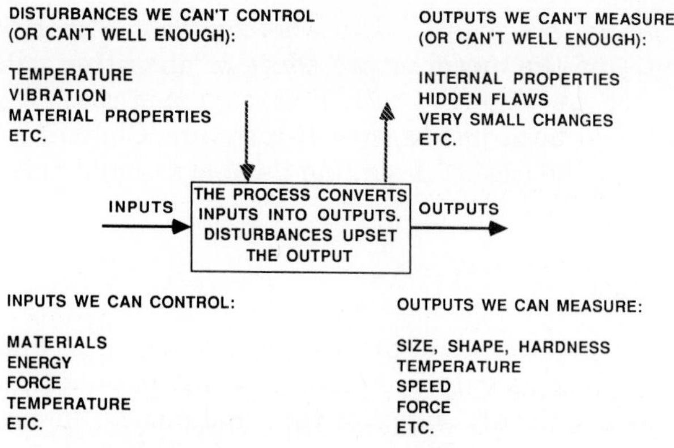

Fig. 4.2 Detailed view of a process model.

preting the measurements, and calculating from the model how to adjust the inputs to obtain the desired behavior and to reduce the effects of disturbances. It is just this progression—from models to control to automation—that underlies the growth of modern manufacturing.

Either situation—design or operation—causes us to search for values of physical parameters. In metal cutting, we may need a new cut depth; in an FMS we may need a new combination of machines or assignment of tasks to machines. Except in rare cases, engineers find the new parameters by the method of *analysis*. Analysis provides us the opportunity to try various parameters until the desired behavior is predicted by the model. Sometimes this comprises trial and error. Other times there is a well-developed procedure. The analysis process is illustrated in Fig. 4.3(*a*).

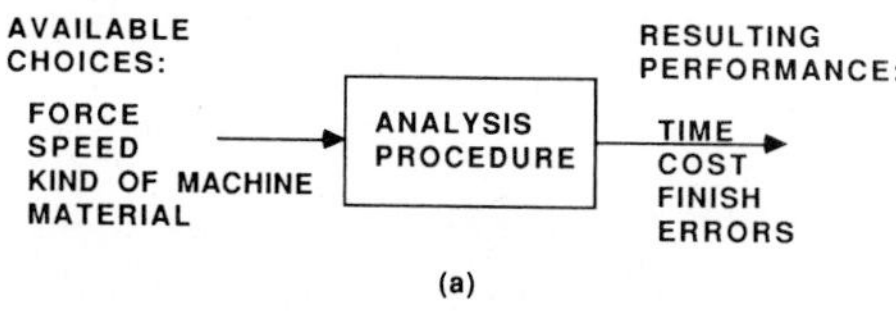

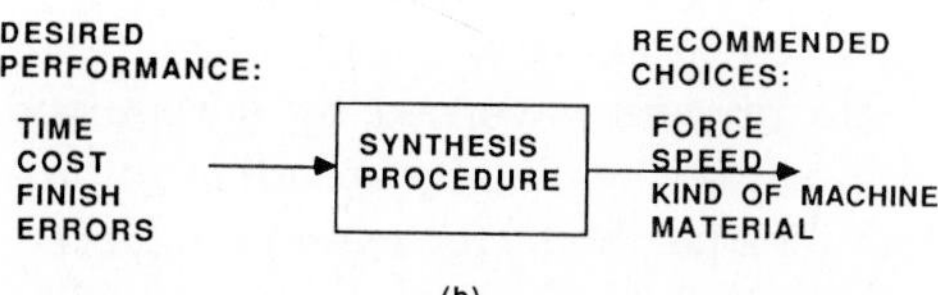

Fig. 4.3 The difference between analysis and synthesis.

Less frequently a design procedure exists whereby we can specify the behavior we want, and the model or procedure or algorithm will *synthesize* a solution for us. Figure 4.3(*b*) illustrates this case. We make a special point of synthesis just because it is so rare. Chapter 14 discusses this problem for the case of designing flexible assembly systems.

Types of Process Models

We may distinguish two main types of process models: technical and economic. Technical models usually comprise physical parameters, whereas economic models typically comprise time and money. In significant ways, the two types of model interact or may be linked, and in such cases we speak of "economic-technical" models.

A familiar technical model is that of metal cutting. The metal removal model represents the forces on a cutting tool while cutting a particular material (Merchant, 1945). This model can be used to predict heat delivered to the workpiece, energy required to cut, resulting surface finish, and the risk of the tool breaking. A physical model of assembly relates the physical variables (size and shape of workpieces, friction during assembly, stiffness of tools and grippers, and relative error between parts) to the performance variables (likelihood of assembly failure and forces exerted on the parts by tools and each other).

A typical economic model of metal cutting predicts the tool's wear rate given the same type of physical variables as the technical cutting model, but the quantities of interest are economic: how long the tool will last, how much a new tool costs, how long it takes to change tools, and so on (Taylor, 1907; Gilbert, 1950). The harder we cut, the faster we create new workpieces, but we may lose our savings back if we have to stop all the time for broken or worn tools.

At their most basic, technical models represent the physical responses of machines and materials, perhaps in great detail, while economic models attempt to capture the economic consequences of those responses, typically with less detail.

Looked at another way, economic models relate an amount of work to an amount of time or money or number of machines. The basic currency of such models is the *work content* inherent in a manufacturing task. In metal cutting or grinding, the content might be represented by the volume of material that must be removed; in assembly, it is the number of assembly operations needed to make one unit of the product. Since manufacturing is a rate process governed by a required quantity in a given time, the work content is usually specified in productive units per unit time (assemblies per hour, for example). Determining the work content of a job is thus a basic step in modeling, whether the job is metal cutting, assembly, testing, or transport. In later chapters, the economic models we give will require data of exactly this kind.

The Relation Between Models and Specifications

As stated above, most models are structured so as to predict behavior given the physical parameters, whereas engineers' problems are posed the other way: Given the desired behavior, what are the correct parameters? If we take a step back, we see that deciding what behavior to seek is itself a crucial question. We speak of this as the issue of setting *specifications* for a process or system. It is surprising but true that many failures in technology and manufacturing arise not from lack of models but rather from lack of well thought out specifications. Too little effort was spent deciding how much output was needed or time was available or how carefully something needed to be handled or inspected. The existence of good models can permit the range of possible specifications to be searched so that good designs result. Merely by listing the parameters that must be specified, a model can encourage the necessary thought. Without a model for a process, we may literally not have the means to think adequately about it.

The Relation Between Specifications and Technology

New manufacturing technology is being developed all the time. New materials, tools, assembly devices, transporters, test methods, and so on continue to appear, offering new possibilities for performance. Process models permit us to decide which process to choose for a given application and tell us what performance to seek in writing our specifications.

Technology also offers the opportunity to demand *uniformity* of process behavior, and better technology should be more uniform. "Uniformity," "repeatability," and "reproducibility" are all words that describe a major feature of manufacturing technology, one that is indispensable for high quality. The degree of uniformity itself is thus often written into well-formed specifications.

The Relation Between Models, Control, Automation, and Process Improvement

"You can't automate something you don't understand." This says it all. Process models are the means by which we attain a level of understanding that supports control, automation, or indeed any effort at process improvement, automated or not. Better understanding of metal-cutting forces and machine tool deflections can lead to better surface finishes and workpiece tolerances. Better understanding of assembly part mating allows prediction of the probability of successful mechanized assembly. This in turn can lead to reliable assembly machines or robots. Better understanding of the design process and the relation between product design and producibility can lead to more efficient production and better products. Too often, a lack of models leads to automation that accomplishes little, to wasteful groping for process improvement instead of a directed effort, or to products that are hard to make.

If we have a reasonably accurate process model and a way of measuring the performance of the process, we are in a position to formulate a strategy for converting the measurements into design or control actions. This is illustrated schematically in Fig. 4.4. Obtaining this strategy is generally a challenging task.

If the process is governed by typical dynamic equations (for example, a robot, a chemical process, or a rolling mill are in this class), the techniques of control theory are available for formulating a strategy (Reid, 1983).

If the process is a factory or FMS, the theory is less well developed. We may be interested either in designing or operating a system. In either case, typical approaches include numerical searches and algorithms such as linear programming and dynamic programming which can rapidly sift through strategy options such as which machine type should do a particular job (Thesen, 1978). When such techniques are insufficient, one usually makes use of computer simulations and trial and error methods.

We will briefly consider two examples that are discussed more thoroughly in later chapters or in the references. The first is robot force control. In this case, the process is assembly of two parts. If the parts

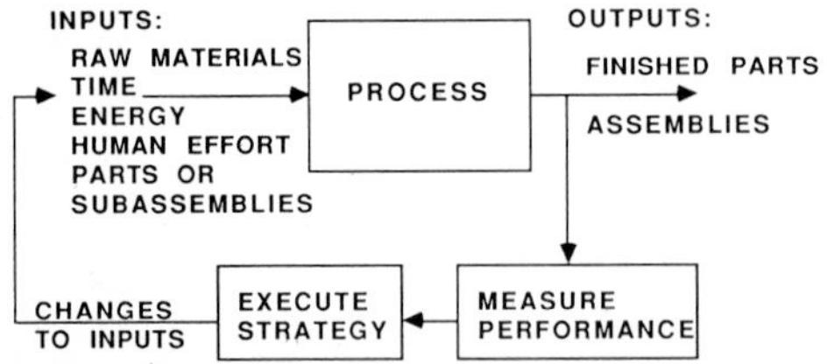

Fig. 4.4 Using a process model as part of a control strategy for automation or process improvement.

are not assembling properly, forces arise that can be measured by a force sensor attached to the robot or the work table. The strategy issue is to decide how to interpret the force and torque measurements so as to create steering commands for the robot. Understanding of the part mating process (Chap. 5) allows us to formulate a strategy in which we interpret the felt forces and torques as if the sensor were at the tip of the entering part (a peg, say), and we steer the robot as if it were holding the part also at the tip, shifting and turning the part about its tip so as to reduce the forces and torques (Whitney 1977). This strategy has been converted into patented spring-loaded devices called "remote center compliances," which are described in Chap. 7.

The second example, also discussed in later chapters, concerns how to design an economical assembly system. Here the issue is to decide how many and what kind of machines, robots, or people are needed to assemble a certain number of items per year at the lowest cost. The process model is an economic one that relates cost and speed of the various alternative assembly methods for each operation. The strategy is a design procedure that evaluates each candidate machine and feasible assembly system design and chooses the most economical one. Despite the apparent complexity of the problem, the algorithms are surprisingly fast.

Fabrication Processes

We turn now from process models in general to the specific processes in manufacturing. Fabrication and assembly processes are described briefly, and then the status of models of these processes is discussed.

Part fabrication is essentially a series of independent steps with minimum interconnections between operations performed on individual piece parts. These operations attempt to enforce a particular geometric configuration on formable materials. The ideal geometry exists in the design, possibly in a CAD system. The output of the fabrication system is an approximation of that ideal geometry perturbed by the statistics of both the process and the materials. These perturbations are supposed to fall within design tolerances.

Today, fabrication processes are many and varied, and new ones are appearing in response to new materials and techniques. It is important to distinguish mature processes from new ones by the degree to which the mature ones are understood and predictable. While no process is completely predictable, the better understood ones are casting, forging, bending, cutting, and heat treating of metals; molding and cutting of plastics; traditional joining processes like screws, rivets, and welds; and common coating processes such as plating and painting.

New processes and materials include composite materials, hybrids of composites and metal parts, powder metal parts, and hybrids of metal and injection molded plastic pieces.

Piecepart fabrication processes may be classified as liquid or plastic solidification, solid deformation, powder compaction, solid shaping by material removal, and composites. A diagram showing some of these processes appears in Fig. 4.5. The earliest processes in industrial technology were casting and solid deformation, whereas powder compaction and composites are the most recent. A major trend is toward net shape or near net shape processing, meaning that at the end of the first or first few process steps, the part has its final shape. Most importantly, little or no material removal is needed in such cases. The result is that a part is created in less time, with less energy, fewer steps, less transport and paperwork, and so on.

In addition, some parts are made by solid joining to other parts, typically using welding, rivets, screws, or adhesives. This method is basic to the construction, shipbuilding, and aircraft industries, but it also occurs in manufacturing. A common application is to parts that are not symmetric or not convex, so that simple lathe turning or casting may be difficult; another application is to very low-volume parts for which it is not economical to incur manufacturing setup costs, such as for making a mold. It is not an efficient manufacturing technique and is usually replaced by molding, casting, or other processes where feasible or economic.

Parts built up of other parts may be symptomatic of poor design practice. More attention is being given to part count reduction, with

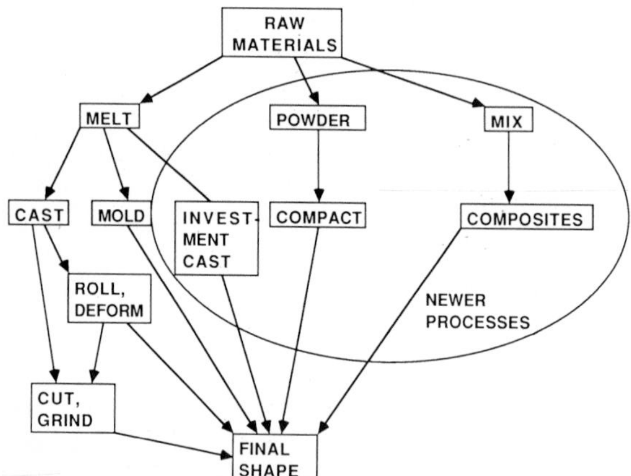

Fig. 4.5 Stages of basic fabrication processes. Note that newer processes often involve fewer steps in arriving at the final shape of a part.

the result that products have fewer but more intricate parts. This trend favors processes like complex stamping, powder compaction, and molding, which can make complex parts that have many surfaces, edges, holes, and so on.

While casting is the oldest process and is usually associated with rough pieces requiring much further work, a recent trend is precision investment casting. Interestingly, the method used is also ancient: the lost wax process. It is now used to make such items as jet engine turbine blades complete with internal cooling passages.

Another recent process is powder compaction. A few years ago this method was associated with rather brittle or porous parts. Today compacted parts have densities of 98 percent of the solid. The reason for interest in these parts is that they possess material and mechanical properties not attainable by conventional means. For example, large metal parts can have high strength and small grain size. Prior methods for making such parts involved forging and subsequent heat treating, resulting in large grain size and low strength. Another unique property is solid alloys of materials such as titanium and aluminum which will not alloy as liquids. One may conclude that powder compaction can create entirely new materials (Scientific American, 1986).

Material deformation methods have advanced rapidly in recent years. Two major trends are visible. First, parts can be made with "deeper draw," meaning that cup-like stampings can be very long in relation to their diameter. A well-known example is the all-aluminum soft drink can, which is drawn to a depth twice its diameter. Pressing is applicable to heavy parts as well as typical sheet metal. Parts with ¼-in wall thickness and 10-in diameter by 6 in deep, formerly practical only as lathe-turned parts, now can be made economically by high-power pressing. This comparison is illustrated in Fig. 4.6(*a*).

Composites are parts made of different materials solidified together. Solid alloy powder parts may be included in this class, but more typical are those made of epoxies with glass or carbon fibers molded in. A typical manufacturing process comprises "laying up" sheets or bundles of fibers with epoxy in between or impregnated into the fibers. The final piece is pressed in a mold and baked. These materials are more expensive than familiar metals or plastics, but their high strength and light weight make them desirable for aircraft and space applications. Composite parts can be designed to have high strength just in those regions where they need it; this is accomplished by carefully arranging the number of layers of fiber and the directions in which they are laid. Composites are also being considered for medium-temperature uses like automotive connecting rods. Their relatively low weight makes them especially attractive here.

A different kind of composite is the insert or outsert molded part.

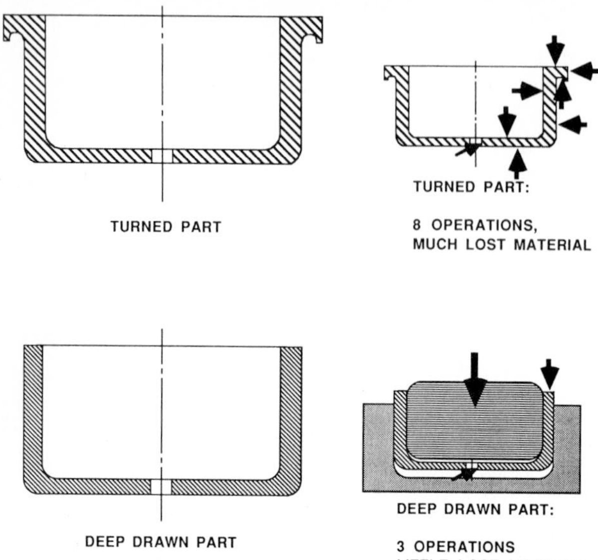

Fig. 4.6(a) Comparison between a lathe-turned part and a deep-drawn part. Each method produces a functionally equivalent part using different methods, amounts of time, energy, and materials.

Such parts are typically metal with plastic pieces molded directly onto or into them. This is accomplished by placing the metal pieces into the molding machine. Typical examples include metal parts with plastic bearings or wheels molded onto shafts, holes in metal sheets with bushings molded in, or plastic springs attached to metal parts. Such parts find uses in electronics, furniture, and electric appliances. Figure 4.6(*b*) is a schematic illustration of this kind of part.

As precision products rise in importance, it becomes necessary to make parts with finer tolerances, clearances, and surface definitions. Figure 4.6(*c*) compares conventional and advanced methods for "machining" parts according to the accuracy they can achieve, with historical trends in capability (Taniguchi, 1983). Note that methods with

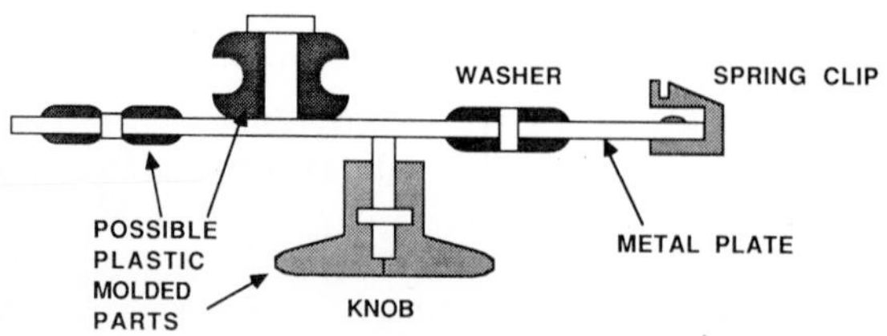

Fig. 4.6(b) Examples of insert and outsert molded parts.

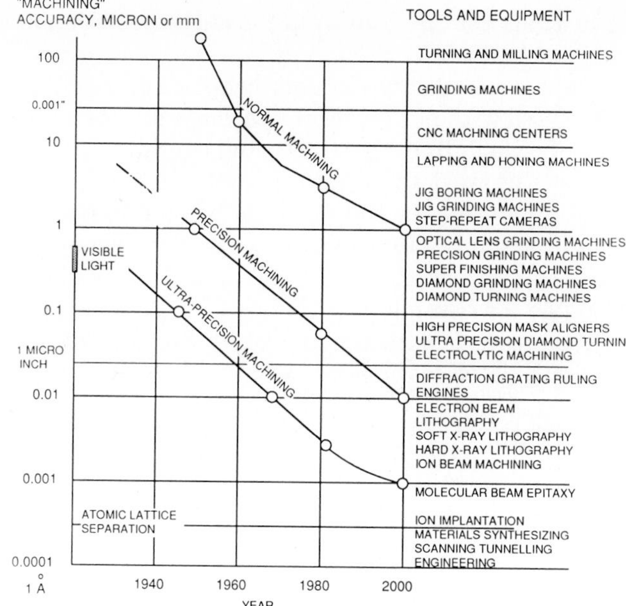

Fig. 4.6(c) Achievable "machining" accuracy (Taniguchi, 1983).

accuracy above 0.1 μm act by direct contact between a tool and the surface while those below (except for ruling engines) act indirectly via fields of ions, x-rays, and so on. At the finest level, the ambition is to "machine" *individual atoms or atomic layers.*

While this section cannot completely cover processing options, one message should be clear. While one may think of manufacturing as metal removal by familiar milling machines or lathes, a wealth of new processes are appearing that offer parts with new properties, net shapes, complex shapes, and composite materials. These processes typically take less time to make a part than older methods. However, they are often associated with long-lasting and costly preparations, such as design of molds, stamping or pressing dies, or composite layup processes. Many of these preparations themselves are in need of process improvement before they can be economical for short design cycles, rapid product evolution, and model mix production. Ongoing research in plastic flow in injection molds has resulted in simulation software that greatly speeds the mold design process (Wang, 1987).

A second important implication is that all of the recent attention to FMS based on metal-cutting machines may be misplaced as a larger percentage of parts is made by other methods. FMS methods have been applied outside of conventional metal cutting only to sheet metal stamping; only two installations are known to the authors. Both make electronic parts such as chassis.

A third implication, discussed later in this chapter, is that short processing times associated with new part fabrication methods will require new approaches to scheduling manufacturing operations. Fabrication used to take days or weeks per part in contrast to assembly, which takes seconds or minutes. In the past, the time disparity between fabrication and assembly often permitted some separation of the two functions; as parts were made they were stocked up until complete sets were available for assembly. As fabrication time per part falls, scheduling of the entire fabrication-assembly process will have to be done in a more integrated manner.

Assembly Processes

Components of the assembly phase of manufacturing

Assembly consists of more than simply joining parts. Many activities must occur to support part mating. In addition, assembly itself may be hierarchical, in which assemblies are joined to assemblies. This hierarchy is shown in Fig. 4.7, where the terms discussed below are illustrated.

The main activities of assembly are:

- Marshalling parts in the correct quantity and sequence
- Transporting parts and partially assembled items
- Presenting parts or assemblies to the assembly workstations
- Mating parts or assemblies to other assemblies
- Inspecting to confirm correct assembly
- Testing to confirm correct function
- Documentation of the process's operation

Marshalling is a logistic function which may be performed according to one of many strategies. These strategies are based on estimates of work schedules, the planned production of various product types, and lists of the parts needed for each type of assembly. Two types of strategies are generally used, the push type and the pull type.

The push type operates on the basis of a planned production schedule of anticipated final needs for finished assemblies. Fabrication or purchase of parts is initiated on the basis of estimated lead times (the time between placement of an order and receipt of the item) for producing or obtaining the parts. Since these lead times are typically weeks or months long, push strategies usually cover long time spans.

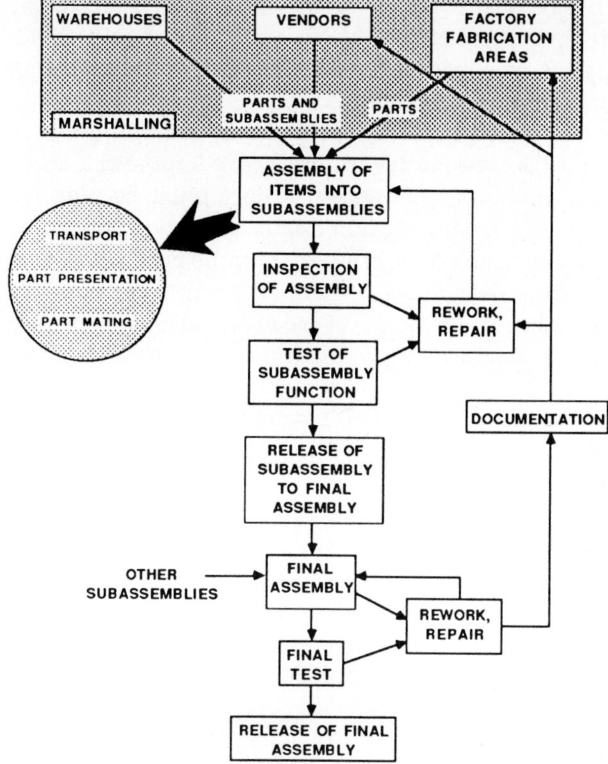

Fig. 4.7 Main steps in assembly.

Material requirements planning (MRP) is a generic name for many such strategies.

Pull strategies operate in reverse of push strategies. The pull method starts with anticipated demand or orders in hand for finished assemblies. As these orders are filled, replacement items are ordered from the next upstream processes. Orders progress upstream in a similar fashion, pulling production downstream as needed. An order is triggered when a rather small safety stock level is reached, often a few hours' or days' work. Because of the much shorter time spans over which such strategies operate, they are called JIT methods. (A more complete description of JIT is in Chap. 3.)

MRP methods tend to work well when there are long production runs of similar or the same items. Large in-process inventories are likely to accumulate. MRP works less well in a model mix environment where orders change rapidly compared to the lead times. MRP also makes assumptions about the availability of production resources that are not possible to fulfill. Unanticipated bottlenecks cause MRP-based schedules to break down, requiring rescheduling. Part of the source of these problems is the fact that MRP is being used as a scheduling tool even though it was originally intended only as a planning tool for placing orders (Lundrigen, 1986).

JIT methods work well when there is a continually changing mix of the same group of items. Because order intervals are kept short, there is less accumulation of inventory. However, orders must be planned carefully, because each upstream station tends to make what was most recently made rather than what will very soon be ordered. A way around this is to keep the orders mixed in proportion to recent history of order mixes. As long as the near-term future order pattern is not too different from the recent past and if production times are kept short and in-process inventories small, errors in anticipating the mix will not have serious consequences. To keep JIT working in the long term requires marketing and engineering discipline to keep the number of models from growing and/or to ensure that new models can be made mostly from existing parts. (Refer to the combinatoric method discussed in Chap. 3.)

Transport is the short-term logistic implementation of marshalling. That is, transport accomplishes the actual carrying of parts or assemblies between stations or work areas. The major options for transporting, including conveyors and automatic guided vehicles, are discussed in Chap. 10.

Part presentation takes parts from the transporter and places and orients them so that assembly can occur with only minor adjustments. An assembly gripper, tool, or robot may grip the part either directly from the transporter or from a part feeder (see Chap. 11), and it carries the part to a point very near where mating takes place.

Part mating is the actual process of fitting parts together. Mechanical mates include peg-hole insertions, interference or force fits (for example, peg larger than hole), insertion of electronic components into sockets or circuit boards, mating of gears, insertion of threaded fasteners, compliant mates like snap fits, and other similar mechanical mates. The physics of such mates is discussed in Chaps. 5 and 6.

Joining accompanies mating and usually involves fastening in some way. Screws, rivets, adhesive bonding, welding, soldering, crimping, staking, and ultrasonic bonding are examples. The implications for assembly, repair, and use of reversible versus irreversible joining methods are discussed under "Product Design" in Chap. 9.

Inspecting usually involves determining that an assembly operation has been completed correctly. One may check the tightness of a screw or freedom of motion of a shaft in its bearings. This is in contrast to *testing,* where the issue is to determine if a subassembly functions correctly. The distinction between inspecting and testing is that the latter may be directly related to a functional specification on the assembly or product.

In addition to the above direct operations, an important indirect operation is *documentation.* Assemblers, inspectors, or testers record data such as test results, number of correct assemblies, reasons for failure of tests or assembly equipment, and so on. These documentary data can be crucial to the correct functioning of the factory over the long term, providing the ability to trace problems back to their causes, maintaining control of the processes, and permitting improvement of the factory's performance.

Assembly Process Models

By contrast with fabrication processes, assembly is relatively poorly understood, mainly because people have routinely been available to do assembly. A process model for assembly needs to describe how parts mate, what the requirements for successful assembly are, how parts are damaged by assembly, and how to design them to maximize success. Beyond models of individual part mates lie models of groups of parts, including assembly sequence options, jigging and fixturing methods, tolerancing of assemblies, and implications for quality control. Given the effort to automate assembly tasks or improve their quality, the need for models is especially acute here.

Difficulties associated with automating manual tasks

If one lacks a model of a manual task, one cannot proceed to automate it by simply mimicking what people do. This approach was taken by many early workers in robotics, often with disappointing results. People are poor examples on which to base automation for several reasons:

1. We do not really know what people are doing in many cases, so we cannot really do a good job imitating them.
2. People are extremely "well engineered" and in most cases we cannot build machines of comparable capability that use or mimic human techniques.
3. People operate by unique means based on their strengths and weaknesses. For example, people have poor ability to return a hand or tool to exactly the same spot—that is, they have poor repeatability—and partly as a consequence they have very good sensors that permit them to search for the correct spot. By contrast, machines usually

have good repeatability, so their lack of sensors may not matter. Designers of machines thus tend to exploit their repeatability instead of bemoaning their lack of sensors. Machines usually go about their work quite differently from the way people do, even if both are doing the same job. The sewing machine is a good example. See Fig. 4.8 and Table 4.1.

4. At a somewhat different level, people can be too innovative or resourceful. They may attempt to "improve" a process, leading to lack of reproducibility, or they may try to "help" by using parts that do not quite meet tolerances, leading to quality problems later. Many factories succeed in continuing to operate only because of such extracurricular activities by the employees. However, this ability to operate is deceptive because the operation is not really under control. It operates

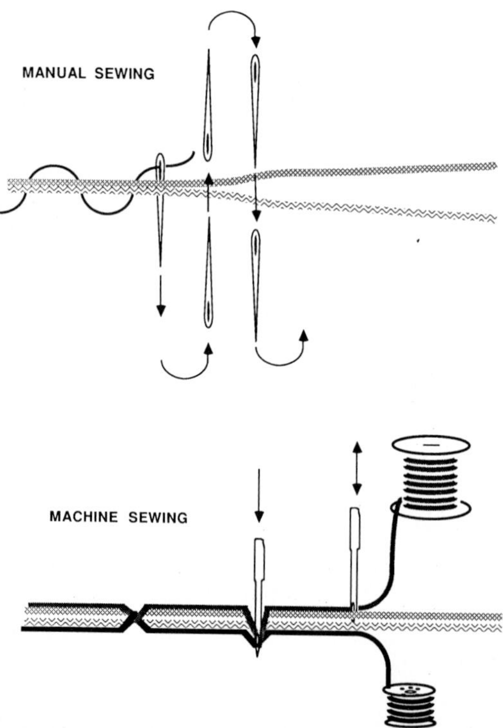

Fig. 4.8 Comparing manual and machine sewing. This figure does not attempt to explain how the sewing machine works. A clever mechanism under the cloth passes a loop of the upper thread completely around the lower thread supply, accomplishing the twisting of the upper thread around the lower one. Detailed descriptions may be found in technical encyclopedias.

TABLE 4.1 Comparison Between Manual and Machine Sewing

	MANUAL	MACHINE
NUMBER OF "HANDS" NEEDED	TWO	ONE
NUMBER OF THREADS	ONE	TWO
GRASP OF NEEDLE	PERSON LETS GO AND REGRASPS REPEATEDLY	MACHINE NEVER LETS GO
MOVEMENT OF NEEDLE	PASSES COMPLETELY THROUGH CLOTH; CHANGES ORIENTATION 180° REPEATEDLY	POINT GOES THROUGH; DOES NOT CHANGE ORIENTATION
LOCATION OF EYE	AT REAR OF NEEDLE	IN POINT OF NEEDLE
JOINING METHOD	ONE THREAD PASSES BACK AND FORTH THROUGH CLOTH	TWO TWISTEDTHREADS TRAP CLOTH BETWEEN THEM; NO THREAD PASSES THROUGH BOTH PIECES

on the basis of undocumented procedures and the granting of exceptions to specifications.

Automation does not have the ability to grant exceptions or use parts that are out of tolerance; thus the introduction of machines into such factories often leads to disaster. The original operations were not really under control; in our terms, they were not modeled correctly. Introducing automation can reveal these problems vividly, but this method is not recommended. Managers may conclude that the factory was operating successfully before and that automation is a poor idea. This is, of course, exactly the opposite of the truth.

The above discussion is not intended to downplay the importance of people in making a factory operate. On the contrary, the resourcefulness of people is essential at a higher planning and supervisory level, so that manual and automatic factories can continue to improve their operations.

We may generalize from the sewing machine case by saying that wherever we can analyze a manual process thoroughly, we have the opportunity to design a totally new way of accomplishing it. In so doing, we may overturn many existing assumptions about how the task ought to be done or what preparations may be necessary. For example, while sewing machines are now over 100 years old, it is only in the last few years that equipment to feed cloth into sewing machines has come into use. Thus people were still necessary to feed the cloth, a step we may regard as a preparation for the actual sewing task.

Similarly, the task of mating parts was mechanized many years ago for certain restricted situations and has now been thoroughly analyzed with the result that optimum methods not used by people are available to machines. The preparation problem, in this case arranging the parts and presenting them to the assembly machine, is still not well understood or widely mechanized. Options in use are discussed in Chap. 10.

Geometric tasks: Easy to model

The part mating problem itself is now well understood. Assembly is a geometric task. That is, if the sizes, shapes, and locations of parts were known exactly, this information would be sufficient to plan 100 percent successful assembly. However, we do not know the geometric information with perfect accuracy. Parts, jigs, grippers, feeders, robots, and other equipment can introduce geometric errors. Since there are such errors, parts will strike each other at the wrong place or angle, giving rise to forces, moments, and friction forces and causing deformations of parts, tools, and grippers. Thus models of assembly are based on predicting the effects of size, shape, and location errors. These effects include assembly failure and damage to parts. Since the required information is often well defined and easily obtained, such models have a good success record. Inconsistency in the shape of workpieces is typically a large source of problems. All too often, such inconsistency is avoidable if sufficient attention is paid during part fabrication and transport.

A class of geometric tasks that is difficult to automate is that of flexible parts. Hoses, wires, cloth, and animal hide are examples. Such items have so many degrees of freedom that controlling them all can be quite difficult. Methods that have succeeded include stretching or freezing the items to stiffen them, holding them on screens with vacuum, and encasing them in a stiff binder that is later washed or melted away.

Note that mere size, large or small, is not a technical barrier. Automatic methods are in use for welding sides of ships, extending over many meters. Similarly, in microelectronics and biotechnology, automatic work is done on items a few wavelengths of light in size or smaller.

Nongeometric tasks: Difficult to model

There are other tasks performed by people that have so far eluded or resisted analysis. Several features distinguish such tasks from sewing or assembly. They may be inherently variable, requiring constant monitoring and adjustment of the process. Welding is such a process. A large number of variables must somehow be observed, measured, and responded to in a coherent and effective way. Not all the variables affecting welding have been identified, or their effect is not well understood.

Alternatively or additionally, some tasks may simply have not been analyzed up to now and are accomplished by people acting on their own experience or in response to vague instructions from other people. Surface cleanup grinding is an example. The body of a car or ship typically has weld beads on it resulting from joining several pieces. These beads must be ground off and the resulting surface must be "fair" and "smooth." The sharpness of the grinding disk must be monitored, and the rate at which it grinds must be observed since it can change because of material changes from piece to piece.

Both welding and grinding are currently the subject of research that seeks to model them and bring them under control for the purposes of automation. Progress has been much greater in welding, but many problems remain. Three main problems block wider automation of welding:

1. Distortion of parts and assemblies caused by heating and cooling
2. Weakness and cracking of the weld itself caused by impurities or foreign particles in the weld
3. Variability of the first two caused by unknown or unmeasured influences

Distortion is typically three dimensional, involving warping and shrinking or stretching. Analytical predictions require careful modeling of the elastic-plastic stress-strain-temperature relations in the metal plus accurate knowledge of the time and space distribution of heat input during welding and subsequent cooling (Goldak et al., 1985). Cracking is caused by many factors, including the presence of extremely small amounts of very common chemical impurities (Sundell et al., 1986).

In such situations, careful analysis may not be rewarded with more accurate predictions because material properties and cleanliness may not be known with sufficient precision or may not repeat sufficiently from piece to piece unless extravagant efforts are made. Practical responses include controlling materials as much as is feasible or economical, recording empirical experiments and planning the work based on past data, and using expert people to do the work. We will return to this topic when we discuss quality control in Chap. 9 and error analysis of workstations in Chap. 11.

Expert systems

In recent years, another approach has arisen to deal with unmodeled processes, the expert system (Hayes-Roth, 1983). Typical expert system developers assume or frankly acknowledge that the process they want to perform has not been modeled and that the only recourse is to "experts," that is, to people who presently perform, or appear to perform, the task now. By one means or another, the experts are questioned until their "rules" are known and translated into computer code. This method is useful when there is no model. A good example is medical diagnosis; lacking models for human physiology, the expert system instead models the doctor and the process of diagnosis itself.

In other situations, the expert system approach may hold some dangers. A prerequisite, of course, is experts, people with real expertise. The lack of expertise cannot be remedied by the expert system, yet this fact is often not appreciated. Second, the "experts" may not in fact be very good at the task in question, even if they are the best available. One may question the wisdom of creating an expert system in such cases, since the result may not be very useful. Third, the problem may be more complex than first realized, and the resulting expert system may have very many rules. A danger here is that up to now there has been no way of ensuring that the resulting system is self-consistent. Problems of this sort are subjects of current research.

An example from product design for assembly will illustrate these issues. In Chap. 6 we discuss the problem of designing the tips of electrical plugs so that they are easy to mate. A manufacturer of such parts used to rely on the experience of its engineers to shape the tips. One could imagine interviewing the engineers, writing down rules like "the length of tip's tapered section ought to be about 3 times the plug's diameter," or "the rule about 3 times the diameter is okay when the plug is gold plated but not when it is tin plated—then the taper should be 4 times the diameter," and so on. However, plug mating is a geometric assembly problem and has been modeled. The result, described in Chap. 6, is a compact set of equations that implicitly includes rules like the whimsical ones above and makes them unnecessary.

When a definitive or mathematical model is lacking, however, expert systems promise to be a useful technology. In particular, the effort to create a knowledge base pays ample dividends in increased understanding of a problem.

Models of Test and Inspection Tasks

Models of test and inspection tasks are not well developed except in the sense of industrial engineering. That is, one can often predict how long it will take or how much it will cost to perform a given test. However, the real modeling issues are not addressed. These include:

1. How long will it take to discover the cause of an observed failure?
2. What methods are the most direct or useful in tracking down a fault?
3. What powers of observation and thought do people use during such tasks?
4. What causes people to make assembly errors, and what methods are most effective at preventing errors?

Because such basic questions remain the topics of research, the automation of test and inspection remains primitive. Specific tests such as measuring voltages, temperatures, forces, and torques are easy to automate in most cases, but these comprise merely the measurement phase, omitting the more difficult processes of diagnosis and repair. A recent approach to diagnosis is the use of expert systems which combine the diagnostic strategies of experienced people with physical models of the item being inspected. This approach is successful because it multiplies the expert and enables inexperienced workers to carry out diagnoses. Creation of these systems is a lengthy process.

A different issue, discussed in Chap. 9, concerns strategy. Given a product design, just what tests should be performed and when? What tests tell the most about existing faults? When is the most opportune stage of assembly to take the item apart? As a design issue, one may ask how to configure the product, establish its assembly sequence, or stage it in subassemblies so as to enable an effective testing strategy to be implemented. Sometimes, questions of this sort can be addressed by statistical decision theory (Raiffa and Schlaiffer, 1961).

By contrast, typical approaches to quality control assume that these questions have been answered already, and they proceed to establish sampling intervals, acceptance and rejection levels, and so on. In fact, these latter techniques focus on *operating* the factory and ensuring that its processes are running within the required tolerances. The issues discussed in the paragraph above are concerned with designing the product and process in the first place so that quality goals can be achieved and verified. The Taguchi method (see Chap. 8) seeks to relate quality control and product design by bringing statistical analysis to bear.

Models of Manufacturing Systems

Manufacturing systems tend to be characterized by a flow of workpieces and assemblies from one location to another. In such industries as paper and cigarettes, this flow can be remarkably fast, often hundreds of miles per hour; in aircraft and shipbuilding, the speed of flow is greatly less, perhaps a few hundred feet per year.

The flows in factory layouts can be unidirectional or quite intricate. See Fig. 4.9 for some typical layout types. Mass production typically involves flow shop organization exhibiting simple linear flows across the factory floor, perhaps folding back and forth to accommodate the length. Work flows from station to station in the sequence in which

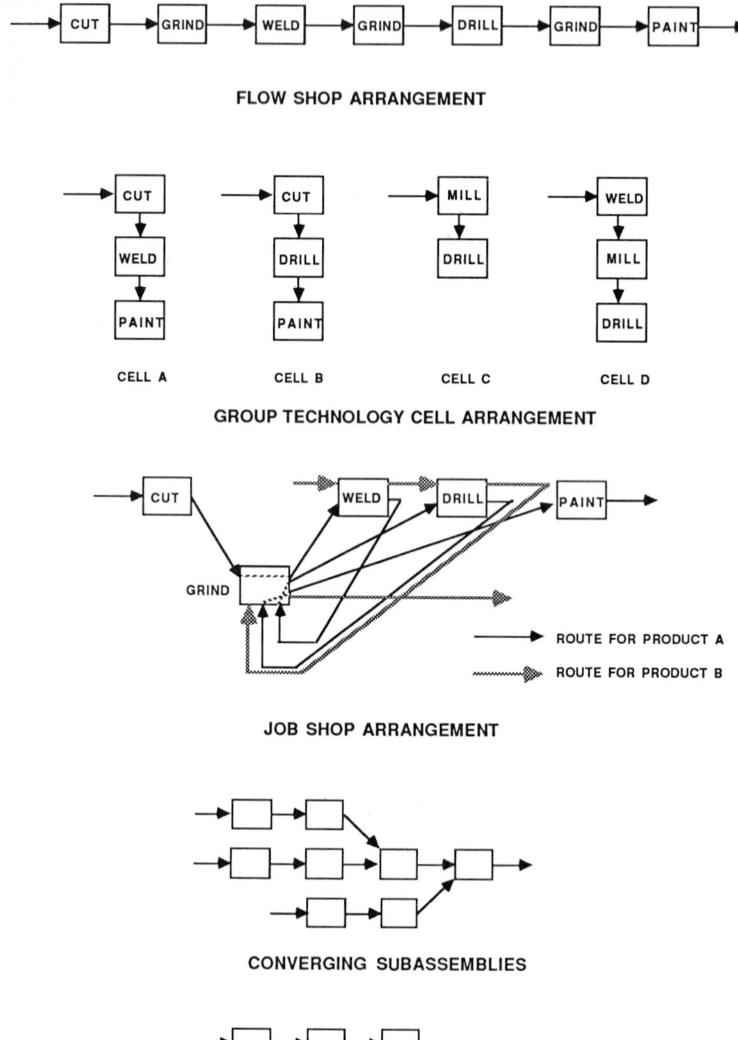

Fig. 4.9 Typical types of factory layouts.

work must be done, and each successive station is equipped to do the work needed next.

In lower-volume manufacturing where there is more model mix, it is not economical to buy several of one kind of machine just because more than one step in the product's manufacture requires that kind of machine. Job shops are appropriate in this case. Parts arrive at a department when they are ready for the kind of work that department does. If families of parts or products with similar processing needs can be identified, specific cells tailored to their needs, called "group technology cells," can be set up. If automatic transport and machine loading are added, such cells become FMSs.

As workpieces flow and are joined, there is a natural convergence of the flow lines. As defective items are identified and reworked, they enter backward flows that rejoin the main flow upstream of where they left. Models of manufacturing tend to mirror these lines of flow, characterizing them as networks, and network flow analysis methods are useful for designing and operating them.

Figure 4.10 is an example of a simple manufacturing network. It contains processes, material-handling links between processes, and queues or waiting places between some of the processes. The issues in system design are to choose the process equipment, locate the equipment on the factory floor, determine the methods for each process so that process times are known and the required production volume can be made, decide how much transport capacity is needed, and how much queue space to provide.

As yet there is no single algorithm or procedure that will start with a family of feasible assembly sequences and applicable resources

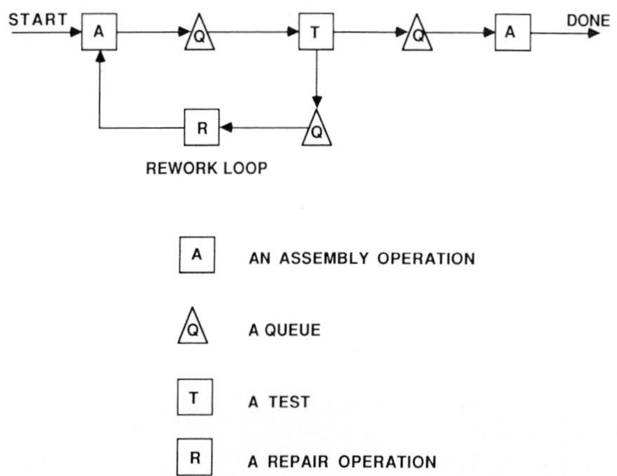

Fig. 4.10 A simple manufacturing network with assembly, test and repair processes, queues, and a rework loop.

(people, robots, fixed automation machines) and completely design an assembly system. Suri (1985) gives a survey of the design tools available. The basic tools are network flow theory, queuing theory, and computer simulation. In Chap. 14 system design algorithms are presented which choose equipment and assign tasks to equipment in order to meet production requirements at minimum cost. Queue sizes and transport capacities are not found by these algorithms. Other aspects of design not covered by these algorithms are equipment reliability and transport capacity. Simulation is the current tool of choice for these problems. Simulation is discussed in Chap. 15.

Summary

This chapter makes the case that understanding manufacturing begins with understanding its basic processes. We use "processes" in the broadest sense, including not only the familiar ones like fabrication and assembly, but the equally important system or interface processes such as design, transport, inspection, and documentation. If we understand processes, we can make engineering or economic models, leading to the ability to design processes to meet specifications on their technical and economic performance. Where explicit mathematical models are not available, it often helps to carefully examine the methods of people and formulate an expert system. A good model and a clear specification are the prerequisites for designing automation, and automation in turn can provide the consistency of output necessary to guarantee adherence to the specifications. Without this understanding, process design, improvement, and control constitute a frustrating grope.

The different manufacturing processes are understood to varying degrees, with the older fabrication processes being the best understood. Assembly processes, those done by people for years, and especially those that are not dominated by geometry, are the least well understood. In the largest sense, the entire system of manufacturing is one big process operated by people—designers, marketers, fabricators, assemblers, inspectors—which is incompletely modeled.

References

Gilbert, W. W.: "Economics of Machining," in *Machining Theory and Practice*, American Society of Metals, Cleveland, 1950, pp. 465–485.

Goldak, J. A. et al.: "Computational Weld Mechanics," *AGARD Workshop Structures and Materials 61st Panel Meeting*, Sept. 8–13, 1985. (Goldak's address is Dept. of Mech. and Aero. Eng., Carleton Univ., Ottowa, Canada. No archived version of this paper is available)

Hayes-Roth, F., D. A. Waterman, and D. B. Lenat (eds.): *Building Expert Systems*, Addison Wesley, New York, 1983.

Lundrigen, R.: "What Is This Thing Called OPT?" *Productivity and Inventory Management*, vol. 27, no. 2, 2d quarter 1986, pp. 2–12.

Merchant, M. E.: "Mechanics of the Metal Cutting Process I. Orthogonal Cutting and a Type 2 Chip," *J App. Physics*, vol. 16, no. 5, May 1945, pp. 267–275.

———: "Mechanics of the Metal Cutting Process II," *J App. Physics,*, vol. 16, no. 6, June 1945, pp. 318–324.

Raiffa, H., and R. Schlaifer: *Applied Statistical Decision Theory*, Harvard University Press, Cambridge, MA, 1961.

Reid, J. G.: *Linear System Fundamentals*, McGraw-Hill, New York, 1983.

Scientific American: "Materials for Economic Growth," *Scientific American*, vol. 255, no. 4, Oct. 1986.

Sundell, R. E., H. D. Solomon, and S. M. Correa: "Minor Element Effects on Gas Tungsten Arc Weld Penetration—Weld Pool Physics," proceedings, 1986 International Conference on Trends in Welding Research, American Society for Metals, Metals Park, OH, 1986.

Suri, R.: "Quantitative Techniques for Robotic Systems Analysis," in *The Handbook of Industrial Robotics*, S. Y. Nof (ed.), John Wiley and Sons, New York, 1985.

Taniguchi, N.: "Current Status in and Future Trends of Ultra-precision Machining and Ultrafine Materials Processing," *Annals of CIRP*, vol. 32, no. 2, 1983.

Taylor, F. W.: *Transactions of the ASME*, vol. 28, 1907, pp. 31–350.

Thesen, A.: *Computational Methods in Operations Research*, Academic Press, New York, 1978.

Wang, K. K., et al.: "Recent Findings in Injection Molding Research," Proceedings of the *14th NSF Conf. on Production Research and Technology*, Society of Manufacturing Engineers, Ann Arbor, Oct. 1987, pp. 421–425.

Whitney, D. E.: "Force Feedback Control of Manipulator Fine Motions," *ASME J Dynamic Systems, Measurement and Control*, vol. 99, no. 2, June 1977, pp. 91–97.

Chapter

5

Assembly of Compliantly Supported Rigid Parts

Introduction

The next several chapters present the basic processes of assembly. The engineering results give a designer the conditions (part size, shape, and part-to-part error) for successful assembly. Basic to concurrent design, this information influences both the design of parts and the design of fabrication and assembly equipment. The logic of the presentation is as follows:

- Conditions for successful assembly (Chaps. 5 and 6)
- Design of grippers and tools to meet those conditions (Chap. 7)
- Design of groups of parts (Chap. 9)
- Design of workstations to carry grippers and fixtures so they can meet the conditions (Chap. 11)

The most common type of assembly involves "rigid parts," which generally do not change shape during assembly. Their assembly is easier to model than that of "compliant parts," which deform in expected and acceptable ways during assembly. Typical examples include snap fits, assembly of electrical plugs, stretching springs or elastic belts over pins or pulleys, and so on. Chapter 6 covers compliant parts.

Types of Rigid Parts and Mating Conditions

Rigid parts and their mating conditions may be classified by the shapes of the parts and the clearance between them. See Fig. 5.1(*a–e*).

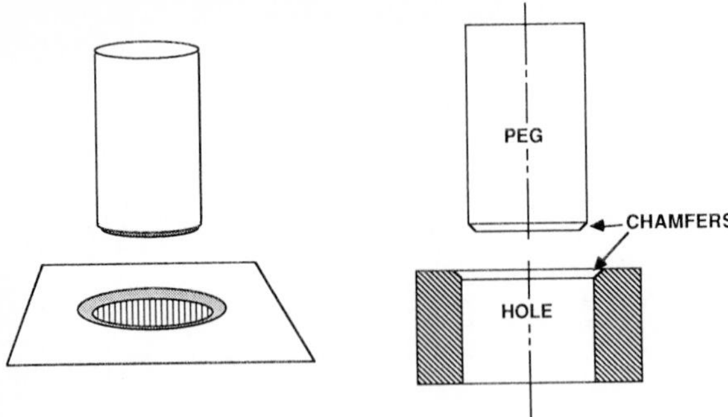

Fig. 5.1(a) Schematic illustration of mating of round pegs and holes with chamfers on both peg and hole.

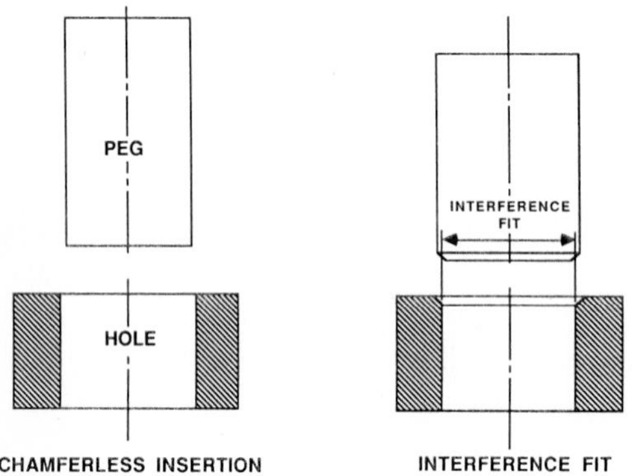

Fig. 5.1(b) Left: Schematic illustration of mating two parts without chamfers. Right: Schematic illustration of interference mating of two parts.

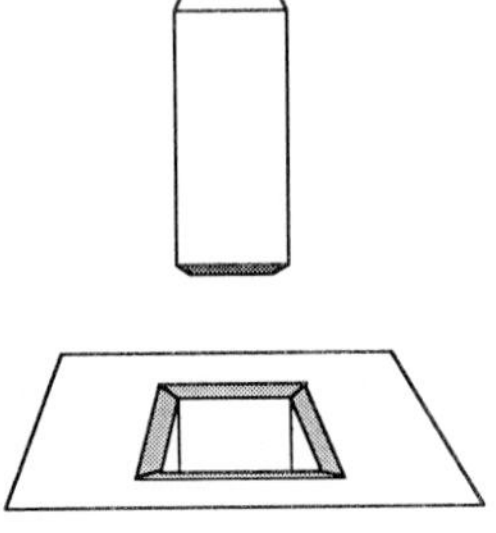

Fig. 5.1(c) Schematic illustration of rectangular peg-hole mate.

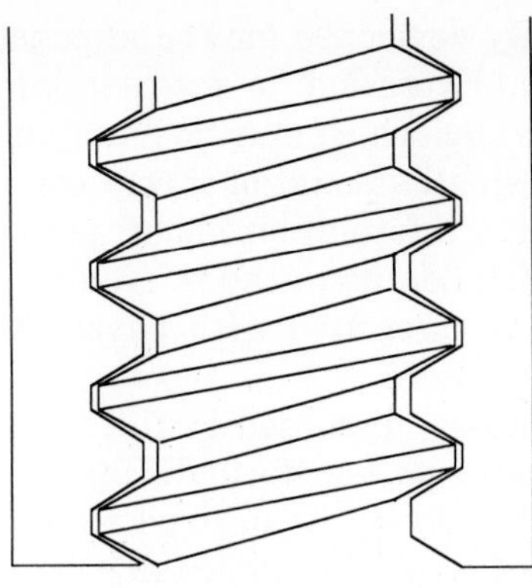

Fig. 5.1(d) Schematic illustration of screw thread mating.

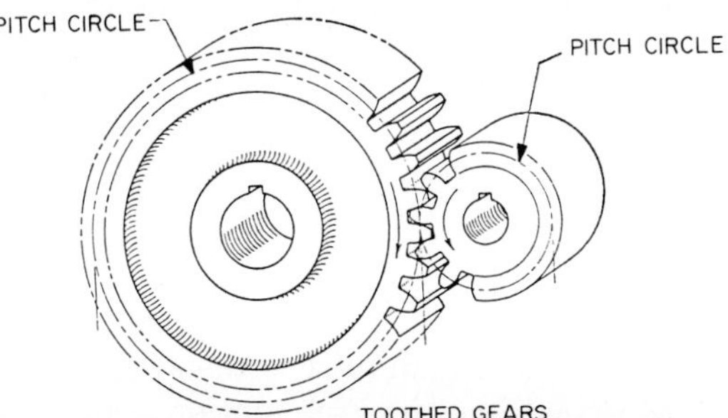

Fig. 5.1(e) Schematic illustration of gear mating (from Gieseke, Mitchell, and Spencer, 1958). The pitch circles of the gears are tangent when the gears are properly mated. The teeth are widest when measured along the pitch circle and are generally narrower when measured along other circles concentric with the pitch circle but having either larger or smaller radii. *(Adapted with permission of Macmillan Publishing Company. Copyright © 1958 by Macmillan.)*

The most common shape is round, although rectangular and tongue-groove shapes are also used. These types usually mate via motion in one direction only. Two simultaneous directions are required to mate threaded parts. Most commonly there is clearance between the parts, although the clearance can sometimes be extremely small. Some parts are made with deliberate interference, effectively, negative clearance. Such parts are assembled by using extra force ("force" or "interference fits") or by cooling one part and/or heating the other to temporarily create positive clearance ("shrink fits"). One may also classify mates by noting whether one or both parts have chamfers. If neither part has a chamfer, the mate is called "chamferless."

Three types of mates will be considered here: pegs and holes, screw threads, and gears. The theory that predicts required mating force and gives error conditions is much more highly developed for round pegs and holes than for any other geometry. Extension to rectangular shapes results in extremely complex equations which may be found in the references (Sturges, 1988). There is a small amount of theory concerning threaded mates and some intuitive information about gears which are summarized in this chapter, with details in the references. Other types of mates, such as push-twists associated with bayonet-base light bulbs, exist but are not discussed here.

The other main classification of part mates, discussed in the next chapter, is compliant part mates, in which the parts deform during assembly. Similar but more complex equations may be derived to describe assembly forces and the influence of errors. A particularly important feature of such analyses is the ability to determine how to redesign the shapes of the mating surfaces or adjust their compliance in order to enhance mating, prevent unmating, deal with alignment errors, and so on. These opportunities also apply to rigid parts but the discussion of them is concentrated in the next chapter.

Gross and Fine Motion

Assembly action or motion can be divided into two types, "gross motion" and "fine motion." Gross motion generally transports a part to the region where assembly itself will occur. Fine motion generally performs the assembly. The transition from gross to fine motion is the first critical phase of assembly. The gross motion must be accurate enough so that certain starting conditions for further mating are met. The fine motions must also meet various conditions in order for the mate to be completed successfully. Both sets of conditions are expressed by equations that relate initial errors, part geometry, stiffness of tools and grippers, and sliding friction between parts. These equations can be used to specify maximum errors between parts beyond which assembly will either not start or not complete. The required mating force can also be obtained. Finally, the equations may be used to develop design criteria for apparatus that holds parts or grippers so that the likelihood of a successful mate is maximized. Both chamfered and chamferless assembly will be discussed.

Gross motion is usually not related to a manufacturing task. Instead, the aim is simply to transfer an object or tool from one place to another while avoiding obstacles. Gross motions are usually about the same size as the mover itself. Often there is little need to follow a path precisely, and the emphasis is usually on speed. Little task-related action occurs.

By contrast, fine motions have the opposite characteristics. They are dominated by information or circumstances from outside the mover, and most of the task-related action occurs during these motions. Whereas the outcome of a gross motion is rarely in doubt, both the outcome and the way the outcome is achieved during fine motion might be unpredictable. Adjustment and reaction are the prime features, rather than speed. The basis for the unpredictability of fine motions is the impossibility (physically) or unfeasibility (economically) of eliminating all geometric errors in and between parts. These errors come from many sources, including part fabrication, the way parts are gripped or placed in fixtures, construction and placement of the fixtures, and motions of the grippers while being carried by tools or robots.

Most assembly operations comprise the following actions:

- Gross motion to a part
- Fine motion to grasp it
- Gross motion to carry it to the assembly point
- Fine motion to place or insert it

The contrasts between gross and fine motion are of interest because it is often necessary to build separate equipment to accomplish the two types of motions. For example, most industrial robots are in fact gross motion devices. Their lack of fine motion capability goes far to explain their limited use in assembly. Where robots are successful assemblers, there is often a tool on the robot's wrist that accomplishes the necessary fine motions. If we include within fine motion at least part of the approach time when the assembly apparatus is slowing down and withdrawal time when it is speeding up, fine motions can take up a sizable portion of the total, perhaps 30 percent. This fact indicates that there may be an economic advantage in designing separate gross motion and fine motion devices so that the assembly actions are done by apparatus suited to the needs of each phase. In a later chapter we will deal with some of the trade-offs involved. For now, we will concentrate on the details of mating parts.

The contrasts are also important in categorizing the phases of assembly, to plan assembly trajectories, and to design and analyze assembly workstations to see if they will reliably accomplish the tasks set for them. This chapter and several later ones will deal with these topics.

Part Mating Theory for Round Parts with Clearance and Chamfers

Figure 5.2 schematically represents assembly of a round peg and hole in two dimensions, although we should remember that assembly is

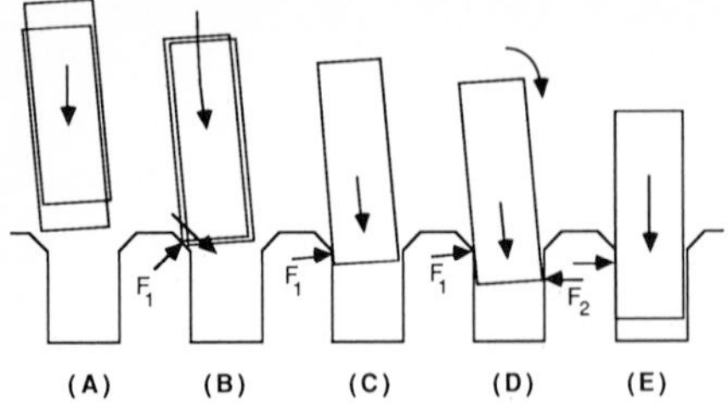

Fig. 5.2 Phases of mating pegs and holes. (*a*) Approach; (*b*) chamfer crossing; (*c*) one-point contact; (*d*) two-point contact; (*e*) line contact. F_1 and F_2 are the contact forces.

three dimensional in general. The various models of assembly derived in this book are mostly two dimensional and are accurate enough for most purposes (Whitney, 1982; Simunovic, 1975; Arai and Kinoshita, 1981). The figure defines five typical phases of an assembly: approach, chamfer crossing, one-point contact, two-point contact, and line contact. Not every assembly contains all of these phases but most do.

Parts typically begin mating with some relative lateral and angular error, so the first contact occurs on the chamfers. During chamfer crossing, the contact point moves down the chamfer toward the rim of the hole as the parts try to move laterally to remove the lateral error. The part is pushed laterally by the force acting on it at the contact point. Once the contact point reaches the rim, it remains there,[1] acting as the "one point" of one-point contact. As the peg advances farther into the hole, it finally strikes the opposite side, establishing a second contact point. During the two-point contact phase, the parts try to rotate with respect to each other to remove angular errors. The part is turned angularly by the torque created by the forces acting at the two contact points. In some cases, two-point contact may be followed by line contact, in which the parts are exactly parallel and in contact along one wall of the hole.

These moves constitute the fine motions of a typical simple assembly. Other assemblies, such as push-twist, snap actions, and thread mating, include other fine motions.

Conditions for successful assembly

The mechanics of part mating are governed by the geometry of the parts, the stiffness of the parts and tooling, the friction between parts as they move past each other during assembly, and the amount of lateral and angular error between the parts as mating begins. The interplay of these factors determines whether assembly will be successful

---

[1] This is what happens if the peg is shifted to the left and tilted to the left, as shown in Fig. 5.2. If it is tilted to the right, the first contact point will travel with the peg's tip down the inside wall of the hole until the second contact occurs on the rim.

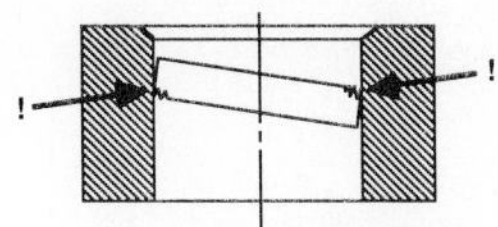

Fig. 5.3 Schematic illustration of wedging.

and how large the forces exerted on the parts by the tooling and each other will be.

The success or failure of a peg-hole assembly depends on how the parts behave while passing through two potential danger zones. First, the lateral or angular errors before assembly could be so large that the parts fail to meet within the bounds of the chamfers (or part diameters if there are no chamfers). Second, there are two forms of failure associated with two-point contact during the fine motion phase; these are called "wedging" and "jamming." While the names sound similar, the events are different and have different causes and cures. Later sections of this chapter will put firm mathematical formulations behind these ideas. For now, we concentrate on an intuitive understanding.

Wedging is an event in which the contact forces between peg and hole can set up compressive forces inside the peg, effectively trapping it part way in the hole. Figure 5.3 is a schematic illustration. To avoid wedging, one must keep the angular error between peg and hole at the moment of first two-point contact small enough. The equations describing successful assembly show that there is a relation between avoiding wedging and ensuring that the chamfers meet.

Jamming is an event in which the peg cannot advance into the hole because the insertion force vector points too far off the axis of the hole. Figure 5.4 is a schematic illustration. To avoid jamming, one must support the peg so that the reaction forces set up by the two contact points are able to turn the peg parallel to the hole's axis. These supports are also important in chamfer crossing and avoidance of wedging.

We turn next to a discussion of supports for parts during assembly. In all of the following discussions, the mathematical results are stated, but the derivations are in an appendix at the end of the chapter.

A model for compliant support of mating parts

During assembly, parts are supported by jigs, fixtures, hands, robots, grippers, and so on. These supports have some compliance, either by

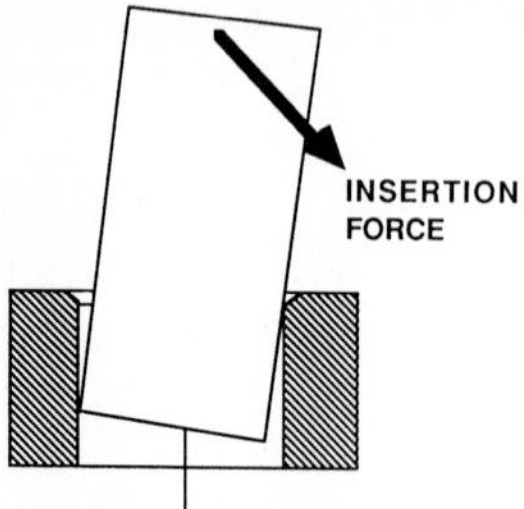

Fig. 5.4 Schematic illustration of jamming.

accident or design. Compliance is the inverse of stiffness: Stiff things are not very compliant and vice-versa. Since the parts also have some compliance in general, we say that rigid parts are those whose compliance is small compared to the compliance of the supports. Correct design of these supports is a crucial issue in successful assembly, along with control of alignment errors between the parts.

Therefore we speak of a deliberately designed assembly tool compliance as an "engineered compliance" to distinguish it from the "undocumented compliance" that always exists in tooling and parts. Unlike a properly engineered compliance, undocumented compliance provides no guarantee of successful assembly or small contact forces between parts. The assembly task may appear to "work" successfully but the reasons why may not be understood. A small change in conditions, such as temperature or part geometry, will cause it to fail. A number of early research experiments in robot assembly depended on undocumented compliance.

The geometry of the peg and hole is defined in Fig. 5.5. It shows an idealized peg and hole with some initial relative lateral error ε_0 and angular error θ_0. Because of these initial errors, the peg must both rotate and translate in order to mate with the hole. The support must

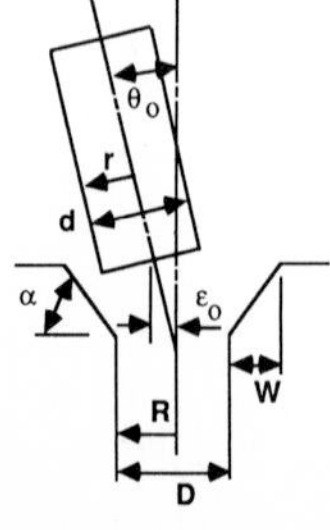

Fig. 5.5 A peg-hole mate modeled as a two-dimensional tab-slot mate. The peg is shown inclined at an initial angular error θ_0 and an initial lateral error ε_0. The diameter of the hole is D, radius R. The diameter of the peg is d, radius r. The width of the chamfer is W, inclined at angle α.

therefore be compliant both laterally and angularly to permit these motions to occur. Thus it is important to be able to model the compliance of the support.

A one-dimensional spring is the simplest example of a compliance. In assembly, forces and torques can act on a part from any direction, so it is necessary to think of multiaxis compliances in order to understand how the parts will move in response to these forces and torques. The force F acting on a part is in general a six-vector (three forces, three torques), and the resulting motion δ is also a six-vector (three translations, three rotations). These two vectors are related by a 6×6 matrix **C** called the "compliance matrix" of the part and its support:

$$\delta = \mathbf{C}F$$

Since the part will move differently depending on the point at which it is pushed, each such point has associated with it its own, usually different, compliance matrix. For a three-dimensional object, the matrix contains 36 generally nonzero entries. In many cases there is a special point at which the matrix is diagonal (only the six entries on the diagonal are nonzero). That is, pushing at this point with a pure force causes only lateral motion, and applying a pure torque about this point causes only rotation. This point is called the "compliance center." The object behaves as if it were supported at this point by three independent lateral springs in the X, Y, and Z directions, plus three independent torsional springs about those axes. The stiffness or compliance of the object when acted on at this point is then simply described by only six numbers, namely the three XYZ lateral stiffnesses and the three angular stiffnesses about the XYZ axes. The origin of these axes is at the compliance center.

In the case of a planar model such as in Fig. 5.5, the compliance at the compliance center consists of just one lateral spring and one an-

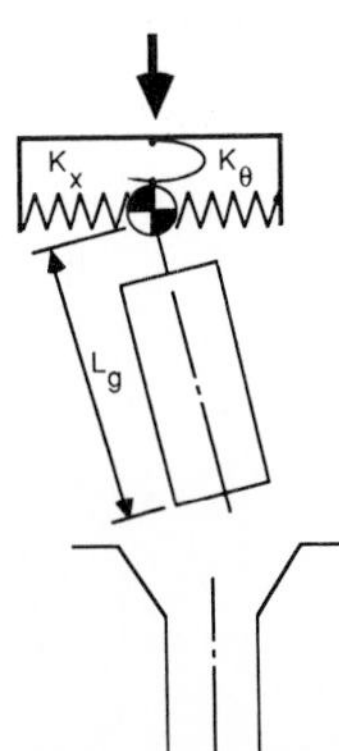

Fig. 5.6 Illustrating the support of the peg at the compliance center. The support consists of one lateral and one angular spring. The compliance center is located a distance L_g from the tip of the peg.

gular spring, as illustrated in Fig. 5.6. The point marked ⊗ in Fig. 5.6 is the compliance center of the support. It might be called the "mathematical support point" for the peg because, in general, it is not the point at which the peg is physically supported. Instead, the physical support has been replaced mathematically and equivalently by one lateral spring of stiffness K_x and one torsional spring of stiffness K_θ located a distance L_g from the tip of the peg.

A part mating event then can be represented by the path of the supported part (constrained by its shape and the shape of the part it mates to), the path of the support (constrained by the machine doing the assembly), the forces and moments applied to the part by the compliances of the support as these paths deviate and the compliances stretch and compress, and the forces applied to the parts by the contact and friction forces during assembly. Figure 5.7 sketches the five phases of assembly again in terms of the angle θ between peg and hole

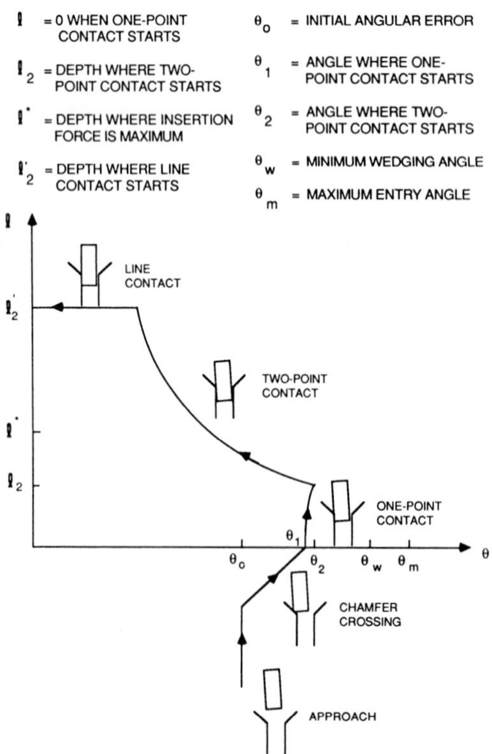

Fig. 5.7 The life cycle of an assembly. This plot traces the history of insertion depth and angle between peg and hole as the peg passes through the five phases of assembly defined in Fig. 5.2.

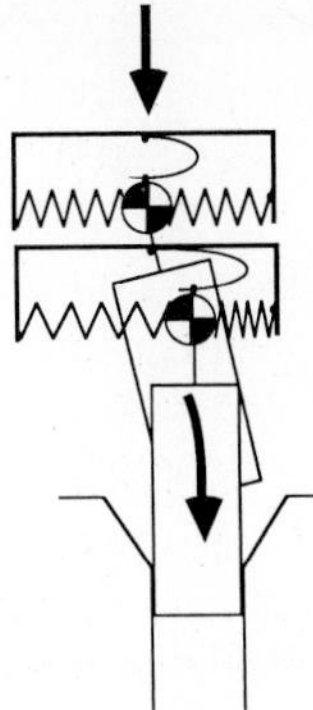

Fig. 5.8 Schematic illustration of the deformation of the lateral and angular springs as assembly proceeds. The deformation of these springs gives rise to contact forces between the tip of the peg and the walls of the hole.

and the depth of insertion l, while Fig. 5.8 shows schematically how the springs deform during assembly.

Kinematic description of part motions during assembly

The behavior of pegs and holes during assembly is strongly affected by the location of the compliance center. To illustrate this, let us consider the two situations depicted in Fig. 5.9. In part (*a*) the compliance cen-

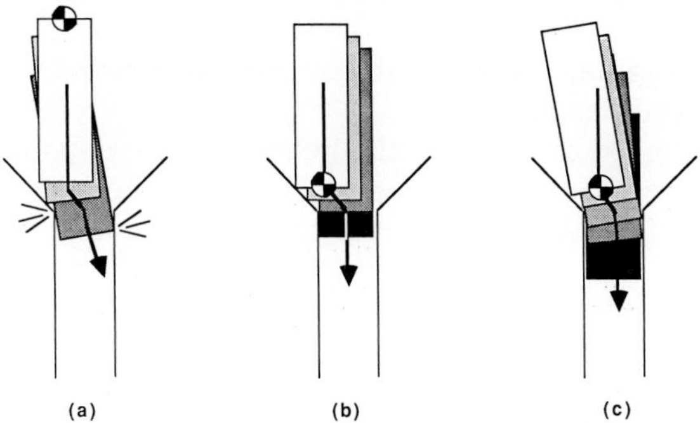

Fig. 5.9 Comparison of part mating behavior for two different locations for the compliance center. In (*a*), the compliance center is at the rear of the peg. Initially the peg has some lateral error but no angular error. The lateral error becomes angular error as the peg passes over the chamfer and one-point contact begins. Wedging or jamming could occur. In (*b*) and (*c*), the compliance center is at the tip of the peg. In (*b*), there is initially only lateral error, which is removed during chamfer crossing without introducing any angular error. In (*c*), there is initially both lateral and angular error. Again, the lateral error is removed during chamfer crossing, while the angular error is removed during two-point contact.

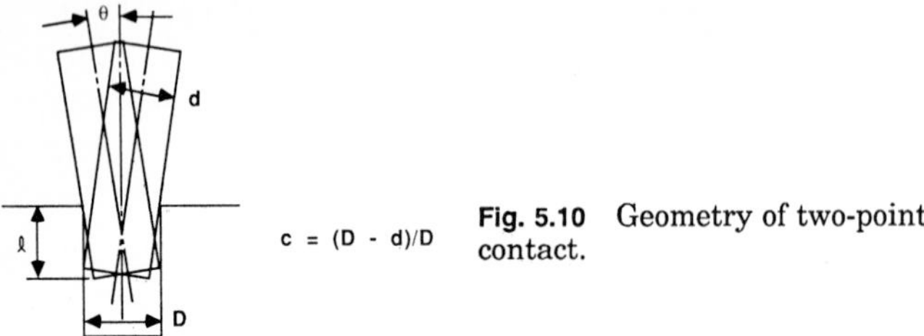

Fig. 5.10 Geometry of two-point contact.

ter is located far from the tip of the peg. If there is some lateral error, the peg will both translate and rotate in response to the contact force between the peg and chamfer. The rotation will combine with any initial angular error and may cause the parts to have a two-point contact. Since two-point contact is a prime danger zone, we would like to prevent this type of contact or delay it until the peg is far into the hole and the risk of wedging and jamming is low. Clearly, the smaller the angular error, the farther into the hole two-point contact will occur.

In part (*b*) the compliance center is approximately at the tip of the peg and an example of pure lateral error is shown. In this case, chamfer crossing removes the lateral error without introducing any angular error, clearly a desirable situation.

In part (*c*) there is both lateral and angular error. Chamfer crossing removes the lateral error while two-point contact removes the angular error. We will show later that (*c*) represents the safest two-point contact situation if there is angular error and that the contact forces between the parts are as small as possible.

To proceed further, we need to consider the geometry of two-point contact in more detail. Figure 5.10 shows a peg part way into a hole. It is easy to show that insertion depth ℓ and wobble angle θ are approximately related by

$$\ell\theta = cD \tag{5.1}$$

where

$$c = \frac{D - d}{D} \tag{5.2}$$

The variable c is called the clearance ratio. It is the dimensionless clearance between peg and hole. Figure 5.11 shows that the clearance ratio describes different kinds of parts rather well. That is, knowing the name of the part and its approximate size, one can predict the clearance ratio with good accuracy. The data in this figure are derived from industry recommended practices and ASME standard fit classes.

Equation (5.1) shows that as the peg goes deeper into the hole, angle

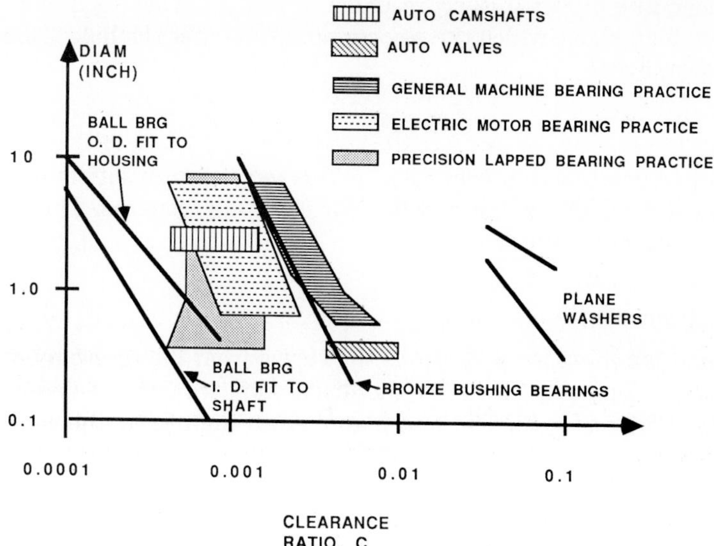

Fig. 5.11 Survey of dimensioning practice for rigid parts. This figure shows that for a given type of part and a two-decade range in diameters, the clearance ratio varies by a decade or less, indicating that the clearance ratio can be well estimated simply by knowing the name of the part.

θ gets smaller and the peg becomes more parallel to the axis of the hole. This fact is reflected in the long curved portion of Fig. 5.7.

Figure 5.12 plots the exact version of Eq. (5.1) for different values of clearance ratio *c*. Note particularly the very small values of θ that apply to parts with small values of *c*. Intuitively we know that small θ implies difficult assembly. Combining Fig. 5.12 with data such as that in Fig. 5.11 permits us to predict which kinds of parts might present assembly difficulties.

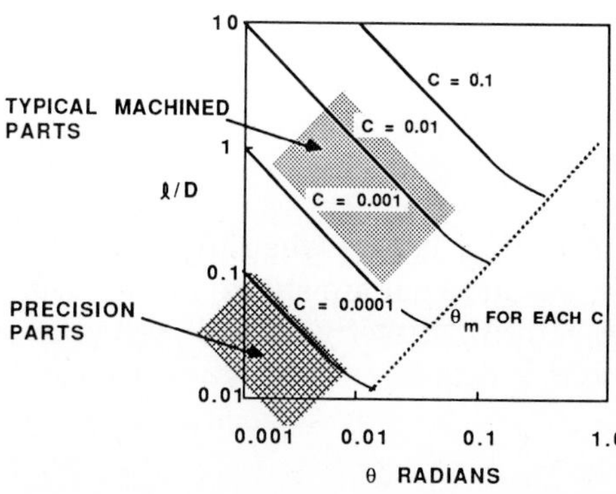

Fig. 5.12 Wobble angle versus insertion depth. Parts with smaller clearance ratios are limited to very small wobble angles during two-point contact, even for small insertion depths. Since successful assembly requires alignment errors between peg and hole axes to be less than the wobble angle and since smaller errors imply more difficult assembly, it is clear that assembly difficulty increases as clearance ratio (rather than clearance itself) decreases.

The dashed line in Fig. 5.12 represents the fact that there is a maximum value for θ above which the peg cannot even enter the hole. This value is given by

$$\theta_m = \sqrt{2c} \tag{5.3}$$

It turns out in practice that condition (5.3) is very easy to satisfy and that in fact a smaller maximum value for θ usually governs. This is called the wedging angle θ_w.

Wedging and jamming

Wedging and jamming are conditions that arise from the interplay of forces between the parts. To unify the discussion, we use the definitions in Figs. 5.6 and 5.13. The forces applied to the peg by the compliances are represented by F_x, F_z, and M at or about the tip of the peg. The forces applied to the peg by its contact with the hole are represented by F_1, F_2, and the friction forces normal to the contacted surfaces. The coefficient of friction is μ. (In the case of one-point contact, there is only one contact force and its associated friction force.) The analyses that follow assume that these forces are in approximate static equilibrium. This means in practice that there is always some contact—either one point or two—and that accelerations are negligible. The analyses also assume that the support for the peg can be described as having a compliance center.

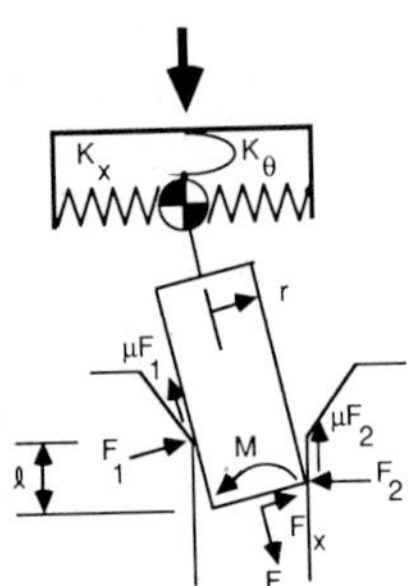

Fig. 5.13 Forces and moments on a peg in two-point contact.

Wedging can occur if two-point contact occurs when the peg is not very far into the hole. A wedged peg and hole are shown in Fig. 5.14. The contact forces F_1 and F_2 are pointing directly toward each other. The smallest value of θ for which this can occur is θ_w, given by

$$\theta_w = \frac{c}{\mu} \tag{5.4}$$

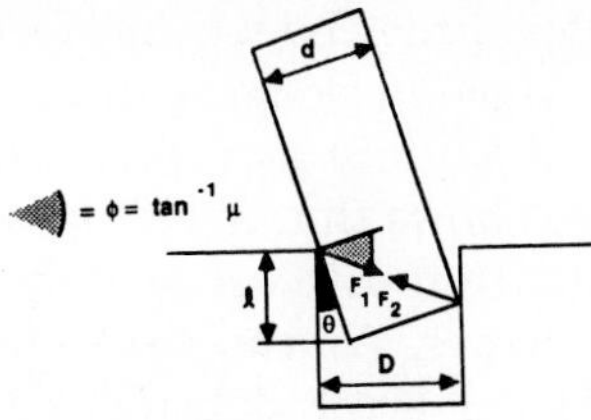

Fig. 5.14 Geometry of wedging condition. The figure is drawn for the case of the smallest θ and largest ℓ for which wedging can occur, namely $\ell = \mu d$.

We can now state the geometric conditions for stage 1, the successful entry of the peg into the hole and the avoidance of wedging, in terms of the initial lateral and angular errors. To cross the chamfer and enter the hole, we need

$$|\varepsilon_0| < W \tag{5.5}$$

where W is the sum of chamfer widths on the peg and hole, and

$$\theta_0 + S\varepsilon_0 < \pm \frac{c}{\mu} \tag{5.6}$$

where

$$S = \frac{L_g}{L_g^2 + K_\theta/K_x} \tag{5.7}$$

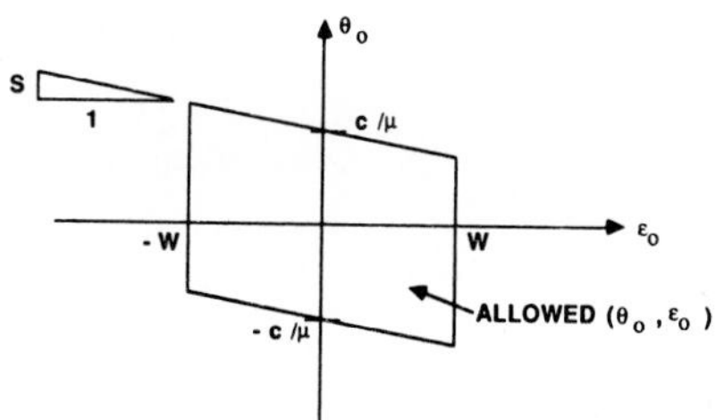

Fig. 5.15 Geometry constraints on allowed lateral and angular error to permit chamfer crossing and avoidance of wedging. Not only must the error angle between peg and hole be less than the allowed wobble angle, as shown in Fig. 5.12, but the maximum error is also governed by the coefficient of friction if wedging is to be avoided. If L_g is not zero, then if there is also some initial lateral error, this error could be converted to angular error after chamfer crossing. So, avoiding wedging places conditions on both initial lateral error and initial angular error. The interaction between these conditions disappears if $L_g = 0$. This fact is shown intuitively in Fig. 5.9.

(L_g is defined in Fig. 5.6.) If parts become wedged, there is generally no cure (if we wish to avoid potentially damaging the parts) except to withdraw the peg and try again. It is best to avoid wedging in the first place. The conditions for achieving this, Eqs. (5.6) and (5.7), can be plotted together as in Fig. 5.15. This figure shows that avoiding wedging is related to success in initial entry, and that both are governed by control of the initial lateral and angular errors. We can see from the figure that the amount of permitted lateral error depends on the amount of angular error and vice versa. For example, we can tolerate more angular error to the right when there is lateral error to the left because this combination tends to reduce the angular error during chamfer crossing. Since we cannot plan to have such optimistic combinations occur, however, the extra tolerance does us no good, and in fact we must plan for the more pessimistic case. This forces us to consider the smallest error window.

Note particularly what happens if $L_g = 0$. In this case the parallelogram in Fig. 5.15 becomes a rectangle and all interaction between lateral and angular errors disappears. This makes planning of an assembly the easiest and makes the error window the largest.

Jamming can occur because the wrong combination of applied forces is acting on the peg. Figure 5.16 states that any combinations of the applied forces F_x, F_z, and M which lie inside the parallelogram guarantee avoidance of jamming. To understand this figure, it is important to see the effect of the variable λ. This variable is related to the insertion depth ℓ and is given by

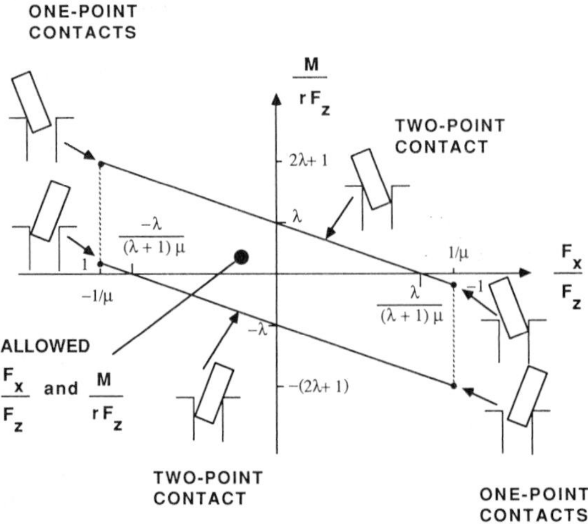

Fig. 5.16 The jamming diagram. This diagram shows what combinations of applied forces and moments on the peg will permit assembly without jamming.

$$\lambda = \frac{\ell}{\mu D} \tag{5.8}$$

As insertion proceeds, both ℓ and λ get bigger. This in turn makes the parallelogram in Fig. 5.16 get taller, expanding the region of successful assembly. The region is smallest when λ is smallest, near the beginning of assembly. We may conclude that jamming is most likely when the region is smallest. (Since the sides of the region are governed by the coefficient of friction μ, the parallelogram does not change width during insertion as long as μ is constant.)

If we analyze the forces shown in Fig. 5.13 to determine what F_x, F_z, and M are for the case where K_θ is small, we find that

$$\frac{M}{rF_z} = -\left(\frac{L_g}{r}\right)\left(\frac{F_x}{F_z}\right) \tag{5.9}$$

which says that the forces and moments on the peg must lie on a line of slope $-(L_g/r)$ in Fig. 5.16. If L_g/r is big, the line will be steep and the chances of the applied forces falling inside the parallelogram will be small. On the other hand, if L_g/r is small so that the line in Eq. (5.9) is about parallel to the sloping sides of the parallelogram, the chance of the applied forces falling inside the parallelogram will be as large as possible. This tells us to make L_g/r approximately equal to μ. Since μ is typically 0.1 to 0.3, we see that the compliance center should be quite near the end but inside of the peg to avoid jamming.

In Chap. 7, a particular type of compliant support called a "remote center compliance" (RCC) is described which succeeds in placing a compliance center outside itself. The compliance center is far enough away that there is space to put a gripper and workpiece between the RCC and the compliance center, allowing the compliance center to be at or near the tip of the peg. The reader wishing to know how the RCC works may read Chap. 7 now, or may continue with this chapter.

Typical insertion force histories

We can get an idea of the meaning of the above relations by looking at a few insertion force histories. These were obtained by mounting a peg and hole on a milling machine and lowering the quill to insert the peg into the hole. A six-axis force-torque sensor recorded the forces. The peg was held by an RCC. The experimental conditions are given in Table 5.1.

Figure 5.17 shows typical histories of F_z for a case where there is only lateral error and the compliance center is about $4r$ away from the tip of the peg. The first peak in the force indicates chamfer crossing. Between ℓ = 1 millimeter (mm) and ℓ = 9 mm is one-point contact,

TABLE 5.1 Experimental Conditions for Part Mating Experiments

Support: Draper Laboratory Remote Center Compliance
Lateral stiffness = K_x = 7 N/mm (40 lb/in)
Angular stiffness = K_θ = 53,000 N · mm/rad (470 in · lb/rad)
Peg and hole: Steel, hardened and ground
Hole diameter = 12.705 mm (0.5002 in)
Peg diameter = 12.672 mm (0.4989 in)
Clearance ratio = 0.0026
Coefficient of friction ≅ 0.1 (determined empirically from one-point contact data)

following which two-point contact occurs. The maximum force occurs at about ℓ = 16 mm, or about twice the depth at which two-point contact began. For many cases, we can prove that the peak force will occur at this depth.

Figure 5.18 shows the insertion force for the case where the lateral error is larger than that in Fig. 5.17, but L_g is almost zero. Here, there is essentially no two-point contact, as predicted intuitively by Fig. 5.9. Also shown is the lateral force F_x. These results show the merit of placing the compliance center near the tip of the peg.

Figure 5.19. summarizes the events and conditions for successful chamfered rigid peg-hole mating.

Comment on chamfers

Chamfers play a central role in part mating. Clearly, wider chamfers make assembly easier since they lessen the restrictions on the permissible lateral error. Chapter 11 discusses the relationships among the various sources of error in an assembly workstation and describes how to calculate the width of chamfers needed.

Also, it is significant that if a properly designed compliant support is used, with its compliance center at the tip of the peg, there will be little insertion force except that generated by chamfer crossing. As the next chapter shows, the magnitude of this force depends heavily on the slope and shape of the chamfers. That is, straight chamfers need not be inclined at 45 degrees, and furthermore, chamfers need not be straight.

While most chamfers are flat 45 degree bevels, some solutions to part mating problems have been based on chamfers of other shapes. Figure 5.20 shows two examples of designs for the ends of plug gauges. Plug gauges are measuring tools used to determine if a hole is the correct diameter. To make this determination accurately requires that

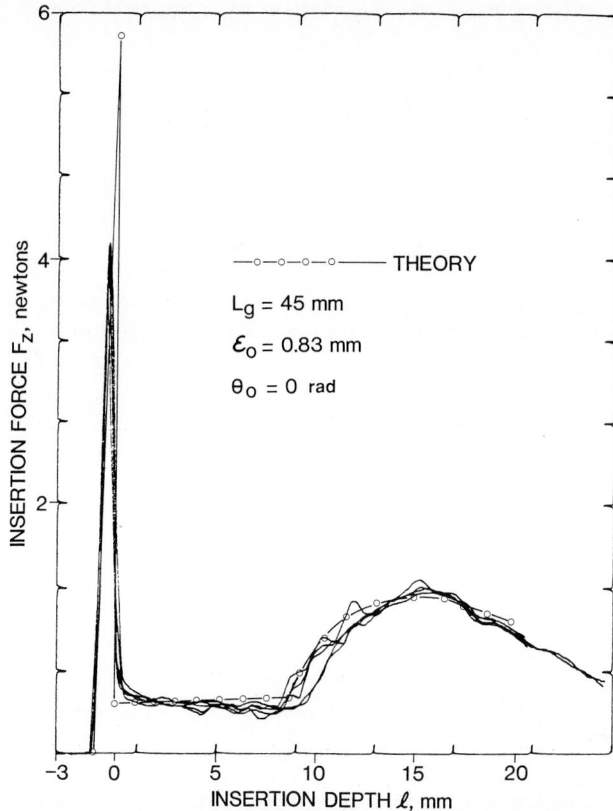

Fig. 5.17 Insertion force history. The compliance center is $4r$ back inside the peg from the tip. There is lateral error only, essentially no angular error. As expected, two-point contact occurs, giving rise to the peak in the insertion force at a depth of about 15 mm. The peak at around 0 mm is caused by chamfer crossing. Also shown on the plot is a theoretical estimate of insertion force based on equations given in the appendix. A computer program in the appendix was used to create the estimate.

the clearance between hole and gauge be very small, making it difficult and time-consuming to insert and remove the gauge and to avoid wedging it in the hole. The designs in Fig. 5.20 specifically prevent wedging by making the ends of the gauges spheres whose radius is equal to the peg's diameter. The small undercut in the second design also helps to avoid damaging the rim of the hole.

Chamferless Insertion

Chamferless insertion is a rare event compared to chamfered insertion because only a few parts have to be made without chamfers. Many of

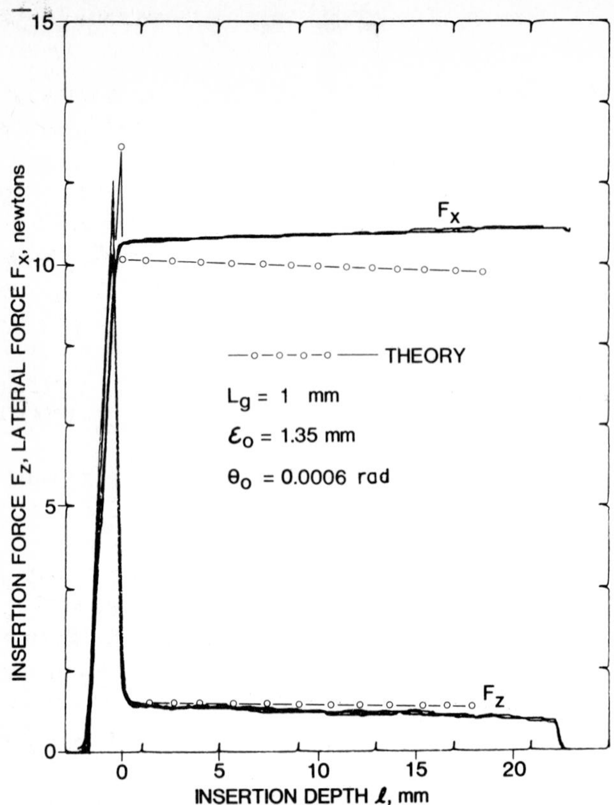

Fig. 5.18 Insertion and lateral force history. The peg, hole, and compliant support are the same as in Fig. 5.17, but L_g is essentially zero. As predicted, two-point contact does not occur even though there is initially more lateral error than in Fig. 5.17. This additional lateral error is also responsible for the larger chamfer crossing force (the large spike at $\ell = 0$) in this case compared to Fig. 5.17.

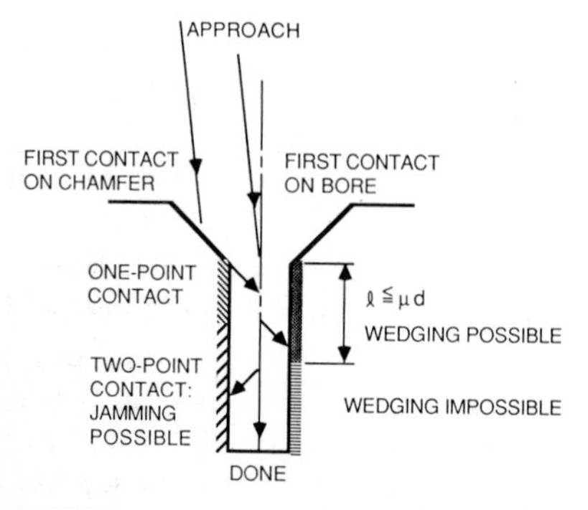

Fig. 5.19 Pictorial summary of conditions for successful clearance assembly of round pegs and holes with chamfers.

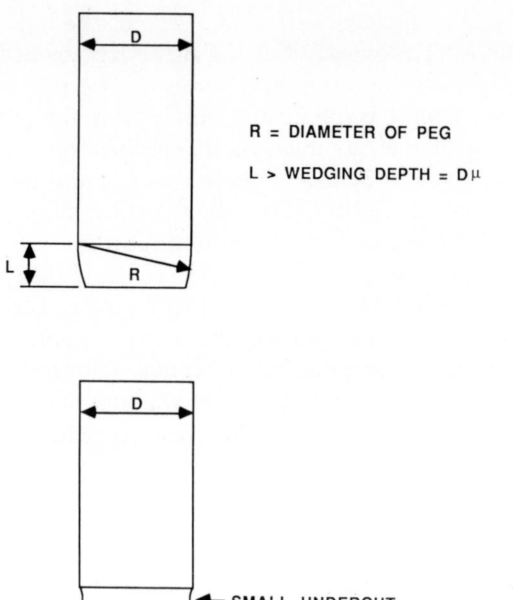

Fig. 5.20 Two designs of chamfer that prevent wedging.

these are parts of hydraulic valves, whose sharp edges are essential for obtaining the correct fluid flow patterns inside the valves. In other cases, chamfers must be very small because of lack of space; a chamfer always adds length to a part, and sometimes there is a severe length constraint, either on a part or on the whole product. Chamferless insertions are, of course, more difficult than chamfered ones because W in Eq. (5.5) is essentially zero. An attempt to assemble such parts by directly controlling the lateral error to be less than the clearance is almost certain to fail. This is especially true of hydraulic parts, whose clearances are only 10 or 20 μm (0.0004 to 0.0008 in).

In spite of their relative rarity, chamferless insertions have attracted much research interest and some overly complex solutions, such as that in Fig. 5.21. This is a multiphase method in which the

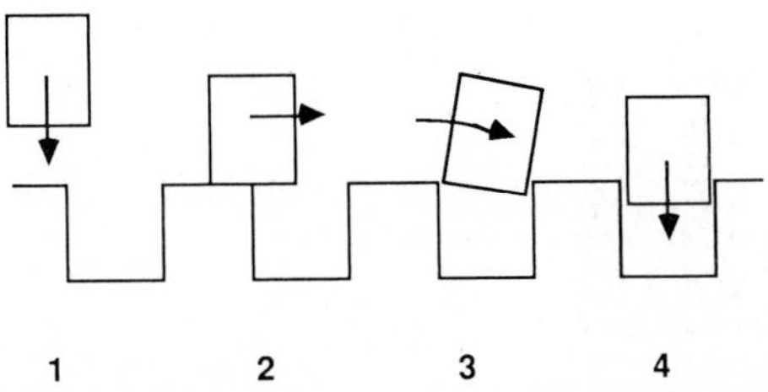

Fig. 5.21 A chamferless insertion strategy. (1) Approach; (2) slide laterally; (3) catch the rim of the hole and tilt; (4) lower peg into hole.

peg is lowered until it strikes the surface well to one side of the hole. The lateral error may not be known exactly but the direction toward the hole is known well enough for the method to proceed. The peg is then slid sideways toward the hole. It is held compliantly near the *top* so that when it passes over the edge of the hole, its tip catches the rim of the hole and it starts to tip over. A sensor detects this tilt and lateral motion is stopped and reversed slightly. This should allow the tip to fall slightly into the hole. The peg is then lowered carefully.

An elaboration of this strategy is employed by the Hi-Ti Hand (Goto et al., 1980), a motorized fine motion device invented by Hitachi, Ltd. In this method, if the peg meets resistance during the lowering phase, it is gently rocked side to side in two perpendicular planes. The limits of this rocking are detected by sensors, and the top of the peg is then positioned midway between the limits. The push and rock procedure is repeated as necessary until the peg is all the way in. In the case of the Hi-Ti Hand, mating time is typically 3 to 5 s. This method is good if the parts are delicate because it specifically limits the insertion force. For parts that can stand a little contact force, however, it is far too slow. Typical assembly times for chamfered parts held by an RCC are of the order of 0.2 s.

Figure 5.22 shows an entirely passive chamferless insertion method (Gustavson et al., 1982). "Passive" means that it contains no sensors or motors. Figure 5.23 is a schematic of the apparatus itself. It has several novel features, including two centers of compliance which op-

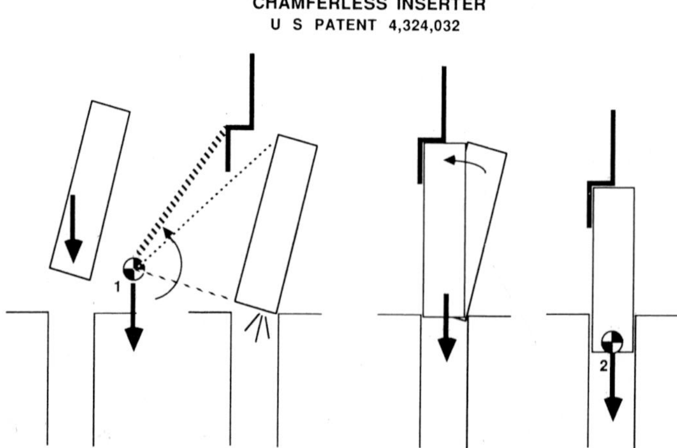

Fig. 5.22 Passive chamferless insertion strategy. The inserter works by first permitting the peg to approach the hole tilted and then to turn up to an upright orientation with one edge slightly in the mouth of the hole. Insertion proceeds from that point with the aid of a conventional RCC. The details of how this is accomplished are shown in Fig. 5.23.

erate one after the other. The operation begins with the peg deliberately tilted into an angular error and as little lateral error as possible. (Note that this is the opposite of the initial conditions for the Hi-Ti Hand, where initial angular error is zero and there is deliberate lateral error.) When the peg is tilted, one side of the peg effectively acts as a chamfer, and it is almost certain that the tip of the peg and mouth of the hole will meet. Once they meet, the gripper continues moving down while the peg tilts up to approximately vertical under the influence of the linkage which creates the first compliance center. Upon reaching vertical, the peg locks into the gripper and comes under the influence of the compliant support above it, having the second center of compliance at the tip of the peg. The peg's tip stays in the mouth of the hole while rotating up to vertical. Insertion then proceeds as if the parts had chamfers, starting from the point at which chamfer crossing is complete.

Examples of the apparatus in Fig. 5.23 are in use installing valves into automobile engines.

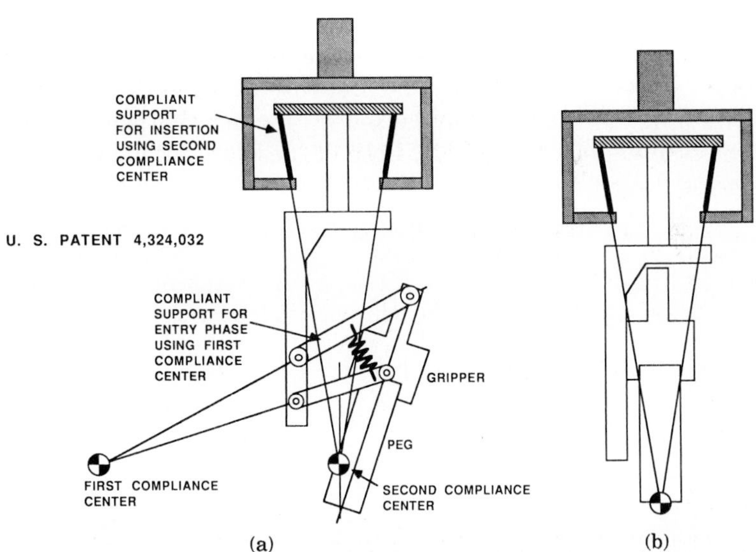

Fig. 5.23 Schematic of passive chamferless inserter. (*a*) Arrangement of the device while the peg is approaching the hole. The first compliance center is active and the part can rotate around it because of the sprung linkage attached to the gripper. The linkage is designed so that the tip of the peg does not move laterally very much while the peg is rotating up to vertical. What little tip motion there is will be in a direction away from the first compliance center so as to keep the tip pressed firmly against the rim of the hole. By this means the peg is most likely to remain in the mouth of the hole. (*b*) The part has engaged the mouth of the hole and is now locked into the vertical position. Insertion proceeds from here the same as if there had been chamfers and chamfer crossing were complete.

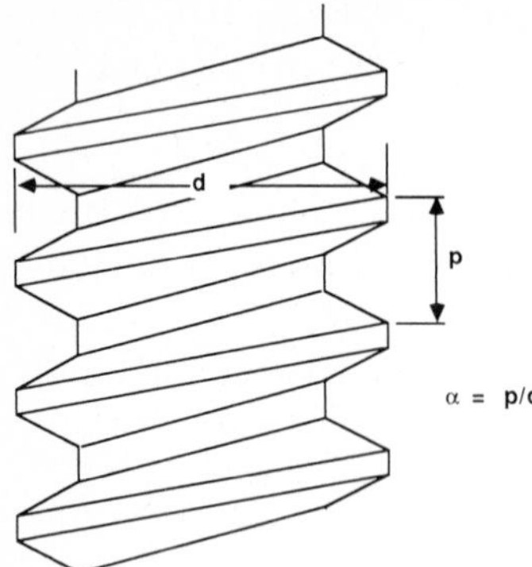

Fig. 5.24 Schematic of screw thread defining p and d. In order for threads to mismate because of tilt angle error, the tilt must be greater than α.

Screw Thread Mating

Figure 5.1(*d*) showed normally mated screws. Assembling screws involves a chamfer mate similar to peg-hole mating followed by thread engagement. The screw (or nut) is then turned several turns until it starts to tighten. The last stage comprises tightening a specified amount.

Aside from missing the mouth of the hole, screw mating can fail in two possible ways. One is a mismatch of threads caused by angular error. The other is a mismatch caused by having the peaks of the screw miss the valleys of the hole. Both of these are interchangeably called "cross threading."

In order for the threads to mismate angularly, the angular error must be greater than the angle between successive peaks or valleys, as shown in Fig. 5.24. If we define the angle between peaks as α, the diameter of the screw as d, and the thread pitch as p threads per unit length, we may write

$$\alpha = \frac{p}{d} \tag{5.10}$$

We may calculate α for different standard screw thread sizes. The results are in Fig. 5.25. They indicate that for very small screws, an angular error of 1.14 milliradians (mrad) or 0.8 degree is enough to cause a tilt mismatch. Angular control required at this level is comparable to that required to mate precision pegs and holes, as indicated in Fig. 5.12. For larger screws, the angles become comfortably large, indicating what is found in practice, namely that this kind of error does not happen very often since angular control as good as a degree or so is easy to obtain, even from simple tools and fixtures.

The other kind of screw mating error is illustrated in Fig. 5.26. Here, the error is also angular, but the angle in question is about the

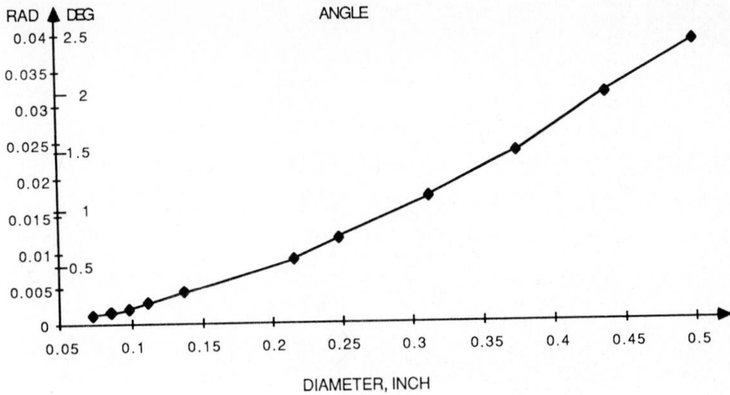

Fig. 5.25 Maximum permissible angular error versus screw size for UNC threads to prevent tilt mismatch between threads. Since angular errors are relatively easy to keep below a few tenths of a degree, angular cross threading is fairly easy to avoid for all but the smallest screws.

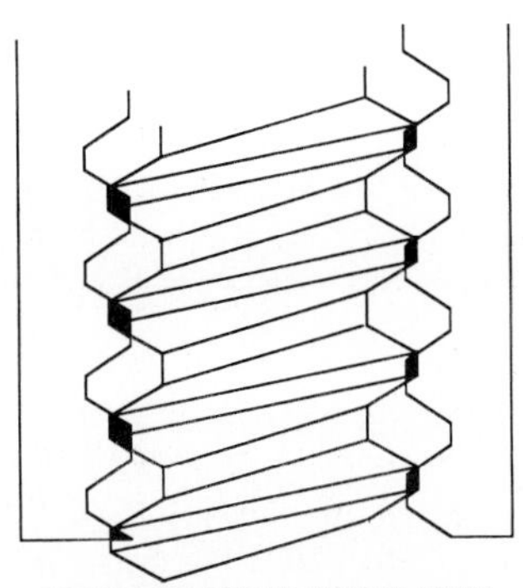

Fig. 5.26 Mismated screws caused by helical phase error.

insertion axis in the twist direction. That is, the thread helixes are out of phase. Unless the materials of either the screw or the hole are soft, this kind of error is also difficult to create.

Some study of this problem may be found in Russian papers. Figure 5.27 is from Romanov (1964). The screw has a taper or chamfer of angle α while the hole thread has a taper of angle γ. The analysis in this paper is entirely geometric, with no consideration of friction. The conclusion is that α should be greater than γ (see Fig. 5.28). This is an interesting conclusion because the Russian standards at the time the paper was written were α = 45 degrees, γ = 60.

Another method of aiding the starting of screws is to drastically

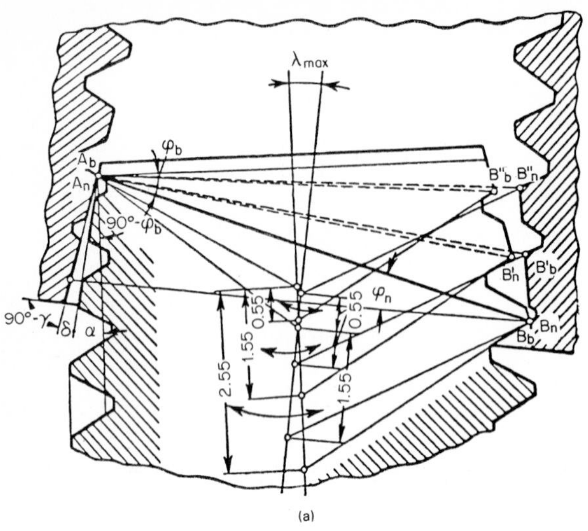

(a)

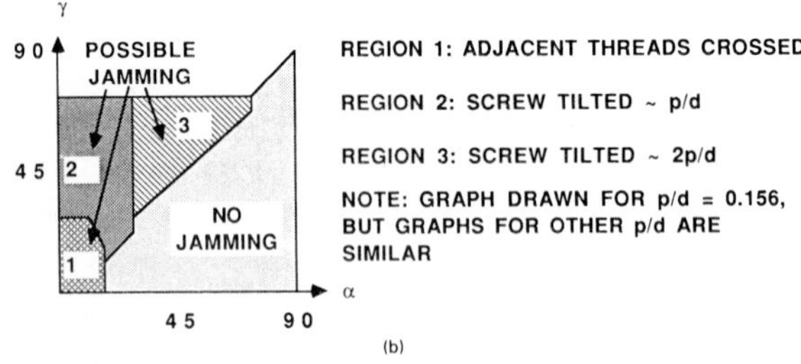

(b)

Fig. 5.27 (*a*) Variables involved in analysis of thread mismating. Both angular and phase error are depicted here; (*b*) Sample diagram of good and bad values of α and γ (from Romanov, 1964).

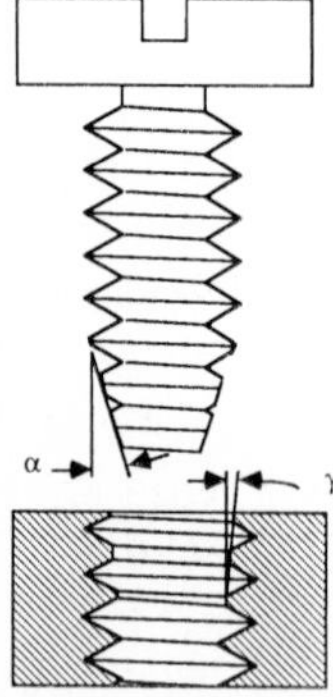

Fig. 5.28 Screw and threaded hole with screw chamfer steeper than hole chamfer.

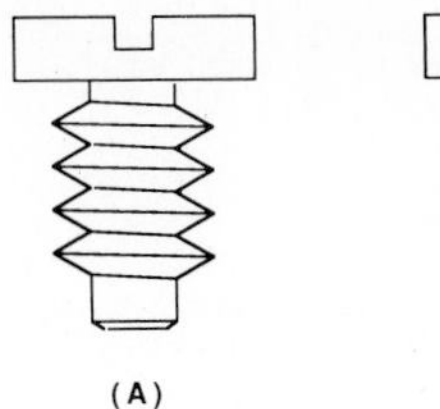

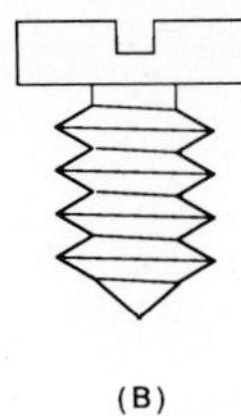

Fig. 5.29 Dog point (*a*) and cone point (*b*) screws.

change the shape of the tip. Two examples are shown in Fig. 5.29. These are called "dog point" and "cone point" screws. (Cone point screws figured in the example of Volkswagen car production in Chap. 3.) Each has two disadvantages: extra cost and extra length, but the advantages are valuable. The dog point is a short cylinder that assures that the screw is centered in the hole and parallel to it. The cone point provides the largest possible chamfer, making it easier to put the screw in a poorly toleranced or uncertainly located hole, such as in sheet metal.

The above methods of starting screws all depend on the helixes mating with the correct phase without doing anything explicit to ensure that correct phase is achieved. A method which searches for the correct phase is the "turn backward first" method, known to work well with lids of peanut butter jars. Usually this method requires sensing. To use it, one places screw and hole mouth to mouth and turns backward until one senses that the screw has advanced suddenly. The magnitude of this advance is approximately one thread pitch. At this point, the threads are in a dangerous configuration, with chamfered peaks almost exactly facing each other. So it is necessary to turn an additional amount back, perhaps 45 degrees. Then it is safe to begin turning forward. If a full turn is made without an advance being detected, successful mating will not be possible, and the parts should be separated. This method is slow and, as stated, requires sensing, but it works well and may be necessary in the case of unusually large diameters and small thread pitches, where even small angular errors can cause mismating.

The last phase of screw mating is the tightening phase. Screw tightening must be done with care in order to obtain a properly and safely secured joint without risking stripping the threads. A commonly used but unreliable method is to measure the torque required to tighten the screw. The unreliability is based on the fact that the felt torque is a combination of tightening torque and friction torque between the head of the screw and the hole face. One typically feels more torque than is actually being exerted on the threads. Errors of 50 percent or more are not unusual.

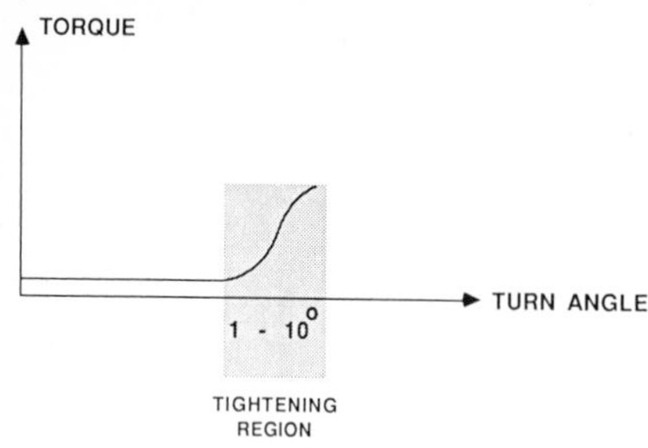

Fig. 5.30 Schematic of screw tightening torque versus screw turn angle. The torque rises very quickly after many turns with little or no torque. Torque is applied until the inflection point on the curve is reached.

A more reliable method measures both turn angle and torque and seeks to set a certain amount of elongation into the screw rather than to achieve a certain amount of torque. To achieve this, it is necessary to plot torque versus turn angle and try to determine the inflection point of the curve. This point is related to the point at which the screw starts to deform plastically, at which it has achieved its maximum safe stretch. For many screws, the entire tightening event occurs within 1 to 10 degrees of turning, as indicated in Fig. 5.30. Since screws are typically turned rapidly by automatic screwdrivers, the measuring apparatus and brakes on the screwdriver must act quickly. Commercial devices are available that operate on this principle. A study of torque-angle-controlled tightening of precision threads by automatic control is given by Dunne (1986).

Gear Mating

The last topic in this chapter is the assembly of gears. This is a complex topic on which only a little research has been done. We will assume that one gear has already been installed and it is necessary to install and mate another or others to it. There are several cases to consider. In each case the common element is that gear mating requires two separate alignments to occur. One is to bring the pitch circles into tangency and the other is to fit the teeth together. These two steps can be done in either order, depending on the circumstances. Pitch circles are illustrated in Fig. 5.1*e*.

The first case analyzed is the easiest. There is plenty of space near the insertion point so the arriving gear may be brought down to one side of its mate as shown in Fig. 5.31. Once it is near, the tool rotates the gear about its spin axis while bringing it laterally toward its mate. The mating direction is perpendicular to the spin axis of the gears. Eventually the teeth mesh and assembly can continue. This method mates the teeth first and then the pitch circles.

If the arriving gear is on a shaft that must be inserted into a bearing, the above method works if the teeth can be mated before the shaft

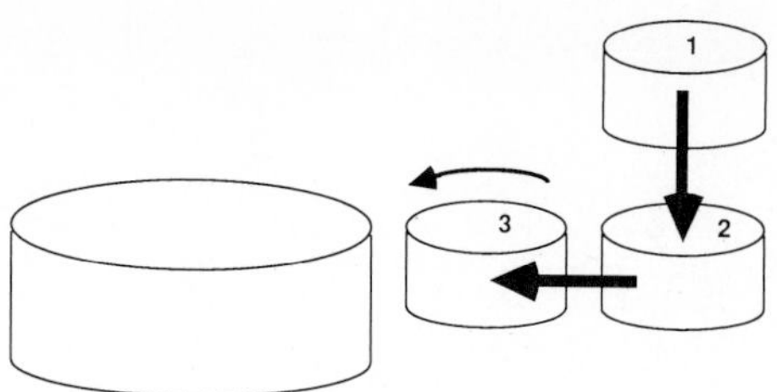

Fig. 5.31 The side-approach method of mating gears.

and bearing. If the shaft and bearing must mate first, the best method is to spin the shaft and gear while inserting along the spin axis in the hope of mating the teeth. The same problem arises if two gears that are linked together must mate simultaneously with a third gear, as shown in Fig. 5.32. Thus this method approximately mates the pitch circles first and then mates the teeth.

However, an approach along the spin axis may not succeed as easily as one perpendicular to it. Gears are designed so that when they are mated, with the pitch circles tangent, there is little or no clearance between adjacent teeth. When gears are inserted along the spin axis, the pitch circles are typically already approximately tangent. This method therefore depends on the teeth mating under conditions in which there is little or no clearance between them. The arriving gear may simply come to rest on top of its mate and spin without mating, especially if the pitch circles slightly overlap.

People typically make such mates either by waiting until a random chance mates the gears or by rocking the arriving gear, tilting its spin axis away from parallel to its final orientation, in order eventually to tilt the tip of a tooth into the space between two teeth on the other gear. These random and unpredictable methods cannot be used by automatic machinery without their being equipped with extra degrees of freedom and sensors. The method also fails to have a predictable completion time, making it an awkward one to include in an otherwise

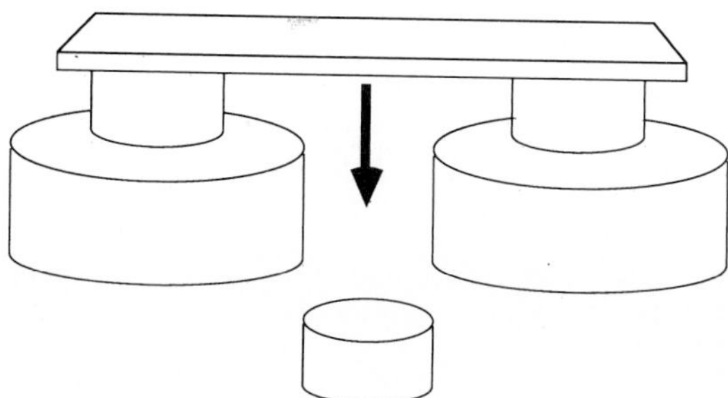

Fig. 5.32 The spin-axis-approach method of mating gears.

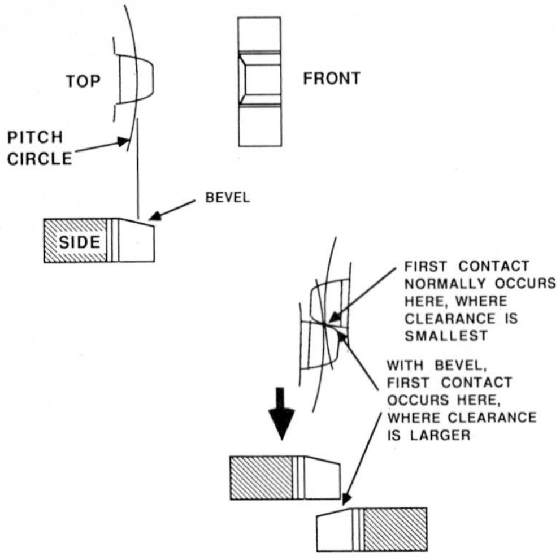

Fig. 5.33 Beveling gear teeth to aid mating.

well-planned and rhythmic production line. In short, the method lacks structure and should be replaced with a better one.

Two solutions are possible. The first is shown in Fig. 5.33. Here, a bevel has been cut on one side of the teeth so that when they meet, the touching places will not be on the pitch circle but instead somewhere else; anywhere else will have larger clearance, so the chance of mating will be much larger.

The second solution is shown in Fig. 5.34. This idea is similar in spirit to the dog point screw. To make it work well, the chamfered pilot on the gear must be well made so that it fits snugly within the teeth of the mating gear. This fit places the pitch circles close to each other. Spinning the arriving gear usually causes the teeth to mate easily.

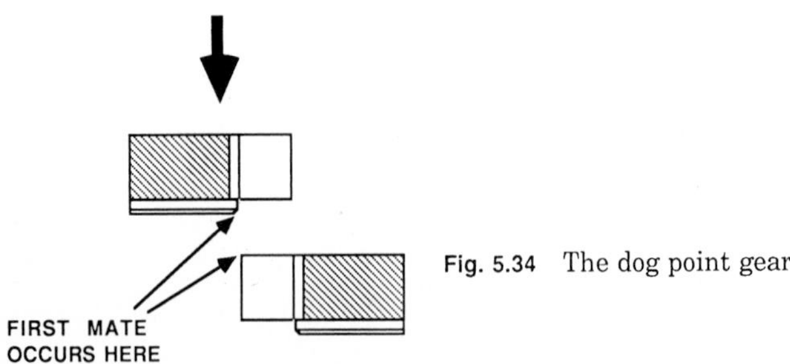

Fig. 5.34 The dog point gear.

Both of these solutions to gear mating have the same disadvantage as dog point screws; they add length to the gears. Since the length of a gear tooth's face is carefully calculated to give the gear adequate load capacity and life, one does not shorten the gear in order to accommodate either the bevel or the pilot. An entire product can become longer if we add length to some of its parts, and the added length can be a problem for other reasons.

The mating of splines is physically similar to mating of gears. Splines are essentially internal gear mates in which all the teeth mate at once since the pitch circles are concentric.

Summary

This chapter has outlined the behavior of rigid parts during assembly. The success of mating was shown to depend heavily on the shapes of the parts, the initial errors between them, the friction coefficient, and the compliance of the supporting tools and grippers. Success for chamfered and chamferless peg-hole mates depends on avoiding wedging and jamming. The mathematical conditions for this were derived. All of the relevant analyses assume that the parts are moving slowly. Conditions given for successful mating of screws and gears are geometrical since the theory is not well enough developed to provide anything else. However, the conditions for successful assembly of simple peg-hole mates that take account of friction are more restrictive than the purely geometrical conditions. That is, the allowed errors are much smaller. Therefore, it is likely that the geometric conditions given for gears and screws are also merely necessary ones and are not sufficient, implying that the true conditions are more restrictive.

References

Arai, T., and N. Kinoshita: "The Part Mating Forces That Arise When Using a Worktable with Compliance," *Assembly Automation,* Aug. 1981, pp. 204–210.

Dunne, B. J.: "Precision Torque Control for Threaded Part Assembly," MIT M.S. Thesis, Mech. Eng. Dept., 1986.

Gieseke, F. E., A. Mitchell, and H. C. Spencer: *Technical Drawing,* 4th ed., Macmillan, New York, 1958, p. 546.

Goto, T., et al.: "Control Algorithm for Precision Insert Operation Robot," *IEEE Trans. on Systems, Man, and Cybernetics,* vol. SMC-10, no. 1, Jan. 1980, pp. 19–25.

Gustavson, R. E., et al.: U.S. Patent 4,324,032, "Operator Member Erection System and Method," 1982.

Romanov, G. I.: "Preventing Thread Shear in Automatic Assembly," *Russian Engineering Journal,* vol. 44, no. 9, 1964, pp. 50–52.

Simunvoc, S.: "Force Information in Assembly Processes," presented at the *5th Int'l. Symp. on Industrial Robots,* Chicago, 1975.

Sturges, R. H., Jr.: "A Three-Dimensional Assembly Task Quantification with Application to Machine Dexterity," *Int'l. J. Robotics Res.*, vol. 7, no. 4, Aug. 1988, pp. 34–78.
Whitney, D. E.: "Quasi-Static Assembly of Compliantly Supported Rigid Parts," *Trans. ASME J. Dynamic Systems, Measurement, and Control,* vol. 104, Mar. 1982, pp. 65–77. This reference contains many other references to part mating theory.

Appendix

This appendix sketches the derivations of the basic equations for rigid part mating when the parts are supported by a support that has a compliance center. More detail may be found in Whitney (1982). The derivations presume that the compliance center is located on the peg's axis an arbitrary distance L_g from the tip of the peg. Chamfer crossing, one-point contact, and two-point contact will be described. The derived equations and computer program treat the case in which lateral error and angular error are both positive as shown in Fig. 5.5.

Chamfer Crossing

Refer to Fig. 5A.1, which shows a peg during chamfer crossing and the forces on it. The support contributes the applied forces and the contact between peg and chamfer provides the reaction forces. The support forces are found by determining how far the compliances described by K_x and K_θ have been stretched or compressed. The initial lateral displacement of the support point with respect to the hole's axis is given by U_0:

$$U_0 = \epsilon_0 + L_g\theta_0 \tag{5A.1}$$

When $U = U_0$ and $\theta = \theta_0$, both compliances are relaxed. As chamfer crossing proceeds, U and θ are related by

$$U = L_g\theta - \frac{z}{\tan\alpha} + \epsilon_0 \tag{5A.2}$$

To find U and θ separately, we have to solve for the forces and moments. Writing equilibrium equations between the applied forces and contact forces yields

$$f_1 = f_N\mathbf{B} \tag{5A.3}$$

$$f_2 = f_N\mathbf{A} \tag{5A.4}$$

$$\mathbf{A} = \cos\alpha + \mu\sin\alpha \tag{5A.5}$$

$$\mathbf{B} = \sin\alpha - \mu\cos\alpha \tag{5A.6}$$

and

$$\left.\begin{aligned} F_x &= -f_1 \\ F_z &= f_2 \\ M &= f_2 r \end{aligned}\right\} \quad \text{Contact forces} \qquad \begin{aligned} &(5A.7) \\ &(5A.8) \\ &(5A.9) \end{aligned}$$

$$\left.\begin{aligned} F_x &= -K_x(U_0 - U) \\ M &= K_x L_g(U_0 - U) - K_\theta(\theta - \theta_0) \end{aligned}\right\} \quad \text{Support forces} \qquad \begin{aligned} &(5A.10) \\ &(5A.11) \end{aligned}$$

Combining the above equations yields expressions for U and θ during chamfer crossing:

$$\theta = \theta_0 + \frac{K_x(z/\tan\alpha)(L_g\mathbf{B} - r\mathbf{A})}{(K_xL_g^2 + K_\theta)\mathbf{B} - K_xL_gr\mathbf{A}} \tag{5A.12}$$

and

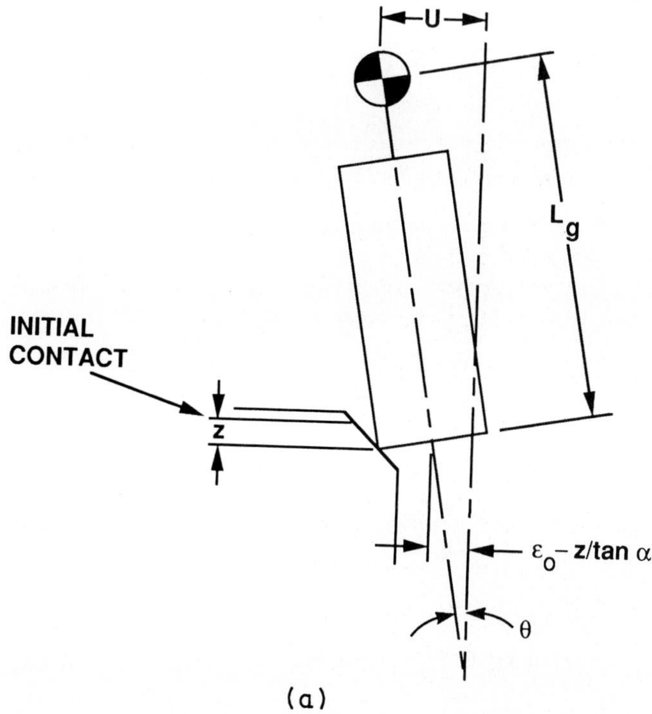

Fig. 5A.1 Geometry (*a*) and forces (*b*) during chamfer crossing.

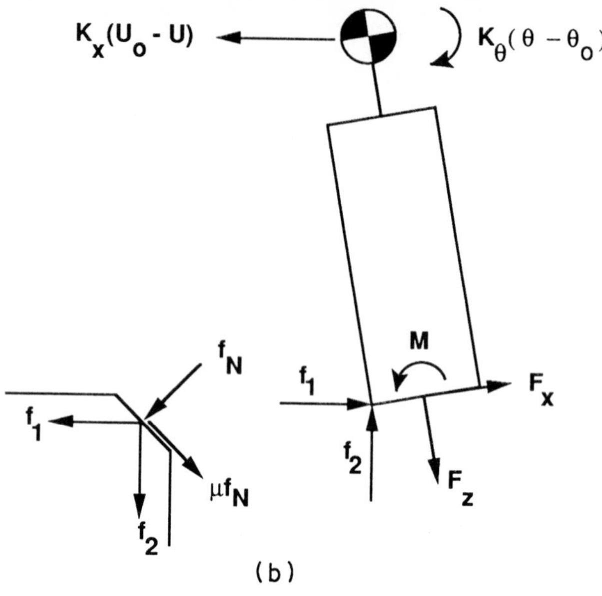

Figure 5A.1 *(Continued)*

$$U = U_0 - \frac{K_\theta(z/\tan\alpha)\mathbf{B}}{(K_x L_g^2 + K_\theta)\mathbf{B} - K_x L_g r\mathbf{A}} \tag{5A.13}$$

One-Point Contact

The forces acting during one-point contact are shown in Fig. 5A.2. A derivation analogous to that for chamfer crossing begins with the geometric constraint

$$U = cR + L_g\theta - \ell\,\theta \tag{5A.14}$$

and yields

$$\theta = \frac{\mathbf{C}(\epsilon_0' + L_g\theta_0) + K_\theta\theta_0}{\mathbf{C}(L_g - \ell) + K_\theta} \tag{5A.15}$$

and

$$U = U_0 - \frac{K_\theta(\epsilon_0' + \ell\theta_0)}{\mathbf{C}(L_g - \ell) + K_\theta} \tag{5A.16}$$

where

$$\mathbf{C} = K_x(L_g - \ell - \mu r) \tag{5A.17}$$

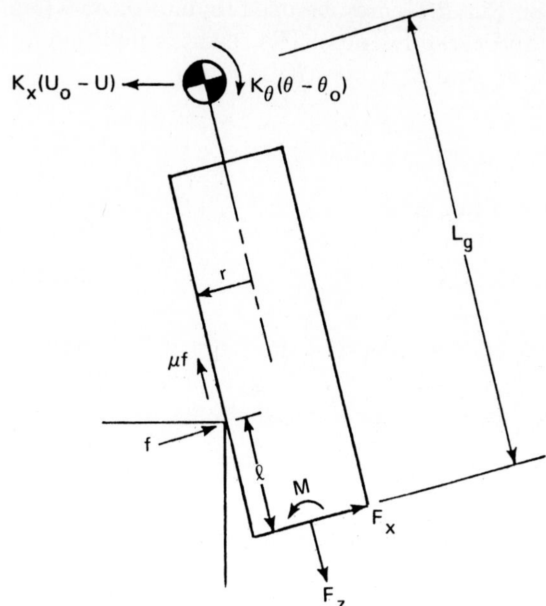

Fig. 5A.2 Forces acting during one-point contact.

and

$$\epsilon_0' = \epsilon_0 - cR \tag{5A.18}$$

Two-Point Contact

Whereas during chamfer crossing and one-point contact we needed to find the forces before we could find U and θ, the reverse is true during two-point contact. We find U and θ via geometric compatibility

$$R = \frac{\ell}{2} \tan \theta + r \cos \theta \tag{5A.19}$$

which reduces to Eq. (5.1) when θ is small. The relation between U, θ, and ϵ during one-point contact is

$$U_0 - U = \epsilon_0' + L_g(\theta_0 - \theta) + \ell \theta \tag{5A.20}$$

If Eq. (5.1) is substituted for θ in Eq. (5A.20), we obtain the corresponding relation for two-point contact:

$$U_0 - U = \epsilon_0'' + L_g(\theta_0 - \theta) \tag{5A.21}$$

where

$$\epsilon_0'' = \epsilon_0 + cR \tag{5A.22}$$

A force analysis based on Fig. 5.13 may be used to determine when two-point contact begins (and possibly ends). The result, simplified for the case in which $K_\theta >> K_x\, L_g^2$ and $K_\theta\theta_0 >> \mu K_x\, \epsilon_0''\, r$ is

$$\ell_2 \cong \frac{cD}{\theta_0} \tag{5A.23}$$

for the onset of two-point contact, and

$$\ell_2' \cong \frac{K_0\theta_0}{K_x\epsilon_0''} - \ell_2 \tag{5A.24}$$

for the termination of two-point contact and the start of line contact. The values of θ at which these events occur may be obtained by substituting Eqs. (5A.23) and (5A.24) into Eq. (5.1).

Insertion Forces

Insertion force during chamfer crossing is obtained by substituting Eqs. (5A.12) and (5A.13) into Eqs. (5A.7) through (5A.11) to yield

$$F_z = \frac{K_x K_0 \mathbf{A}(z/\tan\alpha)}{\mathbf{BD} - \mathbf{E}} \tag{5A.24}$$

where

$$\mathbf{D} = K_x L_g^2 + K_0 \tag{5A.25}$$

and

$$\mathbf{E} = K_x L_g r \mathbf{A} \tag{5A.26}$$

Equations for lateral force and moment are derived similarly.

Insertion force during one-point contact is obtained analogously by substituting Eqs. (5A.15) and (5A.16) into (5A.7) through (5A.11) to yield

$$F_z = \frac{\mu K_x K_0(\epsilon_0' + \ell\theta_0)}{\mathbf{C}(L_g - \ell) + K_0} \tag{5A.27}$$

Again, lateral force and moment may be obtained analogously.

To derive the forces and moments during two-point contact, we begin by writing the force and moment equilibrium equations between the reaction forces and the support forces expressed in peg-tip coordinates:

$$F_x = f_2 - f_1 \tag{5A.28}$$

$$F_z = \mu(f_1 + f_2) \tag{5A.29}$$

$$M = f_1\ell - \mu r(f_2 - f_1) \tag{5A.30}$$

These may be combined to yield

$$\frac{M}{rF_z} = \pm\lambda - \frac{F_x}{F_z}\mu(1 + \lambda) \tag{5A.31}$$

where

$$\lambda = \frac{\ell}{2r\mu} \tag{5A.32}$$

The two equations in (5A.31)—one each for the plus sign and the minus sign—form the diagonal lines of the parallelogram in Fig. 5.16. Substituting Eqs. (5A.21) and (5.1) into Eqs. (5A.9) and (5A.10) yields

$$F_x = -K_xL_g\left(\theta_0 - \frac{cD}{\ell}\right) - K_x\epsilon_0'' \tag{5A.33}$$

and

$$M = \mathbf{D}\left(\theta_0 - \frac{cD}{\ell}\right) + K_xL_g\epsilon_0'' \tag{5A.34}$$

Putting these into Eq. (5A.31) yields

$$F_z = \frac{2\mu}{\ell}\left[\mathbf{D}\left(\theta_0 - \frac{cD}{\ell}\right) + \mathbf{F}\right] + \mu\left(1 + \frac{\mu d}{\ell}\right)\left[\mathbf{G}\left(\theta_0 - \frac{cD}{\ell}\right) - \frac{\mathbf{F}}{L_g}\right] \tag{5A.35}$$

where

$$\mathbf{F} = K_xL_g\epsilon_0'' \tag{5A.36}$$

and

$$\mathbf{G} = -K_xL_g \tag{5A.37}$$

Computer Program

Listing 5A.1 is a computer program that calculates and plots all of the variables discussed in this appendix. This program provided the "theory" lines in Figs. 5.17 and 5.18. The following is a brief discussion of how this program works and how the variable names in it correspond to names used in this chapter.

The first few lines express input data, which may be stored in the program or typed in by the user. Such data include stiffnesses of the supports, clearance ratio between peg and hole, coefficient of friction, location of the support compliance center, and the initial lateral and angular errors. Note that $L_g = 0$ should not be used. To simulate small values for L_g, one may use $L_g = \mu r$.

Next is a short routine that plots axes on the screen.

```
1000 REM  PROGRAM FOR INSERTION FORCE
1010 REM  BASED ON EQUATIONS IN THIS CHAPTER.
1020 REM  THIS PROGRAM IS IN TRUE BASIC FOR THE MACINTOSH.
1030 REM  VALUES OF COEFFICIENTS AND CONSTANTS ARE METRIC AND
1040 REM  CORRESPOND TO EXPERIMENTAL DATA IN TABLE 1.
1050 REM
1060 REM  PRELIMINARY CALCULATIONS
1065 LET SCALF = 100000
1067 LET SCALD = 1000
1070 LET SP$ = "  "
1080 LET KX = .22
1090 LET KT = 6.5000
1100 LET D = .1942
1110 LET C = (.1942-.1941)/.1942
1120 LET MU = .03
1130 LET E0 = .002
1140 INPUT PROMPT "TYPE SP FOR SCREEN PRINT, SG FOR SCREEN GRAPH ":AN$
1150 IF (AN$ <> "SP") AND (AN$ <> "SG") THEN GOTO 1140
1160 INPUT PROMPT "INITIAL THETA ":T0
1170 IF AN$="SP" THEN PRINT "L       FX       FZ        M1        F1"
1180 LET LG = 0.1
1190 LET KL = KX * LG
1200 LET A = KL * LG + KT
1210 LET U0 = E0 + C * D / 2
1220 LET B = KL * U0
1230 LET C1 =  - KL
1240 LET AL = KX * (U0 + LG * T0)
1250 LET BE = AL * LG + KX * LG * C * D - AL * MU * D / 2 + KT * T0
1260 LET GA = (A - KX * LG * MU * D / 2) * C * D
1270 LET L2 = (BE -  SQR (BE ^ 2 - 4 * AL * GA)) / (2 * AL)
1280 LET L4 = (BE +  SQR (BE ^ 2 - 4 * AL * GA)) / (2 * AL)
1290 LET LT = (4 * A + 2 * C1 * MU * D) * C * D
1300 LET LB = 2 * A * T0 + B * (2 - MU * D / LG) + C1 * (T0 * MU * D - C * D)
1310 LET LS = LT / LB
1320 LET L = LS
1330 GOSUB 2060
1340 LET FM = FZ
1350 IF AN$="SP" THEN GOTO 1500
1360 REM
1370 REM PLOT AXES
1380 SET WINDOW -1,4*L2*SCALD + 2,-1,FM +1.5
1390 PLOT 0,0; 0,FM+1
1400 PLOT 0,0; 4*L2*SCALD,0
1410 FOR X = 0 TO 4*L2*SCALD STEP 4*L2*SCALD/12
1420     PLOT TEXT, AT X,-.2:STR$(INT(X+.5))
1430 NEXT X
1440 PLOT TEXT, AT X/2.5, -.5: "INSERTION DEPTH"
1450 FOR Y = 0 TO FM + .5 STEP FM/8
1460     PLOT TEXT, AT .2,Y: STR$(INT(100*Y+.5)/100)
1470 NEXT Y
1480 PLOT TEXT, AT .2,Y+.2: "FORCE"
1490 REM
1500 REM BEGIN MAIN CALCULATION LOOP
1510 FOR L = 0 TO 4*L2 STEP L2/40
1520     IF L >= L2 THEN GOTO 1650
1530     IF L > L4 THEN
1540        PRINT "TWO POINT CONTACT LOST"
1550        GOTO 1800
1560     END IF
1570     LET A1 = KX * (LG - L - MU * D / 2)
1580     LET B1 = A1 * LG + KT
1590     LET EP = E0 - C * D / 2
1600     LET FZ = MU * KX * KT * (EP + L * T0) / (B1 - A1 * L)
1610     LET FX =  - FZ / MU
1620     LET M1 =  - FX * (L + MU * D / 2)
1630     LET F1 =  - FX
1631     LET FZ=FZ*SCALF
```

Listing 5A.1

```
1632      LET FX=FX*SCALF
1633      LET M1=M1*SCALF
1634      LET F1=F1*SCALF
1640      GOTO 1660
1650      GOSUB 2060
1660      IF AN$ = "SP" THEN GOTO 1710
1670      PLOT  L*SCALD,FZ;
1680      GOTO 1700
1690      PLOT L,FX;                    ! CHOOSE THIS ONE TO PLOT FX INSTEAD OF FZ
1700      IF AN$ = "SG" THEN GOTO 1770
1710      LET L =  INT (10000 * L) / 10000
1720      LET FX =  INT (1000000 * FX) / 1000000
1730      LET FZ =  INT (1000000 * FZ) / 1000000
1740      LET M1 =  INT (100 * M1) / 100
1750      LET F1 =  INT (100 * F1) / 100
1760      PRINT L; SP$;FX; SP$;FZ; SP$;M1; SP$;F1
1770 NEXT L
1780 IF AN$ = "SG" THEN GOTO 2040
1790 REM
1800 REM SUMMARY PRINTOUT OF PARAMETERS
1810 LET LL = LG - C*D/2
1820 LET TC = T0 + KX * LL * EP / (KX * LG * LL + KT)
1830 PRINT "TC= ";TC
1840 LET EPP = E0 + C*D/2
1850 LET LLL = LG - L2 - MU * D / 2
1860 LET T2 = KX * EPP * LLL / (KX * LG * LLL + KT) + T0
1870 PRINT "T2= ";T2
1880 LET AA = .707 * (1 + MU)
1890 LET BB = .707 * (1 - MU)
1900 LET FC = KX * KT * EP * AA / ((KX * LG ^ 2 + KT) * BB - KX * LG * D * AA / 2)
1910 PRINT "FC= ";FC
1920 REM  FC IS PEAK CHAMFER FORCE
1930 PRINT "L2= ";L2
1940 PRINT "LS= ";LS
1950 PRINT "FM= ";FM
1960 PRINT "KX= ";KX
1970 PRINT "KT= ";KT
1980 PRINT "LG= ";LG
1990 PRINT "MU= ";MU
2000 PRINT "C= ";C
2010 PRINT "E0= ";E0
2020 PRINT "T0= ";T0
2030 PRINT "D= ";D
2032 PRINT "SCALF= ";SCALF
2034 PRINT "SCALD= ";SCALD
2040 STOP
2050 REM
2060 REM SUBROUTINE TO CALCULATE FORCE DURING TWO POINT CONTACT
2070 LET LD = L / D
2080 LET TT = LD -  SQR (LD ^ 2 - 2 * C)
2090 LET M1 = A * (T0 - TT) + B
2100 LET FX = C1 * (T0 - TT) - B / LG
2110 LET FZ = 2 * MU * M1 / L + MU * FX * (1 + MU * D / L)
2120 LET F2 = M1 / L + FX * (1 + .5 * MU * D / L)
2121 LET M1=M1*SCALF
2122 LET FX=FX*SCALF
2123 LET FZ=FZ*SCALF
2124 LET F2=F2*SCALF
2130 IF (L > L2 + 2) AND (F2 <= 0) THEN
2140    PRINT "TWO POINT CONTACT LOST"
2150    GOTO 1800
2160 END IF
2170 LET F1 = (M1 + .5 * MU * D * FX) / L
2171 LET F1=F1*SCALF
2180 RETURN
2190 END
```

Listing 5A.1 *(Continued)*

The next few lines compute ℓ^* and F_m, the depth at which maximum insertion force occurs and that force. The values of ℓ_2 and ℓ_2' where two-point contact begins and possibly ends are also computed here.

The main program loop is next, stepping through values of insertion depth ℓ from 0 to 4 times the predicted ℓ_2. The first part of this loop calculates insertion forces during one-point contact. When insertion depth exceeds ℓ_2, the corresponding values for two-point contact are calculated. At the end of each pass, values are printed and plotted.

The last part of the program calculates two values associated with chamfer crossing: the value of θ just at the end, where one-point contact begins, and the insertion force at that point. One may assume that chamfer crossing force and angle θ each increase linearly during chamfer crossing, with force starting at 0 and θ starting at θ_0.

Finally, there is a summary printout that repeats input data.

Correspondence of variable names is as follows:

Program names	Equation names
KX	K_x
KT	K_θ
MU	μ
EO	ε_0
TO	θ_0
LG	L_g
A	**D**
U0	e_0''
B	**F**
C1	**G**
L2	ℓ_2'
L4	ℓ_2
LS	ℓ^*
FM	F_z max. during two-point contact
A1	**C**
EP	ε_0'
F1	f_1 (contact force)
F2	f_2 (contact force)
FX, FZ, M1	F_x, F_z, M
TC	θ at end of chamfer crossing
T2	θ when two-point contact begins
AA, BB	**A**,**B** for α = 45°
FC	max. insertion force at end of chamfer crossing

Figure 5A.3 is a sample of graphic output from this program.

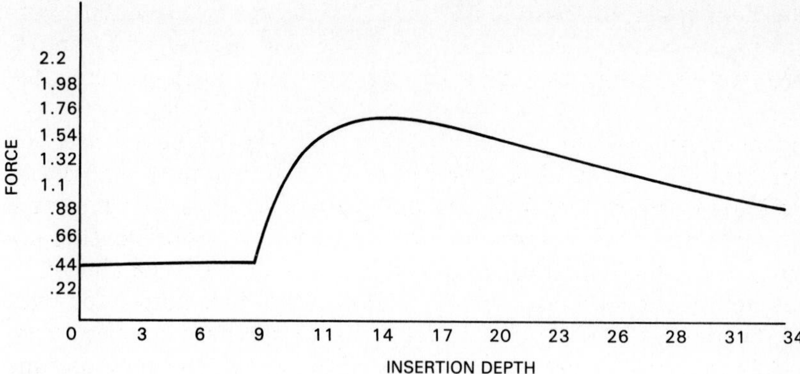
FORCE
2.2
1.98
1.76
1.54
1.32
1.1
.88
.66
.44
.22
0
3
6
9
11
14
17
20
23
26
28
31
34
INSERTION DEPTH

Fig. 5A.3

Chapter 6

Assembly of Compliant Parts

Introduction

Chapter 5 dealt with compliantly supported rigid parts entering rigid holes. Different problems and design opportunities arise when at least one mating part is compliant. Figure 6.1 exhibits numerous applications of compliant parts, including electrical connectors, door latches, snap fits, and light bulb sockets. Figure 6.2 shows two simplified geometries that contain the elements considered in this chapter.

This chapter will explore two theoretical conditions: rigid peg, compliant hole [Fig. 6.2(*a*)] and compliant or compliantly held peg, rigid chamfered hole [Fig. 6.2(*b*)] and demonstrate experimental verification of the theory. Specific cases are shown, but others can be readily derived (Whitney, 1980, 1983, 1988).

Significantly more complex conditions have been solved: compliant peg and compliant hole and minimum energy chamfers by Hennessey (1982) and a three-dimensional part mating theory by Gustavson (1985). The interested reader should consult these references.

Design Criteria and Considerations

Compliant parts are designed to perform various functions in various environments. The parts may be inserted by hand or machine. They may be delicate or rugged. The designer may, for example, wish easy insertion and difficult withdrawal or may wish to signal incomplete mating by having the parts pop apart. There are so many criteria that we list only a few that involve the insertion force (force in the direction of insertion) or withdrawal force. The criteria are

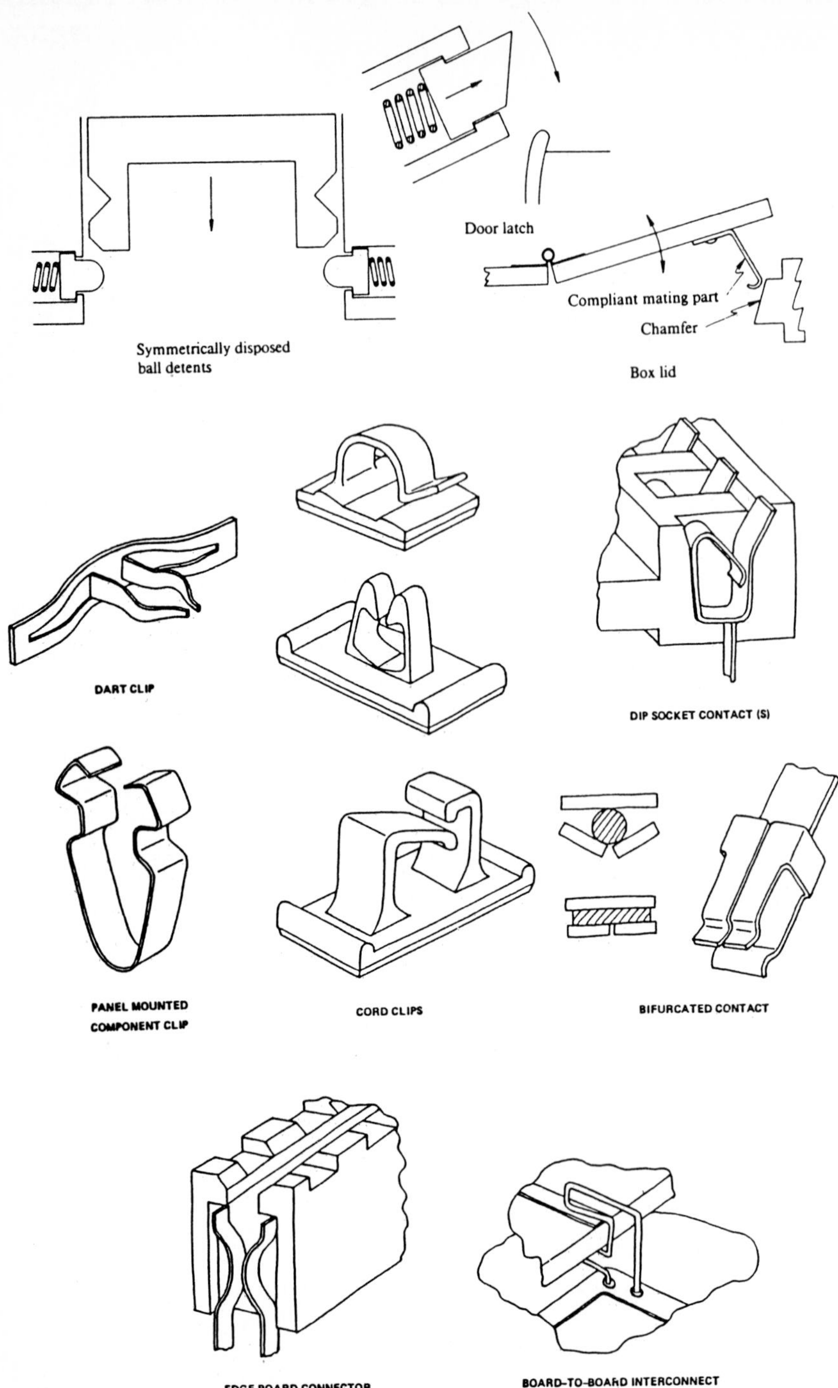

Fig. 6.1 Example compliant part applications.

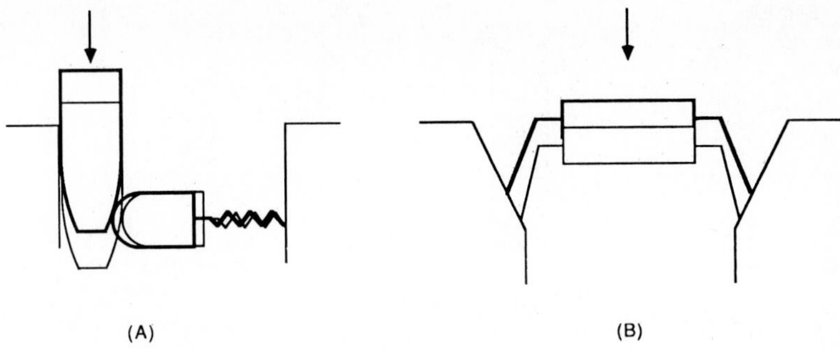

Fig. 6.2 (*a*) Rigid peg-compliant hole model; (*b*) compliant or compliantly held peg, rigid chamfered hole model.

1. Avoid sharp discontinuities in force versus insertion depth
2. Minimize mechanical work during insertion
3. Minimize the peak value attained by the insertion force during insertion
4. Achieve a specific pattern of force versus depth
5. Achieve a specific ratio of insertion force to withdrawal force

A number of design features influence insertion force. They are:

1. Peg nose shape
2. Number of springs (compliant members) making up the compliant hole
3. Entry shape of the spring
4. Speed of entry (quasi-static or dynamic)
5. Type of spring deflection (linear, nonlinear)
6. Spring preload
7. Rigid, compliant, or compliantly held rigid pegs
8. Straight or tilted initial entry of the peg into the hole

The most influential feature is the shape of the contacting surfaces. These surfaces are typically the tips of pegs and the mouths of holes.

Four basic types of insertion force behavior have been identified. Each corresponds to a particular type of mating surface shape. The shapes could be on either the peg or the hole. They are:

1. *Linear shape.* Figure 6.3(*a*) shows the most common shape and provides linear force versus depth behavior. The maximum force occurs at the end of insertion and could be very high.

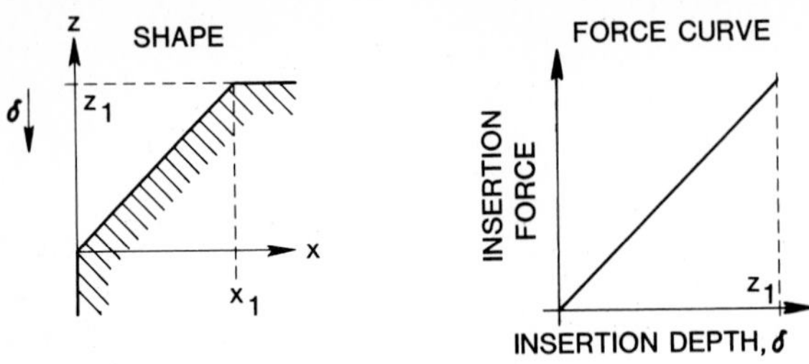

Fig. 6.3(*a*) Force versus depth behavior for linear shape. δ is the direction of insertion motion.

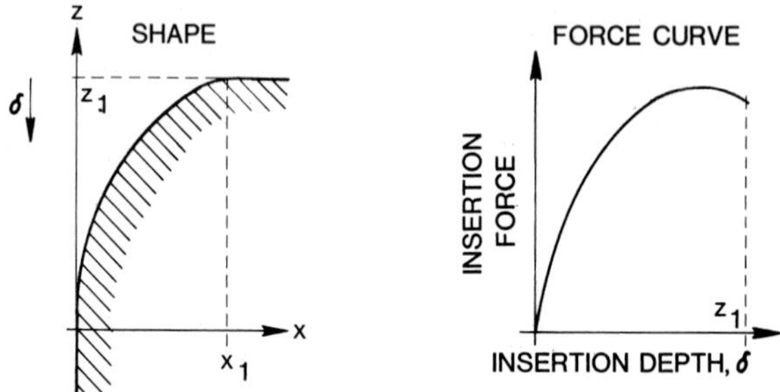

Fig. 6.3(*b*) Force versus depth behavior for convex shape.

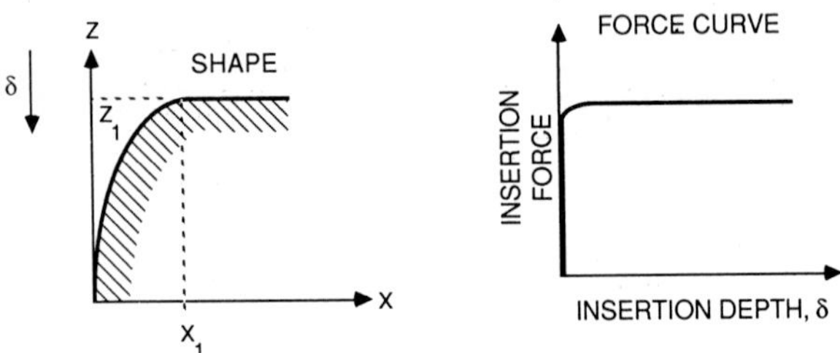

Fig. 6.3(*c*) Force versus depth behavior for constant force shape.

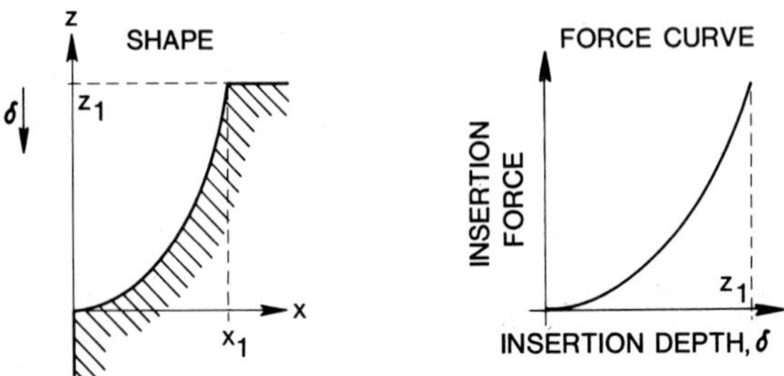

Fig. 6.3(*d*) Force versus depth behavior for concave shape.

2. *Convex shape.* Figure 6.3(*b*), which makes the surface convex, allows shaping of the force versus depth curve. Various geometrical forms have been tried including circular arcs, parabolas, and logarithmic curves.
3. *Constant force shape.* Figure 6.3(*c*) shows a particular convex shape with a complex descriptive equation that can produce constant insertion force throughout the insertion. This behavior results in minimum peak force.
4. *Concave shape.* Figure 6.3(*d*) shows that reversing the arc provides less force for beginning depths but very large forces near the end.

General assumptions

Table 6.1 lists the assumptions used in this chapter. The comments indicate extensions that might be added.

TABLE 6.1 Assumptions for Analysis of Compliant Part Mating

Assumptions	Comment
1. Two-dimensional cases only.	1. Third dimension could be added.
2. Peg travels parallel to centerline of hole.	2. Angular and translational misalignments can be added.
3. Peg has prescribed lateral position: *a.* For one compliance, one rigid wall case [see Fig. 6.7(*a*)], peg rides along wall opposite compliance [see Fig. 6.10(*a*)]. *b.* For two equal symmetrical compliance case [see Fig. 6.7(*b*)], peg and "hole" centerlines are coincident [see Fig. 6.10(*b*)].	3. Alternately *a.* Peg-wall contact may not occur at all. *b.* Compliance may not be shape-symmetric or have equal stiffnesses. Only one compliance may be contacted by peg.
4. Compliance is an integral part of the mounting; friction coefficient is uniform on all contacting surfaces.	4. Compliance(s) could be made of different materials requiring specification of two or more friction coefficients.
5. Deflection of the compliance(s) is rigid body motion with respect to a reference location.	5. Small-deflection beam theory or large-deflection theory can be added.
6. Spring has no preload at initial contact with peg.	6. Spring preload can be added.
7. Conditions are quasi-static; motion does not create need for dynamic considerations.	7. Dynamics may play a role in compliant part mating.

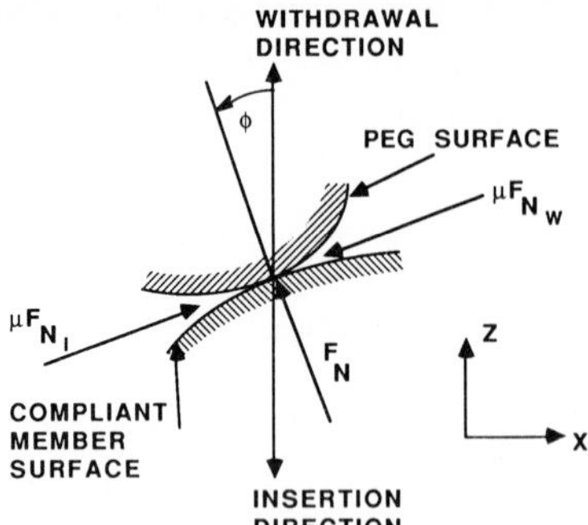

Fig. 6.4 Forces at the peg and compliant member interface.

General force considerations (Whitney, et al. 1980)

While a significant variety of mathematical models for compliantly held peg into hole or peg into compliant mount mating can be created, the complexity lies in describing the orientation geometry and the elastic behavior of the spring(s). If we focus on the peg-compliant member interface at any instant during part mating (see Fig. 6.4), we may write the following basic equations for the vertical and horizontal forces F_X and F_Z (subscript I = insertion, W = withdrawal) acting on the peg during insertion and withdrawal in terms of the normal contact force F_N and interface angle ϕ.

$$F_{XI} = F_N(\sin \phi - \mu \cos \phi) \tag{6.1}$$

$$F_{ZI} = F_N(\cos \phi + \mu \sin \phi) \tag{6.2}$$

$$F_{XW} = F_N(\sin \phi + \mu \cos \phi) \tag{6.3}$$

$$F_{ZW} = F_N(\cos \phi - \mu \sin \phi) \tag{6.4}$$

Ratios of F_X/F_Z versus ϕ are plotted in Fig. 6.5 while F_Z/F_X ratios are plotted in Fig. 6.6. These figures show that the ratio of insertion force to lateral force during insertion is larger for a larger coefficient of friction and smaller for a larger interface angle. During withdrawal, the ratio is again smaller for a larger angle but smaller for a larger friction coefficient. Note that for straight entry shapes, the angle is constant, whereas for curved shapes the angle changes during insertion.

These figures show that three factors control the mating forces of compliant peg-hole combinations:

1. The normal (or contact) force
2. The slope at the interface point [$\phi = \tan^{-1}$ (slope)]
3. The friction coefficient

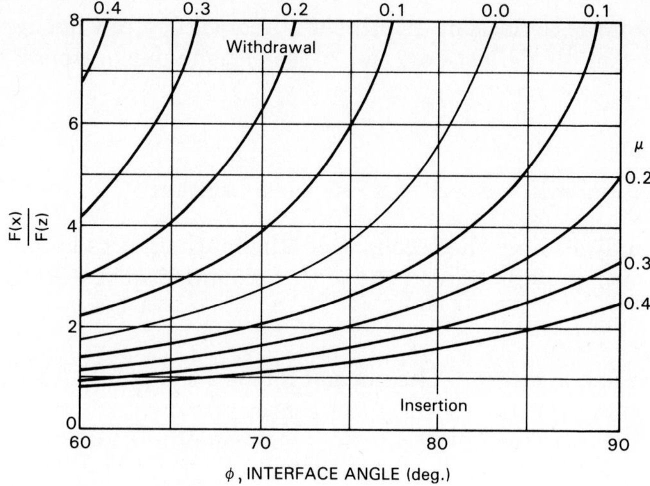

Fig. 6.5 Force ratios occurring at the interface surface(s) (lateral force and insertion force).

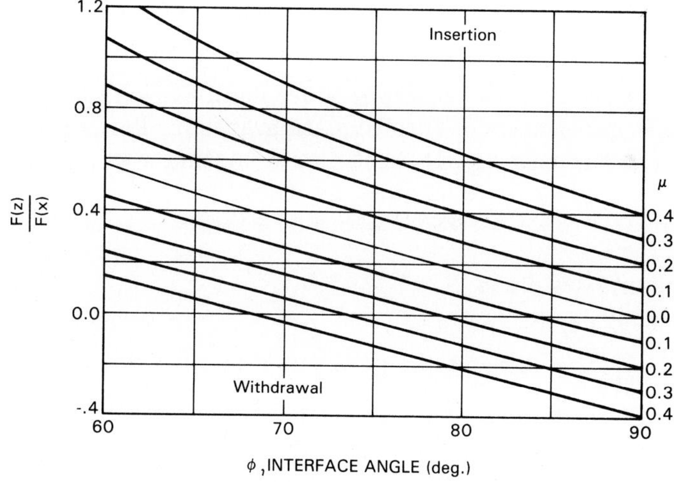

Fig. 6.6 Force ratios occurring at the interface surfaces(s) (insertion force and lateral force).

Establishing and controlling these three factors is fundamental to compliant peg-hole design. They are defined below.

The normal force. The normal force, which produces the insertion force, Eq. (6.2), is created by deflection of the compliant member(s). Certain peg-hole combinations contain a spring whose action can be analyzed only by large-deflection (nonlinear) theory; they are not included here. For "small" deflections, two types of behavior are possible:

1. Elastic deflection
2. Rigid body motion with respect to a reference location

This chapter analyzes only the second type; the mathematics is considerably less complex while agreement with experimental results is good.

Slope at the peg-spring interface. The normal force at the point of contact is oriented along the line joining the center of curvature of the peg's surface and the center of curvature of the compliant member's surface; the slope angle at the contact point is ϕ. Depending upon what insertion force versus depth characteristics are required, the designer may alter the interface slope by increasing or decreasing the angle ϕ or making it variable by using a curved surface. Numerous easily definable shapes may be investigated: straight lines, circles, conic sections, parabolic curves, logarithmic curves, etc.

Friction. Friction interacts with slope to produce nonlinear effects. It can be controlled by lubrication or surface plating. It is modeled very simply for our purposes as a constant throughout a mating event; this has been found experimentally to be quite accurate.

Rigid Peg-Compliant Hole Case (Whitney et al., 1983)

General force analysis

The mating of a rigid peg and a compliant hole is analyzed first. The analysis is based on the assumptions in Table 6.1. Two fundamental compliant wall conditions (see Fig. 6.7) are considered. Each models the compliant wall as a spring-loaded member with a circular nose which is constrained to move only in a direction normal to the insertion direction of the peg (assumed to be along the centerline). The nose radius is r and the spring stiffness is K_x. Numerous other models of mating shape and spring behavior could be used by extrapolating from these models.

The end of the peg is modeled as a circular arc with an arbitrary radius (see Fig. 6.8). The circle is tangent to the side of the peg. This surface is the primary contact with the compliant wall(s) during insertion and withdrawal.

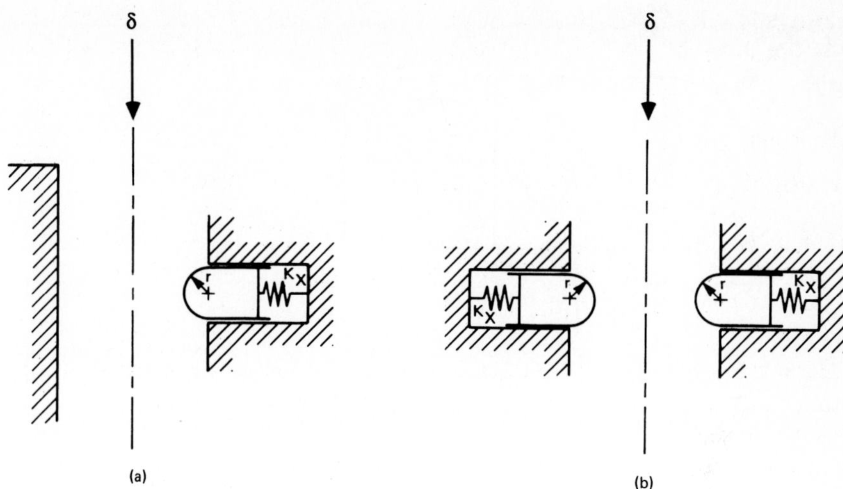

Fig. 6.7 Models for compliant wall conditions. (*a*) one rigid wall, one compliant wall; (*b*) two symmetrical, equal compliant walls.

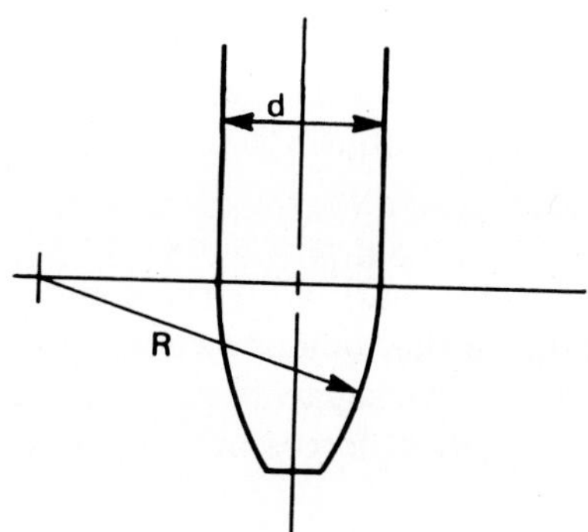

Fig. 6.8 Definition of peg shape parameters.

Forces on compliant member. We begin the force analysis by showing the forces on the compliant member. The peg contact point (see Fig. 6.9) occurs at angle ϕ, which requires the normal force to pass through the center of the radius at the end of the compliant member. The friction forces will be in the direction shown for insertion or in the opposite direction for withdrawal. Thus, as long as friction is present, the insertion normal force is different from the withdrawal normal force. The normal force is caused by the deflection $(L_0 - L)$ of the spring. For insertion we find that the normal force is

$$F_{NI} = \frac{K_x(L_0 - L)}{(1 - \mu^2)\sin\phi - 2\mu\cos\phi} \tag{6.5}$$

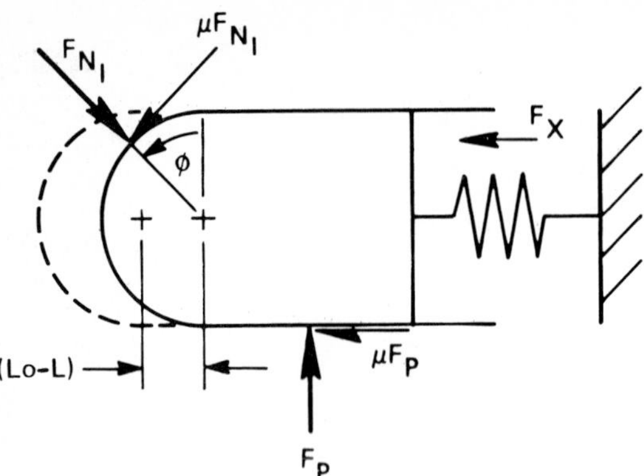

Fig. 6.9 Forces on compliant member during insertion.

while for withdrawal, normal force is

$$F_{NW} = \frac{K_x(L_0 - L)}{(1 - \mu^2)\sin\phi + 2\mu\cos\phi} \tag{6.6}$$

These normal forces are fundamental to the determination of the insertion and withdrawal forces for compliant part mating.

Forces on rigid peg. For present purposes, the peg is assumed to be rigid and constrained to move along a straight path which is coincident with the centerline of the "hole." Since either one or two compliant members exert force on the peg, there are two separate cases to be defined (Fig. 6.10). The insertion and withdrawal forces are given in Table 6.2.

Although the terms in the table could be divided by cos ϕ making the expressions easier to read, problems would arise in computation when $\phi \to \pi/2$ whereas the equations shown in Table 6.2 are always usable.

In order to evaluate the insertion and withdrawal forces, separate calculations for $(L_0 - L)$ and ϕ are needed. These depend on the geometry of the parts and vary in general during mating.

Geometry of mating parts. To determine $(L_0 - L)$ and ϕ we must deal with the one-compliant-member case and the two-compliant-member case separately.

From Fig. 6.11 or 6.12, we may write

$$\phi = \cos^{-1}\left(\frac{Z}{R + r}\right) \tag{6.8}$$

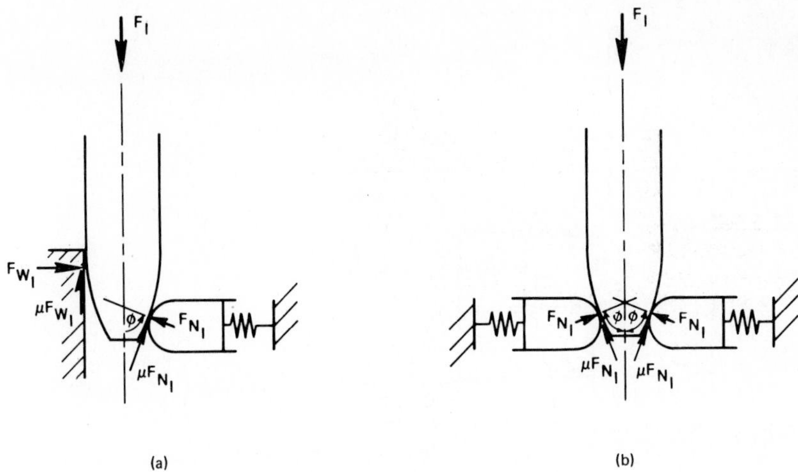

Fig. 6.10 Forces on the peg during insertion. (*a*) one rigid wall, one compliant wall; (*b*) two symmetrical, equal compliant walls.

TABLE 6.2 Formulas for Insertion Force and Withdrawal Force for the Single-Compliant-Member and Two-Compliant-Member Cases

	Insertion force	Withdrawal force
One rigid wall, one compliant member	$\dfrac{K_x(L_0 - L)[(1 - \mu^2)\cos\phi + 2\mu\sin\phi]}{(1 - \mu^2)\sin\phi - 2\mu\cos\phi}$	$\dfrac{K_x(L_0 - L)[(1 - \mu^2)\cos\phi - 2\mu\sin\phi]}{(1 - \mu^2)\sin\phi + 2\mu\cos\phi}$
Two symmetrical equal compliant members	$\dfrac{2K_x(L_0 - L)(\cos\phi + \mu\sin\phi)}{(1 - \mu^2)\sin\phi - 2\mu\cos\phi}$	$\dfrac{2K_x(L_0 - L)(\cos\phi - \mu\sin\phi)}{(1 - \mu^2)\sin\phi + 2\mu\cos\phi}$

[Equations (6.7)]

From Fig. 6.11, we find the deflection of the compliant member is

$$L_0 - L = L_0 - (D - d) - R + (R + r)\sin\phi \tag{6.9}$$

for the first case, and from Fig. 6.12 it is

$$L_0 - L = L_0 - \frac{D - d}{2} - R + (R + r)\sin\phi \tag{6.10}$$

for the second case. In both cases, L_0 is an independent feature of the geometry and must be given in advance.

Two other conditions of particular interest occur; first contact and constant force, which are:

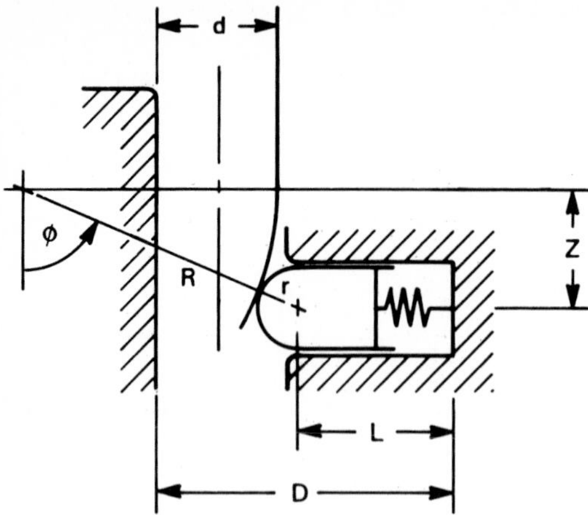

Fig. 6.11 Geometry of mating parts for one-rigid-wall, one-compliant-member case.

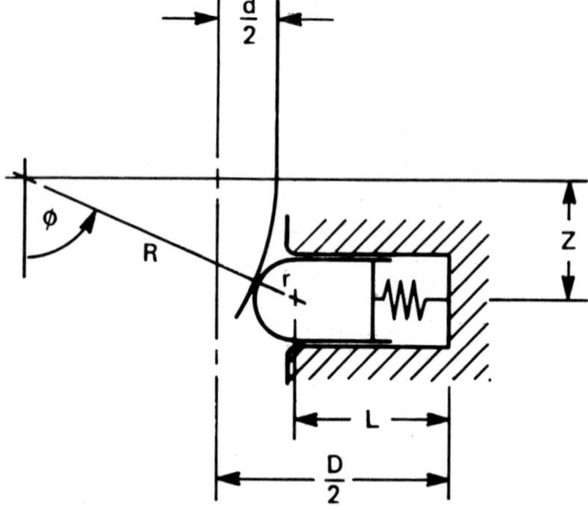

Fig. 6.12 Geometry of mating parts for the two-symmetrical, equal-compliant-members case.

1. First contact occurs when the peg traveling along its path encounters the compliant member radius which has a prescribed initial location because of specification of L_0.
2. Constant force condition occurs when the straight portion of the peg, far from the tip, contacts the compliant member (i.e., movement of the peg up or down does not cause changes in the magnitude of the force values.) This special case occurs at the finish of the peg radius (when $\phi = \pi/2$). Table 6.3 summarizes these two conditions.

TABLE 6.3 Equations for Initial Contact and Constant Force for Two Types of Compliant Part Mating.
Subscript 0 indicates initial contact. Subscript F indicates constant force. Z_0 and ϕ_0 are the initial insertion depth and contact angle respectively. L_F is the final deflection of the spring.

"Hole" case	Figure	Initial contact condition	Constant force condition
One rigid wall, one compliant member	6.11	$\phi_0 = \sin^{-1}\left[\frac{D - L_0 - d + R}{R + r}\right]$ $Z_0 = (R + r) \cos \phi_0$	$L_F = D - d - r$
Two symmetrical equal compliant members	6.12	$\phi_0 = \sin^{-1}\left[\frac{\left(\frac{D - d}{2}\right) - L_0 + R}{R + r}\right]$ $Z_0 = (R + r) \cos \phi_0$	$L_F = \frac{D - d}{2} - r$

[Equations (6.11)]

Critical geometry. Certain geometrical conditions must be avoided or part mating difficulties will result. The most obvious is to avoid the denominator of the normal force [Eq. (6.5)] going to zero. To avoid this, we need to satisfy

$$\phi_{min} = \tan^{-1}\left(\frac{2\mu}{1 - \mu^2}\right) \tag{6.12}$$

This provides a theoretical minimum value of ϕ. However, we have found experimentally that closely approaching this limit gives a very sharp and undesirable peak in the insertion force. A recommended but arbitrary limit is $\phi \geq 30°$. Equation (6.12) yields ϕ that obeys this limit if $\mu \leq 0.268$. If μ is larger than this, ϕ must be kept correspondingly larger. From a practical standpoint, this means that the slope at the contact point must be steeper. Violation of the limit in Eq. (6.12) corresponds roughly to the event of jamming in rigid part mating.

Theoretical results using a digital computer. The equations derived in previous sections are somewhat difficult for hand calculation especially since numerous insertion depths must be investigated for every peg-hole combination of interest. Closed form algebraic solutions might be obtained but would be too complex to permit easy interpretation. A BASIC computer program PEGCMPHL (see App. 6.1) has been written which solves this general class of models; its output can be in the form of plotted or tabular data such as shown in Figs. 6.13 and 6.14. Although the graphs use newtons (N) and millimeters for units, any consistent set of units can be used. The effect of changing a single parameter, while holding all others constant, on the behavior of the insertion and withdrawal force versus insertion depth can be readily found using the program. We next investigate two cases.

One rigid wall, one compliant member. Figure 6.13 shows the characteristics of the X direction and Z direction forces observed during mating and unmating using representative data. In general, varying individual parameters produces the following:

1. End-of-peg radius (R) affects both maximum force values and insertion depth at which constant force occurs. A trade-off between the two may determine the optimum value for R. A minimum value of R may be obtained by combining a specification for the final normal force and the ϕ_{min} condition in Eq. (6.12).
2. End-of-compliant-member radius (r) has similar effects to those described for R with lesser effect on force magnitudes. r may be limited by other geometric values.
3. Friction (μ) has only a slight effect on the insertion depth at which constant force occurs. However, force magnitude increases directly as μ increases.
4. As K_x increases, the maximum force increases proportionately.
5. The program allows the user to specify a desired final normal force. Increasing the value of this force increases the magnitude of the insertion and withdrawal forces as well as the depth at which constant force is achieved.

Two symmetrical equal compliant walls. This case is illustrated in Fig. 6.14 and has characteristics consistent with those described for the one-rigid-wall, one-compliant-wall case. Compatible geometry was used so that the X direction (normal) forces are equal for the two examples. The major difference appears in the greater magnitude of the insertion and withdrawal forces.

Design of Chamfers (Whitney et al., 1983)

Introduction

The chamfer is the hero of mechanical parts assembly. It guides parts together when they are laterally or angularly misaligned. Since misalignment is almost inevitable, chamfers are called into play all the

SAMPLE DATA 401

INSERTION of RADIUS END PEG into COMPLIANT WALL HOLE

One spring, one straight wall

1.00 mm PEG DIAMETER

1.00 mm END of PEG RADIUS

2.00 mm MOUNTING DIMENSION

0.25 mm END of SPRING RADIUS

1.04 mm SPRING INITIAL DIMENSION

0.150 Coefficient of Friction

10.00 N/mm SPRING RATE

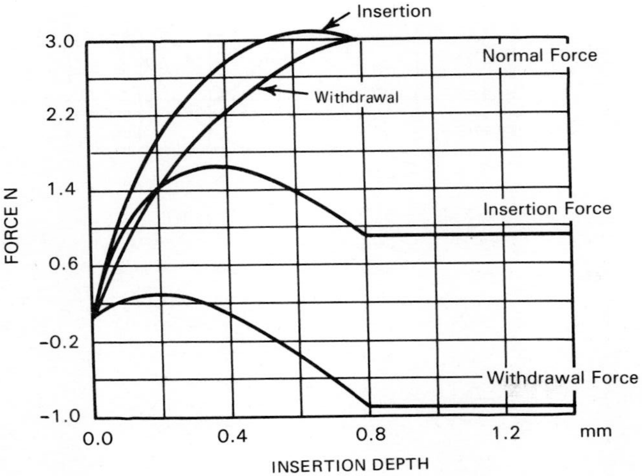

Insertion
Withdrawal
Normal Force
Insertion Force
Withdrawal Force
FORCE N
3.0
2.2
1.4
0.6
-0.2
-1.0
0.0
0.4
0.8
1.2
mm
INSERTION DEPTH

SAMPLE DATA 401

INSERTION of RADIUS END PEG into COMPLIANT WALL HOLE

One spring, one straight wall

1.00 mm PEG DIAMETER

1.00 mm END of PEG RADIUS

2.00 mm MOUNTING DIMENSION

0.25 mm END of SPRING RADIUS

1.04 mm SPRING INITIAL DIMENSION

0.150 Coefficient of Friction

10.00 N/mm SPRING RATE

DEPTH	INSERTION		WITHDRAWAL	
mm	X-Force (N)	Z-Force (N)	X-Force (N)	Z-Force (N)
0.0000	0.0000	0.0000	0.0000	0.0000
0.0322	0.4484	0.3766	0.2742	0.1009
0.0644	0.8295	0.6806	0.5242	0.1767
0.0965	1.1557	0.9256	0.7532	0.2307
0.1287	1.4369	1.1219	0.9635	0.2660
0.1609	1.6803	1.2778	1.1573	0.2848
0.1931	1.8918	1.3995	1.3362	0.2892
0.2252	2.0759	1.4921	1.5018	0.2810
0.2574	2.2364	1.5599	1.6551	0.2615
0.2896	2.3763	1.6063	1.7973	0.2323
0.3218	2.4980	1.6341	1.9292	0.1943
0.3540	2.6036	1.6458	2.0516	0.1486
0.3861	2.6949	1.6434	2.1652	0.0962
0.4183	2.7731	1.6286	2.2704	0.0378
0.4505	2.8396	1.6030	2.3678	-0.0259
0.4827	2.8954	1.5679	2.4577	-0.0940
0.5148	2.9412	1.5245	2.5406	-0.1661
0.5470	2.9779	1.4737	2.6166	-0.2414
0.5792	3.0061	1.4166	2.6861	-0.3195
0.6114	3.0263	1.3539	2.7492	-0.3998
0.6436	3.0390	1.2865	2.8061	-0.4818
0.6757	3.0444	1.2149	2.8569	-0.5650
0.7079	3.0430	1.1399	2.9017	-0.6489
0.7401	3.0350	1.0620	2.9405	-0.7330
0.7723	3.0206	0.9819	2.9733	-0.8169
0.8044	3.0000	0.9000	3.0000	-0.9000
0.8044	3.0000	0.9000	3.0000	-0.9000
1.1022	3.0000	0.9000	3.0000	-0.9000
1.4000	3.0000	0.9000	3.0000	-0.9000

Fig. 6.13 Typical force versus depth behavior for the one-spring, one-straight-wall case.

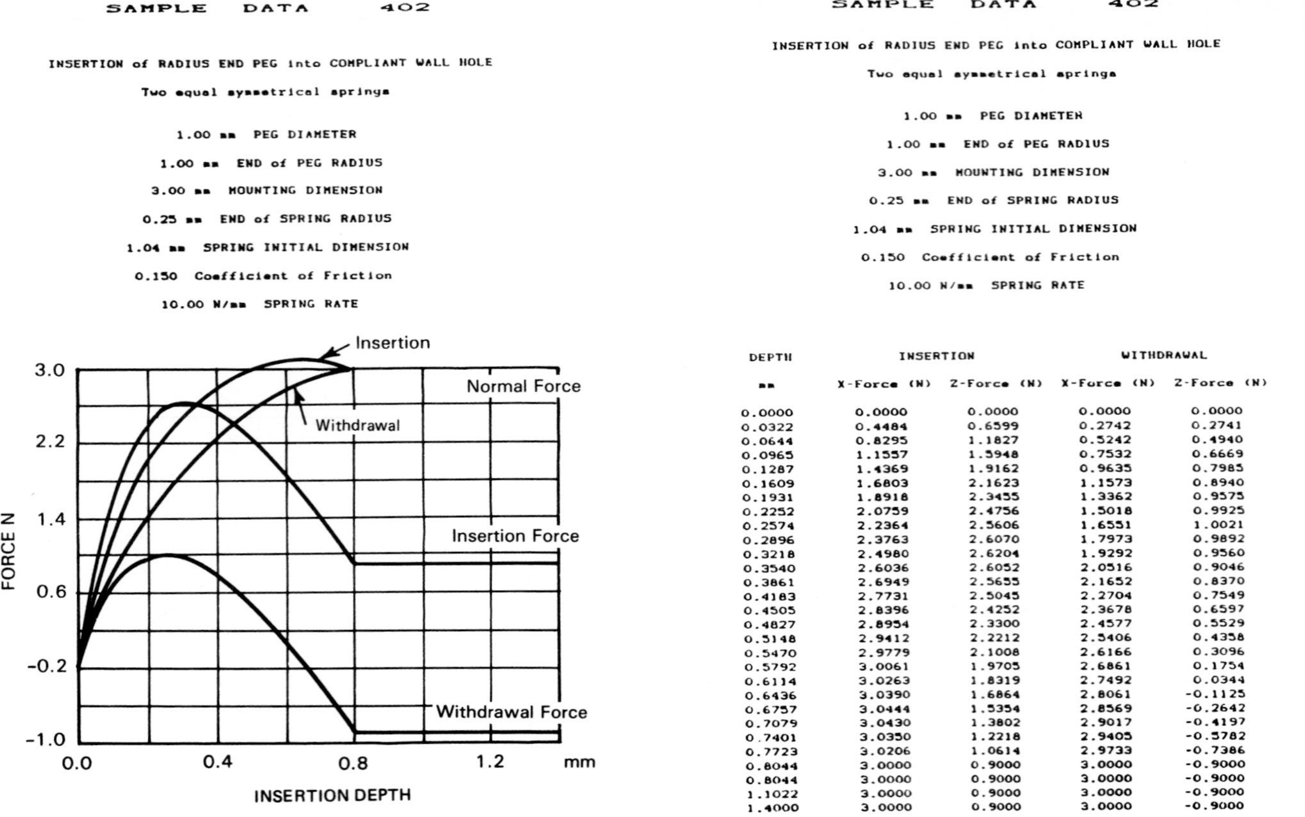

SAMPLE DATA 402

INSERTION of RADIUS END PEG into COMPLIANT WALL HOLE

Two equal symmetrical springs

1.00 mm PEG DIAMETER

1.00 mm END of PEG RADIUS

3.00 mm MOUNTING DIMENSION

0.25 mm END of SPRING RADIUS

1.04 mm SPRING INITIAL DIMENSION

0.150 Coefficient of Friction

10.00 N/mm SPRING RATE

DEPTH	INSERTION		WITHDRAWAL	
mm	X-Force (N)	Z-Force (N)	X-Force (N)	Z-Force (N)
0.0000	0.0000	0.0000	0.0000	0.0000
0.0322	0.4484	0.6599	0.2742	0.2741
0.0644	0.8295	1.1827	0.5242	0.4940
0.0965	1.1557	1.5948	0.7532	0.6669
0.1287	1.4369	1.9162	0.9635	0.7985
0.1609	1.6803	2.1623	1.1573	0.8940
0.1931	1.8918	2.3455	1.3362	0.9575
0.2252	2.0759	2.4756	1.5018	0.9925
0.2574	2.2364	2.5606	1.6551	1.0021
0.2896	2.3763	2.6070	1.7973	0.9892
0.3218	2.4980	2.6204	1.9292	0.9560
0.3540	2.6036	2.6052	2.0516	0.9046
0.3861	2.6949	2.5655	2.1652	0.8370
0.4183	2.7731	2.5045	2.2704	0.7549
0.4505	2.8396	2.4252	2.3678	0.6597
0.4827	2.8954	2.3300	2.4577	0.5529
0.5148	2.9412	2.2212	2.5406	0.4358
0.5470	2.9779	2.1008	2.6166	0.3096
0.5792	3.0061	1.9705	2.6861	0.1754
0.6114	3.0263	1.8319	2.7492	0.0344
0.6436	3.0390	1.6864	2.8061	-0.1125
0.6757	3.0444	1.5354	2.8569	-0.2642
0.7079	3.0430	1.3802	2.9017	-0.4197
0.7401	3.0350	1.2218	2.9405	-0.5782
0.7723	3.0206	1.0614	2.9733	-0.7386
0.8044	3.0000	0.9000	3.0000	-0.9000
0.8044	3.0000	0.9000	3.0000	-0.9000
1.1022	3.0000	0.9000	3.0000	-0.9000
1.4000	3.0000	0.9000	3.0000	-0.9000

Fig. 6.14 Typical force versus depth behavior for the two-equal-symmetrical-spring case.

time. Yet they are often carelessly designed, routinely chosen to be 45 degrees if straight and given a pleasing shape if curved. Furthermore, many surfaces act as chamfers unbeknownst to the designer. The result is that parts are often much more difficult to assemble than need be.

This section presents analyses and design guidelines for chamfers used in contexts where the part engaging the chamfer, or its supports, deforms during insertion. The models highlight the relationships between the force-deformation characteristics of the compliant piece, the shape of the chamfer, and friction. These analyses may be combined with one- and two-point contact analyses in Chap. 5 to obtain complete part mating histories of compliantly supported rigid parts.

Basic model for insertion force

The problem of inserting a compliant or compliantly held part across a rigid chamfer can be modeled as shown in Fig. 6.15. Variations on the model can represent other common geometries. The model assumes that the chamfer is rigid and lies between $X = 0$, $Z = 0$ (the "root"), and $X = X_1$, $Z = Z_1$ (the "top"). The compliant part is modeled as a rigid, straight thin piece with length L. Its supported end is held by a frictionless bearing that travels along the Z axis, the insertion direction. The compliance is represented by a torsional spring of stiffness K_α at the bearing. The contacts of dual in-line electronic packages (DIPs) or the contact springs of electrical connectors may be modeled

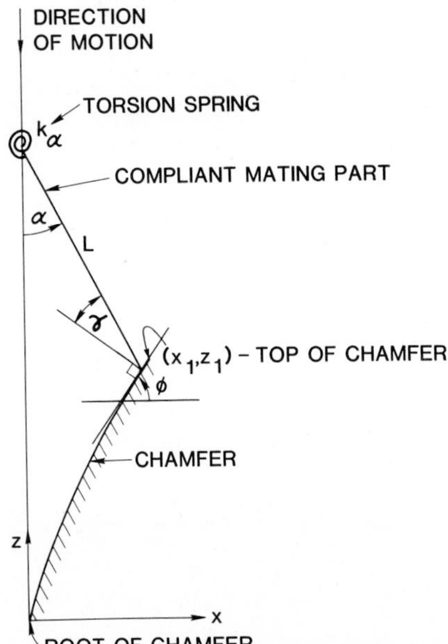

Fig. 6.15 Basic characteristics for the design of chamfers.

this way. The other end (the tip) of the compliant part contacts the chamfer first at the point (X_1, Z_1) and is the only portion of the compliant part to touch the chamfer. The tip travels from the top to the root during insertion. Friction coefficient μ acts between the tip and the chamfer surface and is assumed constant. The insertion force F_I is assumed to be positive along the insertion direction (negative Z).

The insertion force is given by

$$F_I = \frac{K_\alpha(\alpha_1 - \alpha)(\cos\phi + \mu \sin\phi)}{L[\sin(\phi - \alpha) - \mu\cos(\phi - \alpha)]} \tag{6.13}$$

where $\alpha_1 = \sin^{-1}(X_1/L)$

The force exerted by the compliant part on the chamfer parallel to the X axis is represented by the term $K_\alpha(\alpha_1 - \alpha)/L$. All other parameters relate that force to the insertion force. Since the slope of the chamfer at any point equals tan ϕ, Eq. (6.13) can be revised to show that it is the slope and not the shape that determines insertion force (see Fig. 6.3).

Physical models for normal force

We present equations for two cases shown in Figs. 6.16 and 6.17 because they represent physical apparatus used in our experiments and behave similarly to real parts. Figure 6.16 shows a compliant part made of a rigid rod loaded by a linear spring and having a radius at the end in the form of a nonrolling bearing. Normal contact force is

$$F_N = \frac{K_s \ell_s^2 \cos\alpha\,(\sin\alpha_1 - \sin\alpha)}{L\sin(\phi - \alpha) - \mu[L\cos(\phi - \alpha) + r]} \tag{6.14}$$

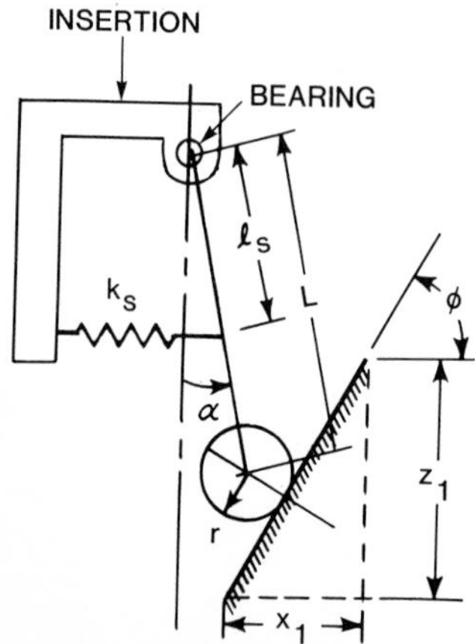

Fig. 6.16 Characteristics for test setup number 1.

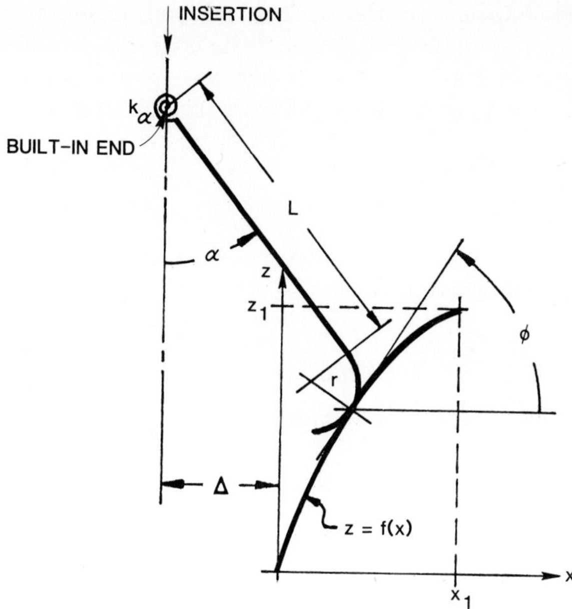

Fig. 6.17 Characteristics for test setup number 2.

The insertion and lateral forces may be obtained from Eqs. (6.1) through (6.4). Figure 6.17 shows a compliant part comprising a cantilever with a radius end. The normal (contact) force is

$$F_N = \frac{K_\alpha(\alpha_1 - \alpha)}{A} \tag{6.15}$$

where $A = \cos\alpha\{(L + \mu r)\sin\phi + (r - \mu L)\cos\phi\}$
$\quad - \sin\alpha\{(L + \mu r)\cos\phi - (r - \mu L)\sin\phi\} - \mu r$

$K_\alpha = 3EI/\ell \qquad E, I =$ elastic parameters of the beam

$\ell = \{L^2 + 2r^2 + 2r\sin\alpha(L\sin\phi + r\cos\phi)$
$\quad + 2r\cos\alpha(L\cos\phi - r\sin\phi\}^{1/2}$

$$\alpha = \cos^{-1}\left[\frac{-r(\Delta + X - r\sin\phi) + L\sqrt{(L^2 + r^2) - (\Delta + X - r\sin\phi)^2}}{L^2 + r^2}\right]$$

Solutions to chamfer-design problems

Three types of solutions will be given. Each has potential uses, advantages, and drawbacks. The three types involve integral criteria, point criteria, and synthesized shapes. The first uses calculus of variations to encompass the entire insertion-force history in the criterion and to recommend a chamfer shape. The second deals with one point on the force history, while the third is a family of shapes parametrized by a single variable.

Minimum-insertion-work chamfers

Calculus of variations has been used to determine the shapes of chamfers that minimize the insertion work:

$$\min \int_{z=0}^{z_1} F_z(X, Z')\, dZ$$

where Z' is the slope $= \tan \phi$.

Whitney et al. (1983) contains the derivation of the optimum shape $Z(X)$:

$$Z = \mu X + \sqrt{1+\mu^2}\left[\sqrt{X_1(X_1 + C')} - \sqrt{(X_1 - X)(X_1 + C' - X)} + C' \log\left|\frac{\sqrt{X_1 + C'} - \sqrt{X_1}}{\sqrt{X_1 + C' - X} - \sqrt{X_1 - X}}\right|\right] \tag{6.16}$$

where C' must be determined to match the boundary condition at (X_1, Z_1).

To find C', we must employ numerical techniques because Eq. (6.16) is transcendental. We will express the shape $Z(X)$ in terms of the baseline slope S defined as

$$S = Z_1/X_1$$

and the slope at the root, $Z'(0)$, given by (Whitney et al., 1983)

$$Z'(0) = \mu + \sqrt{\frac{1+\mu^2}{1+d}} \tag{6.17a}$$

where

$$d = C'/X_1 \tag{6.17b}$$

We also define an auxiliary variable R, the shape factor, as

$$R = Z'(0)/S \tag{6.18}$$

Thus, for straight chamfers $R = 1$, for convex chamfers $R > 1$, and for concave chamfers $R < 1$. Substituting (X_1, Z_1) into Eq. (6.16) and using Eq. (6.17b), we obtain

$$S = \mu + \sqrt{1 + \mu^2}\left[\sqrt{1 + d} + d \ln\left|\frac{\sqrt{1 + d} - 1}{\sqrt{d}}\right|\right] \tag{6.19}$$

Equations (6.17), (6.18), and (6.19) can be solved simultaneously to produce a table of R, given μ and S. Figure 6.18 shows sample results and demonstrates that:

1. For given μ, S is allowed to have a limited range of values.
2. At each end of the range, $R = 1$.
3. Maximum values of R vary from about 1.1 for $\mu \cong 3$ to 1.25 for $\mu \cong 0.25$, approaching $R = 1.5$ as μ approaches 0, and $R = 1$ as μ approaches infinity.

These observations will be discussed in turn. First, the lower limit on the value of S is

$$S = \mu$$

The upper limit is

$$S = \mu + \sqrt{1 + \mu^2}$$

The insertion work is in fact smallest when S has this value. The work is then

$$E^* = 0.5\,K\left(\frac{X_1 S}{L}\right)^2 \tag{6.20}$$

The optimum value of S is called S^*:

$$S^* = \mu + \sqrt{1 + \mu^2}$$

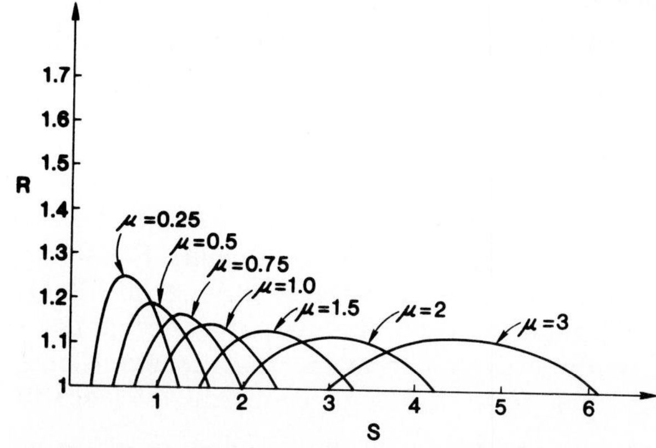

Fig. 6.18 Shape factor R versus S for different μ for minimum insertion work chamfers. The aspect ratio is $S = Z_1/X_1$, and the shape factor is $R = Z'(0)/S$.

This does not mean that steeper chamfers cannot be made or used but only that for each μ, chamfers with $S > S^*$ will not be optimal with respect to insertion work.

Second, at each end of the allowed range of S, the value of R is unity. That is, the slope of the chamfer at $Z = 0$ is the same as the baseline slope. When $S = \mu$, the slope at the root is μ. Since the slope at the top is also μ, the chamfer is straight with the slope equal to μ. We can show that when $S = S^*$ the chamfer is also straight.

Third, the fact that R ranges from about 1 to about 1.5 as μ ranges from very large to very small values shows that for S between the allowed limits the chamfers are gently convex. Criteria discussed below yield generally larger values of R, ranging from $3/2$ to 10 as μ ranges from 0 to 1. Such chamfers are more sharply arched, yield higher insertion work, and require lower peak insertion force.

Taken together, these results mean that the minimum-insertion-work "curved" chamfer with given μ and optimally chosen S is in fact straight, having E given by Eq. (6.20). If S is fixed rather than being chosen optimally and $\mu < S < S^*$, a gently convex chamfer with higher insertion work is obtained. If a continuous-slope chamfer with $S > S^*$ is desired, one must design one's own; it will yield larger work. The calculus of variations will also return a chamfer with $S > S^*$, but its slope will be discontinuous. The chamfer will consist of a straight line of slope S^* between (0, 0) and (X_1, S^*X_1) followed by a straight vertical line from (X_1, S^*X_1) to (X_1, SX_1). Since there is no insertion force associated with the vertical segment, the work is again given by Eq. (6.20) and in effect we have a straight chamfer of slope $S = S^*$. These results and relationships are summarized in Fig. 6.19.

Minimum-peak-force chamfers

The force model [Eq. (6.13)] was attacked numerically to determine chamfers whose maximum peak value of insertion force anywhere during insertion was minimized. The result was constant force substantially below the peak-force values of straight chamfers or those obeying the above integral criteria.

Turning the problem around, we can solve for constant-force chamfers analytically. For $\mu = 0$ the shapes are parabolas. Equations for their top and root slopes are easy to find [see Whitney et al. (1983) for details]. The slope equations are useful for simplified design techniques. We have no analytic proof, however, that constant-force chamfers minimize the peak force, although empirical evidence is strong.

To obtain solutions for $\mu > 0$ requires a technique similar to that used for minimum-insertion-work chamfers. The resulting shape

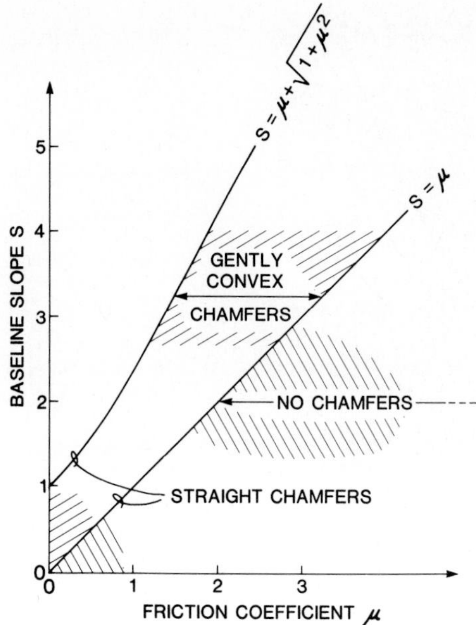

Fig. 6.19 Minimum insertion work chamfers. Range of usable chamfer shapes.

equation $Z(X)$ for force model [Eq. (6.13)] is

$$Z = -\frac{X}{\mu} + \frac{L^2C(1 + \mu^2)}{K\mu^2} \ln \left[\frac{L^2C/K\mu - X_1 + X}{L^2C/K\mu - X_1}\right] \tag{6.21}$$

where C, still to be determined, is the value of the constant insertion force. The slopes are

$$Z'(X_1) = \mu \tag{6.22}$$

and

$$Z'(0) = \frac{X_1 + \mu L^2C/K}{L^2C/K - \mu X_1} \tag{6.23}$$

To determine the constant insertion force C, we put Eq. (6.18) into Eq. (6.23) to obtain

$$C = \left(\frac{\mu RS + 1}{RS - \mu}\right)\left(\frac{KX_1}{L^2}\right) \tag{6.24}$$

Then, put the boundary condition (X_1, Z_1) in Eq. (6.21) to obtain

$$\frac{\mu(\mu S + 1)(RS - \mu)}{(\mu^2 + 1)(\mu RS + 1)} = \ln\left(\frac{\mu RS + 1}{\mu^2 + 1}\right) \tag{6.25}$$

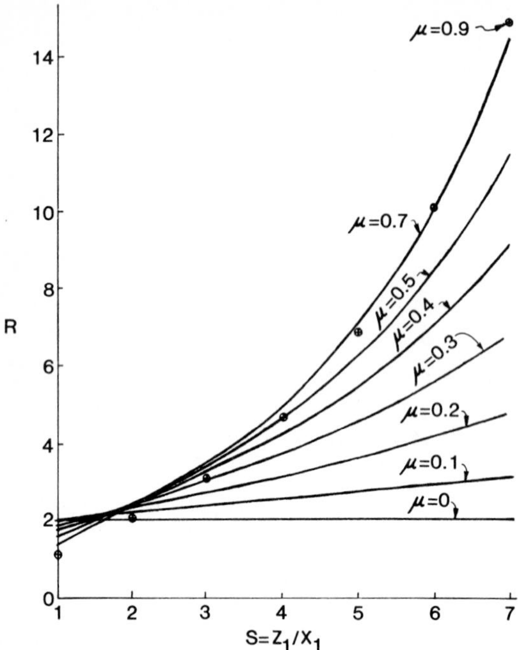

Fig. 6.20 Shape factor R versus S for different μ for minimum-peak-force chamfers. The aspect ratio is $S = Z_1/X_1$, and the shape factor is $R = Z'(0)/S$.

This can be solved numerically to yield tables of R versus μ and S (see Fig. 6.20).

The convex chamfers may be summarized conveniently by their top slopes (if one assumes $\mu > 0$ and finite but small X_1/L) and their root slopes. A more general analysis than that given here yields this formula for top slopes of *all* the chamfer types analyzed above:

$$Z'(X_1) = \frac{\mu + X_1/L}{1 - \mu X_1/L}$$

The root slopes depend on R

$$Z'(0) = RS$$

and are different for each type of chamfer, as follows:

Straight chamfer	$\min \int F_1\, dZ$	$\min \int F_1\, dX$	Constant force
$R = 1$	$1 \le R \le \sim 1.5$	$R \sim 3/2$	$R = 2$ if $\mu = 0$ $R > 2$ if $\mu > 0$ (value depends on S)

It is interesting to compare the various solutions. Figure 6.21(*a*) shows three chamfers having $S = 3$, while Fig. 6.21(*b*) shows their force versus insertion-depth behavior and the value of their normalized insertion work. The minimum-work chamfer has a discontinuity because $S = 3$ is larger than $S^* = 1.22$ corresponding to $\mu = 0.3$.

Figure 6.22 shows the ratio of the minimum constant force to the peak force of a straight chamfer having the same S and μ. The ratio plotted is

$$r = \left(\frac{\mu RS + 1}{RS - \mu}\right)\left(\frac{S - \mu}{\mu S + 1}\right)$$

From Fig. 6.22 we see that we cannot reduce the insertion force below half that of a straight chamfer (for the same S and μ) no matter what chamfer shape we use. The advantage of the minimum-force chamfer is reduced as S and μ increase.

Synthesizing chamfer shapes

A simple formula with a single parameter will yield a family of chamfers containing members similar to each of the above analytically determined shapes. Similar force characteristics are, of course, also obtained. This gives an easy though approximate design technique.

It is useful to note that exponential curves of the form

$$Z = \alpha(1 - e^{-bX}) \tag{6.26}$$

exhibit most of the properties required for chamfer shapes. Since such a curve must pass through (0,0) and (X_1, Z_1), the parameter α is easily found:

$$\alpha = \frac{Z_1}{1 - e^{-bX_1}}$$

By letting

$$n = bX_1$$

the exponential chamfer can be defined as

$$Z = \left(\frac{Z_1}{1 - e^{-n}}\right)(1 - e^{-nX/X_1}) \tag{6.27}$$

It is not only the geometry of the chamfer but also the slope at any particular point during insertion that prescribes the required force behavior. The slope at any point on Eq. (6.27) is

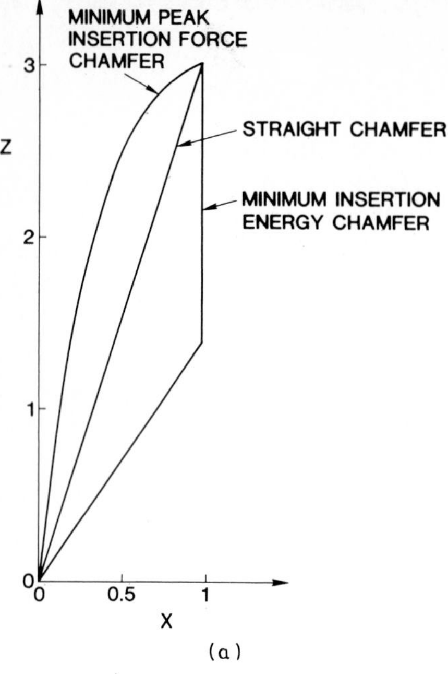

(a)

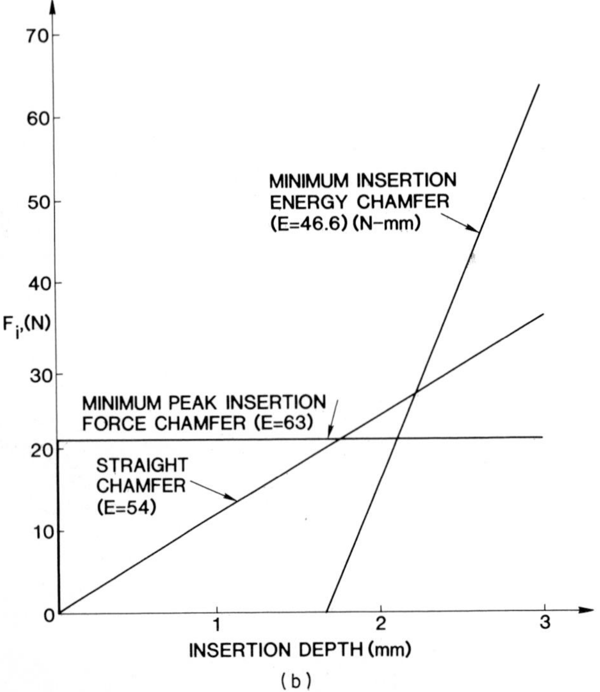

(b)

Fig. 6.21 Comparison of chamfer shape (a) and insertion force versus insertion depth characteristics (b for three different design criteria.

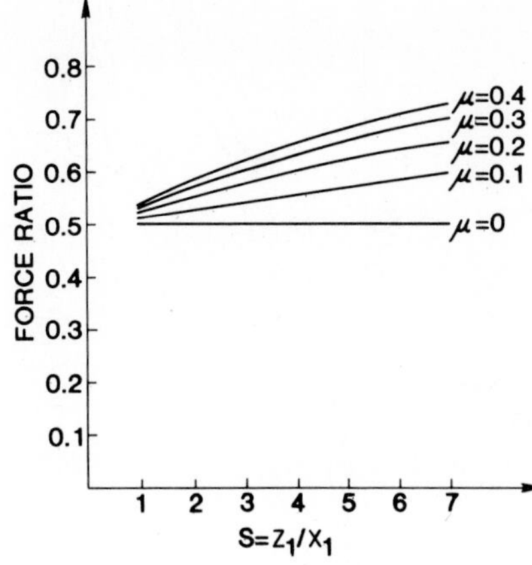

Fig. 6.22 Minimum peak force when compared to straight chamfer having the same aspect ratio and friction coefficient.

$$\frac{dZ}{dX} = \tan\phi = \left(\frac{Z_1}{X_1}\right)\left(\frac{n}{1 - e^{-n}}\right)e^{-nX/X_1} \tag{6.28}$$

For a particular part-mating situation, the baseline slope Z_1/X_1 will be known. To design a chamfer, all one need do is prescribe parameter n subject to the limitations

$$0 < n \le n_{\max}$$

The constant n can theoretically equal 0 (for the straight-line chamfer), but this causes problems since n appears in the denominator of the initial-angle equations. Very small values for n yield very nearly straight-line chamfers. The maximum value for n can be established numerically from

$$e^n \le 1 + \left[\frac{n(Z_1/X_1)}{\mu + \left[\dfrac{(1 + \mu^2)(X_1 / \sqrt{L^2 - X_1^2})}{1 - (\mu X_1 / \sqrt{L^2 - X_1^2})}\right]}\right] \tag{6.29}$$

Equation (6.29) expresses the condition that the denominator of the force equation [Eq. (6.13)] not equal zero. As in all the chamfer-design formulations, that condition is equivalent to requiring that the line joining the compliant part's tip and support not fall inside the contact force's friction cone.

Typical results for various values of n (for prescribed X_1, Z_1, L, K, and μ) are shown in Fig. 6.23. These graphs clearly show the relation-

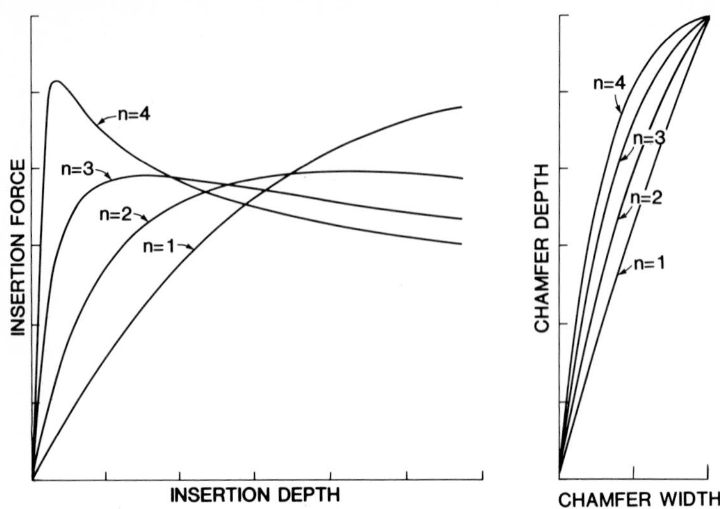

Fig. 6.23 Synthesized chamfer shape geometry and force versus depth characteristics.

ship between chamfer shape and the resulting insertion-force versus insertion-depth behavior.

Correlation of Experimental and Theoretical Results

How well can the predicted (theoretical) behavior of insertion and withdrawal force versus depth be matched by experimental results? Five sample cases are exhibited which show that carefully controlled experiments can verify theory and certain assumptions. The test apparatus used is described in Chap. 5.

Rigid peg entering hole with compliant member

Figure 6.24 shows sketches of two peg end shapes that were extensively tested. They were inserted into or withdrawn from a "hole" containing one rigid wall and one cantilever spring with radius end. The two peg end shapes are dissimilar enough that recognizable variations in force versus depth behavior should occur.

Four insertion and withdrawal sequences were performed for each

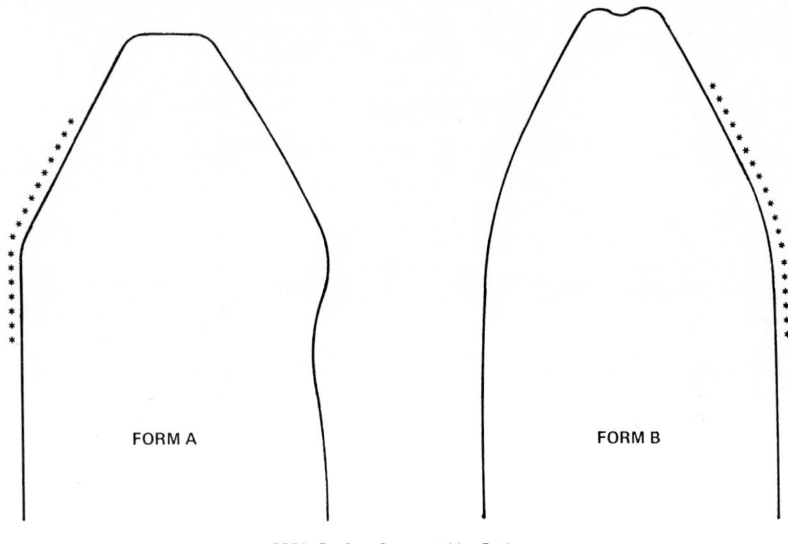

Fig. 6.24 Peg shape (electrical connector pin) used in experiments.

of the two pegs (form A and form B). The computer-plotted test results in Fig. 6.25 clearly reveal the phenomenon: the more streamlined the mating surface shapes, the smoother the insertion and withdrawal force characteristics.

To compare these results with theory, we need to determine the actual sizes and shapes of the parts and the coefficient of friction. The physical dimensions for the peg-hole combination can be determined by various methods. Data for final contact force and friction coefficient must be obtained from experimental results.

The effective friction coefficient can be derived from the information in Fig. 6.25. An elementary force analysis of the "constant contact-insertion force" area beyond a depth of about 1.25 mm shows that the insertion force F_I is related to the steady-state contact or normal force F_c by

$$F_I = 2\mu F_c \tag{6.30}$$

Also, the withdrawal force can be expressed as

$$F_W = -2\mu F_c \tag{6.31}$$

These equations are special cases of Eqs. (6.2) and (6.4).

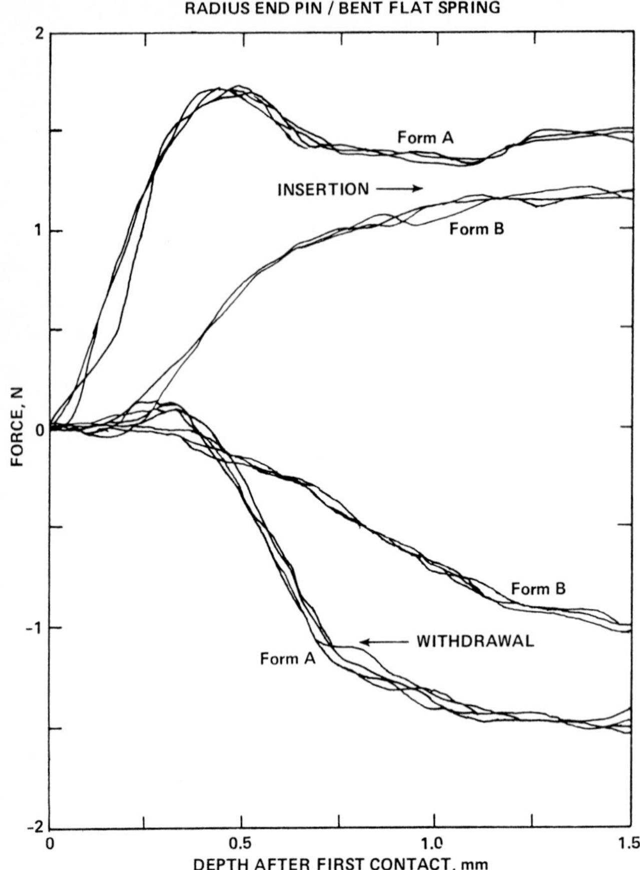

Fig. 6.25 Experimental results for single pin and socket mating.

Since the normal force is derived from the deflection of the spring, one can write the equation for a simple spring for this case:

$$F_c = K_x(d_p - d_c) \tag{6.32}$$

where $d_p - d_c$ is the difference between the peg diameter d_p and the relaxed position of the spring. The spring rate K_x was measured by deflecting the actual spring used. The result is

$$K_x = 14.6 \text{ N/mm}$$

F_I, K_x, and d_p are known for two conditions, which are

$$F_{IA} = 2\mu K_x(d_{pA} - d_c) \qquad \text{for form A}$$

$$F_{IB} = 2\mu K_x(d_{pB} - d_c) \qquad \text{for form B}$$

Solving for μ yields

$$\mu = \frac{F_{IA} - F_{IB}}{2K_x(d_{pA} - d_{pB})} \tag{6.33}$$

For the physical case at hand

$$F_{IA} = 1.39 \text{ N} \qquad F_{IB} = 1.02 \text{ N}$$

$$d_{pA} = 1.600 \text{ mm} \qquad d_{pB} = 1.549 \text{ mm}$$

Then Eq. (6.33) yields

$$\mu = \frac{1.39 \text{ N} - 1.02 \text{ N}}{2(14.6 \text{ N/mm})(1.600 \text{ mm} - 1.549 \text{ mm})} = 0.248$$

This value of μ is used below. Also, Eq. (6.30) yields

$$F_{cA} = \frac{1.39 \text{ N}}{2(0.25)} = 2.78 \text{ N} = 10 \text{ oz}$$

$$F_{cB} = \frac{1.02 \text{ N}}{2(0.25)} = 2.04 \text{ N} = 7.3 \text{ oz}$$

Theoretical and experimental data comparison

Using data from part measurements and calculations above, a digital computer program produced the results in Fig. 6.26. These theoretical results can be superimposed on the experimental results of Fig. 6.25, as shown in Fig. 6.27, where the initial contact point is defined as zero depth.

Compliant member or compliantly supported rigid member traversing a rigid chamfer

For this case, the experimental apparatus looks like Fig. 6.16. Again we must determine μ. It is possible to determine μ from a knowledge of $F_{Z\text{-DOWN}}$, $F_{X\text{-DOWN}}$, $F_{Z\text{-UP}}$, and $F_{X\text{-UP}}$[1] at any particular depth, since for insertion [see Eqs. (6.1) and (6.2)]

$$\frac{F_{Z\text{-DOWN}}}{F_{X\text{-DOWN}}} = \frac{1 + \mu \tan\phi}{\tan\phi - \mu} \tag{6.34}$$

and, for withdrawal (signs on μ are reversed),

$$\frac{F_{Z\text{-UP}}}{F_{X\text{-UP}}} = \frac{1 - \mu \tan\phi}{\tan\phi + \mu} \tag{6.35}$$

[1] $F_{Z\text{-DOWN}}$ and $F_{X\text{-DOWN}}$ are forces during insertion; $F_{Z\text{-UP}}$ and $F_{X\text{-UP}}$ are forces during withdrawal.

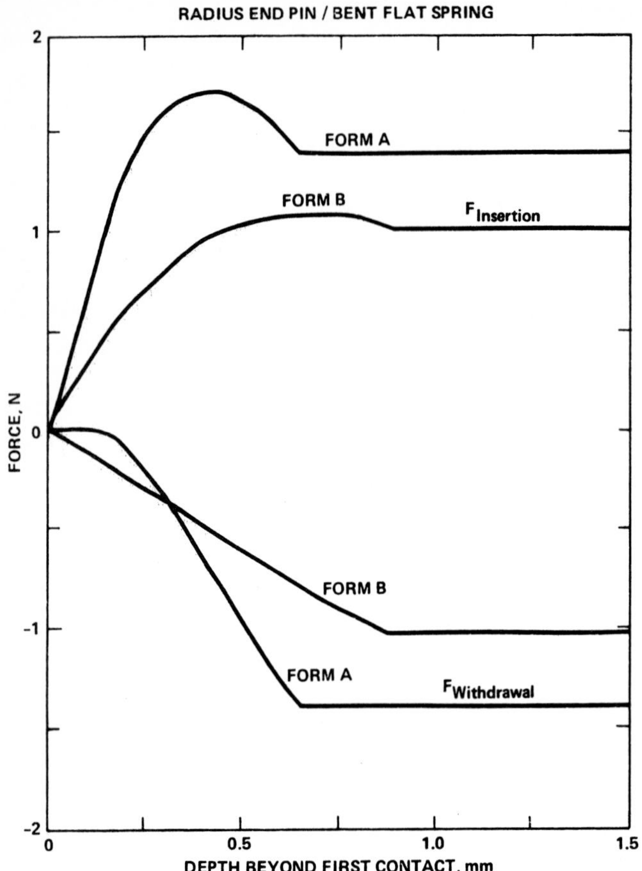

Fig. 6.26 Theoretical part-mating results using measured and calculated parameters for single pin and socket.

Let

$$\gamma_D = \frac{F_{Z\text{-DOWN}}}{F_{X\text{-DOWN}}} \qquad \text{and} \qquad \gamma_U = \frac{F_{Z\text{-UP}}}{F_{X\text{-UP}}}$$

Then tan ϕ can be eliminated from Eqs. (6.34) and (6.35) and the following equation obtained for μ:

$$\mu^2 + 2\left(\frac{1 + \gamma_U\gamma_D}{\gamma_D - \gamma_U}\right)\mu - 1 = 0 \tag{6.36}$$

A check on consistent behavior of the experimental data can be performed by taking a number of data slices (at arbitrary insertion depths), calculating μ using Eq. (6.36) for each, and determining the mean and standard deviation for the resulting μ data. This procedure

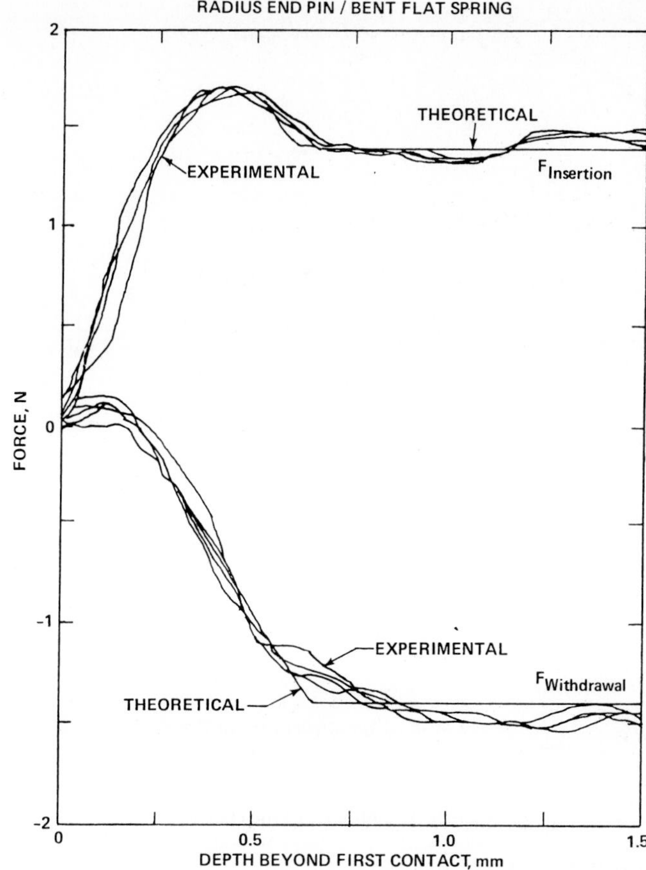

Fig. 6.27 Comparison of form A theoretical data to experimental data.

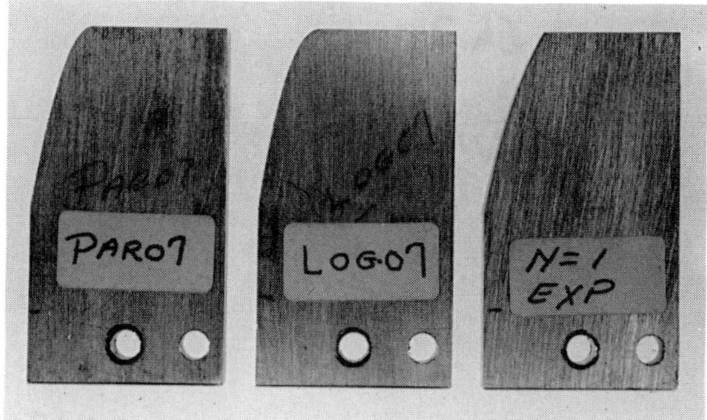

Fig. 6.28 Chamfer shapes used for experiments. All three have $S = 3$. PAR07 is a constant-insertion-force chamfer based on assuming $\mu = 0$. LOG07 is a constant-force chamfer with $R = 2.4$ based on $\mu = 0.1$. EXP is an exponential chamfer with $n = 1$.

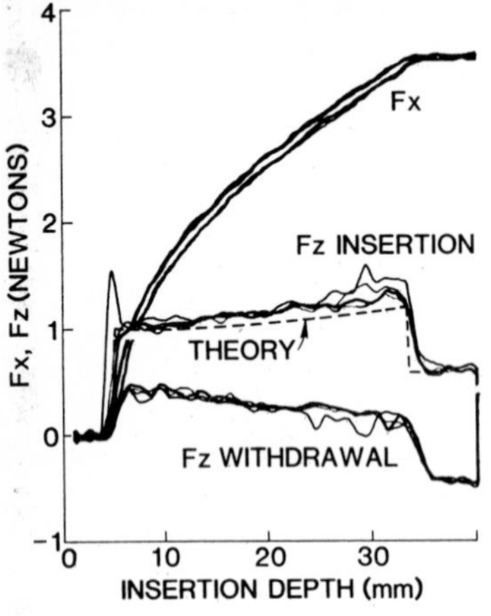

Fig. 6.29 Comparison of theory to experimental results for the PAR07 shape (constant force if $\mu = 0$). Theory line is based on $\mu = 0.14$, which is the actual value.

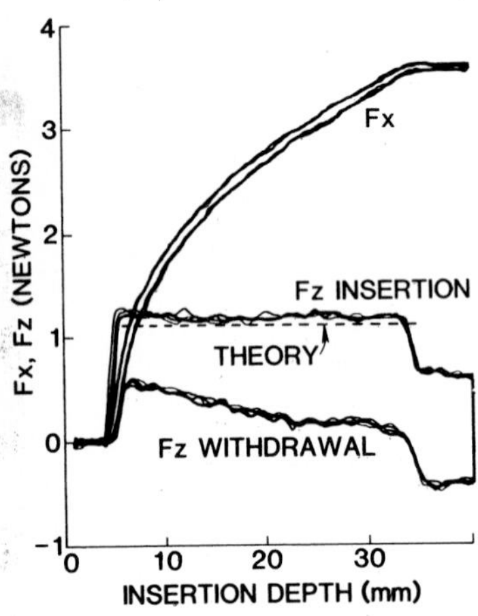

Fig. 6.30 Comparison of theory to experimental results for the LOG07 shape (constant force if $\mu = 0.1$). Theory line is based on $\mu = 0.15$, which is the actual value.

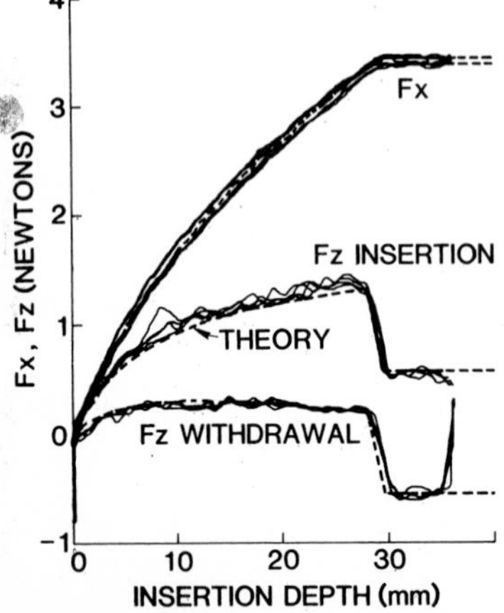

Fig. 6.31 Comparison of theory to experimental results for the $n = 1$ EXP shape (exponential chamfer). Theory line is based on $\mu = 0.15$, which is the actual value.

was used on the experimental parts in Fig. 6.28, yielding almost constant $\mu = 0.15$, which helps to explain the close match between theoretical and experimental results.

Experimental results

The three chamfer shapes shown in Fig. 6.28 were NC milled to produce specific insertion-force behavior. Shape LOG07 [constant-force logarithm obeying Eq. (6.21)] was intended to produce constant insertion force if $\mu = 0.1$. Shape PAR07 (constant-force parabola) was intended to produce constant insertion force if $\mu = 0$. Since $\mu \cong 0.14$ to 0.15, neither experimental result yields constant force but is close to what theory would predict for those shapes at that value of μ (see Figs. 6.29 and 6.30). Experimental results for an exponential chamfer with $n = 1$ are shown in Fig. 6.31 and compare to the predicted theoretical results with reasonable agreement.

Discussion and Conclusions

Underlying this work is the premise that robot operations, like assembly, can be analyzed to the point at which effective tools, strategies, and product designs can be created. In the case of compliant parts, the focus is on product design. The main design features of a chamfer that affect mating force are its shape, the coefficient of friction, and the stiffness of the mating part. The results presented here indicate that, of the three factors, shape is the most influential. In addition, small changes in shape can make large changes in insertion-force behavior, a statement that is not true of stiffness or friction, except in some limiting cases.

It appears that, if fabrication costs permit, slightly convex chamfers are preferable to straight ones. If the chamfer must be straight and if space permits, long chamfers are preferable to short ones.

References

Gustavson, R. E.: "A Theory for the Three-Dimensional Mating of Chamfered Cylindrical Parts," *ASME J. Mechanisms, Transmissions, and Automation in Design,* June 1985.

Hennessey, M. P.: "Compliant Part Mating and Minimum Energy Chamfer Design," S M Thesis, MIT Mech. Eng. Dept., Sept. 1982.

Whitney, D.E.: "Part Mating Theory," in *International Encyclopedia of Robotics: Applications and Automation,* R. Dorf (ed.), John Wiley, New York, 1988.

———, R. E. Gustavson, and M. P. Hennessey, "Designing Chamfers," *Int'l. J. of Robotics Research,* vol. 2, no. 4, Winter, 1983, pp. 3–18.

———, et al.: "Part Mating Theory for Compliant Parts," C S Draper Laboratory Report R-1407, Oct. 1980.

Appendix

Computer program PEGCMPHL for analyzing the behavior of a single peg entering a variety of compliant holes

```
10 REM                          PEGCMPHL                  Rewritten 3 AUGUST 1987
20 REM
30 R9=57.29578:  SCREEN 0:  WIDTH 80:  COLOR 14,0,0:  CLS:  FOR I=1 TO 10:  PRIN
T:  NEXT
40 PRINT TAB(15) "INSERTION of RADIUS-END PEG into COMPLIANT HOLE.": PRINT:  PRI
NT:  PRINT TAB(17) "Two fundamental types can be investigated : ": PRINT: PRINT
50 PRINT TAB(22) "1     One spring, one straight wall":  PRINT
60 PRINT TAB(22) "2     Two symmetrical springs":  PRINT: PRINT: PRINT TAB(33);
70 INPUT "Which ";STYP
80 PRINT:  PRINT:  PRINT:  PRINT TAB(18);
90 INPUT "TITLE (40 Char. Max.) : ",T$
100 CPTR=INT(41-LEN(T$))
110 PRINT:  PRINT:  PRINT:  PRINT TAB(25) "All dimensions are   mm !":  PRINT:
PRINT:  PRINT:  PRINT TAB(32);
120 INPUT "Peg Diameter : ",DIAP:  PRINT:  PRINT TAB(29);
130 INPUT "End of Peg Radius : ",RADP:  PRINT:  PRINT TAB(28);
140 INPUT "Mounting Dimension : ",DIAH:  PRINT:  PRINT TAB(27);
150 INPUT "Friction coefficient : ",MU:  PRINT:  PRINT TAB(25);
160 INPUT "Spring initial dimension : ",LEN0:  PRINT:  PRINT TAB(27);
170 INPUT "End of Spring Radius : ",RADS
180 DIFF=DIAH-DIAP:  RCHK=2*LEN0+RADS-2*DIFF:  IF STYP=2  THEN RCHK=RCHK+DIFF
190 IF RADP>RCHK  THEN 220
200 PRINT:  PRINT:  PRINT TAB(19) USING "###.###  Minimum usable peg end radius
!";RCHK:   PRINT:  PRINT TAB(29);
210 GOTO 130
220 PRINT:  INPUT "                          Spring rate (N/mm) : ",SPRT
230 REM
240 REM     ****    PARAMETER CALCULATION for SPECIFIED CONTACT FORCE
250 REM
260 M5=1-MU*MU:  PRINT:  PRINT:  PRINT:  PRINT TAB(14) "You may specify the Fina
l (constant) Normal Force ,":  PRINT:  PRINT TAB(18) "Spring dimension will then
 be calculated .":  PRINT:  PRINT:  PRINT TAB(27);
270 INPUT "Do you want to (Y or N) ";ANS$:  IF ANS$="N"  THEN 340
280 IF ANS$="n"  THEN 340
290 PRINT:  PRINT:  INPUT "                        Final (constant) Normal Force - N
 : ",FFR
300 LCHK=DIFF-RADS:  IF STYP=2  THEN LCHK=LCHK-.5*DIFF
310 RCHK=M5*FFR/SPRT:  LEN0=LCHK+RCHK: RCHK=2*RCHK-RADS: IF RADP>RCHK  THEN 340
320 PRINT:  PRINT:  PRINT TAB(19) USING "###.###  Minimum usable peg end radius
!";RCHK:   PRINT:  PRINT TAB(29);
330 GOTO 130
340 RSUM=RADP+RADS
350 PRINT:  PRINT:  INPUT "                 Maximum Insertion Depth (beyond first c
ontact) : ",ZMAX
360 REM
370 REM     ****    DETERMINE DEPTH for START of CONSTANT INSERTION FORCE
380 REM
390 IF STYP=2  THEN 410
400 DCHK=RADP+DIFF:  LCHK=DIFF-RADS:  GOTO 420
410 DCHK=RADP+.5*DIFF:  LCHK=.5*DIFF-RADS
420 S5=(DCHK-LEN0)/RSUM:  PRINT:  PRINT:  PRINT TAB(22) USING "###.### mm  INITI
AL SPRING DIMENSION";LEN0:  PRINT:  PRINT:  PRINT TAB(23) USING "###.### mm  FIN
AL SPRING DIMENSION";LCHK
430 PHI0=ATN(S5/SQR(1-S5*S5)):  ZMIN=SQR(RSUM*RSUM-(DCHK-LEN0)^2):  IF ZMIN<ZMAX
 THEN 480
440 PRINT:  PRINT:  PRINT TAB(15) "MAXIMUM DEPTH SPECIFIED IS NOT LARGE ENOUGH !
":  GOTO 350
450 REM
460 REM     ****    DETERMINE FINAL CONTACT and INSERTION FORCES
470 REM
480 G9=SPRT*(LEN0-LCHK)/M5:  FINS=2*MU*G9:  FWDL=-2*MU*G9
490 PRINT:  PRINT:  PRINT TAB(19);
500 INPUT "DO YOU WANT GRAPHICAL OUTPUT (Y or N) ";ANS$
510 IF ANS$="Y"  THEN 950
520 IF ANS$="y"  THEN 950
530 LPRINT CHR$(27);CHR$(71)
540 LPRINT TAB(CPTR) CHR$(14);T$
550 LPRINT CHR$(27);CHR$(72)
560 LPRINT:  LPRINT TAB(15) "INSERTION of RADIUS END PEG into COMPLIANT WALL HOL
E":  LPRINT:  IF STYP=2  THEN 580
570 LPRINT TAB(25) "One spring,  one straight wall":  LPRINT:  LPRINT: GOTO 590
580 LPRINT TAB(26) "Two equal symmetrical springs":  LPRINT:  LPRINT
590 LPRINT TAB(28) USING "###.## mm  PEG DIAMETER";DIAP:  LPRINT
600 LPRINT TAB(26) USING "###.## mm  END of PEG RADIUS";RADP:  LPRINT
610 LPRINT TAB(25) USING "###.## mm  MOUNTING DIMENSION";DIAH:  LPRINT
620 LPRINT TAB(24) USING "###.## mm  END of SPRING RADIUS";RADS:  LPRINT
630 LPRINT TAB(22) USING "###.## mm  SPRING INITIAL DIMENSION";LEN0:  LPRINT
640 LPRINT TAB(25) USING "#.###  Coefficient of Friction";MU:  LPRINT
650 LPRINT TAB(24) USING "######.## N/mm  SPRING RATE";SPRT:  LPRINT:  LPRINT
660 REM
670 REM     ****    COMPUTE INSERTION / WITHDRAWAL CHARACTERISTICS for 0<Z<ZMIN
680 REM
690 ZINC=ZMIN/25
700 LPRINT:  LPRINT:  LPRINT TAB(12) "DEPTH            INSERTION
 WITHDRAWAL":  LPRINT
710 LPRINT TAB(10) "  mm       X-Force (N)  Z-Force (N)  X-Force (N)  Z-Force (
N)":  LPRINT
720 FOR I=0 TO 25
730 Z=ZINC*I:  ZDIF=ZMIN-Z:  C6=ZDIF/RSUM:  IF I<25  THEN 750
740 PHI1=90/R9:  GOTO 760
750 PHI1=ATN(SQR(1-C6*C6)/C6)
760 S4=SIN(PHI1):  C4=COS(PHI1)
770 L=DCHK-RSUM*S4:  K1=SPRT*(LEN0-L):  XFI=K1/(M5*S4-2*MU*C4):  XFW=K1/(M5*S4+2
```

Listing 6A-1

```
*MU*C4):  IF STYP=2  THEN 790
780 ZFI=XFI*(2*MU*S4+M5*C4):  ZFW=-XFW*(2*MU*S4-M5*C4):  GOTO 800
790 ZFI=XFI*2*(C4+MU*S4):  ZFW=-XFW*2*(MU*S4-C4)
800 LPRINT TAB(8):  LPRINT USING "####.####    ";Z;XFI;ZFI;XFW;ZFW
810 NEXT I
820 REM
830 REM     ****    DATA for CONSTANT FORCE SECTION
840 REM
850 LPRINT TAB(8):  LPRINT USING "####.####    ";ZMIN,G9,FINS,G9,FWDL
860 ZMDL=(ZMIN+ZMAX)/2:  LPRINT TAB(8):  LPRINT USING "####.####    ";ZMDL,G9,FI
NS,G9;FWDL
870 LPRINT TAB(8):  LPRINT USING "####.####    ";ZMAX,G9,FINS,G9,FWDL
880 LPRINT CHR$(12)
890 CLS:  FOR K=1 TO 10:  PRINT:  NEXT:  INPUT "  DO YOU WANT TO CONTINUE (Y or
N) ";ANS$:  IF ANS$="Y"  THEN 30
900 IF ANS$="y"  THEN 30
910 CLS:  END
920 REM
930 REM     ****    GRAPHICAL OUTPUT
940 REM
950 DEF SEG=&HB800:  SCREEN 1:  COLOR 8,0:  CLS
960 XRNG=ZMAX:  YRNG=G9-FWDL
970 SCFAX=XRNG/14:  FCTRY=YRNG/10
980 YMID=(G9+FWDL)/2
990 PWR=INT(LOG(FCTRY)*.434295):  BSE=FCTRY/10^PWR
1000 FOR K=0 TO 2
1010 IF BSE<2^K  THEN 1030
1020 NEXT K
1030 SCFAY=(2^K)*(10^PWR):  IF K>2  THEN SCFAY=10^(PWR+1)
1040 FOR K=5 TO 19 STEP 2:  CLM=2+(K-1)*16:  LINE(CLM,4)-(CLM,164),1:  NEXT K
1050 FOR K=1 TO 11:  ROW=4+(K-1)*16:  LINE(66,ROW)-(290,ROW),1:  NEXT K
1060 XMIN=0: XMAX=ZMAX: YMIN=INT(10*YMID-50*SCFAY)/10
1070 FOR K=1 TO 6:  LOCATE 25-4*K,3:  YVL=YMIN+2*(K-1)*SCFAY:  PRINT USING "###.
#";YVL:  NEXT K
1080 LOCATE 7,1:  PRINT "F":  LOCATE 8,1:  PRINT "o":  LOCATE 9,1:  PRINT "r":
LOCATE 10,1:  PRINT "c":  LOCATE 11,1:  PRINT "e":  LOCATE 14,1:  PRINT "N":  LO
CATE 23,38:  PRINT "mm"
1090 FOR K=1 TO 4:  LOCATE 23,-1+8*K:  XVL=XMIN+4*(K-1)*SCFAX:  PRINT USING "##.
#";XVL:  NEXT K
1100 ZINC=ZMIN/200
1110 FOR I=0 TO 200
1120 Z=ZINC*I:  ZDIF=ZMIN-Z:  C6=ZDIF/RSUM:  IF I<200  THEN 1140
1130 PHI1=90/R9:  GOTO 1150
1140 PHI1=ATN(SQR(1-C6*C6)/C6)
1150 S4=SIN(PHI1):  C4=COS(PHI1)
1160 L=DCHK-RSUM*S4:  K1=SPRT*(LENO-L):  XFI=K1/(M5*S4-2*MU*C4):  XFW=K1/(M5*S4+
2*MU*C4):  IF STYP=2  THEN 1180
1170 ZFI=XFI*(2*MU*S4+M5*C4):  ZFW=-XFW*(2*MU*S4-M5*C4):  GOTO 1190
1180 ZFI=XFI*2*(C4+MU*S4):  ZFW=-XFW*2*(MU*S4-C4)
1190 XP=(66+Z*16/SCFAX):  YP=164-(XFW-YMIN)*16/SCFAY:  PSET (XP,YP),2
1200 XP=(66+Z*16/SCFAX):  YP=164-(XFI-YMIN)*16/SCFAY:  PSET (XP,YP),3
1210 XP=(66+Z*16/SCFAX):  YP=164-(ZFW-YMIN)*16/SCFAY:  PSET (XP,YP),2
1220 XP=(66+Z*16/SCFAX):  YP=164-(ZFI-YMIN)*16/SCFAY:  PSET (XP,YP),3
1230 NEXT I
1240 YP=164-(XFW-YMIN)*16/SCFAY:  LINE (XP,YP)-(290,YP),2
1250 YP=164-(XFI-YMIN)*16/SCFAY:  LINE (XP,YP)-(290,YP),3
1260 LOCATE YP/8+2,34:  PRINT "Normal"
1270 YP=164-(ZFW-YMIN)*16/SCFAY:  LINE (XP,YP)-(290,YP),2
1280 LOCATE YP/8-1,30:  PRINT "Withdrawal"
1290 YP=164-(ZFI-YMIN)*16/SCFAY:  LINE (XP,YP)-(290,YP),3
1300 LOCATE YP/8-1,31:  PRINT "Insertion"
1310 DEF SEG=&HB800:  BSAVE "PICTURE",0,&H4000
1320 LOCATE 23,5:  INPUT "DO YOU WANT A HARDCOPY (Y or N) ";ANS$
1330 IF ANS$="N"  THEN 1540
1340 IF ANS$="n"  THEN 1540
1350 LPRINT CHR$(27);CHR$(71)
1360 LPRINT TAB(CPTR) CHR$(14);T$
1370 LPRINT CHR$(27);CHR$(72)
1380 LPRINT:  LPRINT
1390 LPRINT TAB(15) "INSERTION of RADIUS END PEG into COMPLIANT WALL HOLE":  LPR
INT:  IF STYP=2  THEN 1410
1400 LPRINT TAB(25) "One spring,  one straight wall": LPRINT: LPRINT: GOTO 1420
1410 LPRINT TAB(26) "Two equal symmetrical springs":  LPRINT:  LPRINT
1420 LPRINT TAB(28) USING "###.## mm  PEG DIAMETER";DIAP:  LPRINT
1430 LPRINT TAB(26) USING "###.## mm  END of PEG RADIUS";RADP:  LPRINT
1440 LPRINT TAB(25) USING "###.## mm  MOUNTING DIMENSION";DIAH:  LPRINT
1450 LPRINT TAB(24) USING "###.## mm  END of SPRING RADIUS";RADS:  LPRINT
1460 LPRINT TAB(22) USING "###.## mm  SPRING INITIAL DIMENSION";LENO:  LPRINT
1470 LPRINT TAB(25) USING "#.###  Coefficient of Friction";MU:  LPRINT
1480 LPRINT TAB(24) USING "######.## N/mm  SPRING RATE";SPRT:  LPRINT:  LPRINT
1490 CLS:  BLOAD "PICTURE",0
1500 DEF SEG=&H1FFF:  DATA &H55,&HCD,&H05,&H5D,&HCB
1510 FOR ADDR=0 TO 4:  READ INS:  POKE ADDR,INS:  NEXT
1520 RESTORE:  PSUB=0:  CALL PSUB:  DEF SEG=&HB800
1530 LPRINT CHR$(12)
1540 CLS:  FOR K=1 TO 10:  PRINT:  NEXT:  INPUT "  DO YOU WANT TO CONTINUE (Y or
N) ";ANS$:  IF ANS$="Y"  THEN 30
1550 IF ANS$="y"  THEN 30
1560 CLS:  END
```

Listing 6A-1 *(Continued)*

Chapter

7

Engineered Compliance and the Strategy of Compliant Assembly

Introduction

This chapter is in two parts. The first part describes the *remote center compliance* (RCC), a device that provides engineered compliance for tools and parts to be assembled. The second part extends the RCC idea to encompass the strategy of *compliant assembly*, a strategy that employs engineered compliance, part and product design, and error analysis to guarantee reliable assembly. Embodying this strategy in assembly workstations is the subject of Chap. 11.

The Remote Center Compliance

The RCC is a compliant interface between a workpiece and a tool that helps the tool function or helps assemble the workpiece to another piece. Its basic function is to act as a general error absorber in six dimensions and to provide a part or tool with organized compliance, that is, a particular and unique force-deformation behavior. The following sections give the history of the RCC, explain how it works, give simple design rules, and illustrate its use in typical applications. The presentation also repeats some of the material in Chap. 5 in an intuitive rather than a mathematical way.

History

The RCC was invented by Paul Watson, Samuel Drake, and Sergio Simunovic of Draper Laboratory (Watson, 1976; Drake, 1977) as a response to the need to perform assembly of parts that are not perfectly aligned laterally or angularly. In typical mechanical assembly machines, great care is taken to ensure that the parts are aligned. This is accomplished by holding the parts rigidly in grippers and fixtures. Grippers and fixtures are usually built especially for the parts and are expensive. But if the parts are slightly misshapen or gripped slightly crookedly, they will strike each other as shown in Fig. 7.1(*a*) and will not assemble correctly or will be damaged. Also, if a robot is used for assembly, misalignment may occur simply because robots cannot be built economically to be as rigid and accurate as mechanical assembly machines. Finally, some parts fit together so closely that even a tenth or a hundredth of a millimeter error will cause misassembly.

Manual assemblers use their eyes to guide parts near each other and then use their fingers to wiggle the parts together. While these methods could be used by robots, there are several reasons why alternate methods should be sought. First, vision systems and articulated fingers cost money and wiggling takes time which, in a factory environment, translates into money. Second, to imitate human methods unquestioningly is not necessarily a good guide to engineering design. Third, if we set aside the human method, we are free to take a new and better approach which people cannot use. The RCC is an excellent example of this.

Before the RCC was invented, researchers at Draper had studied part mating and determined conditions for successful assembly. These studies divided assembly into two stages—*chamfer crossing* and *insertion*, with the latter divided into substages. During chamfer crossing [see Fig. 7.1(*b*)], the parts try to move laterally with respect to each other to correct lateral errors. However, angular errors may be intro-

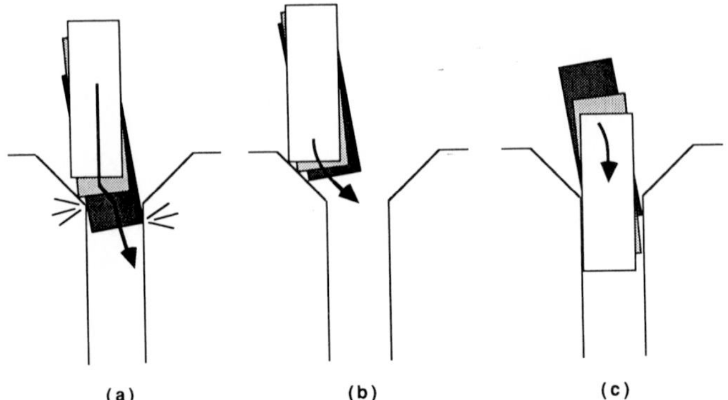

Fig. 7.1 (*a*) Attempt to assemble misaligned parts; (*b*) parts try to move laterally during chamfer crossing; (*c*) parts try to move angularly during insertion.

duced or increased by these lateral motions. During insertion [see Fig. 7.1(*c*)], the parts try to rotate with respect to each other to correct angular errors. If the parts are held rigidly, however, they will not be able to move as they need. In this case, forces and torques will build up—lateral forces caused by lateral errors and torques caused by angular errors.

The lateral forces, acting at single contact points during chamfer crossing and one-point contact, push in the direction opposite to the lateral error. Similarly, the torques arise from pairs of contact forces acting during two-point contact and exert a twist in the direction opposite to the angular error. Thus the forces can be thought of as signals indicating which way the parts should move or be moved actively or be allowed to move passively in order to facilitate assembly. For this reason, various "force feedback" algorithms have been devised to sense these force signals and maneuver the parts into the correct relative positions. Whitney (1987) contains summary descriptions of many force control algorithms.

The essence of the Draper force feedback algorithm was to sense forces and torques with a sensor located just behind the gripper, as shown in Fig. 7.2 (Drake and Watson, 1975). This sensor can detect forces along X, Y, and Z axes aligned to the sensor, as well as torques about these axes. Using the appropriate coordinate transformations, one can calculate what forces and torques are being exerted at or about the tip of the part where it contacts the other part. Using coordinated motion control algorithms (Whitney, 1972), one can program a robot to maneuver the tip of the part laterally or angularly in response to the sensed forces along or about these axes. The behavior of this algorithm is illustrated in Fig. 7.3.

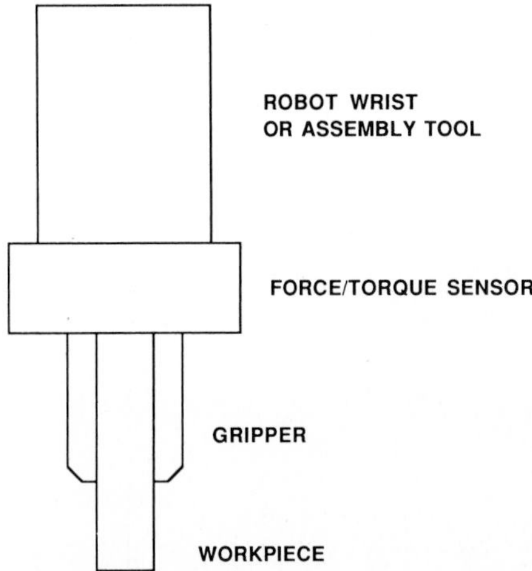

Fig. 7.2 Typical configuration of force-torque sensor on assembly tooling.

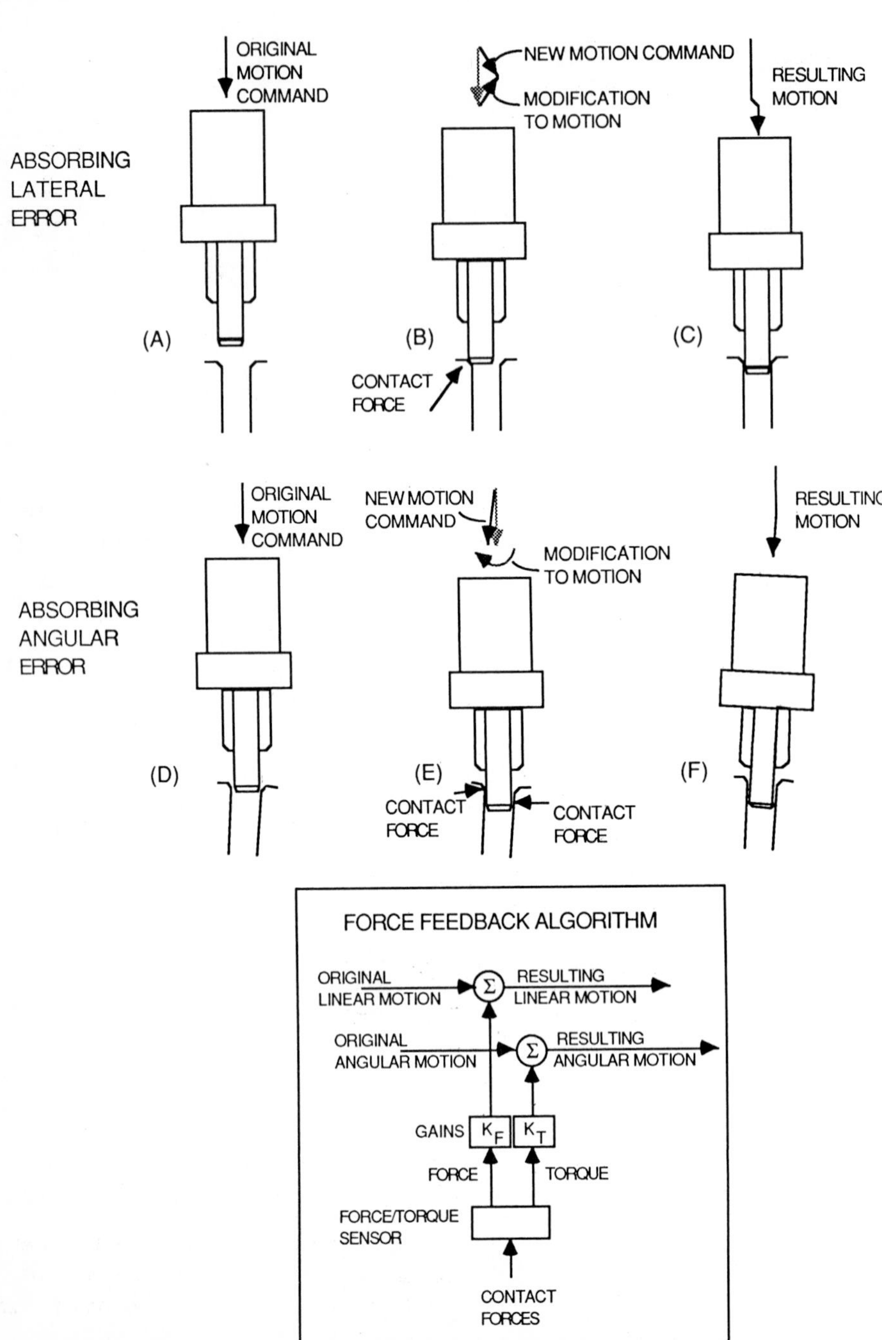
ORIGINAL
MOTION
COMMAND
NEW MOTION COMMAND
MODIFICATION
TO MOTION
RESULTING
MOTION
ABSORBING
LATERAL
ERROR
(A)
(B)
(C)
CONTACT
FORCE
ORIGINAL
MOTION
COMMAND
NEW MOTION
COMMAND
MODIFICATION
TO MOTION
RESULTING
MOTION
ABSORBING
ANGULAR
ERROR
(D)
(E)
(F)
CONTACT
FORCE
CONTACT
FORCE
FORCE FEEDBACK ALGORITHM
ORIGINAL
LINEAR MOTION
Σ
RESULTING
LINEAR MOTION
ORIGINAL
ANGULAR MOTION
Σ
RESULTING
ANGULAR MOTION
GAINS
K_F
K_T
FORCE
TORQUE
FORCE/TORQUE
SENSOR
CONTACT
FORCES

A crucial ingredient of this method is to move the part laterally without rotating if it is acted upon only by a single contact force at its tip (such as occurs during chamfer crossing or one-point contact) or to rotate it about its tip without translating if it is acted on only by a pair of contact forces that generate a torque about its tip (such as occurs during two-point contact insertion). The mechanics of this action as it relates to part mating is explained in Chap. 5. The force feedback algorithms are discussed in Whitney (1977).

The force feedback algorithm was explained because the RCC attempts to permit parts to maneuver themselves passively just as this force feedback algorithm would have maneuvered them actively.

Compliance and the Remote Center

It is important to understand the difference between the RCC and ordinary ways of holding workpieces during assembly. Every gripper, robot, or assembly machine is compliant to some degree. In most cases this compliance can be described by a center (or centers) of compliance, together with its lateral and rotational stiffnesses.[1] This compliance center is usually inside the structure of the gripper, and the associated stiffnesses are usually large.

The optimum way (see Fig. 5.9) to hold parts differs from this in two ways: First, the center of compliance should be at or near the tip of the part. Second, the stiffnesses should be low, making it easier for the

---

[1] The center of compliance of a compliant structure is defined as the point at which a pure force applied there will cause the structure to translate without rotating; similarly, if a pure torque is applied there, the structure will rotate but that point will not translate. Centers of compliance are discussed in Chap. 5.

Fig. 7.3 (OPPOSITE) The Draper force feedback algorithm. Top: Absorbing lateral error. (A) The robot, carrying a peg, approaches the hole which is laterally offset from the approach path. (B) When the peg strikes the chamfer, a contact force arises. This force is sensed in vector form by the sensor. The force vector is converted via matrix multiplication into a motion modification vector, and this modification vector alters the commanded motion. (C) As a result of the modification, the robot moves laterally as well as ahead, and the peg enters the hole. If the commanded modification is not large enough, the peg will continue to contact the chamfer, forces will continue to be sensed, and more motion modifications will be generated. Middle: Absorbing angular error. (D), (E), and (F) repeat (A), (B), and (C) for the case where angular error exists. The modification to the motion is a rotation which is programmed so as to rotate the peg about its tip so that the modification will not introduce any lateral error. Bottom: Summary of the force feedback algorithm. Motion commands are represented as separate linear and angular motions. The vector force-torque sensor senses the contact force vector and separates it into its lateral and angular components. Forces and torques are scaled by gains K_F and K_T to create motion modifications. Pure lateral error, pure angular error, or both types of error at once can be accommodated. In more complex versions of the algorithm, both forces and torques are used together to determine both lateral and angular motion modifications.

part to move while keeping the contact forces low. The result is that a lateral contact force at the tip of the part causes it to move laterally; a torque about the tip causes it to rotate. These are the desired responses according to the theory of part mating. The RCC accomplishes these by virtue of its mechanical design.

The theory on which these conclusions are based models round pegs and holes as flat tabs and slots. Experimental agreement with real round pegs and holes is very good. The RCC has been used successfully with parts of many other shapes as well, but the theory is either less well developed or nonexistent. Placing the center of compliance near the tip of the part still seems to be a good rule. Mating of parts with noncircular cross sections is aided by the fact that RCCs are also compliant about the insertion axis.

Practical Remote Center Compliances

The RCC is an axially symmetric passive device (that is, it contains no sensors, computers, or actuators). It is entirely mechanical and derives its properties from its geometry and the elasticity of its parts. "Compliance" means that it is compliant. "Remote center" means that its lateral and angular displacements are independent at a compliance center which is remote from the device itself.

The RCC is mounted on the wrist of robots or assembly equipment and is located just behind the gripper or tool (see Fig. 7.4). In some applications, it is mounted on the work table under the other mating part. Usually, the size of grippers or tools is arranged so that the tip of

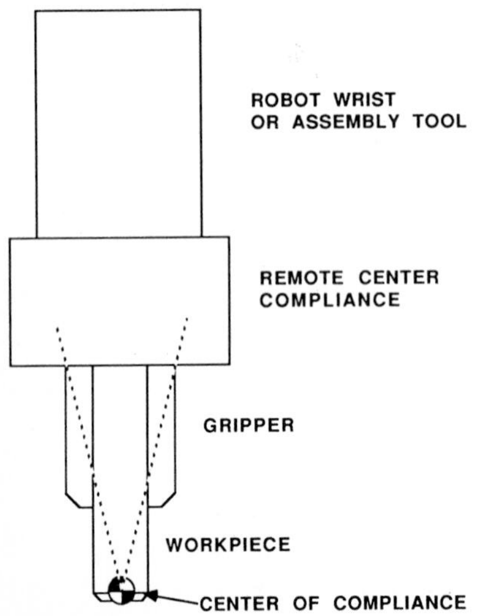

Fig. 7.4 Typical configuration of remote center compliance on assembly tooling.

the part will lie at or near the compliance center. Preferably, the RCC is much more compliant than the other objects it is connected to, so that its compliance matrix and center location will dominate over theirs, and the center will be where we want it to be. If the other objects are not at least 10 times stiffer than the RCC, the compliance center will shift back into the tool or robot, and its beneficial effect will be lost.

We can also think of the RCC as a mechanical way of implementing the force feedback algorithms described in the previous section of this chapter.

RCC Construction

Two generic ways of building RCCs are known: linkages and compliant structures. Linkages are easier to understand and are illustrated in Fig. 7.5 (Watson, 1976). A linkage RCC has three rigid platforms, of which one connects to an assembly machine or robot, the second attaches to the part or gripper, and the third is suspended between the first two. Linkages or flexures which are parallel to each other [see Fig. 7.5(*a*)] connect the first and third platforms, allowing parallelogram-like deformation (i.e., lateral deformation without rotation) in response to a force at the tip of the part but no response to a torque applied there. Linkages or flexures arranged so that their axes intersect at the remote center [see Fig. 7.5(*b*)] permit rotation of the second platform on the surface of a sphere whose center is at the remote center. This set of focused links will deform rotationally when a

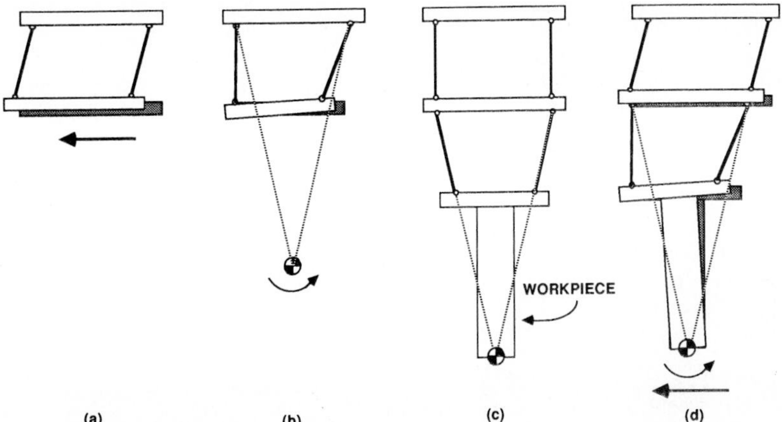

Fig. 7.5 (*a*) Lateral motion portion of linkage RCC; (*b*) angular motion portion of linkage RCC; (*c*) complete linkage RCC; (*d*) linkage RCC undergoing lateral and angular deformation.

torque is applied to the tip of the part but will not deform when a force is applied there. A linkage RCC is made by connecting one linkage set of each type together [see Fig. 7.5(*c*)].

Compliant structure RCCs, the second generic type, exist in many forms. Figure 7.6 shows two types made of metal. In Fig. 7.6(*a*), there are two distinct compliant elements, the top and the focused wires (Drake, 1977). The top alone behaves as if it had a remote center inside itself, whereas the wires alone behave as if they had a remote center at their focus. The net effect of this is a combined remote center between the first two whose location depends on the relative lateral and angular stiffnesses of the separate elements. In Fig. 7.6(*b*), there is only one kind of compliant element, comprising several curved

(a)

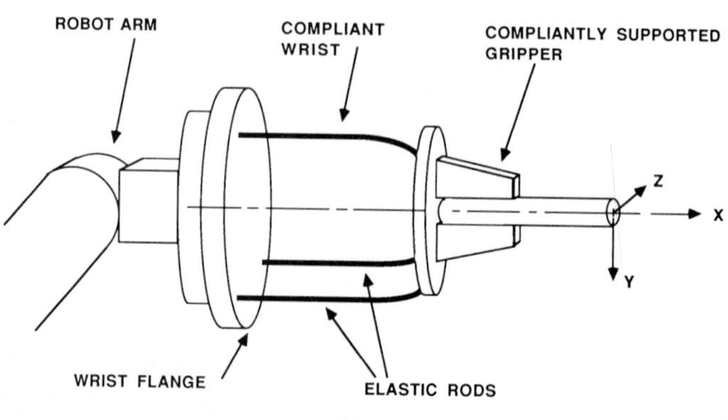

(b)

Fig. 7.6 (*a*) One type of compliant structure RCC. (*b*) Another type of compliant structure RCC (Havlik, 1983).

Fig. 7.7 Shear-pad-type RCC.

wires (Havlik, 1983). The spacing of these wires, the length of the straight portions, and the radius of the curved portions, together with the wires' elastic properties, determine this RCC's stiffness and the location of its remote center.

Figure 7.7 shows another type of compliant structure RCC. Again it has three rigid platforms linked by compliant elements. Here the compliant elements are known as shear pads. These are stacks of rubber-metal sandwiches that deform laterally rather easily in comparison to their axial stiffness. Three of these pads arranged parallel to each other behave similarly to the parallel links of the linkage RCC, and the three others in a focused arrangement behave similarly to the focused links.

However, because the shear pads also deform axially, it is possible to build an RCC using only three of them and only two platforms, as shown in Fig. 7.8. The result is a less expensive unit, although it is somewhat stiffer than a six-pad RCC. All commercial RCCs to date are of the shear pad type with either three or six pads.

Design Equations

This section presents, without derivations, simplified design equations for two types of RCCs, the compliant structure (or "wire") unit of

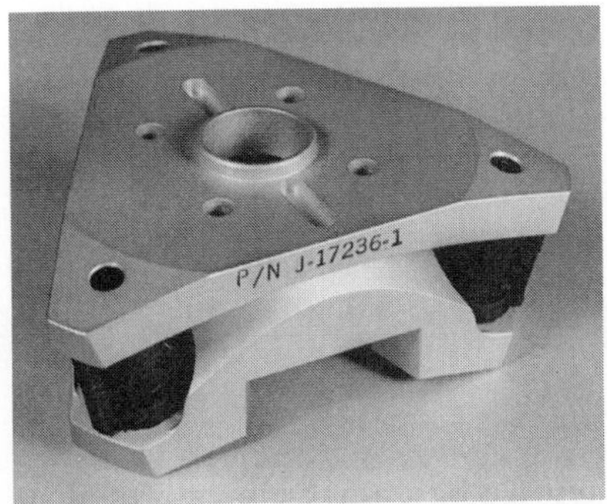

Fig. 7.8 Another shear-pad-type RCC.

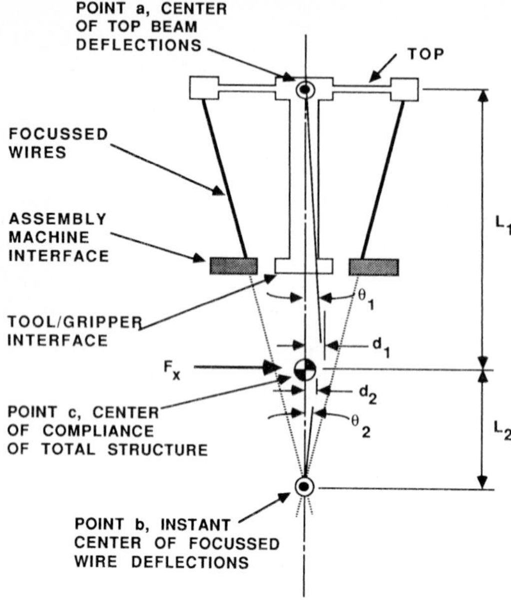

Fig. 7.9 Definition of terms for analysis of compliant structure RCCs.

Fig. 7.6(*a*) and the three-pad type of Fig. 7.8. These equations are linearized and are valid for small deflections only. The reader is advised to read the references for details. It should also be kept in mind that real RCCs do not have perfectly diagonal compliance matrices. Because of various nonlinearities and construction errors, there are always some small off-diagonal terms in the matrix.

Equations for wire RCCs follow (Drake, 1977)—see Fig. 7.9 for definition of terms. Design specifications are

K_L = desired lateral stiffness

K_θ = desired angular stiffness

L_1 = desired compliance center location

Then

$$L_2 = K_\theta/L_1 K_L$$

Let

$$K_{L2} = F_x/d_2 = \text{lateral stiffness of focused wires}$$

Then

$$K_{L2} = (L_1 + L_2) K_L/L_2$$

Let

$K_{\theta 1} = F_x L_1/\theta$ = angular stiffness of top structure measured at point c

Then

$$K_{\theta 1} = (L_1 + L_2) K_\theta / L_1$$

The focused wires can be assigned angles geometrically so as to point to the focus, called point b. Their length and radius can be determined from simple beam theory by regarding them as approximately parallel built-in beams. Usually three equally spaced wires are used, set at an angle of a few degrees off parallel.

The top structure may be a three- or four-beam cross or a diaphragm. Designing it to yield angular stiffness $K_{\theta 1}$ is an elementary problem in beam theory.

If L_1 and L_2 are each about 3 in (7.62 centimeter, cm), the diameter of the top structure is typically about the same 3 in.

Design equations for three-pad RCCs (Whitney and Rourke, 1986) follow. See Figs. 7.10 through 7.12 for definition of terms. Design specifications are

K_x = desired lateral stiffness

K_α = desired angular stiffness

P = desired compliance center location

Let K_{ss} = lateral stiffness of one shear pad = F_s/S

K_E = compression stiffness of one shear pad = F_E/ℓ

$K_{\alpha s}$ = cross moment-force stiffness of one shear pad = $F_s/\alpha = M/S$

$K_{\alpha\alpha}$ = angular stiffness of one shear pad = M/α

θ = angular offset of each shear pad from parallel

r = radius of mounting circle of shear pads

Then, using three such pads equally spaced, we have

$$K_x = 3/2[K_{ss}(1 + \cos^2\theta) + K_E \sin^2\theta]$$

$$P = 3/2[K_{\alpha s}(1 + \cos\theta)\cos\theta + r\sin\theta\cos\theta\,(K_E - K_{ss})]/K_x$$

$$K_\alpha = (1 + 2\cos^2\theta)K_{\alpha\alpha} + 3/2r(K_E r\cos^2\theta + K_{ss} r\sin^2\theta - 2K_{\alpha s}\sin\theta) - P^2 K_x$$

Rebman (1979) and Whitney and Rourke (1986) discuss the design trade-offs necessary in using these equations. One finds, for example,

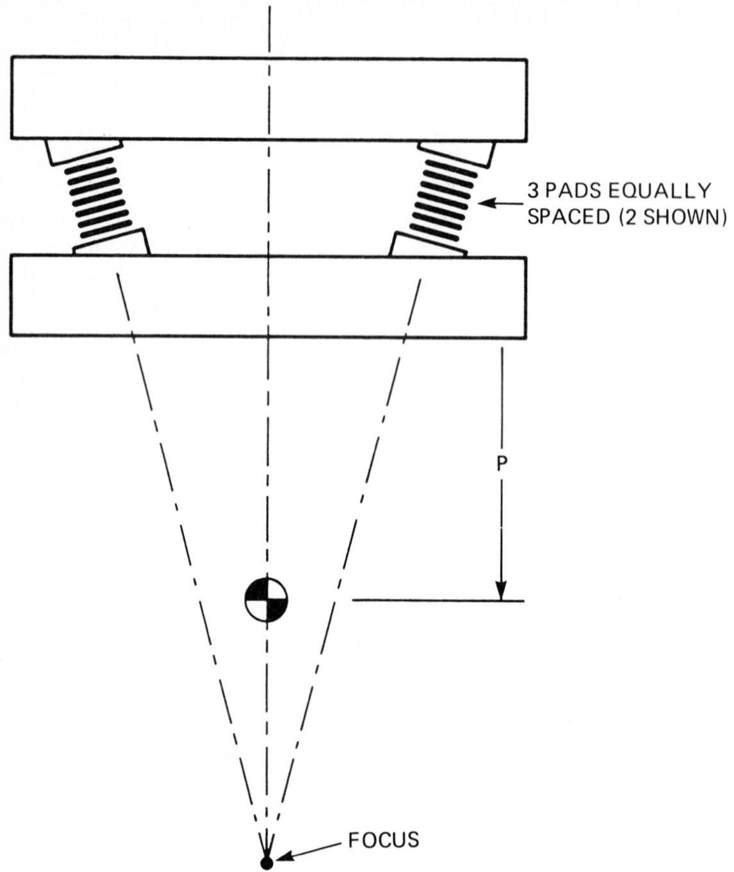

Fig. 7.10 Three-pad shear-pad-type RCC.

that r is usually similar to $P/2$, that one value of θ maximizes P, and that large P, small r, small K_x, and small K_θ are difficult to achieve in one design.

Table 7.1 gives values for the parameters and performance of a typical commercial three-pad RCC.

Whitney and Rourke (1986) discuss the limitations of the linear RCC equations given above. They are sufficient to describe the nominal behavior of the RCC if there is practically no lateral displacement. However, the nonlinear character of the shear pads in compression causes wide deviations from predicted performance as lateral displacement grows. For the above parameters, the value of P will fall from 117 to 85 mm as lateral displacement reaches 0.75 mm in one direction but will stay nearly unchanged for similar lateral displacements in the opposite direction. That is, the compliance center location may

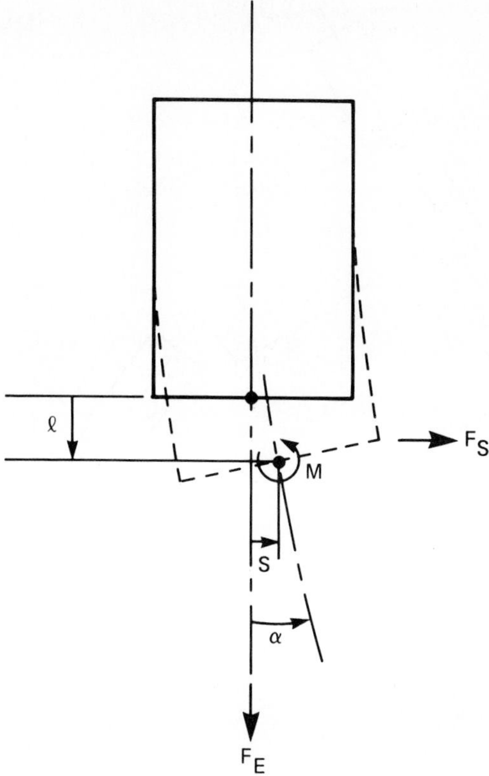

Fig. 7.11 Definition of terms for force-deformation model of a shear pad.

actually shift inward toward the RCC as it absorbs lateral error. These effects are direction dependent and are sensitive to the properties of individual shear pads. RCC designers and users should be aware of them.

Applications of RCCs

The RCC is now a mature product widely used around the world. It has been commercially available since 1978, and over 1000 are now in use in industry. New applications are continually being found. This section categorizes and illustrates some of the possibilities.

RCCs may be mounted behind either of the items that are being mated. An RCC on a work surface behind a growing assembly can be as large and heavy as needed but as the assembly grows, the remote center will not always be in the correct location. An RCC mounted to a workhead must be more limited in size and weight but can be sized,

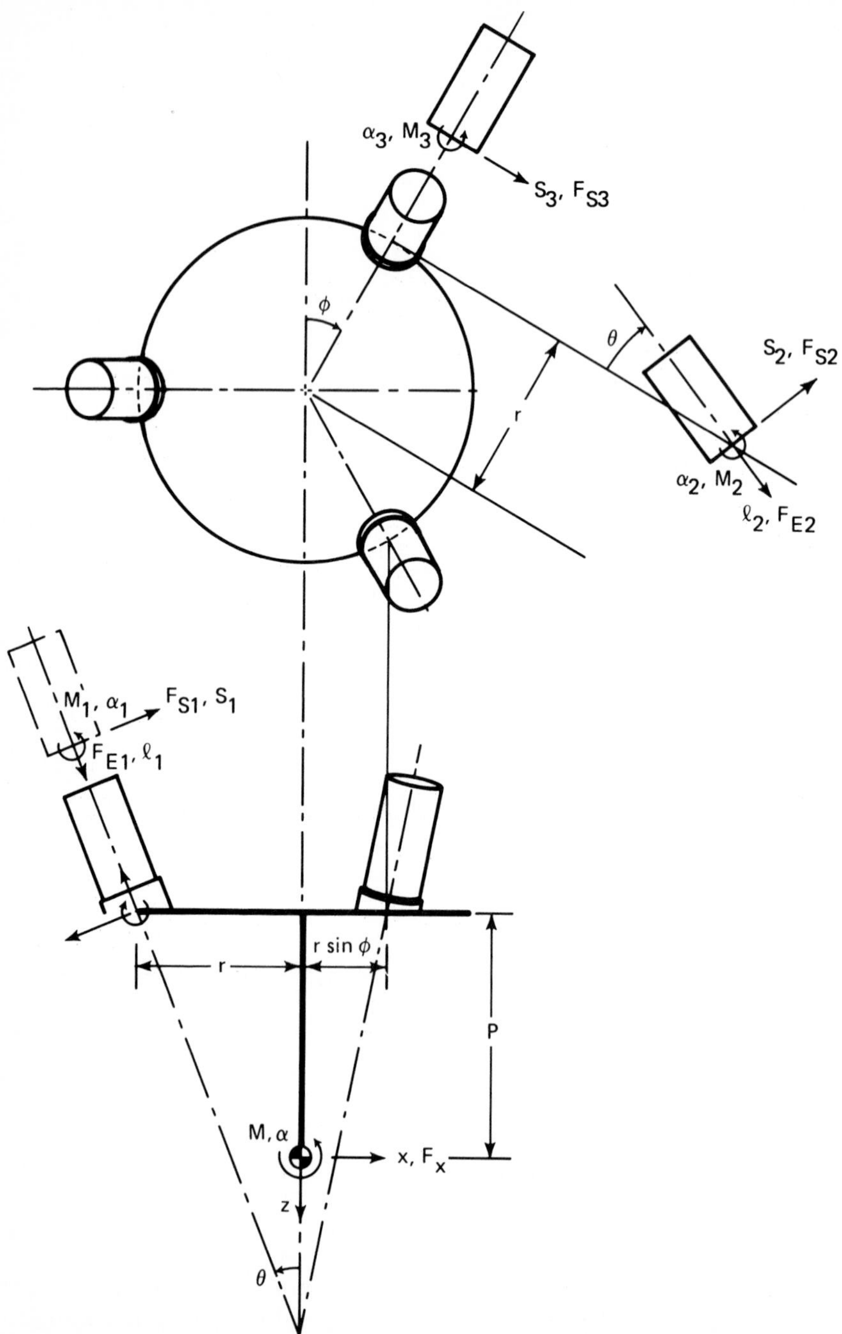

Fig. 7.12 Terminology for three-pad RCC analysis. When expressions are evaluated, $\phi = 30°$ is used.

TABLE 7.1

Parameter	Value (English)	Value (metric)
K_{ss}	15 lb/in	2.63 N/mm
K_E	2400 lb/in	420 N/mm
$K_{\alpha s}$	−11 lb/rad	− 49 N/rad
$K_{\alpha\alpha}$	30 in-lb/rad	3390 N-mm/rad
θ	0.12 rad	
r	1.125 in	28.575 mm
	Performance	
K_x	96 lb/in	16.85 N/mm
P	4.63 in	117.6 mm
K_α	2521 in-lb/rad	2.85×10^5 N-mm/rad

together with tools, to place the compliance center correctly. Economics encourage a tool changing robot to have its RCC inside the tool socket so that all tools share one RCC. All of the above approaches have been used. Exact coincidence of the compliance center and the tip of the peg is not necessary; tests have shown that location deviations of 50 to 100 percent of peg radius do not seriously degrade performance.

Assembly actions are not the only ones that can be aided by the error-absorbing properties of an RCC. Any mate between two items is a feasible candidate. Examples include mating a tool to its storage rack or to a robot tool socket, mating a part to its fixture, mating a gripper to a part, removing a casting from a mold, and so on.

Designers contemplating using the RCC should bear in mind the following limitations: (1) It is not designed to cope with the case where relative error is so large that the chamfers do not meet. (2) At present, commercial RCCs have a fixed compliance center location, although varying the location is possible. (3) If the RCC is to be used to perform insertions along a horizontal axis, some counterbalancing against gravity may be necessary. Also, there are limits to the amount of lateral and angular error that can be absorbed by an RCC of a given size because of the need to keep its internal stresses within design limits. Finally, the RCC can prevent jamming, but a priori control of initial errors is needed in order to prevent wedging.

Equipment with Which the RCC Can Be Used

The following examples are intended to illustrate, but not limit, the possible applications of the RCC. Examples are grouped into clearance fits, interference fits, tooling interfaces, and some speculative possibilities. Examples that have actually been verified at Draper Laboratory are marked with an asterisk (*).

Clearance fits

*Bearing into housing**. The bearings can be laterally displaced 2 mm (0.08 in) and still successfully enter a 40-mm (1.6-in) diameter hole with 0.01-mm (0.0004-in) clearance. One mm (0.04 in) of this lateral error is caused by tolerance stackups between the location of the hole and the location of jig points. During robot mating, engagement of chamfers and insertion occurs in 0.2 s (Nevins and Whitney, 1978).

*Shaft into bearing**. The shaft easily enters the bearing despite the existence of threads on the end of the shaft (see Fig. 7.13).

*Gear onto spline shaft**. Here the RCC's ability to comply about the insertion axis is utilized.

Rivet into hole. Here the holes may be imprecisely located, or the thin material containing them is variable in shape.

*Screw into threaded hole**. This is similar to plain peg and hole except that torsional stops on the RCC allow torque to be exerted on the screw.

Cover onto box. The RCC can mate rectangular cross-sections as well as circular ones. The amount of angular misalignment about

Fig. 7.13 Tool-changing robot wrist with RCC inserting rotor shaft of automobile alternator into bearing.

the insertion axis must be controlled so that chamfers on the cover and box engage.

Rivet tool over rivet head. The RCC allows mating to a convex part, too. Similarly, donut onto peg can be performed.

Forging into die. Rough forgings are of unpredictable shape. Often they can be dropped into the die and will land correctly. If they land incorrectly, the die may be destroyed during forging. If one depends on hidden float, the forging may not seat firmly. The RCC will permit the forging to nestle into place.

Unmachined side of casting onto pallet locating pins.* The casting may be grasped on a machined surface, but the pins will mate with unmachined surfaces whose location is uncertain. The RCC will absorb the difference.

Precise assembly of delicate parts.* The errors will be quite small here but so are the clearances. The parts are fragile and have easily spoiled surfaces. The RCC serves to guide them together while protecting them from jamming and large contact forces. Figure 7.14 shows a manually operated inserter based on this idea.

Interference fits

Nozzle into housing.* The nozzle is brass, about 3 mm (0.12 in) in diameter by 5 mm (0.2 in) long. The housing is aluminum. The interference is about 0.02 mm (0.0008 in). The hole in the housing can be improperly located by as much as 0.5 mm (0.02 in), and rigid tooling tends to use the nozzle as a broach during insertion, ruining the assembly. Mounting the tool on an RCC solved the problem with no increase in insertion time (about 0.1 s; see Fig. 7.15).

Fig. 7.14 Manually operated inserter for precise assembly. The inserter contains an RCC, six-axis force-torque sensor and brake. Electronic controls activate the brake if insertion force exceeds a preset level.

Fig. 7.15 Inserter station for putting nozzles into housings. The insertion tool is pneumatically powered and exerts about 100 pounds (lb) insertion force.

Shaft into laminate stack of motor rotor. Essentially this is a force fit of a round peg into a round hole. The laminations must be supported to avoid peeling them apart. The RCC does not solve this part of the problem.

*Thread-rolling screws into untapped holes**. This is no different from screws into threaded holes.

Snap fit of sheet metal parts. Here it is important that the parts not be too compliant compared to the RCC or else they, and not the RCC, will bend in response to the contact force.

Tooling interfaces

*Tool into machine tool changer or tool into storage socket**. Here the RCC functions as in any clearance, light press or snap fit. Once the tool has been grasped by the machine, however, the RCC may have to be locked tight for the tool to function.

Tool onto guide pins. The pins may be on the fixture which holds the workpiece. The tool is seated on the pins and then is activated. The RCC helps the seating process and assures that no large hidden stresses build up in the tool, pins, or fixture. This helps reduce fixture wear.

Drill into drill bushing. Here the ability of the RCC to guide the drill into the bushing with little side force greatly reduces bushing wear. It also allows relatively imprecise drilling equipment to drill very precisely located holes.

*Tool onto part held in escapement**. The escapement may be at the end of a feeder track, from which the tool must pick up the part. The RCC allows for error in the angular and lateral location of the feeder, wear in the escapement, and part-to-part differences.

*Force sensor into contact with object**. Here the goal may be to perform force feedback assembly, to test for presence of a part, or to do an operation where the force exerted must be measured. If there is uncertainty as to the object's location or if the position resolution of the device carrying the sensor is coarse, forces larger than the sensor's operating limit may be encountered, and no meaningful readings will be obtained. This is especially likely if small forces are sought and a sensitive sensor is in use. The RCC acts as a multiaxis cushion, providing small forces in response to large displacements, keeping the exerted forces small and allowing them to be measured.

Possible, but speculative uses

Alignment of press, stamp, or mold dies. Alignment is provided by guide pins or rods, and the RCC holds half of the die as it engages the pins. This makes construction of the machine much easier since initial alignment of the separated die halves is not so critical.

Universal joint for laterally and angularly misaligned shafts. Torsional stops would, of course, be necessary.

Coupling space manipulators to precessing, rotating satellites to aid retrieving them.

Related concept

"Projected elastic center" technique for shock mounting machinery and aircraft engines. This concept has been a major product of Lord Corporation, Erie, Pa., for many years. It permits an engine to be held from the outside as though it were suspended from its center of mass.

Other RCC Applications in Manufacturing

The RCC can be used for assembly and material handling in conjunction with conventional powered workheads, manually operated workheads, industrial robots, and remote manipulators. The alignment, setup, and maintenance problems in such equipment are also eased.

Robot assembly is a most fruitful area for RCCs because the robot must reach to so many different places. The ability to absorb the errors at all these places with the same RCC makes setup of complex assembly stations easier and faster.

Patents

RCCs and several adaptations of them are covered by numerous U.S. and foreign patents. They are:

4098001	Remote Center Compliance System
4155169	Compliant Assembly System Device
4202107	Remote Axis Admittance System
4242017	Passive Mating System
4283153	Compliant Apparatus with Remote Smeared Centers
4337579	Deformable Remote Center Compliance Device
4355469	Folded Remote Center Compliance Device
4379363	Damped Remote Center Compliance Device
4400885	Locking System For a Remote Center Compliance Device
4414750	Single Stage RCC Device
4439926	Transferable Center Compliance System
4477975	Adjustable Remote Center Compliance Device
4485562	Variable Stiffness Remote Center Compliance Device
4537557	Remote Center Compliance Gripper System
4556203	Remote Center Compliance Device

Related Devices

A sensor has been designed using the RCC as the basis. Three to six displacement sensors operating on magnetic or optical principles are placed inside an RCC. These sensors report the relative displacements of the platforms. One can interpret these displacements in either of two ways. One can relate them to the lateral and angular displacements of the part as it is being assembled. Or one can combine the displacement with the known stiffnesses of the RCC and interpret the results as forces and torques exerted on the part at its tip. Thus the RCC can be made into a displacement or force sensor. A sensor-equipped RCC is called an "instrumented RCC" (IRCC) [see Watson (1982) and De Fazio, Seltzer, and Whitney (1984)].

A Strategy for Compliant Assembly

The RCC is a simple, inexpensive, and effective device for aiding mechanical assembly. It acts as a bridge between the assembly error requirements of parts and the accuracy and repeatability capabilities of assembly machines and robots. It is now routine for parts with clearance x to be assembled by RCC-equipped robots with resolution or accuracy worse than 100 times x. For parts that can withstand mild impacts, insertion times on the order of 100 milliseconds (ms) are typical. For delicate parts, the insertion speed must be slow, but that is usual for delicate parts anyway.

Let us consider how to use this capability to build a comprehensive approach to mechanical assembly. We stated in Chap. 5 that assembly would be a matter of mere geometry if there were not a variety of errors in shape, position, angle, trajectory, and so on. Even in the structured environment of a factory, we are faced with errors. Alternate approaches to eliminating or mitigating them may be grouped as follows:

1. Sensory-based methods that seek to remove error by detecting it in all its forms in real time and calculating corrective actions on the fly. A wide variety of circumstances can be accommodated but the resulting systems could well be slow and costly.
2. A priori methods that seek to eliminate the error sources in advance by controlling tolerances on all the elements of an assembly station, such as by precise design of parts, jigs, fixtures, and so on. The "advantage" is that the errors do not occur, but achieving this could be too costly or impossible.
3. Hybrids of the above in which errors are analyzed by source and either real-time or a priori methods are chosen to eliminate or accommodate them. The advantage is that one can make the best match of methods and needs, but a lot of thought and engineering may be needed.
4. A subset of the hybrid method in which real-time error removal is accomplished by compliant tooling, that is, by using an RCC. This approach will be cheaper and faster than actively controlled hands, fingers, robots, and so on.

At this point we have enough information to understand parts of the hybrid approach. This chapter and the ones before it tell how to predict the behavior of combinations of part size, entry surface shapes, clearance between parts, friction, part compliances, compliance of supports, compliance center locations, and amounts of lateral and angular error. Thus the problem in any one situation is to:

1. Determine how much error is likely to be encountered
2. Decide how to reduce the error enough so that the entry conditions

on wedging are met—perhaps by widening chamfers, adding lubricant, tightening part, jig, or gripper tolerances, adding a vision sensor, etc.—and note how much each will cost

3. Determine how much error will remain after reasonable effort has been expended in step 2
4. Decide how much force in the contact and insertion directions the parts can stand
5. Adjust the shapes of entry surfaces and the stiffnesses of the RCC so that actual forces developed at maximum remaining error conditions will not exceed the limits in step 4.

The computer programs included in prior chapters are useful for evaluating forces on parts during assembly given the initial errors and other physical parameters. In Chap. 11 we describe the mathematics necessary for predicting the error of an entire workstation plus strategies for making economic combinations of the error-control methods.

The essence of this strategy is illustrated in Fig. 7.16. Assembly consists of passing from the initial state (1) to a preassembly state (2), crossing the chamfer, and finally to an assembled state (3). State (2) is described by the wedging conditions. To successfully meet these con-

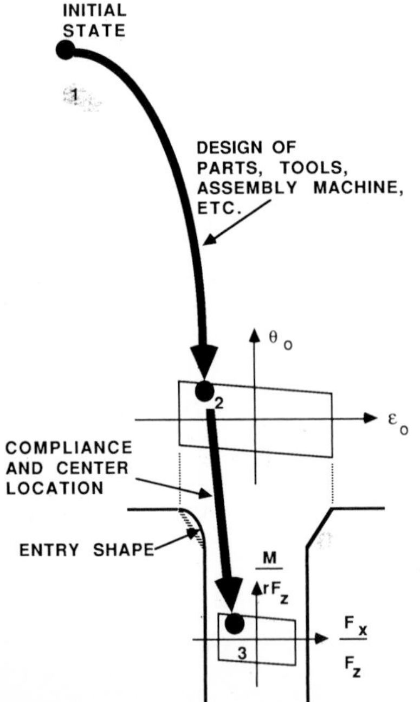

Fig. 7.16 A consistent assembly strategy. From state 1, achieve state 2 (ready to enter hole, avoiding wedging) by means of a priori error control, friction control, and part design. From state 2, achieve state 3 (fully assembled) by means of entry surface shape, compliance, and compliance center location.

ditions requires the proper combination of friction, compliance center location, initial lateral error ε_0, and initial angular error θ_0. Successful chamfer crossing requires careful design of the width, slope, and shape of the chamfer and the tip of the entering part. State (3) is described by the jamming conditions. To meet these conditions requires supporting the part correctly so that the right combination of forces and torques is exerted on it during two-point contact. Using an RCC and ensuring that the compliance center is at or near the tip of the entering part is the easiest way to accomplish this.

The clear implication is that, while we do not need a tool or robot of accuracy x to assemble parts of clearance x, we do need to consider a variety of issues—part design, assembly method, economics and so on—in order to resolve the issue intelligently. In particular, we need to carefully consider structuring the task, since this is central to the a priori approach. Sound engineering practice dictates that every advantage should be sought to use the environment of a task, including design of the parts themselves, to enhance the efficiency, reliability, and predictability of the task within economic feasibility.

References

De Fazio, T. L., D. S. Seltzer, and D. E. Whitney: "The Instrumented Remote Center Compliance," *The Industrial Robot,* Dec. 1984, pp. 238–242.

Drake, S. H.: "Using Compliance in Lieu of Sensory Feedback for Automatic Assembly," *IFAC Symposium of Information and Control Problems in Manufacturing Technology,* Tokyo, 1977.

———, and P. C. Watson: "Pedestal and Wrist Force Sensors for Industrial Assembly," *5th International Symposium on Industrial Robots,* Chicago, 1975.

Havlik, S.: "A New Elastic Structure for a Compliant Robot Wrist," *Robotica,* vol. 1, 1983, pp. 95–102.

Nevins, J. L., and D. E. Whitney: "Computer Controlled Assembly," *Scientific American,* vol. 238, no. 2, Feb. 1978, pp. 62–74.

Rebman, J.: "Compliance for Robotic Assembly Using Elastomeric Technology," proceedings, *5th International Symposium on Industrial Robots,* Washington, 1979.

Watson, P. C.: "A Multidimensional System Analysis of the Assembly Process as Performed by a Manipulator," proceedings, *1st North American Robot Conference,* Chicago, 1976.

———: U.S. Patent 4316329, "Instrumented Remote Center Compliance Device," 1982.

Whitney, D. E.: "The Mathematics of Coordinated Control of Prosthetic Arms and Remote Manipulators," *ASME Journal of Dynamic Systems, Measurement, and Control,* Dec. 1972, pp. 303–309.

———: "Force Feedback Control of Manipulator Fine Motions," *ASME Journal of Dynamic Systems, Measurement, and Control,* June 1977, pp. 91–97. Also U.S. Patent 4243923, "Servo-Controlled Mobility Device," by Daniel E. Whitney and James L. Nevins.

———: "Historical Perspective and State of the Art in Robot Force Control," *International Jouranal of Robotics Research,* vol. 6, no. 1, Spring 1987, pp. 3–14.

———, and J. M. Rourke: "Mechanical Behavior and Design Equations for Elastomer Shear Pad Remote Center Compliances," *ASME Journal of Dynamic Systems, Measurement, and Control,* Sept. 1986, pp. 223–232.

Chapter

8

The Strategic Approach to Product Design: The Basic Issues

Introduction

In this chapter, we describe in some detail, with examples, how the new concept of concurrent product design may be carried out. "Concurrent" means that the design of the product and its manufacturing system are carried out more or less simultaneously. Until recently, it was thought that at most it was necessary to consider only how each part was to be made. Now we know how important it is to consider pairs and groups of parts during design, that is, to consider assembly.

We in fact focus the entire concurrent design (CD) process on assembly itself because of the ability of assembly to force integration of many diverse and complex issues. Within assembly, we place emphasis on the design of an assembly sequence because sequence design raises specific problems that no other aspect of design raises.

As we describe this process, we will refer to particular techniques that are described in detail in later chapters. In addition, we will make clear the evolving nature of the intellectual base that underlies the process and show where new knowledge and techniques are emerging or are still needed.

Serial and integrated approaches to product-process design

Engineering schools teach a fairly straightforward version of how something is designed (see Fig. 8.1). Engineers are given a technically oriented view which emphasizes determining the need, preparing

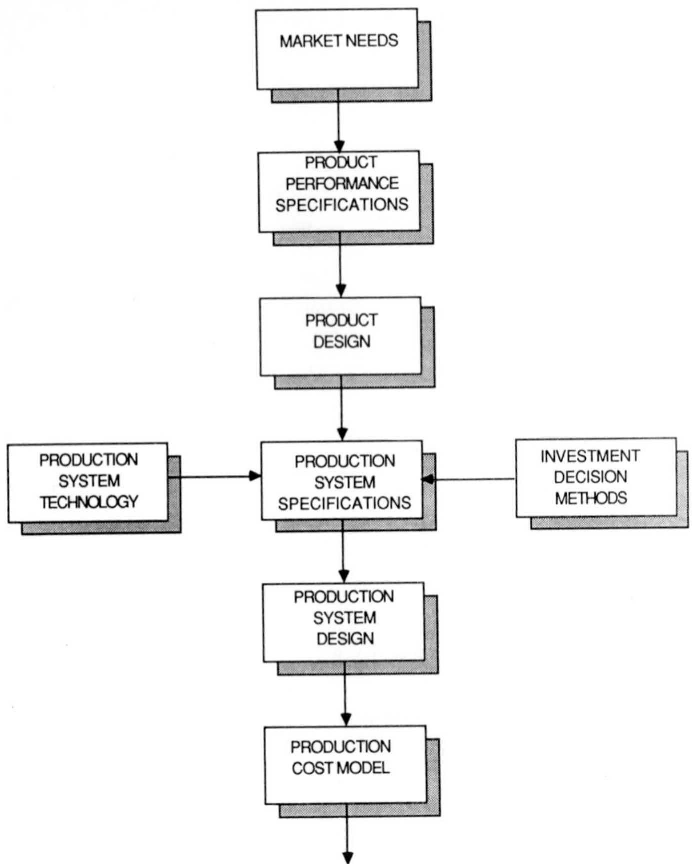

Fig. 8.1 The conventional product-process design method.

product specifications, and making trial designs, then prototypes for bench test, then final designs, then a manufacturing process plan. There is a good deal of feedback as problems are uncovered and resolved. But in the main the process is self-contained from need to final design, with little outside interference.

What's wrong with this method? It has too much linearity—need-design-make-sell. It is too technical. It is too compartmentalized, assuming that design is the domain of the designer, manufacturing the domain of the manufacturing engineer, purchasing the domain of the purchasing manager, and so on.

Consider, for example, the role of the Purchasing Department. The heart of a high-tech product we recently studied is an infrared detector. Purchasing switched to the lower cost of two detector vendors, with disastrous consequences for production. Subtle differences between detectors cannot be found until the product is partially assembled with optics, power supplies, and so on. For ruggedness and cost reasons, the unit is glued together, making disassembly to replace detectors very expensive. Naturally, the product could be redesigned to make detector replacement easier. But the product is a single-use weapon; its shelf life is several years, during which it is ignored because it is too complex for field repair; it must work the first time; its useful life is 10 s. Repair is simply not in character for this product.

The point is that a seemingly minor decision, made to optimize a corner of a company's operations, can have a pervasive effect on how a product is made or used, with severe consequences for operating costs or the customer's perception of the company. These decisions can completely defeat the designer's intentions. Top management, engineering, purchasing, personnel, and manufacturing can each contribute to the success or failure of a product.

On a deeper level, the linear method depicted in Fig. 8.1 cannot lead to truly producible products unless those products are rather simple. Converting a concept into a complex, high-technology product is an involved procedure consisting of many steps of refinement. The design requires a great deal of analysis, investigation of basic physical processes, experimental verification, complex trade-offs, and difficult decisions. The initial idea never quite works as intended or does not perform as well as desired. The designers must therefore make many modifications to the original concept. Along the way, they make increasingly subtle choices of materials, fasteners, coatings, adhesives, and electronic adjustments. Expensive analyses and experiments may be carried out to verify portions of the design. In many cases, the choices become more and more difficult as the design gradually works its way toward acceptability. Furthermore, the choices become more interdependent and take on the character of an interwoven historical chain in which later choices are conditioned or forced by ones made previously. The earlier decisions have the most influence on the later course of the design.

Imagine that a production engineer comes into this increasingly detailed debate late in the process and begins asking for changes. It is likely that, if the product designers accede to these requests, a large portion of the design will simply unravel, and many difficult choices will have to be made all over again. Where some close calls went one way, they now may go another in view of the new criteria which the manufacturing engineer brings to the table. New analyses and experiments may be needed.

As an example, a research scientist at a large chemical company spent a year perfecting a process at laboratory scale. His process operated at atmospheric pressure. When a production engineer was called in to scale it up, he immediately asked for higher pressures because atmospheric pressure would require huge pipes, pumps, and tanks. Unfortunately, the researcher's process failed at elevated pressures and he had to start over.

In other cases, the production engineer's requests might not be possible to grant, resulting in an awkward or unrobust process. We worked on a product that contained delicate spinning parts that had to be dynamically balanced to high tolerances. Because of the design, the rotating elements had to be partially disassembled after balancing in order to finish the assembly. The result was that the final assembly was not well enough balanced, requiring a lengthy adjustment procedure. Only a fundamental redesign of the whole product would have eliminated this awkward step. Since total redesign was not an option, we analyzed the uncertainty in reassembly from the point of view of restoring balance and recommended tightening some tolerances and reshaping certain part-mating surfaces to minimize the problem. Simple adjustments were then sufficient to restore balance to within the desired tolerances.

How can problems like this be avoided? If manufacturing engineers are participants in the design debate from the start, their criteria can be given weight as the difficult choices are being made, and the design process could turn out differently. If repair engineers, purchasing agents, and other knowledgeable people are represented, a better, more integrated design will result on the basis of a similar debate. Again, the design would represent an interconnected web of decisions, but more parties would make the web better balanced.

There is at present no perfected method for designing products so that all of the constituencies can have their say, much less get everything they want. It is unlikely that any such method will ever exist. There will always be trade-offs and compromises between the designer who asks "What good is it if it doesn't work?," the production engineer who asks "What good is it if I can't make it?," the marketer who asks "How can I sell it if it costs too much?"

The approach taken in this book to address this problem is to describe a methodology comprising specific steps which are supported at several points by computer algorithms. The essence of the approach is to increase the quality of the influential early decisions by making more downstream consequences of these decisions known to the designers. Such consequences include product function predictions, estimates of fabrication and assembly costs, concept designs of fabrication and assembly systems and equipment, methods of testing, and so on. Our main way to force early decisions into prominence is to emphasize assembly processes in early design. The integrative nature of assembly seems to be a powerful force in raising the level of integration in all aspects of early product design. Other typical product design methodologies tend to leave assembly to later in the process. As experience with integrated product-process design grows, the methodology will be modified, will improve, and more opportunities for computer aids will be recognized.

At the present, the state of the art in CD is the team approach. The methods being used by competitive companies vary according to their traditions and experience, but they share attributes with the procedure shown in Fig. 8.2. This diagram emphasizes the degree to which decisions made by the different parties affect each other's activities and alter the product's design. No single designer can have all the knowledge needed to carry out such a comprehensive activity alone. Neither do we have superintelligent computer programs that can design products and manufacturing processes. For the time being, at least, we must rely on teams of specialists to pool their knowledge to create superior products and manufacturing systems.

Engineers are taught early on that design is an iterative process, but rarely are they taught about the iterations between design and

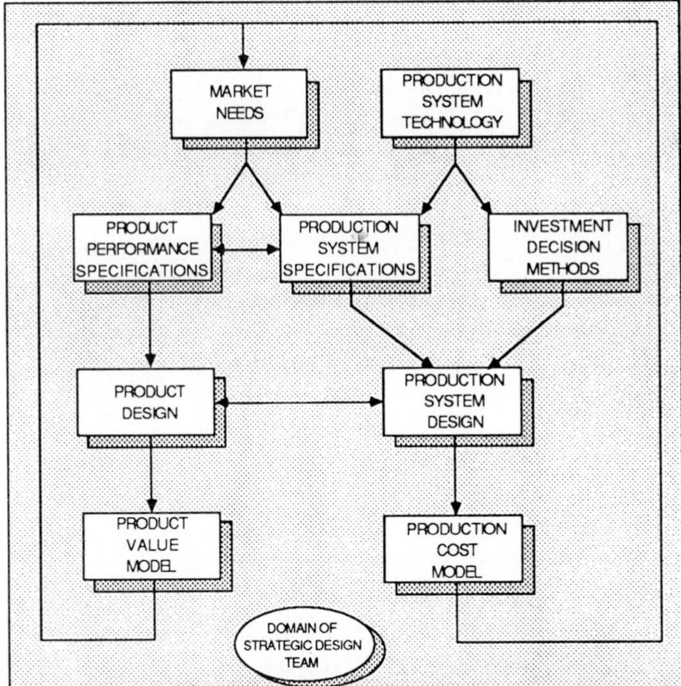

Fig. 8.2 The strategic method of product and production system design. Product and production system design proceed along parallel tracks and comprise coordinated activities: First specifications are established, then design occurs to meet the specifications, and finally both designs are evaluated and compared to the requirements.

production or between production and marketing. Perhaps this is the cause of the traditional time separation between product design and manufacturing system design. The real *concurrency* of concurrency team work cannot be overemphasized. It is not too early to begin the process before there are engineering prototypes, because the essence of a sophisticated design can depend on careful choice of tolerances, materials, or novel fabrication methods that cannot be separated from the design of the manufacturing process.

Practical limitations to integrated product-process design

Notwithstanding the advantages of using CD, it can be difficult to convince people to carry it through. Not only is this true when a new product is being designed, when there may be a true struggle to achieve function, but it is also true for an existing product where the designers do not wish to disturb the level of function they have achieved.

Two classes of limitations, engineering and institutional, may degrade the ideal of integrated product-process design. Engineering limitations include the fact that certain decisions cannot be made until others have been. Institutional limitations include the large size of typical companies and the difficulty of coordinating the activities of the many people involved in the design of complex products. Other institutional difficulties include ingrained habits and training of engineers and managers and the lack of experience in participating in or managing teams. Finally there is the paradox that early decisions, while extremely influential, do not themselves constitute a costly activity, so it can be difficult to convince managers that they are important.

Many very different activities are performed by many people who carry a design concept from recognition of the need to start of manufacture. Figure 8.3 represents this process along with certain precedences that typically must be observed. Some functions cannot begin until others have been considered and at least preliminary results are available. It is not the purpose of CD to ignore or obviate these precedences but rather to organize the flow of debate and decisions so that the impact of decisions, especially the influential early ones, is understood by all constituencies. It is especially important that people whose decisions come *later* in the process are involved in the decisions that come *earlier*.

Perhaps because of both these precedences and the organizational requirements of large companies, the strict sequential method of carrying out these steps has evolved. Often this is called "throwing the design over the wall."

MANAGEMENT	DESIGN ENGINEERING		MANUFACTURING ENGINEERING		QUALITY CONTROL
DETERMINE MARKET NEED:	PRELIMINARY DESIGN	DETAIL DESIGN	MANUFACTURING PLAN	ASSEMBLY PLAN	TEST AND INSPECTION PLAN
DESCRIPTION PERFORMANCE COST QUANTITY DESIGN SCHEDULE PRODUCTION SCHEDULE	TECHNIQUE PHYSICAL PRINCIPLES AND LAYOUT ENERGY STORAGE AND TRANSMISSION LOAD BEARING SIZES, DIAMETERS, LENGTHS SPEEDS CRITICAL MATERIALS MAJOR COMPONENTS VOLTAGES, PRESSURES, FLOWS	LAYOUT DETAILS TOLERANCES PITCHES DRAFTS CHAMFERS MATERIALS FINISHES FASTENERS SEALS CIRCUIT COMPONENTS	MAKE/BUY MFR EQUIPMENT VENDOR CHOICES MFR LOCATION SHIFTS LABOR, TRAINING	IN-HOUSE OR OUT ASSY METHODS SHIFTS LABOR, TRAINING	WHAT TO CHECK HOW TO CHECK WHEN TO CHECK

GENERAL PRECEDENCE OF DESIGN DECISIONS

Fig. 8.3 Precedence of decisions in product-process design.

The functions of marketing, design engineering, manufacturing engineering, quality control, and so on describe organizational boundaries and involve many people. Even if the people in the various departments have similar technical backgrounds, they are likely to think and work differently. Making them work together on a team can be a challenge. There is at present no consensus on such matters as how many teams one person should be a member of at one time, how far into the design process a team should remain active, or how to improve a team that does not function well.

Moreover, major choices of fabrication or assembly technology often hinge on design details; quality problems or the need to include a particular test or check in the process hinges on details of the manufacturing or assembly method, or on details about a part's design. The feasible assembly methods for a key assembly step, whether manual or automated, can depend on the choice between a roll pin, snap ring, press fit, or set screw. The ability of a seal to stop leaks depends on details of geometry, tolerances and finishes associated with the installation and seating of the seal, the details of the assembly sequence, and path the seal traverses while being installed, including the possibility of damaging it, and so on. The point is that not only do design, manufacturing, and quality interact but they do so at extremely detailed levels extending over the entire design. A great deal of attention and persistence and a willingness to consider details and negotiate over them is required to make the CD process succeed. Naturally, these details are important and present if the serial design method is used, but resolving them is likely to be difficult, costly, time consuming, or impossible.

Steps in the Strategic Approach to Product Design

To bring some structure to a detailed description of strategic design, the following breakdown of topics is used in this chapter:

1. Determining the character of the product to see what kind of product it is and thus what design and production methods are appropriate.
2. Subjecting the product to a product function analysis so that the design can be made rationally.
3. Carrying out a design for producibility and usability study to determine if its producibility and usability can be improved without impairing its desired functions.
4. Designing a fabrication and assembly process for the product that takes account of its character. This involves creating a suitable as-

sembly sequence, identifying subassemblies, integrating a quality control strategy with assembly, and designing each part so that its functional tolerances and tooling tolerances (gripping and jigging surfaces) are compatible with the assembly method and sequence and its fabrication cost is compatible with the product's cost goals.

5. Designing a factory system that fully involves the production workers in the production strategy, operates on minimum inventory, and is integrated with the methods and capabilities of the vendors.

Creative design, while an essential step, is not mentioned because it is outside the scope of this book.

Figure 8.4 sketches the activities of the CD team and shows how the activities interact. The main targets of the team are:

- Convert the product concept into a manufacturable, salable, usable product design by clearly articulating all the associated goals, expectations, and constraints (often called constraint-based design)
- Anticipate fabrication and assembly methods and problems
- Simplify the design, fabrication, use, and repair by, for example:
  - Reducing the number of parts
  - Identifying and increasing the number of parts common to different models while decreasing the number of parts that are unique to one model
  - Identifying subassemblies (or single parts) within the product that contain the major differences between models so that model mix production can be obtained by substituting one well-defined subassembly for another
  - Standardizing types of fasteners or their sizes or creating a hierarchy of fastening methods, with expensive reversible ones like screws where the user makes adjustments or changes and low-cost irreversible or specialized ones like glue or rivets where only a skilled service person should work
- Improve the robustness of product and process by, for example:
  - Identifying process steps which, because of design or process choices, are difficult, likely to require high skill, or whose outcome is uncertain so that process times and costs cannot be predicted accurately
  - Designing the product within the capabilities of existing or reasonably anticipated processes and facilities so that product yield will be high [the essence of the Taguchi method (Taguchi and Byrne, 1986)]
  - Breaking product and processes into self-contained modules, designed to meet clear functional specifications, that can each be

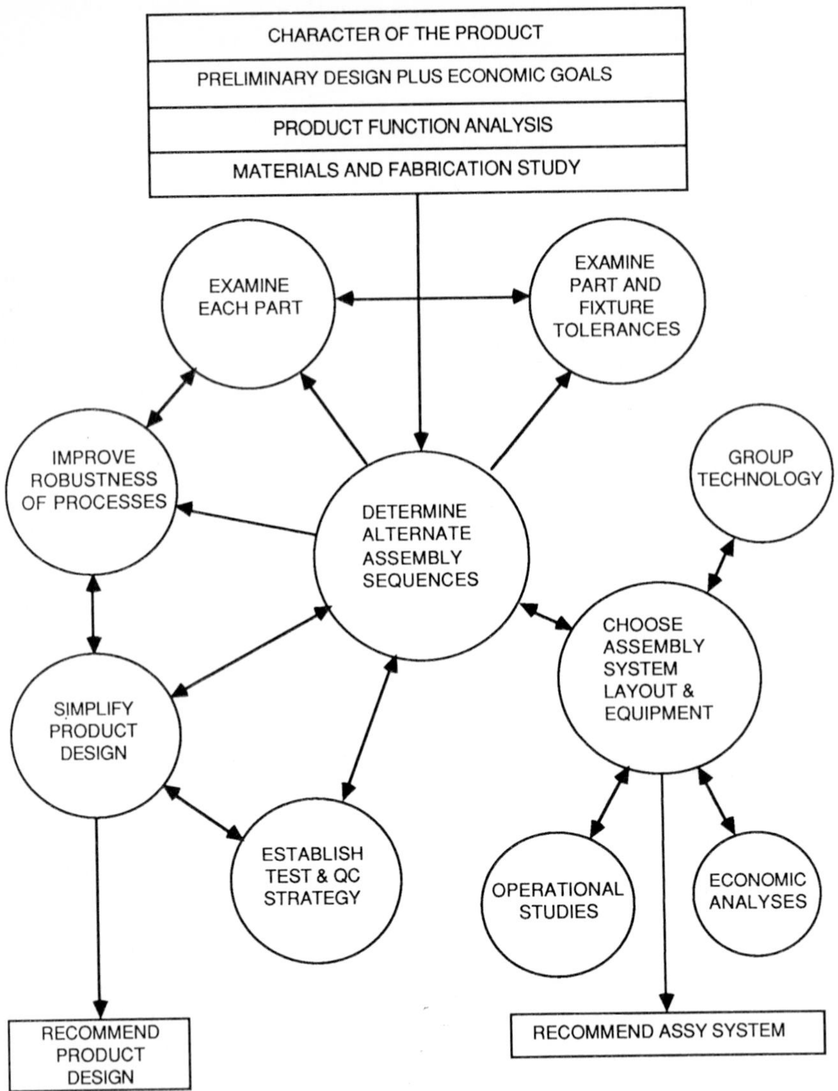

Fig. 8.4 Activities of the CD team.

bought or built on its own line and tested for proper function before being added to the final assembly
  - Adjusting tolerances to eliminate chance failures during assembly
  - Identifying places where tests can be made

- Making assembly easier by:
  - Designing the product and each module so that assembly is possible without turning the item over during assembly

- Designing each part so that it is easy to feed to the assembly station and easy to insert

The next few sections of the chapter consider these activities in more detail.

The character of a product

The story of the single-use weapon introduced the idea of a product's character. By this we mean basic features of how the product will be made, sold, and used. There is an endless list of possible characters. Here are two, together with their consequences for product design and production method:

Character	Consequence
Complex item, no model mix, used by untrained people, must have 100 percent reliability, used once, thrown away (hand grenade, fire extinguisher)	Make high-quality parts, glue or weld them together, don't try to fix it after manufacture
Complex item, model mix and customer options, used by untrained people, lasts for years (motorcycle, sewing machine)	Make high-quality parts, screw them together, provide replacement parts and field repair service

The character is the basis for forming the strategy of design and production. This strategy will help everyone involved in the design make the necessary decisions, since they can compare alternate choices to see which ones support the strategy or are consistent with the character and which are not. Failure to define the character and communicate it to all the designers can result in irrational products.

Naturally, the product's character depends on nonmanufacturing factors such as marketing, finance, relationships with dealers, and so on, which are beyond the scope of this book. The following sections deal with product design as it applies to production and direct use of the product. This limitation of the book's focus does not diminish the importance of these other factors.

Product function analysis

The full potential of CD cannot be realized until team members fully understand how the product is supposed to work and be used. They achieve this understanding through product function analysis. The manufacturing and purchasing personnel must be fully involved in this activity so that they will be able to make meaningful contributions in the next phase, the producibility-usability study.

The product designers may not appreciate the value of including these other constituencies in their previously private domain of design, but they will be pleased later by the higher quality of the other people's suggestions. These suggestions will be formulated with full knowledge of the product designers' constraints and goals, saving the designers valuable time explaining why they did as they did. The credibility of the manufacturing and purchasing people in the eyes of the product designers will be greatly enhanced, improving the chances that their concerns will receive a fair hearing.

Once the product's character has been defined, at least provisionally, true product design can begin. Product function analysis is an activity in which designers and engineers seek ways of simplifying or rationalizing a product's design by starting from what it *should do* rather than how it does it *now* or did in previous designs or was considered during early concept design.

We recently saved a client several million dollars a year by eliminating *one part* from a subassembly. This product has three operating states, called low, medium, and high. It happened that, in the original design, five parts were involved in setting the state. Analysis of the design showed that the actions of one of these parts always followed or imitated the actions of two other parts. The redundant part was eliminated by slightly altering the shapes of the other two parts. All three states are still attainable.

Although a mechanical engineer came up with the new design, an electrical engineer did the analysis that revealed the extra part. He recognized the similarity between the multiple discrete states of this product and typical electric logic circuits. Electrical engineers are taught methods of simplifying such circuits, reducing the number of components while retaining the functions. This example thus shows an additional feature of team dynamics, namely the great benefit of having different technical backgrounds represented on the team.

We have included this example in the section called "Product Function Analysis" because the engineers had to understand how the product was intended to work before they could make the redesign. That is, while the story seems on the surface to be about product simplification, achieving this simplification required more than the usual application of design guidelines. Typical guidelines for simplification do not consider the overall function of the product but rely instead on rules that apply either without regard to function or in terms of the function of only a few contacting parts.[1]

---

[1] For example, a part is a candidate for elimination if (1) it does not move relative to adjacent parts, (2) does not have to be a different material, or (3) does not have to be separated from them to aid assembly or use of the product. (Boothroyd and Dewhurst, 1985).

Regardless of the technical aspects of this story, it is important to ask how come this company made the product for *X* years with an unnecessary part, and how much did it cost them to do so? One should also note that no automation or capital improvement proposals we anticipate for this product have the faintest chance of saving as much money as the elimination of that part.

The above example illustrates the effect on the manufacturing process of making design changes. In some cases, however, the process heavily conditions or even *is* the design. Here are two examples:

1. A complex electro-optical-mechanical product must be made in moderate quantities for a very low price. Yet it contains several precision parts and will not work unless some very close tolerances are achieved. Normally this would be impossible at such a low price, but here an ingenious approach has succeeded. The parts are made to medium tolerances and the mechanical errors are removed after assembly by totally electronic adjustments. To accomplish this required a complete change in design philosophy.
2. The Japanese have revolutionized shipbuilding. As discussed in Chap. 3, their philosophy is that design is a subset of production. That is, once a ship's functional characteristics have been determined and the outside shape, internal bracing, and propulsion method decided upon, much of the rest of the design is determined by how it will be built. In most products, the reverse is true; how it will be built is determined by its design.

Producibility-usability study

This is the stage where product and process designers do their most intense interacting, because here is where design modifications to suit producibility may impinge on function. It is quite difficult to generalize about approaches to this step. In particular, we have found it difficult to formulate rules or guidelines. As indicated in the examples in Chap. 3, commonly quoted rules are often broken once the advantages of doing so are understood.

Unlike a rule-driven process, design for producibility and usability is a top-down process. This means that the process is guided by the strategy developed for the product during the determination of its character. The distinction can be seen in many so-called examples of design for assembly, which are in fact just good (sometimes very good) reengineering of the product. Innovative engineers can always come up with "improvements." Without a guiding strategy, there is no way to tell which improvements really support the strategy and which merely look like improvements when considered in isolation.

Once we had a client whose complex consumer product was put together entirely with dozens of screws. Screws are among the most troublesome kinds of parts, and replacing screws with other kinds of fasteners—glue, rivets, bent tabs, force fits, and so on—can often save money and aggravation. We suggested that the client color code the screws on a drawing of the product as follows:

Red = any screw tightened by an assembler that is never loosened again

Orange = any screw that is tightened by an assembler but may be loosened and retightened during final adjustment

Yellow = any screw that might have to be loosened for repair

Green = any screw that the customer might have to loosen

We then predicted that most of the screws in this product would be red or orange and suggested that these should be the subject of intense redesign activity. The red ones could be replaced by any permanent alternative, like rivets or making the parts in one piece to begin with. The orange ones might be eliminated by providing other ways of doing the adjustments, assuming that there was a cost advantage and that the adjustment would not drift once it was set.

The point of this story is, of course, that decisions regarding fabrication or assembly method can affect users as well as factory personnel, field costs as well as factory costs. They are *design*, not manufacturing, decisions. Because they affect the character of the product, they are strategic in their impact. Because they jointly affect both producibility and usability, they should not be made according to one or the other factor alone. No one department should make these decisions, nor can the decisions be parcelled out for decentralized action.

In another case, we determined that the disassembly sequence for repair of a product should not be the reverse of the factory assembly sequence. In fact, if the factory sequence were merely reversed, the repair person risked injury. The design was therefore modified so that only a safe repair disassembly sequence could be used.

Like the other steps in CD, this step is not without its difficulties. The manufacturing people work under some disadvantages compared to the product design people. First, product function naturally has first place, so production people make little progress unless they can show either no effect on function or, best of all, an improvement, possibly related to quality. Second, product designers have the advantage of many well-developed computer tools to aid their design studies and give weight to their arguments, whereas the manufacturing people often have only hunches or experience. The algorithms in this book are a beginning toward redressing this imbalance.

Third, and perhaps inherent in the process, designers can consider, model, react to, and predict the functional results and effects of many proposed design changes more quickly than manufacturing, assembly, or quality control people can predict the producibility impacts. The disciplines designers depend on are well developed and accurate, and it is typical that small configurational changes lead to small functional changes. For example, reversing the direction in which screws hold two parts together is transparent to function. However, such a minor change sends shock waves through assembly analysis since the assembly sequence may now require the product to be turned over to gain access to the screws. Days or weeks of work designing the assembly system and predicting assembly costs must be redone. Not only must the line balance and floor layout be redesigned but even the choice of assembly technology and method of testing the product are affected.

Assembly processes

The CD team must also address assembly processes. Among the most important activities are:

1. Establishment of an assembly sequence
2. Division of the product into subassemblies
3. Selection of an assembly method for each step
4. Integration of a quality control strategy
5. Economic analysis and choice of assembly method

There is no set order in which to consider these activities, since the choices interact, and making them may trigger more design changes. We will take up items 1 and 2 together first. (Throughout the next several sections, the reader should use Fig. 8.5 to help visualize the interactions of the activities being discussed.)

Determining the assembly sequence. Choice of assembly sequence and identification of subassemblies focus attention on so many aspects of product design that they provide a natural launch pad for integrative detailed design. Assembly sequence studies require identification of potential jigging and gripping surfaces, grip and assembly forces, clearances and tolerances, and other issues that must be accounted for in piece part design. It is significant that these issues were not considered important when manual assembly was used. They are most relevant to machine assembly.

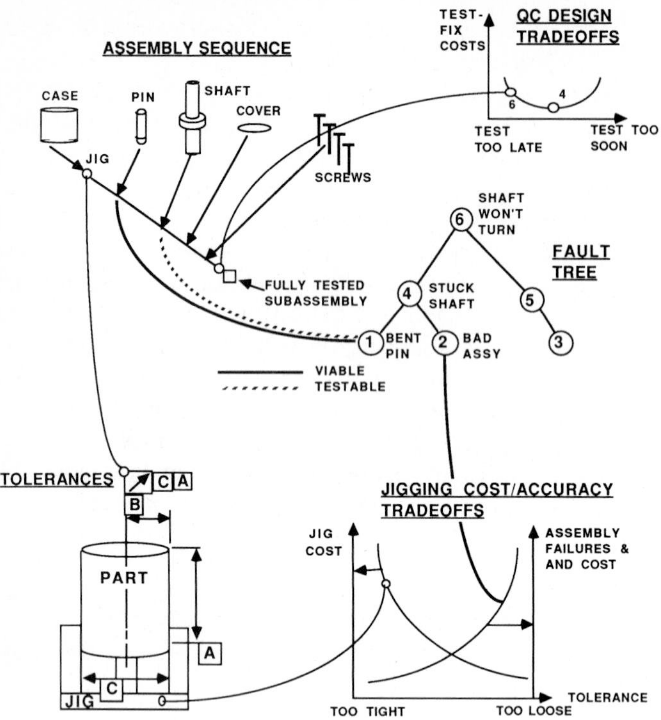

Fig. 8.5 Schematic of the interactions between assembly sequence, tolerances, and quality control. Upper left: An *assembly sequence* for a hypothetical product. The case is first, then the pin, shaft, cover, and screws. If the pin is bent, the shaft will not turn. The fault is viable as soon as the bent pin is installed, but it cannot be tested until the shaft is installed and a turn test is attempted. The *fault tree* shows that a stuck shaft could be caused by either a bent pin or a bad job of assembly. Upper right: The *QC design trade-off*. If we test at step 6, near final assembly, we will have a hard time distinguishing all the causes of "shaft won't turn." If we test too soon, we may not observe all the faults that are viable at that time. Either test point may cost more than testing at step 4, when we can tell why the shaft is stuck with one additional test, such as an attempt at reassembly. Lower left: A possible cause for bad assembly is inaccurate *jigging* caused by poor *tolerances* on those portions of the parts that mate with the fixtures. Correct tolerances relate those jigging surfaces to the mating surfaces, in this case the centerline that describes the orientation of the hole that the shaft will be inserted into. Lower right: As with QC design, there are trade-offs in tolerancing. Tolerances that are too tight raise part and jig fabrication costs, whereas tolerances that are too loose will increase the likelihood of assembly failures.

Imagine a hypothetical product of six parts. We can build it many ways, among them bottom up, top down, or from three subassemblies of two parts each. What makes any way better than the others?

There are construction reasons, such as access to fasteners or lubrication points. Similar considerations apply to ease of assembly, since some sequences may include some tricky part mates whose success may be doubtful or whose failure might damage some parts.

There are quality control reasons, such as the ability to test the function of a subassembly or the avoidance of a sequence that installs fragile parts early in the process. Some sequences might not offer the opportunity to test some function until it is buried beneath many other parts, making rework expensive.

There are process reasons. Some sequences may not allow a part to be jigged or gripped from an accurately made surface, making assembly success doubtful. Some sequences may require many unproductive moves, such as fixture or tool changes or the need to flip a subassembly over. Flipovers may be unavoidable, but some sequences may require flipping before the subassembly is fully fastened together, risking the possibility that it will disassemble spontaneously unless extra fixtures are provided. Additionally, flipovers may be easy for people but difficult, awkward, or costly for machines because of extra axes and controls needed. Thus a sequence without flips may be sought if automatic assembly is a goal. Product redesign may be necessary to permit such a sequence.

Finally, there are production strategy reasons, such as being able to make some subassemblies to stock, since they are common to many models, so that final assembly to order can be done quickly on only the remaining parts.

These points are illustrated by the automobile alternator shown in Fig. 8.6. The figure shows three different assembly sequences. Sequences 1 and 2 build the product right side up, while 3 builds it upside down. Sequences 2 and 3 use a subassembly. Many other sequences are possible, and the reader is invited to think some up.

Figure 8.7 shows the great differences that can exist between an assembly sequence for people and one for a machine. The product is an igniter for an explosively activated product, which is an emergency splice for high-voltage power lines. The igniter contains a small amount of gunpowder which is set off electrically by heating a thin fuse wire to incandescence. The small explosion is directed at a larger charge which then explodes, activating the product. Note in particular the way in which the fuse wire must be bent around the ends of the housing mid-way through assembly.

Figure 8.8 shows the existing manual assembly sequence. The only tools are wire cutters and a small press for the tight fits.

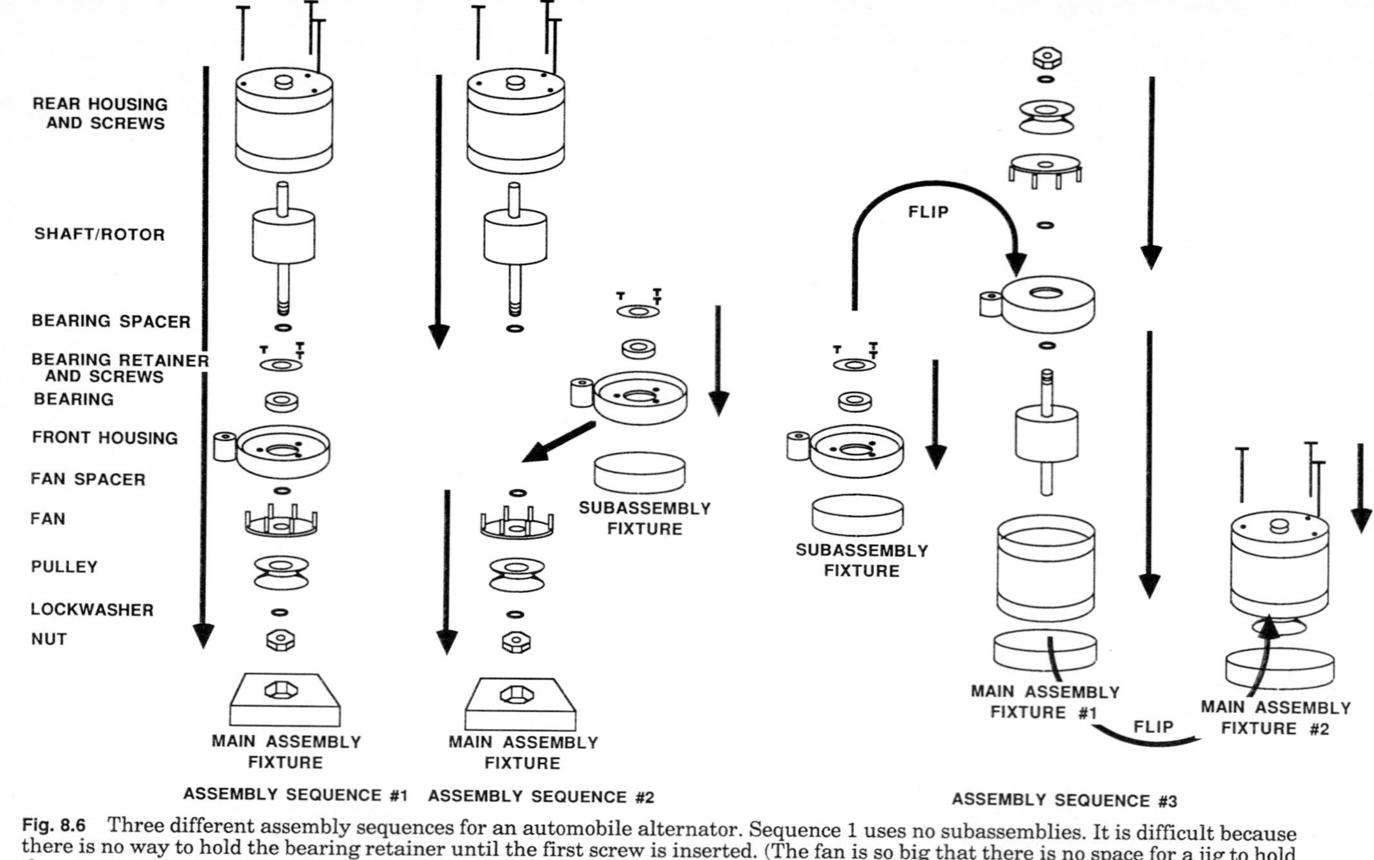

Fig. 8.6 Three different assembly sequences for an automobile alternator. Sequence 1 uses no subassemblies. It is difficult because there is no way to hold the bearing retainer until the first screw is inserted. (The fan is so big that there is no space for a jig to hold the retainer.) Sequence 2 solves this problem by building the front housing as a subassembly on a fixture that contains brackets to hold the retainer. Sequence 3 follows the rule that one should begin the sequence with a large base part. However, this sequence requires two flipovers. The second flip involves an unstable subassembly.

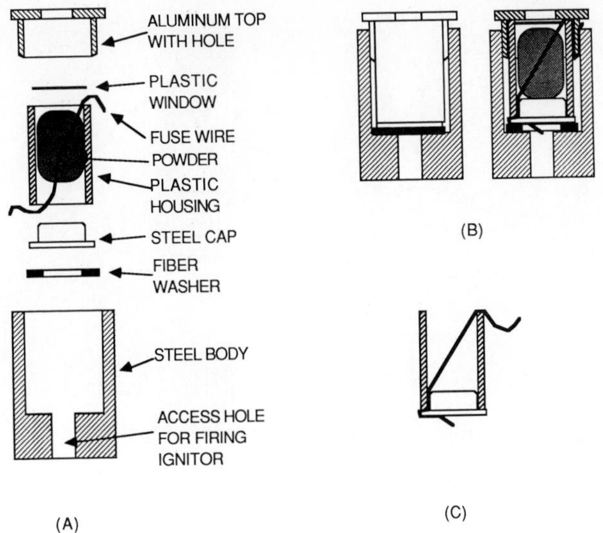

Fig. 8.7 (*a*) Parts of the igniter. The igniter is about the size and shape of a spool of thread. Assembly is entirely done by interference fits. The gunpowder poses some danger to people until assembly is complete. (*b*) The ingiter fully assembled. Because the housing and washer are insulators, the top end of the wire is in electrical contact with metal but the bottom end is not. To fire the igniter, one puts an electrical probe through the hole in the body, touching the cap and completing the circuit. The fuse wire ignites the powder, which blows the plastic window out and explodes through the hole in the top, igniting a larger charge of powder on the other side. (*c*) Partially assembled igniter. This illustration shows how the wire must be bent around the housing part way through assembly so that it will contact the cap and top properly.

The challenge of automating this assembly is to deal with the wire. The manual methods require two hands, and automating this robotically would require a research project to re-create the two-hand coordination. Other than this barrier, the parts are light, well-provided with chamfers, and generally easy to assemble.

The approach taken is to completely redesign the assembly sequence, moving some late steps to the front and holding some parts upside down in comparison to the manual method. Figure 8.9(*a*) and (*b*) shows the result. It can be mechanized with very simple fixed-stop robots or fixed-sequence automatic machinery.

Comment. In traditional industrial engineering, a major influence on choice of assembly sequence is line balance. Relevant to manual assembly, line balance means that each worker's total task time per cycle is as close to that of the other workers as possible. To achieve line

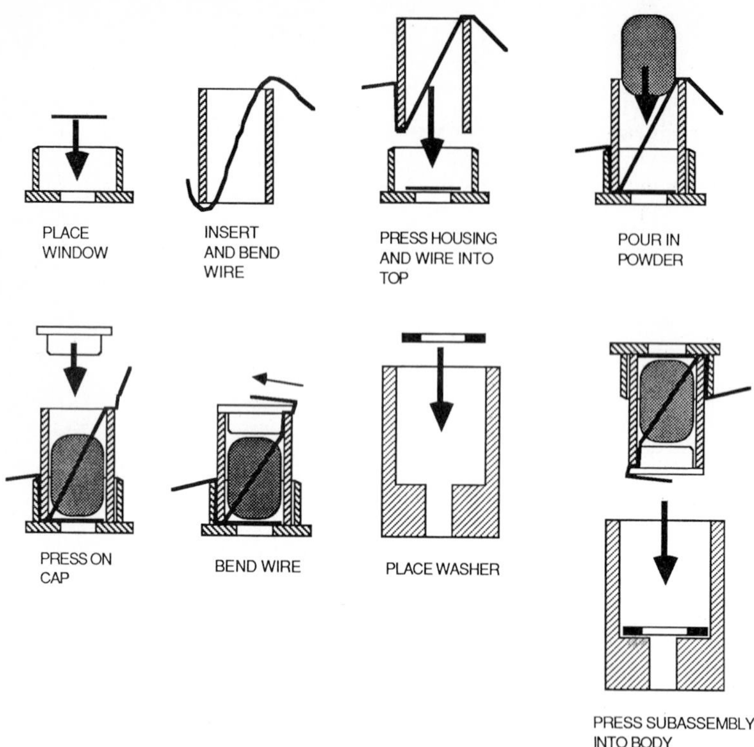

Fig. 8.8 Manual assembly sequence for the igniter. The assembly is accomplished entirely by hand except for wire cutters and presses.

balance, the industrial engineer sequences and groups the tasks and assigns the groups to the workers. It should be clear from the above discussion that much broader issues can be brought to bear on such choices, ranging from testing options to market strategy. It should also be clear that a sequence that is good for human workers may be totally irrelevant for machines, whose strengths and weaknesses are totally different from those of people.

Generating assembly sequences. We have discussed above the importance of having a good assembly sequence. To do so requires that we can generate alternatives and then evaluate them in some rational way.

This is not a trivial problem. In the past, we generated assembly sequences almost literally by hand, using either real parts of the product if available or cutouts of drawings of the parts if not. This cumbersome process rarely led to a large set of alternatives from which to choose. On the other hand, we can show that the maximum number of sequences is very large, and different sequences can be totally different in character from each other. Some will involve heavy use of subassemblies, while others will have none but will begin with different first parts. The extreme difference between alternate assembly sequences and the great differences in resulting assembly time, usable methods, and floor layouts offer great incentive to the manufacturing

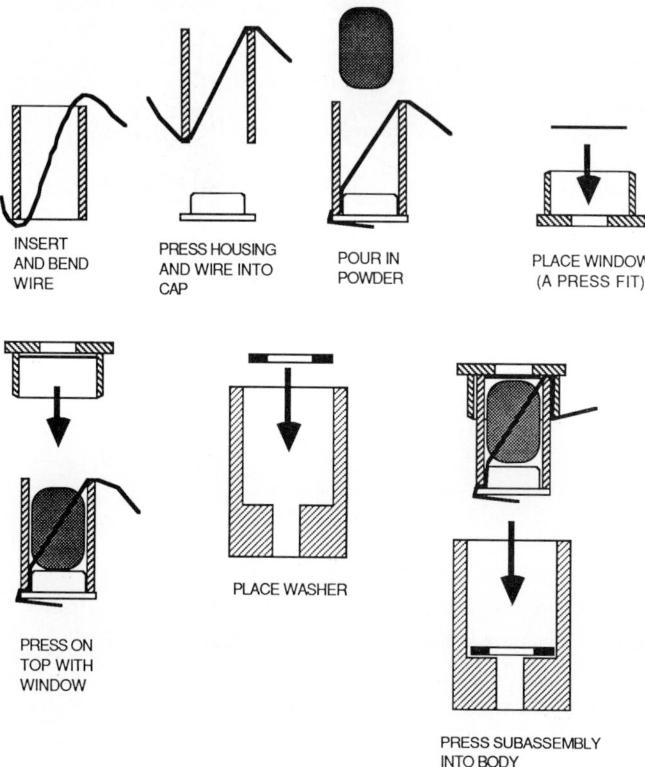

Fig. 8.9 (*a*) Igniter assembly sequence for automatic assembly. Note the differences from the manual sequence. (1) To convert the assembly method so that the wire could be inserted mechanically into the housing, a kinematic inversion was used. In the manual method, the housing is kept more or less stationary while the wire is maneuvered around. In the mechanized version, the wire is kept more or less stationary while the housing is maneuvered. The mechanized method also depends on the ability of the wire to stay bent without being held in shape by jigs or fixtures. (2) In the mechanized sequence, the cap is put on first, with the top being put on later. Since the top is face down, the window is redesigned to be a press fit into the top so it will not fall out during assembly. In the manual sequence, the window was simply dropped into the top and it was joined to the housing before the cap was. The reader is invited to think up other ways of mechanizing this assembly, including other sequences.

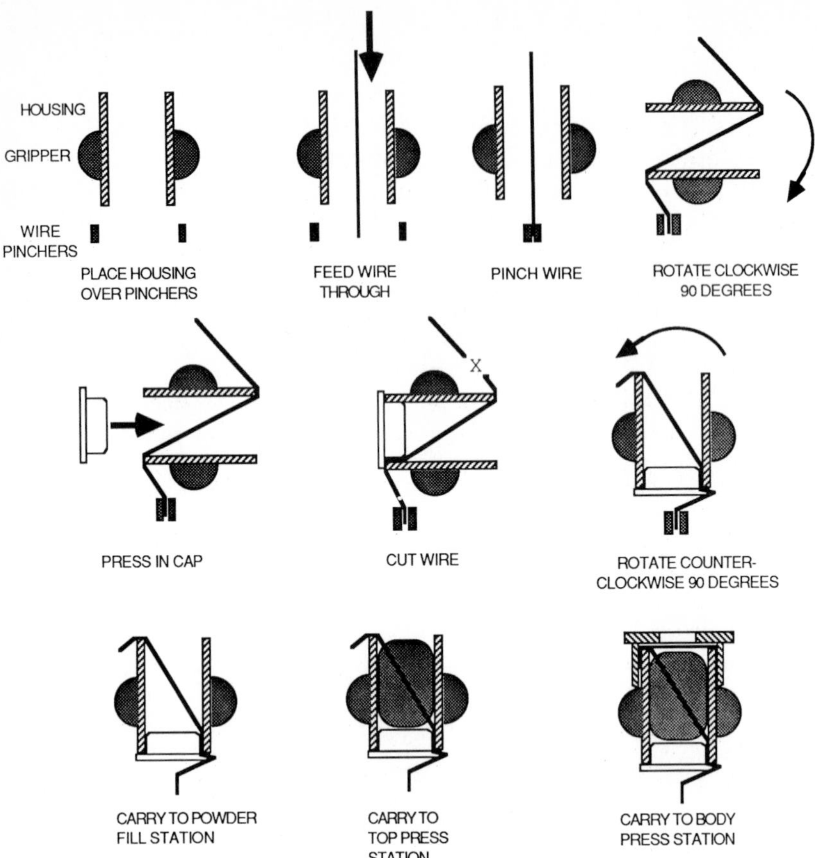

Fig. 8.9 (*b*). Schematic of how automatic assembly is done. This is a concept that has never been tested. It depends on wire-handling equipment and grippers that can make precise rotations and position changes. During the second rotation, it is useful to have the wire-feeding apparatus take up the slack in the wire. Equipment with these capabilities exists in industries that make electrical components. The concept here is also aided by the fact that the cap is steel so that a magnetic holder can place it into the housing at 90 degrees to vertical.

designer to be sure all the sequences are known so that a good choice can be made.

Traditionally, industrial engineers have used a drawing called a precedence diagram to represent the geometric and other constraints that limit how a product may be assembled. However, precedence diagrams do not themselves generate assembly sequences, and many real products cannot be represented by precedence diagrams. Furthermore, the methods used to create assembly sequences have traditionally been haphazard rather than algorithmic. Typically, the analyst starts with a rule, such as "begin with the base part," where "base part" is not rigorously defined but might be any part that is large or that will end up on the outside of the assembly or to which the most parts are added or that can be fixtured securely. One then begins exploring trees of assembly sequences from this root. The exploration resembles a chess game, with many dead ends that must be discovered one by one. A technique that guarantees generating all sequences is the disassembly method (Homem de Mello and Sanderson, 1986; Ko and Lee, 1987). In this method, one starts with the completed product and systematically disassembles it by every possible path. There is no possibility of dead ends by this method, but it is exhaustive and will become too cumbersome to use if there are more than a very few parts.

Based on prior work in Bourjault (1984) and De Fazio and Whitney (1988), we have created an algorithm that will enable an engineer to generate all of the physically possible assembly sequences for a product. The result is typically many hundreds or more sequences. We also have methods for reducing these to a manageable number of interesting sequences by applying judgment criteria such as how many subassemblies or flipovers are required. This algorithm is described in more detail in Chap. 9.

The influence of assembly sequence on part tolerances. Any time a part is designed, the accuracy of its manufacture must be specified. Some of its surfaces are important to its function, so the designer states tolerances on them for this purpose. However, grip and jig surfaces deserve to be toleranced as well so that assembly can take place with confidence that the parts will mate properly. There already exists a large body of theory on how far parts can be misaligned from each other and still be assembled (see Chap. 5). Thus the designer must see that the surfaces on which one part rests and the other is grasped are made accurately enough. Naturally, depending on the assembly sequence, the resting and grasping surfaces will be different (see Fig. 8.10 for some examples).

In addition, sequence issues highlight assembly machine and tooling design problems, such as part approach directions, tolerance buildup due to prior assembly steps, access for grippers, stability of subassemblies, number of tools needed, tool change requirements, and so on. This means that the assembly sequence must be known to the parts designer very early in the design process. By contrast, the usual practice has been to delay consideration of assembly sequence until after the parts are designed and fabrication methods have been chosen. Since different fabrication methods cost different amounts and are capable of making parts to different tolerances, these choices, if made without assembly process knowledge, can render an assembly sequence unrealizable.

Currently, these complex decisions are made manually and require

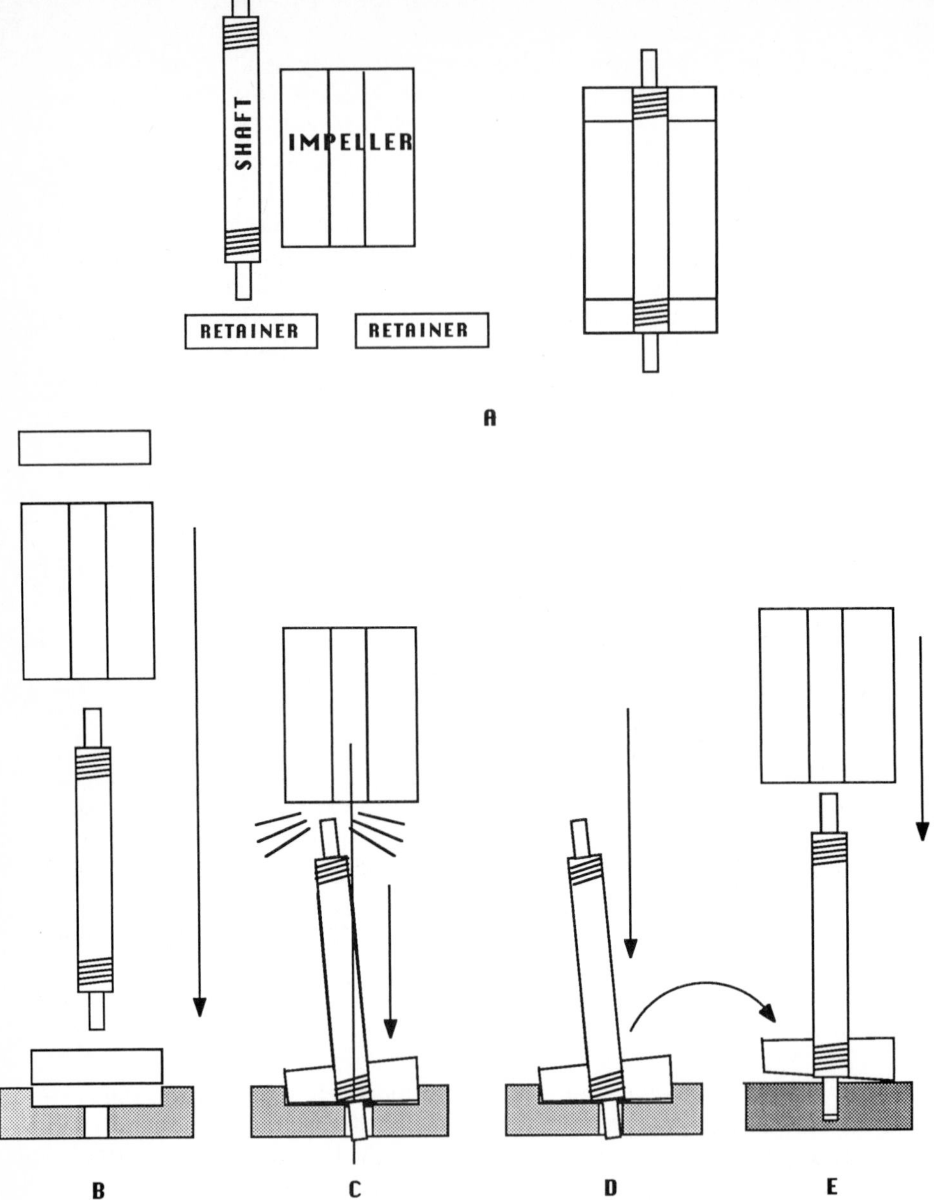

Fig. 8.10 Example of an assembly sequence defeated by poor parts tolerances. (The deviations shown are exaggerated for clarity.) (*a*) The parts are shown disassembled and assembled. (*b*) The desired sequence. This sequence uses the back of the retainer as a jigging surface. The front, being a functional surface, is well toleranced to be perpendicular to the hole so that the shaft will be perpendicular to the retainer. The back is not a functional surface. (*c*) The sequence in (*b*) is defeated by the fact that the back of the retainer, not well toleranced, tilts the shaft so far that the impeller cannot be assembled by bringing it down over the center of the fixture. Note that even if the angle of tilt might be predictable, the actual location of the end of the shaft will be random around a circle. A wasteful search would be necessary to find it. (*d*) As a remedy, a different sequence is used: After the shaft and retainer are mated, the subassembly is transferred to a second fixture (*e*) that grips the shaft, guaranteeing that it will be upright when the impeller is added.

teamwork and lots of calculations. If N dimensions or tolerances combine to create the relative locations of two parts about to be mated, there are 2^N candidate worst cases to evaluate. Among these may be some that will prevent the parts from being assembled. Thus, we run the risk of having "good" parts that cannot be assembled. Statistical simulations have been used to estimate the probability that all parts within tolerance will mate, but as yet there is no deterministic solution to the problem.

In summary, we may say that consideration of alternate assembly sequences, normally considered very late in the *process* design, really belongs in the early stages of *product* design, where each can heavily affect the other. For these reasons, determination of alternate assembly sequences occupies the center of Fig. 8.3.

Creating a quality control strategy. Integrating a quality control strategy into product and process design involves many decisions, including purchasing options and personnel policies that are beyond the scope of this chapter. We will touch on only three aspects related to topics already discussed: determination of a test and repair strategy, definition of subassemblies, and modular assembly line design. All three are linked intimately to choice of assembly sequence.

It is not uncommon for a teardown at final assembly to cost as much as half the total *manufacturing* cost. Thus companies put considerable emphasis on detecting faults before the product is completely assembled.

Every product can experience failures because of poorly made parts or problems during assembly. Some of these failures can be detected by inspecting the parts, while others do not exist until the parts are mated with others, fed electric power or fluid pressure, or pushed or twisted. Thus the failures become viable at certain points in the assembly process, depending on the assembly sequence.

Test and repair strategy. Formulation of a test and repair strategy for manufacturing involves deciding which of many possible assembly stages to choose as test points. To make these choices, one must have some idea of the likelihood that each failure will occur, the cost of test equipment and labor, and the cost of repair at that stage of assembly. Then the designer must relate the assembly sequence to the product's fault tree (a diagram of failures and combinations of failures as well as their manifestations at test points) so that test opportunities, test costs, and rework costs can be assigned to each candidate assembly sequence. Even for one candidate assembly sequence, there are many alternatives. The required knowledge and calculations are discussed in detail in Chap. 9.

Definition of subassemblies and modular assembly lines. We have seen that a way to define subassemblies is to define stages in the assembly where an object with a definable function has been built. Since that function is related to the product's specifications, we should be able to define a test for that subassembly so that we know it will do its job when mated to the rest of the parts. Corresponding to the modules of the product are modular assembly systems. Each produces, tests, and guarantees the correct function of one subassembly. An assembly system made of such modules is preferable to its opposite, a long line that starts with single parts and ends with the final product. This line is not modular, making it difficult to isolate problems or to rearrange parts of the line in response to new technology or a partial redesign of the product.

There are no easy solutions to the QC strategy problem of identifying modules and determining what tests to make. While the required calculations may be readily written down, algorithmic ways of finding the optimum combination do not exist. Curiously, there is a large literature on how to conduct the tests, once their need has been determined. The methods are largely statistical and recommend sampling intervals, sample sizes, alarm levels that signal the fact that an error has reached its limits, and so on.

Economic analysis and choice of assembly method. The fundamental issue in manufacturing system design is the rational choice, from among *many* alternatives, of a method for accomplishing each step. The greatest influences on choice of assembly method are operational or economic: anticipated production volume, the need for flexibility in model mix, part count or options, the method of treating units that fail tests, and so on. There is some literature on this topic, centering mainly on the technical aspects and capabilities of different methods, such as different types of machines or robots, but without much hard-headed comparisons of accuracy or reliability. There is also a dearth of economic data, such as the actual speed of task accomplishment or the rate of breakdowns. The result is that one cannot always make a convincing prediction of the cost and throughput of candidate assembly systems. In certain specialized cases, good estimates can be made. These cases include manual systems or those consisting of specialized "assembly machines." Even in these cases, there are few data and models, and most decision making is based on informed estimates by experienced individuals, with little or no computer support. In recent years, some computer simulations of robots have become commercially available. These are valuable in permitting accurate layout of workstations and calculating nominal motion times, but they do not include predictions of accuracy or repeatability and cannot predict dynamic variables like stopping time or accuracy as a function of payload.

In later chapters we will describe in detail several computer-based tools for designing and analyzing assembly systems. The algorithms are simple enough that they can be available early in product design, when their information feedback can be the most useful. Given adequate data, these tools permit the following issues to be addressed:

1. What is the best economic mix of machines and people to assemble a given model mix of parts for a product, given each machine or person's average cost and time to do each operation, plus production rate and economic return targets? A recent study showed that different manual assembly sequences for the same product could differ by 5 to 20 percent in minimum assembly cost (Klein, 1986).
2. How much can one afford to spend on an assembly system given an anticipated revenue stream? The revenue stream typically comes from cost savings such as labor, rework, or quality, which the assembly system might generate.
3. How much extra time, machines, money, raw materials, or product inventory are required to meet a net production rate target if a certain mix of failures and repair can be anticipated during production? Some companies have estimated that these "costs of quality" can be as much as 20 percent of sales (Martin, 1987). Even a fraction of this amount is large enough to warrant better data and a focussed response.

All of the above design issues have economic consequences which become part of the evaluation process by which alternate fabrication and assembly systems are judged. Different product designs support different assembly sequences, require different tolerances on different surfaces, and require or invite various test and repair strategies. The economic choices presented must be added to those normally made when product designs are evaluated and methods are chosen.

Summary

The above discussions should convince the reader to avoid slogans and encourage a clear-headed search for the manufacturing system that suits the character of the product and best meets the needs of the marketing and manufacturing strategy. Naturally, management must formulate this strategy and monitor its diffusion through the company to see that it properly influences the decisions we have been discussing. Management must also establish and maintain the institutional environment that permits CD to thrive. Technology alone cannot create a productive manufacturing organization. In fact, rationalizing the design of the product and processes can often save more money and time than automation.

Finally we hope it is clear that a great deal of work is required to think through these options and arrive at a good final design of product and process. The new tools for part mating, assembly sequence, and economic modeling and analysis, described in other chapters, have created a knowledge base to support this work.

Comparison to Other Product Design Methods

In addition to the concurrent product-process design method focused on assembly, there are other approaches with advantages and disadvantages that one should be aware of. Discussed briefly below are design axiomatics, "design science" methods, "design for assembly," value engineering, design for logistics, and the Taguchi method. Several of them can play important roles in CD.

Design axiomatics

This is an attempt to focus the designer on constructive ways of meeting a product's requirements by providing general principles to guide thinking and creativity. These guidelines are posed in the form of "axioms" such as "The optimal design has the minimum information content" (Suh, 1978). By itself this statement may not mean much to the reader, but it becomes specific in actual cases, where it may be reinterpreted to mean that each part in the product should perform one and only one function. This advice forces a designer to simplify as well as to consider function very carefully while designing. As we shall see when the Taguchi method is discussed, this approach can have clear advantages in terms of yielding a design that functions well. However, there may be obvious conflicts with producibility considerations, such as the wish to reduce parts count. In order to have fewer parts, one may combine some functions in one part. Complex plastic molded parts are an obvious example.

Design science

Design science has many manifestations, including teaching creativity as well as teaching the use of "design catalogs" that present designers with somewhat standardized ways of accomplishing familiar functions (Roth, 1987). A typical design project may proceed from need statement to identification of generic functions a product must perform (its control functions, energy conversion, or other physical attributes) to identification of various ways of carrying out each function, cataloged by morphology, energy medium, or mechanical type. In Germany, this technique has led to the creation of elaborate catalogs and standardized procedures approved by the VDI (German Standards Institute) and promulgated throughout industry (VDI 2221, 1986). This effort is focused almost totally on product function and contains little about producibility except the injunction that producibility must be considered at a certain step in the process.

Design for assembly

Design for assembly (DFA) has gained acceptance and popularity rapidly in the last few years. It consists of two parts. One is a catalog of generic part shapes and types, classified by group technology methods to indicate which are easiest to feed by means of automatic parts feeders and which are easiest to assemble (Boothroyd and Dewhurst, 1985). The assembly data consist of estimated manual or automatic assembly times: straight push insertion is faster than push-twist or push-twist-tilt, and so on. A designer can test the ease of assembly of a design by describing its assembly steps to a computer which will then calculate approximate relative assembly time and cost (compared to manual) and advise the designer of part mates that should be simplified. A checklist for identifying redundant parts is also included. Three reasons why a part must be separate or cannot be consolidated with others were listed earlier in this chapter.

At a higher level, the method contains rules, advice, or prompting questions to a designer on matters that should be of concern during design (Sturges, 1988). The goals of these rules are those discussed in this chapter, namely better producibility. Sample prompts for parts in this category include:

1. Has the design been simplified and standardized as much as possible?
2. Have subassemblies been limited to 12 parts?

For assemblies, they include:

1. Has the number of parts been minimized?
2. Can the assembly be performed entirely without flipovers?
3. Is there a base part to which the other parts can be assembled?

While these are good questions, it is unlikely that a designer can answer them all optimally from the point of view of producibility alone. For this reason, we prefer starting with a product's character so that there is a basis for answering. In addition, CD does not use ease of assembly as an end in itself but rather uses assembly as a focus for studying all aspects of the product's design, production, and use.

Design for assembly is similar to a method marketed by Hitachi called the Assemblability Evaluation Method (AEM). This method exposes each part mate to an analysis similar to DFAs and deducts points from a perfect 100 based on certain demerits such as push-twist or crowding. Mates with scores less than 90 are subjected to redesign. Several companies, including Ford, General Electric, and Xerox, have adopted this or similar methods and are actively teaching them to their designers.

Value engineering

Value engineering (VE) originated in the 1950s and 1960s and has goals similar to those of CD. For a more complete description, see Salvendy (1982). The main focus of VE is cost reduction while maintaining quality and function. Originally it was intended to be applied to entire products and has in common with CD the ideas of multidiscipline teams and careful analysis of each function and part of the product. It differs from CD in that it begins with an existing design and attempts to improve it. More recently, the method has been applied to single parts, with much less comprehensive effect on the product as a whole. Standard descriptions of VE do not give a strong place to producibility and do not emphasize the fact that producibility interacts with design strongly, but there is no reason why VE teams cannot work with these additional goals in mind.

The heart of the VE method is the functional statement. For the product as a whole and for each part a very brief and focused function statement is formulated. The ability of the item to perform the function at a cost is then evaluated, with savings based either on eliminating nonessential functions or by redesign. The value of the function is also estimated, usually by pooling the opinions of team members. Items which cost too much in relation to the value they contribute are targeted for improvement.

Naturally the ability to estimate costs and values is basic to this method, but the inability to do so accurately may not be an impediment. The reason is that the interactions of the team members and the depth of the study will almost certainly result in improvements. The inability to estimate costs and values also extends to other methods that require such information. This is true of CD as well.

Design for logistics

Design for logistics is not intended to replace other design methods. Instead, it is intended to sensitize designers to the influence of purchasing, stocking, delays, and lead times on the ability to produce a design. A spokesperson for this technique (Mather, 1987) whimsically refers to "mushroom products," as indicated in Fig. 8.11. The height of the mushroom denotes the lead time or delay in obtaining a part after it is ordered. The width of the mushroom denotes variability between product models. If particular models are distinguished from each other by long lead time parts, the manufacturer will always be late responding to orders or market swings. The ideal is a product in which the long lead time parts are used in every model so that they can be ordered well in advance. Small errors in delivery time or amount needed will not stop production of any one model. The models are distinguished by parts that have short lead times or are so cheap that they can be stocked in large quantities with little economic penalty.

The Taguchi method

This method has many elements in common with those described in this chapter. It is based on mathematical analysis and is intended to aid the designer in creating a product that can be produced within economical tolerances on economical equipment and still function as desired (Taguchi, 1986). It is often referred to as a method for achieving quality control, but it is much deeper than that.

Taguchi identifies three elements in product design: "system design," meaning concept design of the product and engineering analysis of it to determine that it will function; "parameter design," meaning the selection of dimensions and tolerances so that the product can be made; and "tolerance design," a step he does not recommend, consisting of tightening performance specifications on materials, workpieces, and processes so that the product will work. The latter is not smart design, merely spending money unnecessarily. According to Taguchi, American designers tend to do system and tolerance design, skipping over parameter design and losing the opportunity it provides for designing a robust product-process system.

System design comprises not only product concept design but also the separation of design factors into controllable ones and uncontrollable ones, or "noise." Controllable factors are things like time or weight that can be easily made to conform to desired levels and tolerances. Noise is a variable that is hard to control or has an inherently unpredictable component that is large compared to desired tolerances. Taguchi warns that trying to control noise is futile and expensive. Instead, one should design product and process to be as immune to noise as possible. This is called "reducing the product's sensitivity." Another term for this approach is "offline quality control," or the QC that is designed into the product. This is contrasted to online QC, the typical

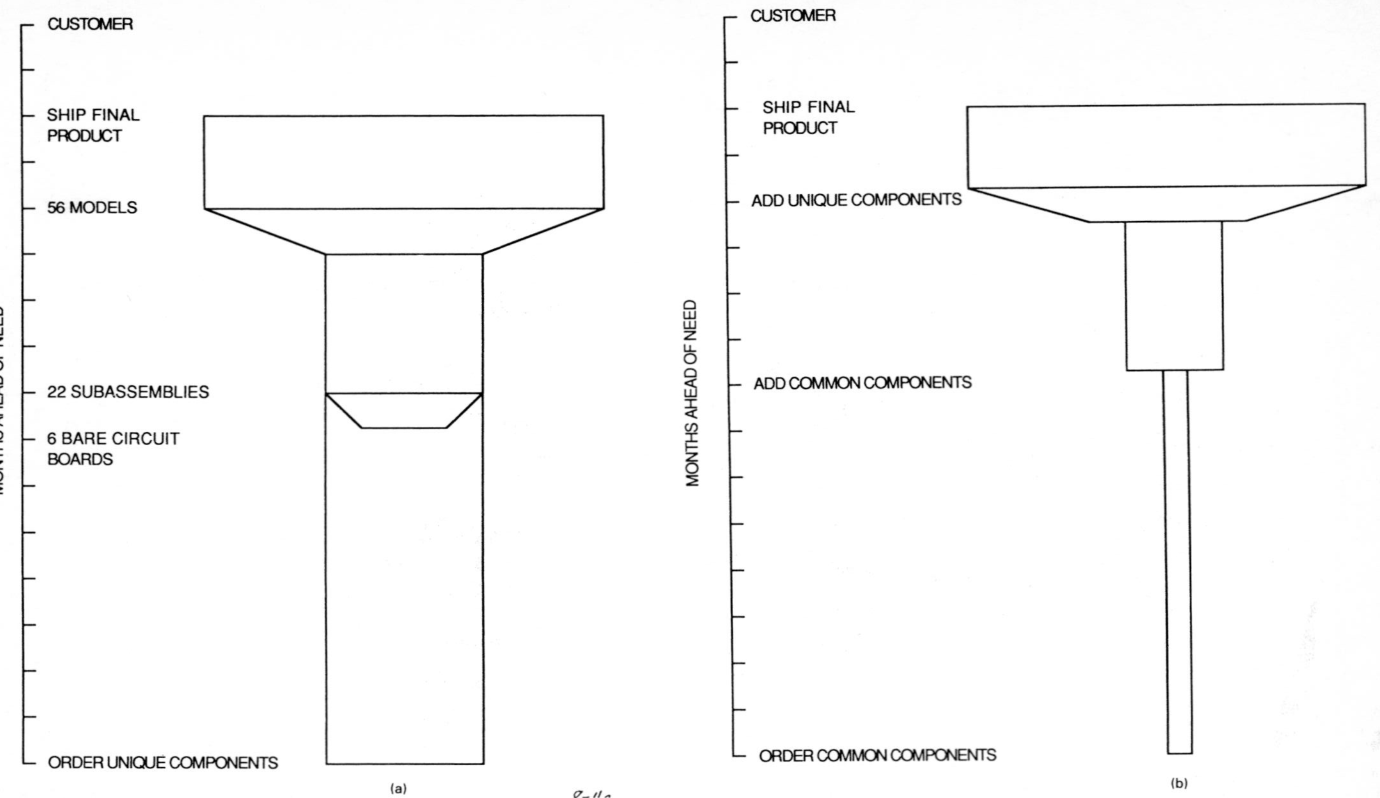

Fig. 8.11 Comparison of logistically "unfriendly" and "friendly" products. Unique parts turn 6 types of bare circuit boards into 22 different finished types. Selecting among these types allows 56 models of product to be made and shipped. (*a*) The unfriendly product. Forecasts must be made of the relative numbers of each type of circuit board needed because the required components must be ordered far in advance. These are added to the boards early so that a large stock of unused boards is built up. (*b*) The friendly product. The long lead time components are common to all boards. Boards are built up with common components and are ready any time to have the unique ones added as orders arrive. Inventory can be used as fast as it is created. The cycle from customer order to delivery is shorter even though the overall lead time is the same as in (*a*). (*Adapted by permission of IFS Publications, Ltd.*)

attempt to keep machines running at toleranced performance or improving their behavior to reach tighter tolerances.

Parameter design is an attempt to deal with unpredictable factors, so the Taguchi approach is statistical. It consists of identifying the probable noise factors and the controllable factors associated with the product's function. Using standard statistical methods, one designs a set of experiments to determine how both the controllable and uncontrollable factors affect performance. (The uncontrollable ones must be controllable during the experiments in order for this technique to work.) The results are analyzed to determine which settings of the controllable ones produce the least variations in product performance in the face of variations in the uncontrollable ones. These or similar settings are preferred because they are less sensitive.

For example, a company that made ceramic tiles found through experimentation that it could overcome shrinkage problems caused by bake oven temperature fluctuations by changing the chemical composition of the tiles. Thus they did not have to buy a better and more expensive oven.

The importance of the Taguchi approach is that it provides an analytical base for designing some aspects of the product to ensure its producibility and especially its robustness. As such, it deserves a place in the producibility-usability study.

Summary

In this chapter we have described a new strategy for improving productivity. It is based on using the assembly process as the focal point and integrator of all the complex decisions required to create a producible product. To verify, improve, extend, and implement this strategy, it is not enough simply to try harder. Deeper understanding of fundamental technical and institutional problems is needed.

CD is not just a product design method but also a way of systematizing the way people and manufacturing functions interact. It provides a basis for these new concurrency teams to exist. The method is not an end in itself. Instead, the application of the method provides visibility into manufacturing systems and their interactions not presently analyzed or understood by any other method. Application of new technology without an integrated approach has proved to be a disaster.

References

Boothroyd, G., and P. Dewhurst: *Design for Assembly Handbook,* Boothroyd and Dewhurst Associates, Kingston, RI, 1985.

Bourjault, A.: "Contribution á une Approche Méthodologique de l'Assemblage

Automatisé: Elaboration Automatique des Séquences Opératoires," Thesis for Grade de Docteur en Sciences Physiques at l'Université de Franche Comté, November 12, 1984.

De Fazio, T. L., and D. E. Whitney: "Simplified Generation of All Mechanical Assembly Sequences," *IEEE J. Robotics and Automation,* RA-3, no. 6, Dec. 1987, pp. 640–658.

Homem de Mello, L. S., and A. C. Sanderson: "AND/OR Graph Representation of Assembly Plans," Carnegie-Mellon University Robotics Institute Report CMU-RI-86-8, 1986.

Klein, C.: "Generation and Evaluation of Assembly Sequence Alternatives," Master of Science Thesis, MIT Mech. Eng. Dept., 1986.

Ko, H., and K. Lee: "Automatic Assembling Procedure Generation from Mating Conditions," *Computer-Aided Design,* vol. 19, no 1, Jan.–Feb. 1987, pp. 3–10.

Martin, J. M.: "Developing a Strategy for Quality," *Mfr. Eng.,* vol. 99, no 2, Aug. 1987, pp. 40–45.

Mather, H.: "Logistics in Manufacturing: A Way to Beat the Competition," *Assembly Automation,* vol. 7, no. 4, 1987, pp 175–178.

Roth, K.: "Design Models and Design Catalogs," *Proceedings 1987 International Conference on Engineering Design,,* ASME, Boston, pp. 60–67.

Salvendy, G. (ed.): "Value Engineering," in *Handbook of Industrial Engineering,* John Wiley, New York, 1982.

Sturges, R. S.: "A Quantification of Manual Dexterity: The Design for Assembly Calculator," submitted for publication to the *J. of Robotics and Computer Integrated Manufacturing,* 1988.

Suh, N., et al.: "On an axiomatic Approach to Manufacturing Systems," *ASME J. Eng. for Industry,* vol. 100, 1978, p. 127.

Taguchi, S., and D. Byrne: "The Taguchi Approach to Parameter Design," *Proceedings, 1986 ASQC Quality Congress.* Also, Taguchi, G., and Y. Wu, *Introduction to Off-Line Quality Control,* American Supplier Institute, Romulus, MI, 1980.

VDI 2221: "Systematic Approach to the Design of Technical Systmes and Products," VDI Standard 2221, available from VDI-Verlag GmbH, Dusseldorf, FRG, 1986.

Chapter

9

Technical Aspects of Product Design

Introduction

This chapter provides technical details on the following five important issues raised in Chap. 8:

- Algorithms for generating assembly sequences
- Identification and correction of high-risk part mates
- The influence of part tolerances on assembly success
- Part design for assembly, feeding, and material handling
- Creation of a quality control and testing strategy

Assembly Sequence Generation

As discussed in the previous chapter, there are many reasons for seeking a good assembly sequence for a product as well as for making assembly sequence choice a topic of early design rather than delaying it. A little study shows that generating assembly sequences manually can be a tedious process with no guarantee that all the good ones will be discovered. This section describes an algorithm that is guaranteed to generate all physically possible sequences.

Assembly sequence generation can be a challenge even for a *modular* product that has been conveniently divided into subassemblies because assemblies with as few as 10 parts can have hundreds of feasible sequences. The difficulty is compounded if the product design is *integrated* because there are no subassemblies and one must deal with dozens or hundreds of parts.

Once one has all the candidate sequences, the issue becomes one of choosing a good one. Here the issues are drastically different if one anticipates manual versus mechanical assembly. The choices must be identified and evaluated economically as well as technically. For this reason, the *generation* of sequences should be kept separate from the *choice* of a good one.

A simple case of manual sequence generation

Often assembly sequence generation is no issue or the issue is transparent in the sense that sequence alternatives, if any, are easily identified and evaluated. Preparation of the head subassembly of a pushrod overhead valve engine is a simple case in point (see Fig. 9.1). The operations are:

- Press in valve guides (if any)
- Cut valve seats concentric with guides (if needed)
- Install valve stem seals
- Install valves
- Install springs
- Install seals
- Install keepers
- Install rockers and studs

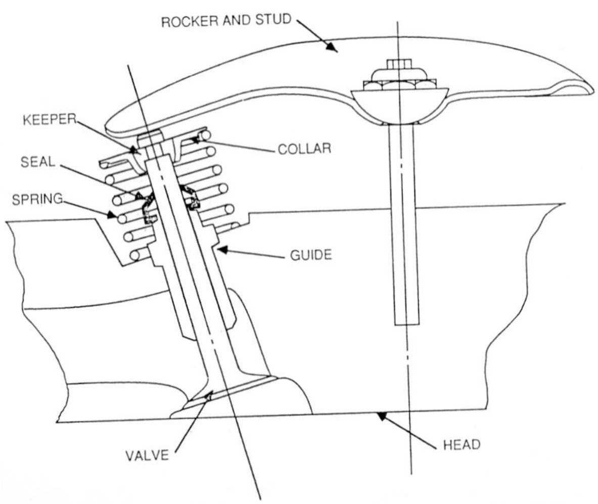

Fig. 9.1 Portion of head assembly of overhead valve engine.

Little useful variation in order can be imagined. A wholly satisfactory assembly sequence is easily found by examination, and attempts to better it by varying sequences simply or radically go unrewarded.

A complex example done manually

In contrast to the head subassembly, we can find examples of modular subassemblies where assembly sequence is a serious issue and a major factor in the ease or difficulty of assembly. The automobile alternator shown in Fig. 8.6 is a case in point. The Draper Laboratory demonstrated robot assembly of this alternator in 1977, using a single low-cost 4-degree-of-freedom tool changing robot equipped with a remote center compliance (Nevins and Whitney, 1978; Nevins et al., 1977). In this case the candidate assembly sequence was found by trial attempts with the real parts in hand. The sequence used (no. 2 in the figure) started with the nut and required no flipovers. Absence of flips permitted use of the low-cost robot rather than a more expensive one with 6 degrees of freedom. Since the nut can hardly be called a "base part," it is unlikely that a scheme for finding sequences based on the rule "start with the base part" would have generated this sequence.

An algorithmic approach

The systematic method for algorithmically generating all physically possible assembly sequences involves characterizing the assembly by a graph in which nodes represent parts and lines between nodes represent relations or liaisons between parts, either as connections or contacts. The method does not precisely create assembly sequences but rather creates *liaison sequences*. Thus there is no "first part," but instead a first liaison, in each sequence. This major departure from conventional practice in generating assembly sequences is essential in separating the creation of sequences from the choice of a good one, since each may begin with a different first liaison comprising two or more parts each, with different jigging problems or opportunities.

Bourjault (1984) demonstrated how the yes-no answers to a large number of questions could be used to give birth to a series of logical statements or rules describing the precedence or allowed order in which the liaisons could be established; these logical statements could then be used to generate all physically possible assembly sequences.

Bourjault's question-answer method is designed so that no unnecessary questions are asked. Since no question is redundant and each has a yes-no answer, the question or answer count is a measure, in bits, of the information content of all the assembly sequences. Bourjault's method reflects and quantifies the fact that the information content of assembly sequences can rise very quickly with parts count; there can be many questions, although the exact number depends on the product.

De Fazio and Whitney (1987, 1988) developed an alternative to Bourjault's method which reduces the question count greatly; there are exactly two questions for each liaison. One can show that the number of liaisons ℓ is related to the number of parts by

$$n - 1 \le \ell \le \left(\frac{n^2 - n}{2}\right) \tag{9.1}$$

where n is the number of parts. So, for an assembly with five parts there are between 8 and 20 questions; for 10 parts, between 18 and 90 questions. Each of the two following questions is addressed to each of the liaisons:

- Q1: What liaison(s) need be *done* already to allow doing liaison i?
- Q2: What liaison(s) need be left *undone* to allow doing liaison i?

Answers are in the form of precedence relations between liaisons and/or logical combinations of liaisons; for example, "liaisons 2 and 5 or 6 must be done before liaison 10 is done" or "the combination of liaisons 7 and 9 must remain undone until liaison 10 is done." A simple shorthand for these questions and answers is

REAR AXLE ASSEMBLY SEQUENCE CONSTRAINTS

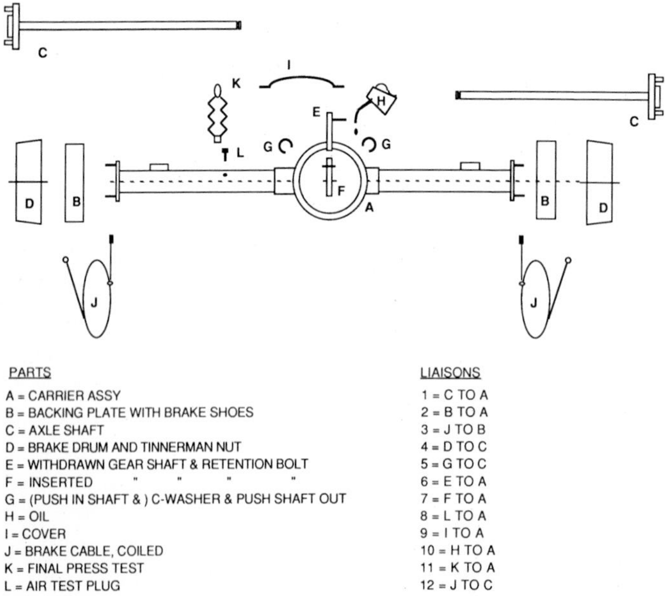

Fig. 9.2 Parts of the rear axle. Some of the interferences are obvious; for example, axle shafts block access for the backing plates.

$$\text{Q1 for liaison 10?} \qquad 2 \text{ and } (5 \text{ or } 6) \rightarrow 10 \tag{9.2A}$$

$$\text{Q2 for liaison 10?} \qquad 10 \rightarrow (7 \text{ and } 9) \tag{9.2B}$$

In the second answer, an alternative verbal equivalent is that either 7 or 9 could be done before 10, but 10 must be done before both 7 and 9 have been done.

These answers are constraining logical relations which permit certain liaison sequences and forbid certain others. The former represent physically possible assembly sequences (strictly speaking, sequences of liaison establishment) and the latter represent physically impossible sequences. As of this writing, we generate the set of answers manually by systematically answering the questions. A PC program has been written (Lui, 1988) to convert the answers into a list of the possible sequences plus a graphical representation shown later in this chapter.[1]

As an example, consider the final assembly sequence of a typical rear axle of a car or small truck (see Figs. 9.2 and 9.3). This axle is typical of what is called the "unitized carrier housing" type, as illustrated in sec. 28, p. 28.25 of the *SAE Handbook* (1981). For the purposes of analysis, the hypoid and differential gearset is assumed to be already assembled and in place in the gear carrier casting. To this casting have been added the axle tubes, and together these comprise the carrier subassembly A. Our analysis begins at the point where the carrier receives the axle shafts with hubs (C in the figure), the axle shaft retainers (called "C" washers) which hold the axles in (G), the brake shoe assemblies (B) (called "backing plates"), the brake drums

[1] An additional issue beyond the scope of this book is liaisons that are accomplished simultaneously. (For example, a screw that holds two parts together will make its liaisons with them simultaneously for our purposes when it is installed.) One of the many ways to handle simultaneity is to modify Q2 to say "left undone or be done simultaneously with liaison *i*." Then, for example, one might interpret 10 → (7 and 9) to include 10 being done simultaneously with 7 or 9 or both. This might be written 10 ≥ (7 and 9). Simultaneities are detected by identifying loops in the liaison diagram. Simultaneous accomplishment is required of the last two undone liaisons in a loop but only if the participating parts are rigid.

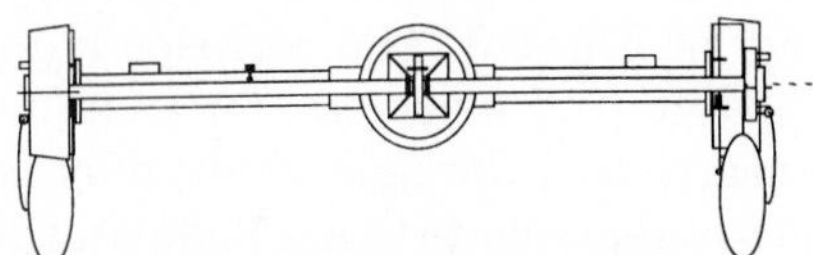

Fig. 9.3 Fully assembled rear axle.

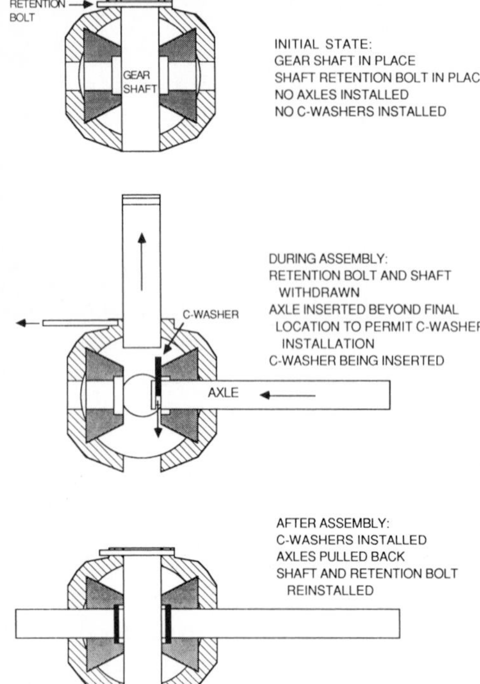

Fig. 9.4 Drawing of shaft retention by C washers.

(D), the brake cables (J), oil (H), a cover (I), an air pressure leak-test (K), and an air test hole plug (L). The drums are retained on the hub studs by pairs of Tinnerman nuts (spring clips), which are not shown.

Additionally, minor disassembly and reassembly must be done in connection with axle-shaft installation because of the method of axle-shaft retention, as shown in Fig. 9.4. The axle shafts are supported against axial outward forces by the C washers and against axial inward forces by the differential gear shaft (E, F). The C washers are secured in recesses in the differential side gears and ride in grooves cut in the ends of the axle shafts. To gain access for C-washer installation, one must push the axle shafts in beyond the gear shaft's surface; for this purpose, the gear shaft must be partly removed. Furthermore, the differential shaft retention bolt securing the differential gear shaft must also be partly removed to allow freedom for removing the shaft.

A liaison-sequence analysis begins with an assembly drawing and a parts list, shown schematically above in Fig. 9.3. The corresponding liaison diagram is shown in Fig. 9.5. Note that a process, for example the leak test or the removal and reinsertion of the gear shaft, may be treated as if it were a part. Each part is represented as a node on the liaison diagram; each connection or liaison with another part is rep-

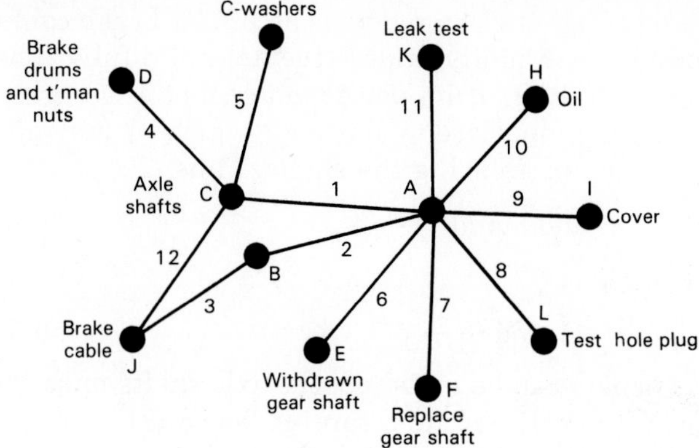

Fig. 9.5 Liaison diagram for the rear axle.

resented by a numbered branch. Liaison 12 represents coiling the free ends of the brake cables and clipping them to an axle-shaft stud to secure them for shipping.[2]

The analysis proceeds to ask question 1 (Q1) for each liaison. What needs to be done to allow doing liaison 1 (Q1-1?) can be addressed as follows. Installing axle shafts blocks access for backing-plate installation (2) so that liaison 2 must precede liaison 1 or

$$2 \rightarrow 1 \tag{9.3}$$

It should be noted here that each part that exists in a pair is given one name (the drums are both D, the axle shafts both C). This convention is based on the assumption that each pair will be installed at the same time or at least at the same station. It might also be noted that if one withdrew the gear shaft (liaison 6) before installing the axle shaft, the shaft would go all the way in to the point where C washers could be installed. However, if the shaft is installed this far too fast, there is a chance that the bearing seal could be damaged. To prevent this, the constraint $6 \rightarrow 1$ is omitted.

For Q1-2? and Q1-3? the answer is that nothing needs to be done prior to liaisons 2 or 3; the consequence is that either operation, backing plates to carrier or cables to backing plates, may be done first.

For Q1-4? one notes that installing the drums and Tinnerman nuts on the hubs of the axle shafts precludes C-washer installation if the backing plates are in place (as they must be) or precludes backing-

[2] Simultaneity is not required by the loop 1-2-3-12 because part J is not rigid.

plate installation once the axle shafts and C washers are placed in the carrier, so at least 5 → 4. Also, the drum denies access for brake cable installation, so (3 and 5) → 4. Finally, unless the axles are fully constrained axially by the gear shaft, drum placement cannot be securely done. The last condition is summarized by liaison 7, which we may anticipate will be the last step in securing the shafts. Thus,

$$(3 \text{ and } 5 \text{ and } 7) \rightarrow 4 \tag{9.4}$$

Q1-5? yields

$$(1 \text{ and } 6) \rightarrow 5 \tag{9.5}$$

That is, before the C washers can be installed, the axle shafts must be in the carrier and the gear shaft and its retaining bolt must be withdrawn.

Q1-6? yields nothing since this operation could be done first.

Q1-7? is answered by noting that before the gear shaft is replaced, it must have been withdrawn, the axles inserted, and the C washers inserted. Thus

$$(1 \text{ and } 5 \text{ and } 6) \rightarrow 7 \tag{9.6}$$

Q1-8? easily yields

$$11 \rightarrow 8 \tag{9.7}$$

Q1-9? yields

$$(7 \text{ and } 10) \rightarrow 9 \tag{9.8}$$

That is, before we put on the cover, we must have added the oil and completed the C-washer operations.

Q1-10? yields

$$(7) \rightarrow 10 \tag{9.9}$$

That is, unless we want a mess, we should finish C-washer installation before adding the oil.

Q1-11? yields

$$(1 \text{ and } 9) \rightarrow 11 \tag{9.10}$$

The three places we want to test for air leaks are the cover seal and the bearing seals around the axle shafts, plus the previously assembled drive pinion seal in the carrier.

Since the brake cable attaches temporarily to a stud on the shaft that pokes through a hole in the brake drum, Q1-12? yields

$$4 \rightarrow 12 \tag{9.11}$$

In this example, Q2 does not add any constraints not already present in the above list. The reader who is interested in a more complex example that illustrates all the features of the method should consult De Fazio and Whitney (1987, 1988). The reference also discusses the fact that the answers to the questions are not unique, as the reader may discover upon trying the method. However, all correct sets of answers will yield the same set of liaison sequences.

The combined precedence constraints are now

$$\begin{aligned} 2 &\rightarrow 1 \\ (3 \text{ and } 5 \text{ and } 7) &\rightarrow 4 \\ (6 \text{ and } 1) &\rightarrow 5 \\ (1 \text{ and } 5 \text{ and } 6) &\rightarrow 7 \\ 11 &\rightarrow 8 \\ (7 \text{ and } 10) &\rightarrow 9 \\ (7) &\rightarrow 10 \\ (1 \text{ and } 9) &\rightarrow 11 \\ 4 &\rightarrow 12 \end{aligned} \tag{9.12}$$

Once the precedence rules are available, one can generate a graphical representation of all the assembly sequences. Scanning down the right-hand side of the precedence relations, we note that liaisons 2, 3, and 6 are unprecedented and may be established first. With liaison 2 established, liaisons 1, 3, or 6 may be established next and so forth. Figure 9.6 represents all valid assembly sequences that result from pursuing the precedence relations in this fashion. Each block represents a single unique state of assembly, with established liaisons being represented by marks in the (numbered) cells. Each line represents an assembly move, the establishment of a liaison. Full disassembly is represented by the top (empty) state, full assembly by the bottom (full) state. Each path through the diagram (there are 330) represents a valid assembly sequence. Some are better than others, and an advantage of the application of liaison-sequence analysis is that no valid assembly sequence is overlooked.

To count the number of sequences, start at the bottom of the diagram and proceed as follows:

1. Write a 1 underneath the rectangle in the last rank (the one with the highest rank number).
2. Go to the next rank above (with the next lower rank number) and consider each rectangle R in turn. Follow each line descending from rectangle R and ending on a rectangle RL in the rank below. Note

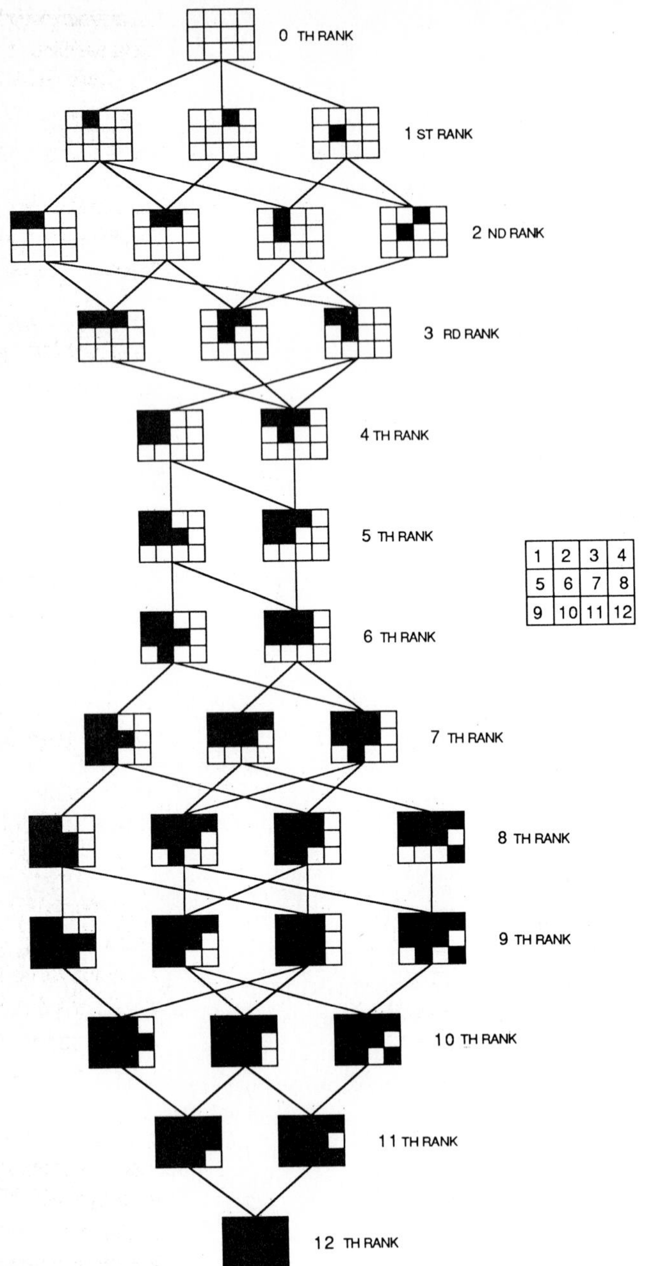

Fig. 9.6 Rear axle assembly sequences.

the number under rectangle RL. Add the numbers noted under each RL connected to R and write the total under R.

3. Repeat procedure 2 with each rank upward, including the top rank.
4. The number under the top rectangle is the number of sequences.

Choosing a Good Assembly Sequence

Having the means to generate all of the physically possible sequences of assembly of a complicated subassembly or assembly allows the manufacturing engineer the confidence of knowing that no potentially best assembly sequence will be overlooked. The manufacturing engineer must then be prepared to handle the result: very, very many candidate assembly sequences. This is the issue discussed in this section: how engineers choose the best assembly sequence from the wealth of choices they are faced with.

The entire procedure of liaison-sequence analysis yielding the viable assembly sequences, followed by the winnowing to one or a few assembly sequence candidates, is represented in the schematic diagram in Fig. 9.7. The winnowing process can be judgmental, qualitative, quantitative, or a combination of these and can follow any or several of four paths, as shown in the lower third of the figure.

First, the engineer can eliminate unacceptable assembly moves, the equivalent of eliminating corresponding lines or branches from the assembly-sequence graph. (Note that if all the branches either entering or leaving a particular state are removed, that state is also removed.) Assembly moves may be eliminated when an acceptable alternative path exists and the move in question is difficult to accomplish or puts a part or parts at risk of damage.

Second, the engineer can eliminate unacceptable assembly states, the equivalent of eliminating corresponding nodes or boxes from the assembly-sequence graph. (Note that if a state is removed, all transitions or branches entering or leaving that state are also removed.) Assembly states may be eliminated when an acceptable alternative path exists and the state in question is awkward, unstable or conditionally unstable under assembly conditions, or requires undue time, cost, or equipment to maintain it between assembly moves.

Third, the engineer can enforce any of several assembly-sequence constraints. Such constraints can be arbitrary and may be based on the engineer's own concept of good practice. Example constraints include ordering of a subsequence of assembly steps or forbidding assembly sequences which create lots of disconnected subassemblies which are joined later. The first may be used, for example, where an assembly step leaves an objectionable condition which can be remedied by

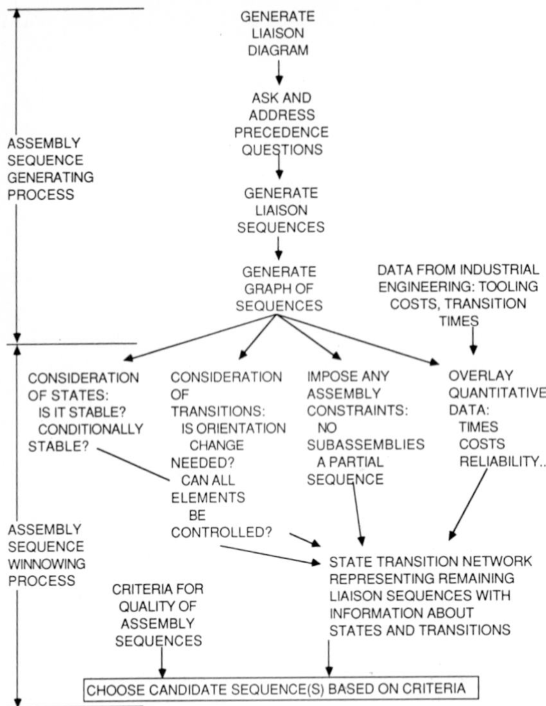

Fig. 9.7 Schematic representation of finding all physically possible assembly sequences and winnowing them down to a small set of candidates.

another particular step; say, an oil fill to be followed immediately by capping. The second can be used when the items being assembled are themselves subassemblies and the engineer wishes to consider only final assembly of these subassemblies. Constraints of the first sort are often expressed in terms of "menus" which suggest which liaison or liaisons may follow a particular liaison. The basic precedence relations remain true in the presence of any such menu, of course. Constraints of the second sort are imposed by referring to the liaison diagram and requiring that the next liaison be one attached to a node that belongs to the partial liaison diagram representing previously accomplished assembly steps. Since subassemblies are equivalent to isolated fragmentary liaison diagrams, this constraint will eliminate such fragments.

Fourth, the engineer may make the assembly-sequence graph into a network by overlaying quantitative data from various sources, data such as fixed costs, variable costs, tooling costs, labor costs, or assembly step times, and use network techniques to find an acceptable path or the optimum path by some criterion.

In the authors' experience, the combination of the first three options, invoking constraints and eliminating awkward states and moves, has been so effective in digesting rich and complicated assembly-sequence choices down to a few easily-considered candidates that the network conversion and network-optimization techniques have seldom had to be used.

An example of winnowing the axle sequences by this method is as follows. Four "common sense" orders to state transitions or assembly moves are imposed:

1. The axles shafts are to be secured with the C washers immediately following axle-shaft insertion. This constraint avoids certain unstable or conditionally stable states in favor of fully stable states. Symbolically, this means that whenever liaison 1 appears, it should be immediately followed by liaison 5.
2. The brake cables are to be wrapped and secured to the axle-shaft studs as soon as possible. The cables are 3 to 7 feet (ft) long and a damage hazard in an assembly area until secured. In light of other constraints, this second constraint is that whenever liaison 3 appears, it is to be immediately followed by liaison 4, which is in turn to be immediately followed by liaison 12.
3. The differential-carrier cover should be placed immediately after filling the carrier with oil. This is a straightforward precaution against contamination either by spillage outward or foreign objects in the carrier and lube. Liaison 9 thus should immediately follow liaison 10.
4. Seal the axle by applying the test-hole plug immediately following a successful leak check, a simple precaution against leakage. Liaison 8 should immediately follow liaison 11.

Imposing these four liaison subsequences prunes the tree from 330 sequences to 6, shown in Fig. 9.8. Choosing among six sequences may be fairly easy. There are three branches to consider. Considering the top region (A), one may prefer taking the left-hand branch, representing adding backing plates, before the right-hand branch, withdrawing the retention bolt and gear shaft, on the basis that it represents avoiding one unstable or conditionally stable state. That is, the gear shaft could fall back into the gearbox.

The choice implied by the first branch perhaps should be made in the light of ideas about the layout and technology of choice for assembling the rear axle. For example, pulling out the retention bolt and gear shaft is much easier manually than mechanically unless the parts are redesigned. People could do this operation at the head of the line, keeping them away from robots or other mechanization within the line. Given redesign, replacing the gear shaft is easier mechani-

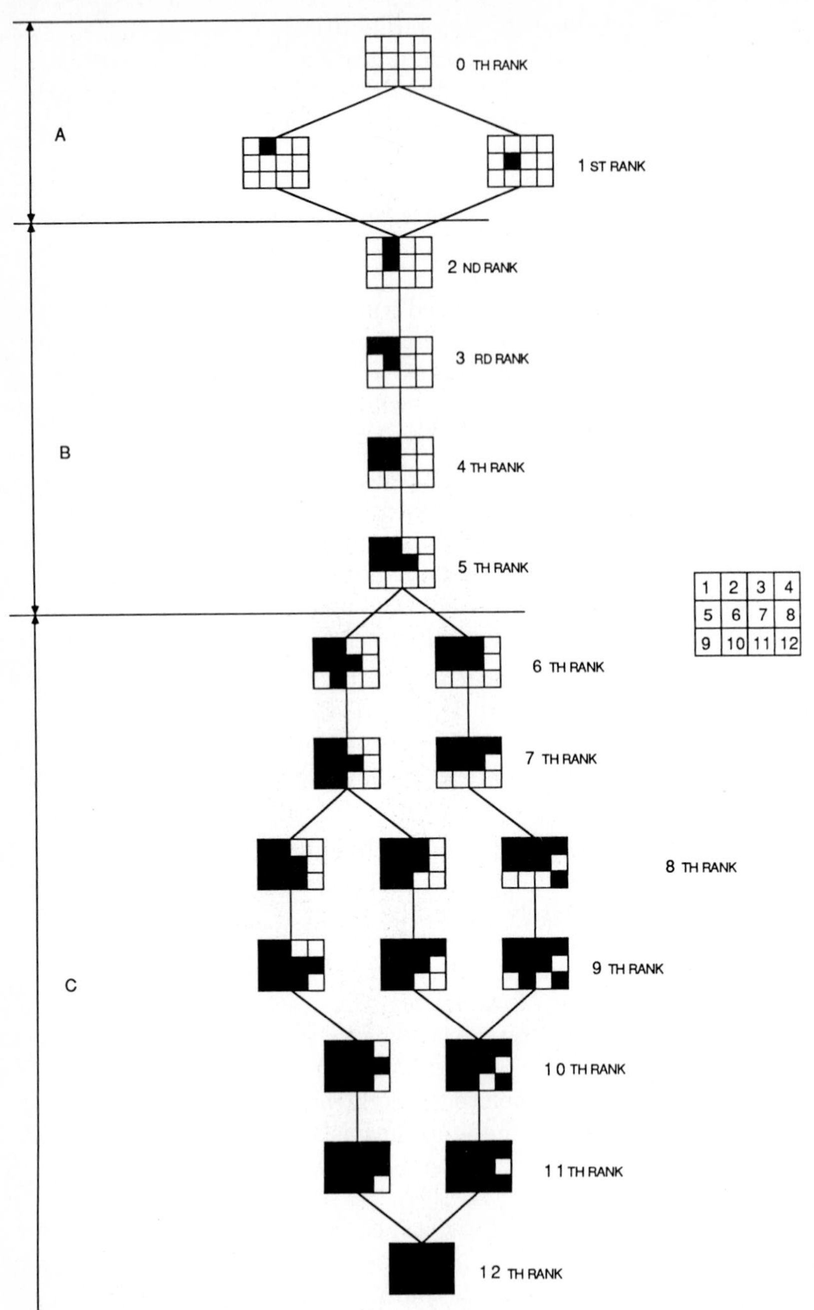

Fig. 9.8 Remaining rear axle assembly sequences after imposing four common sense constraints.

TABLE 9.1 **Representation of Part C of Fig. 9.8**

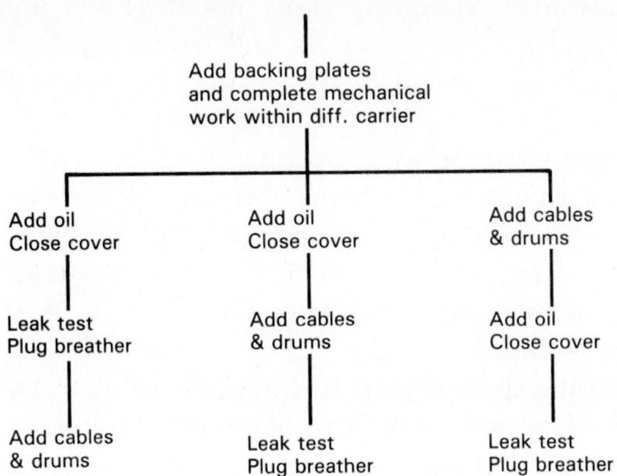

cally than removing it, so possibly an entire stretch of the line could be free of people, an important safety consideration. However, if the necessary redesign cannot be accomplished, people will be needed, eliminating any advantage from putting liaison 6 first.

The top stem of the tree, portions A and B, implies first finishing all mechanical work *within* the differential carrier, followed by any of the three sequence choices for region C represented in Table 9.1.

Again, choices of sequence are best made in context of consideration of layout and assembly technology choice for the assembly line. Notwithstanding, some observations influencing sequence choice can be made. First, all the operations are fairly easily automated, except those involving assembling and securing the cables, which are quite difficult to automate. If automation is to be considered, it is generally convenient to separate manual and automated stations to the extent possible. This consideration suggests the left branch of Table 9.1. Second, the leak test is an operation which is followed by an implied but not shown branch, allowing any failed units to be reconsidered and reworked. Where rework is a possibility, one may wish to branch as early in the assembly as possible or, more precisely, at a state of minimum value added. This again is consistent with choice of the left-hand branch of Table 9.1.

The above discussion does not by any means exhaust the issues raised by assembly-sequence generation and choice. More detail is in the references. It should be noted that only a full economic analysis, simulation, and consideration of the proper roles of people on the line will tell which assembly sequence is the best one. The value of considering assembly sequence early in design is shown by the discussion of the effect of a redesign of the gear-shaft retention method on the choice of feasible assembly method and the option to place people far from assembly machinery.

Not at all represented in the winnowing methods displayed here are quantitative network techniques: assigning data about times and costs to appropriate states and state transitions and using shortest-path or other network optimization routines for choosing the assembly sequence candidate.

Where quantitative network estimation or optimization techniques are to be used, it is important to use real network data or estimates of dimensioned quantities (time in seconds, money in dollars, etc.). The temptation, if any, to characterize the ease or difficulty of a state transition (assembly move) on an arbitrary nondimensioned scale, from one to ten, say, should be avoided. We prefer that questions of judgment be treated as such rather than trying to quantify what is not necessarily quantifiable. The engineer may face the judgmental issues in a binary way: Good states and transitions are kept, bad ones are cut.

Summary

Liaison-sequence analysis produces a representation of all possible sequences of assembly which is the framework for serious consideration of elimination of high-risk mates and awkward states. The analysis is often triggered by a knowledge of certain difficult states and transitions, and as soon as the framework is complete, the engineer may consider alternatives. Often an effective winnowing process is to address first all the judgmental issues including both constraints that are perceived beneficial and the elimination of states and mates which are perceived to be unacceptable. If a choice does not emerge from those sequences remaining in the pruned framework, the assembly sequences should be considered quantitatively and in light of one's choices of assembly technology.

Tolerances and Their Relation to Assembly

Dimensioning philosophy and choice of tolerances is a design function which affects not only the product's function and performance but also manufacture and assembly. Tolerances constrain feasible methods of manufacture, strongly influence cost of manufacture, affect ease and sequence of assembly, and determine the specifications of assembly technology such as jigs and fixtures, assembly machines, robots, and grippers. Dimensioning and associated tolerances potentially affect assembly in many different ways:

- Prevent assembly of some fraction of the parts
- Assure that assembly is uniformly difficult, uniformly easy, occa-

sionally difficult, possible, or easy for one technique or technology but not others

- Assure that assembly is easy by some sequences of assembly and difficult or impossible by others

Often the engineer must consider the relevant dimensions and tolerances on a mate-by-mate basis for the nominal design and nominal assembly sequence, assuming reasonable fixturing where appropriate. This is clearly a concurrent design issue in the sense that design, manufacturing, assembly, quality control, and cost accounting interests are each involved. Design engineers are typically responsible for the general and detailed shape, functional analysis, dimensions, and tolerances of parts and assemblies. Manufacturing engineers are typically responsible for making the parts and are knowledgeable regarding manufacturing costs for different processes and tolerances. Assembly engineers are responsible for the general and detailed specification of the assembly system and choices of assembly technology. All are responsible for calculating the cost of making the product.

The dimensioning and tolerancing issues associated with assembly are different from those associated with single parts considered individually. Multiple dimensions are involved, including translations and rotations. Even with the best current CAD solid modeling systems it is difficult to analyze the interactions.

Dimensioning and choosing tolerances for successful assembly involve these issues:

1. *The analysis of dimensions, tolerances, and clearances of pairs, sets, or multiples of parts.* The analyses must consider relative positions representing approach, contact, partial engagement, and full engagement of one part to another or others
2. *The order or sequence of assembly.*
3. *Analysis of tables, jigs, fixtures, assembly machines, or robots as well as the set of multiple parts.*
4. *Choice of assembly technique.* Every mechanic has the experience of the same nominal assembly move occurring smoothly or not so smoothly, requiring care and effort, or requiring care, effort, and force, all varying from one part set to the next. If the assembly move is done manually, the assembly worker can usually quickly analyze and "reconfigure" the assembly technique.

Ideally such adaptive reconfiguring ability can be a feature of sensor-based computer-controlled robotic assembly as well; however, practically it is not. Such capabilities have indeed been demonstrated in research laboratories but are typically expensive to implement, time consuming, and often not robust. The conclusion is that parts earmarked for manual assembly can typically display wide ranges of assembly behavior, that parts earmarked for automated or robotic assembly generally must have dimensions, tolerances, and qualities such that every example of their assembly "feels" and behaves quite the same as every other. This issue has historically been a major stumbling block for those who would automate assembly.

Clearly there is room for a great deal of ingenuity and imagination in the dimensioning and tolerancing of parts being prepared for automatic assembly, the prime challenge being to manufacture parts which will contribute to the product's final quality as well as assemble in a reproducible and predictable way. A few examples will give the reader a flavor.

Example 1—Inserting axles

The first example is taken from motor vehicle assembly practice and it addresses the insertion of the axle shaft of a solid rear axle through the outboard bearing into the axle carrier and on into the differential gearcase (see Fig. 9.9). The assembly phases of interest are noted in the figure as phases 1 and 2, that is, to get the axle shaft to and into the lips of the gearcase.

Done manually, this assembly step is reasonably easy, so it is reasonable to assign a standard time to it. Several techniques are used, and most involve one or two grip changes, effectively assembly system reconfigurations, in completing the assembly step. For example, an assembler may start off with a two-hand grip, supporting the bulk of the hub end with one hand and guiding the spline end through the carrier outer seal and outboard bearing with the other. Once the spline end is into the bearing, a one-handed grip on the hub end is used to push the axle shaft until the spline-end bangs into the lips of the differential gearcase. The assembler must now contrive to manipulate the hub end in such a way that the inaccessible spline climbs or

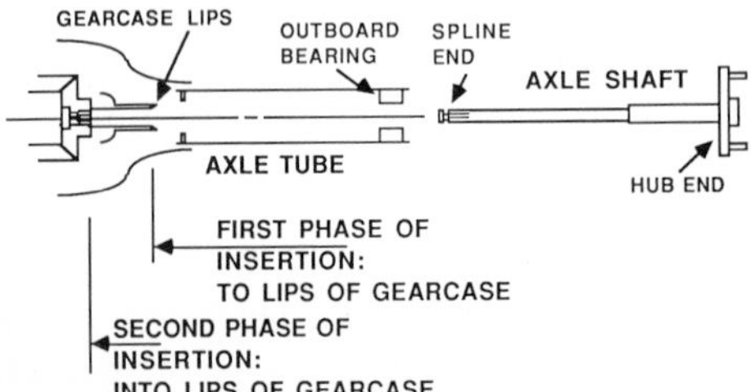

Fig. 9.9 Schematic representation of axle shaft insertion into axle carrier.

jumps through the lips of the case. This typically requires a change in force direction and magnitude if not also a change in grip.

Tolerances for the described manual assembly are not a critical issue nor in this case is the provision or size of chamfers. Burrs can make the assemblers' work more difficult but will not generally preclude success. The issue, if any, is that for unassisted manual assembly, there should be no interference fits. Note in particular that manual assembly is fully tolerant to any error in perpendicularity between the shaft centerline and the plane of the hub.

Now consider assembly by a robot with a gripper. First consider some basic robotic facts of life:

1. "Open-loop" pick-and-place robotic moves (that is, preprogrammed moves unmodified by force or vision feedback) are typically fast, robust, and inexpensive.
2. The addition of vision sensing to a robot move is costly in spite of off-the-shelf hardware availability. In addition, there are reliability problems, at least associated with cleanliness, lighting, and damage.
3. The addition of force sensing to a robot move is also costly and can result in a very slow operation. Reliability will likely be an issue. There is currently a dearth of off-the-shelf hardware and software.
4. Assembly system reconfiguration, as typified by changing grips or modes, generally depends on force, displacement, or vision sensing. The need to reconfigure can add its own intrinsic difficulties to those of sensing, including additional grippers, transfer of grip from one gripper to another, and so on.

Robot lore thus either discourages us from attempting axle insertion by robots or strongly guides us toward figuring out how to implement open-loop pick-and-place robotic moves for the axle-shaft insertion step. The components of a successful open-loop pick-and-place robotic assembly move include:

1. A single grip on the axle suffices from first pick-up to completion of the move (i.e., to the completion of phase 2).
2. The assembly move can be made from initiation to completion of phase 2 either (1) with no part-to-part contact except chamfer crossings or (2) with dimensions, shapes, tolerances, and compliances such that part-to-part contact will halt the assembly and forces will not rise to an extent that might cause damage.

In terms of the assembly task at hand, these components can be interpreted as follows:

1. The axle shaft must be gripped across the hub flange, since the shaft all but disappears as the task approaches completion.
2. Part-to-part contact must be limited to either (1) line-to-line contact between axle shaft and outboard bearings or (2) chamfer-to-chamfer contact between axle shaft and differential-case lips.

Both of these components of a successful open-loop pick-and-place robotic assembly move are directly interpretable in terms of nominal dimensions and tolerances of details of the parts in question as well as the uncertainties in the robot's own motion. These are important only at two places during the process of the assembly. The first is as the spline end enters the outboard bearing; the second as the spline end enters the lips of the case.

The first place, no less important, but a bit less interesting, is not addressed here. There is a lot of clearance between the spline end and the outboard bearing and we will assume that analysis will verify that success is assured.

The second place is where the axle shaft and the entrance of the case meet chamfer to chamfer; assembly will fail if the parts meet flat to flat. So, the question that is asked of the combination of parts dimensions, tolerances, and assembly jigging, manipulator, and gripper is: "Is axle-tip to case-lip contact chamfer to chamfer or is it flat to flat?" This is illustrated schematically in Fig. 9.10. Assume that the workstation supports the shaft tube with a block under the outboard bearing and has a nominal centerline which passes through the center of the bearing. Define variables *A, B, C, D,* and *E* as follows:

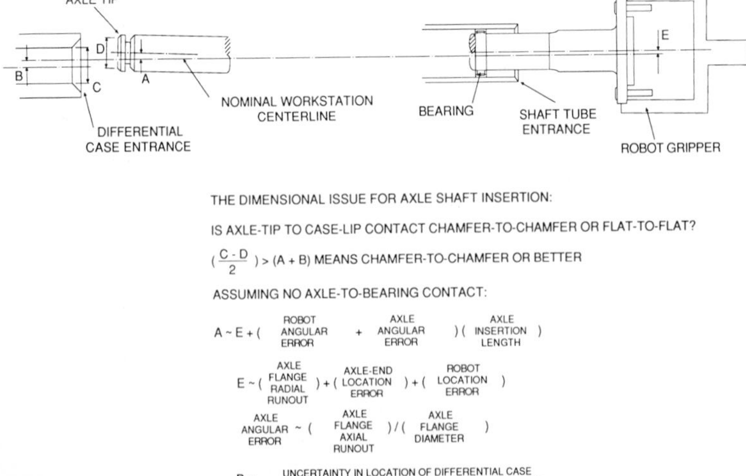

Fig. 9.10 Dimensional issues for axle insertion.

A	Lateral deviation of the centerline of the axle shaft tip from the nominal centerline of the workstation
B	Deviation of the center of the differential case from the nominal centerline of the workstation
C	Outside diameter of the female-part chamfer
D	Inside diameter of the male-part chamfer
E	Lateral offset of hub end of axle from nominal workstation centerline

Then the stated question can be restated algebraically as follows:

$$\left(\frac{C - D}{2}\right) \overset{?}{>} (A + B) \tag{9.13}$$

Clearly, if this inequality is true, the first contact is chamfer to chamfer and assembly proceeds; if not, contact is flat to flat and assembly stops. To resolve this, we must characterize A, B, C, and D quantitatively in terms of the part dimensions and tolerances and the dimensional deviations of the chosen assembly technology.

The chamfer dimensions, C and D, are represented on parts drawings. Note here that it is the authors' experience that drawings do not always represent parts accurately. True part dimensions are outside tolerances often enough that sampling of actual parts, if they are available, is warranted prior to any decisions regarding assembly. Looked at the other way, an analysis like this will reveal which dimensions must always obey tolerances and what those tolerances must be in order that assembly will be successful.

The question in Eq. (9.13) is answered literally by a worst-case calculation, generally involving adding absolute values of errors and deviations rather than by a mean square deviation calculation. What the assembly engineer wants to know is whether first contact will be chamfer to chamfer in every case, whether the parts will assemble in every case. It should be clear that the worst-case C is the minimum possible value of C, even to include the case of no chamfer (if this can occur). Thus the worst-case C is the minimum bore diameter. Similarly, the worst-case D is the maximum possible value of D, even out to the maximum diameter of the shaft's tip, if the chamfer can be missing.

The philosophy of evaluating A and B is the same. However, the values are not exclusively intrinsic to the parts. For example, A, the deviation of the axle-tip centerline from the workstation's nominal, includes components of part and robot position error and also part and robot angular error multiplied by the lever arm contributed by the length of the axle shaft. In this context let us represent the axle-to-nominal centerline deviation at the hub as E. Also, assume that the robot grips the axle by the outside diameter of the hub flange. Then

E = radial run out and nonconcentricity of the flange with respect to the axle shaft's centerline plus the robot's inherent end-point position error plus the error in location of the fixture with respect to the robot. We then can say:

$$A \cong E + (\psi_R + \psi_A)L \tag{9.14}$$

Here, ψ_R is the angular error between the robot and the fixture nominal centerline. ψ_A is the angular error from the robot grip to the tip of the axle shaft (essentially a manufacturing error comprising the deviation of the axle shaft from perpendicularity with respect to the hub). L is the axle shaft's length. B can be similarly evaluated; it can be described verbally as the location error of the differential case centerline with respect to the nominal workstation centerline. It depends not only on how the parts were made but how the gearcase and axle tubes were assembled.

For an example drawn from a small sample of actual axles, we found the following for parameters measured from parts:

$$\left(\frac{C - D}{2}\right) \cong 0.185 \text{ in} \tag{9.15}$$

This represents a worst measured case from the sample and is substantially less (worse) than called for in parts drawings.

$$\psi_A \cong \frac{0.022 \text{ in}}{7 \text{ in}} \cong 0.00314 \text{ rad} \tag{9.16}$$

This represents a worst measured case from the small sample and is very substantially more (worse) than suggested in parts drawings.

$$\text{Axle radial runout} \cong 0.007 \text{ in} \tag{9.17}$$

This represents a worst measured case from the sample and, measured on an uncontrolled surface cut on the same pass as a concentric controlled surface of revolution, is very close to maximum permissible runout.

$$L \cong 24 \text{ in} \tag{9.18}$$

This is a confirmed nominal.

$$B \cong 0.060 \text{ in} \tag{9.19}$$

This is an estimate based on estimates about the machine that presses the tubes into the central casting.

For a parameter depending on parts plus quality of stationary fixturing we found:

$$\text{Tube-end location error} \cong 0.050 \text{ in} \tag{9.20}$$

This represents an estimate based on parts, geometry, and typical good-quality fixture-construction practice.

For parameters depending on assembly technology choice we found

$$\text{Robot position error} \cong 0.015 \text{ in} \tag{9.20}$$

$$\Psi_R \text{ Robot angular error} \cong 0.0008 \text{ rad} \tag{9.21}$$

These numbers represent estimates based on composite robot characteristics including effects out to the gripping interface. They are not thought to be conservative.

The result is shown in Table 9.2. The conclusion is that pick-and-place robotic task automation would not be successful without changes. Axle angular runout is the dominant error. If all axles met the standards suggested in the parts drawing, the 0.075 in Table 9.2 would be merely 0.035, virtually assuring pick-and-place feasibility. Whether axles can be made to drawing standards economically is aquestion for the manufacturing department to answer. Clearly though, if an automation decision were based on drawing dimensions without a parts survey, a wrong decision would be a likely possibility. Upgrading angular runout of the hub is not an easily resolved issue because of the mix of shape-generating machining operations which

TABLE 9.2 Summary of Numerical Example of Axle Insertion Analysis.

The result is that we cannot guarantee that the axle can be inserted open loop by pick-and-place methods.

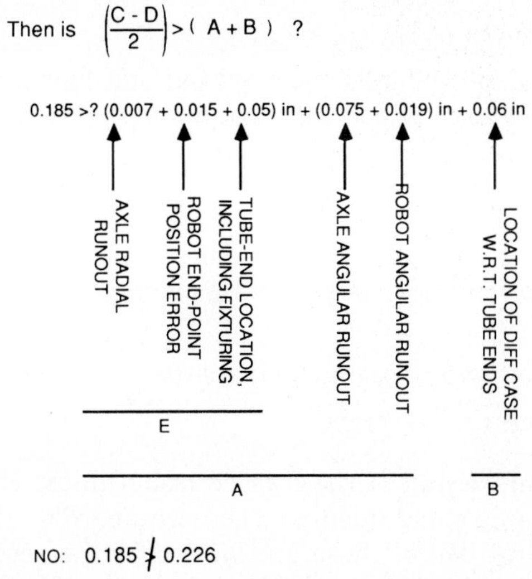

Then is $\left(\frac{C - D}{2}\right) > (A + B)$?

0.185 >? (0.007 + 0.015 + 0.05) in + (0.075 + 0.019) in + 0.06 in

- 0.007: AXLE RADIAL RUNOUT
- 0.015: ROBOT END-POINT POSITION ERROR
- 0.05: TUBE-END LOCATION, INCLUDING FIXTURING
- 0.075: AXLE ANGULAR RUNOUT
- 0.019: ROBOT ANGULAR RUNOUT
- 0.06: LOCATION OF DIFF CASE W.R.T. TUBE ENDS

E = (0.007 + 0.015 + 0.05)

A = (0.007 + 0.015 + 0.05) + (0.075 + 0.019)

B = 0.06

NO: 0.185 $\not>$ 0.226

may relieve residual stresses in forged blanks and hardening and heat-treating operations which may also involve distortions.

Other significant errors include the shape of the carrier (dimension B) and the tube-end location which includes the effects of stationary fixturing. Some improvement in each element may be possible, especially the latter.

Two robust conclusions seem evident from the quantitative analysis. First, not much seems to be gained by substituting a more repeatable and accurate manipulator; its contribution is small. Second, making pick-and-place feasible could be simply a matter of concentrating on the left side of the inequality. In particular, having the left-side as small as 0.185 in is the consequence of a small female chamfer that could be made larger at little physical or economic cost and of a male chamfer that occasionally disappears because of correctable manufacturing difficulties.

What, then, have we shown? We have shown an example of an assembly step for which the most casual of tolerance and error analysis is suitable as a prelude to manual assembly but for which a somewhat painstaking and extensive tolerance and error analysis is a necessary prelude to automated assembly. The analysis for automated assembly is useful not only as a go/no-go decision tool for automation but also as a sensitivity analysis. It allows a quick answer to questions like: "If the errors of dimensions G and H rise to $0.00X$ and $0.00Y$, can the insertion still be done by pick-and-place technique?" or "Which tolerances need be improved and by how much to assure that pick-and-place techniques allow certain assembly?"

Example 2—A three-part product

Most generally, part dimensions and tolerances are but one element in a quartet of interacting elements which affect automated assembly. The quartet includes:

1. Part dimensions and tolerances
2. Dimensions, tolerances, and stability of the elements of the assembly machinery loop comprising grippers, moving elements, and fixtures
3. Provision of and choice of jigging and gripping surfaces on parts
4. Sequence of assembly and process steps

For manual assembly, the second of these is no issue unless each part in the assembly task is jigged, guided, and constrained. The first example emphasized the first two of these and hinted at the second two, which can interact strongly. An example that emphasizes the last two is a three-part precision-instrument assembly which can be characterized as a core with shaft ends similar to a motor armature, an enclosing housing supporting one end of the shaft, and an end cover closing the housing and supporting the other end of the shaft (see Fig. 9.11). Each part is a body of revolution. In this case, manual assembly is not possible because alignment of the core with both the housing and the end cover must be extremely precise. Only a delicate electrical measurement can detect if alignment is correct. An additional bar to manual assembly is the fact that assembly takes place in an oven with extra heaters that solder the parts together.

In this assembly all of the four elements listed above are at issue. The core may be installed first in the housing or first in the end cover, soldering may be done joint by joint as soon as surfaces to be soldered are brought into proximity, or all joints may be soldered simultaneously after assembly. Of these combinations there are some that are better than others and some that do not permit automated completion of assembly under all possible conditions.

The designer of the instrument wishes to hold all three parts suspended in the oven, adjust them using the electrical measurements, and solder them all at once. The assembly machine builder wants to avoid such a complicated mechanism, preferring to solder the parts one at a time, starting with core to end cover. An analysis of the tolerances to which the parts are made shows, however, that properly made parts assembled one at a time could, under some combinations of tolerances, prevent proper adjustment of the last part. If it were

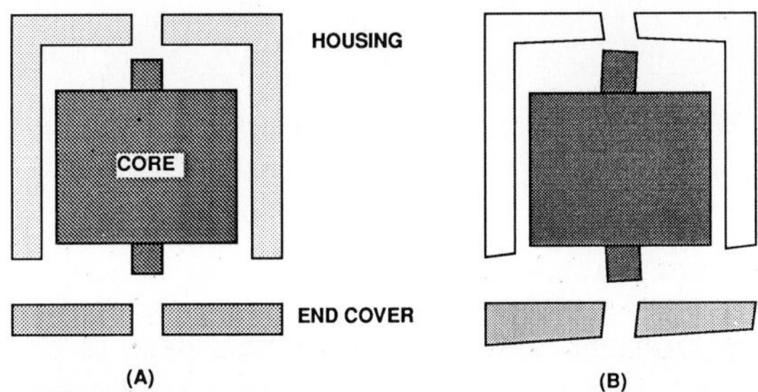

Fig. 9.11 Three-part assembly. (*a*) Nominal part shapes. (*b*) Exaggerated part shapes within nominal tolerances. If the core is soldered to the end cover first and the shaft is centered in the hole, it is possible that we will not be able to assemble the housing over the core and center the shaft in the upper hole while simultaneously centering the core in the housing. A complex fixture that holds all three parts and maneuvers them simultaneously will be needed. To avoid this complexity, the parts must be redesigned, giving them better tolerances or better grip surfaces.

necessary, for reasons of cost or equipment reliability, to adopt the sequential assembly and process sequence (which cannot guarantee successful completion), reconsideration of part dimensions and tolerances is needed. This reconsideration may need to address part-to-part interfaces, part-to-assembly grip and jigging interfaces, the dimensional loop of the assembly machinery, or all three.

Design for Material Handling and Part Mating

Whether a product is assembled manually or automatically, its design should be evaluated with respect to the ease by which parts are fed and oriented to the assembly station and mated to each other. This is often called "design for assembly" (Boothroyd and Dewhurst, 1987). A good rule of thumb is that a product which is easy to assemble automatically will be easy to assemble manually; however, it is not necessarily true that easy manual assembly implies easy automatic assembly. Therefore, in the absence of further information, it is wise to assume automatic assembly.

Design for material handling

Parts must be transported to both manual and automatic assembly stations. Handling involves several factors, including the following:

- Efficiency in terms of parts carried per carrier
- Protection of the parts from contamination or from handling damage
- Separation or spacing between parts to protect the parts from each other and to allow grasping
- Counting, checking identity, and otherwise accounting for the parts and documenting their arrival and use
- Recovery and reuse of the carrier

The anticipated handling method influences how the part is designed. This chapter deals with part design issues, while part feeding alternatives are discussed in Chap. 10.

To increase or maintain "structure" in the production operation, it is preferable to arrange parts uniformly rather than heaping them in bins. The latter appear more efficient because more parts may be packed into a carrier, but almost none of the other factors listed above is supported by this technique. The advantages of bins almost always accrue to the person or company that puts them in the bin, while the disadvantages fall on the one who must get them out. Figure 1.13 illustrates the contrast.

At the moment of assembly, the most important factor is obtaining control of the part by grasping it. Grasp must not only be firm but must be accomplished on a designated gripping surface. The importance of this can be seen by referring to "Tolerances and Their Relation to Assembly" earlier in this chapter as well as to Chap. 11 where it is pointed out that the dimensional uncertainties contributed by the gripping action, the gripper, and the grip surface increase the uncertainty concerning the location of the mating surfaces, possibly rendering assembly impossible.

The best way to ensure accurate grasping is to arrange parts in the carrier in consistent locations and orientations, with some separation between them. The separation permits fingers or grippers to reach around the part; uniform spacing and consistent placement and orientation allow predictable gripping. It is then up to the product designer to know the assembly sequence and identify and properly tolerance the grip surfaces and then to specify how the parts are to be arranged in the carrier so that the grip surfaces are accessible. Parts need not be located in the carrier to the accuracy or repeatability required for assembly. It is necessary only to design the grippers with a wide enough opening and suitable grip surface shape so that the part is gripped accurately.

Sometimes, the nature of the parts permits quite dense packing with excellent uniformity. This result is achieved when parts can be made to nest or stack directly on top of one another. Stamped metal parts often can be designed this way even when they are not flat. Figure 9.12 shows some examples. Location may be provided by pins which pass through holes in the parts; these holes may serve a functional purpose or they may be used exclusively for handling and feeding. The former is probably less costly.

A second example illustrates another common material-handling problem, that of flexible parts. In this case the flexible item is a ribbon cable with a plug on each end. The issue is to insert a circuit board into a computer chassis, plug one end of the cable to the circuit board, and plug the other end of the cable into a socket on the chassis near the board. This is no problem for manual assembly but is essentially not feasible for robot or automatic assembly unless the plugs are constrained in some way. The solution adopted is shown in Fig. 9.13. The board-end plug was redesigned so that the chassis-end plug could be attached to it temporarily by the cable's manufacturer. The robot assembly sequence consists of inserting the board into the chassis, then picking up the cable assembly with the plugs joined, inserting the

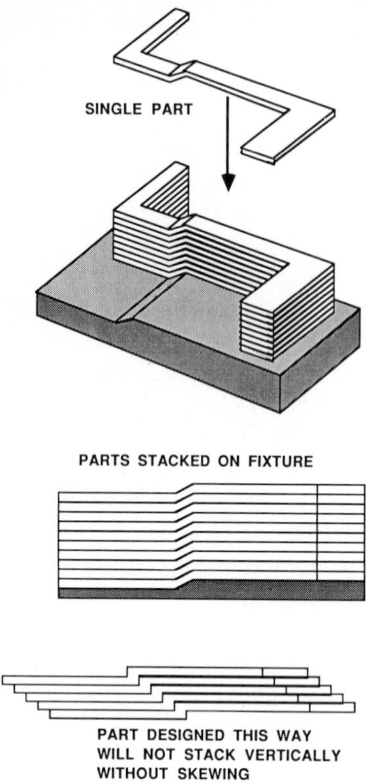

Fig. 9.12 Parts designed to stack in a carrier. The parts at the top of the figure will stack vertically because the bend in the part is made at an angle other than 90 degrees to the flat portion of the part. A vertical stack permits the gripper to grip each part at the same location, except vertical, which is easily adjusted in the program or with a simple contact sensor on the gripper. The parts at the bottom of the figure also stack, but the stack skews to one side. The amount of skew depends on the number of parts remaining in the stack. This, too, could be accounted for by sensors and/or programming, but it would be more complex. In particular, the number of parts delivered in each stack would have to be exactly the same each time or a sensor would be needed to determine how many were delivered.

board-end plug into the board, then detaching the chassis-end plug from temporary storage and plugging it into the chassis.

The example illustrates a larger point, namely that the designer may have to deal with an external parts supplier in order to achieve the goals of easy assembly. Often a vendor will ask a higher price to provide redesigned parts or special packaging.[3] But special packaging may be the only way to achieve automatic assembly because such packaging is the key to automatically feeding the parts. There is a ripple effect to this, since automatic assembly may be the only economic alternative, even accounting for the vendor's penalty, other than buying the entire assembly from a foreign supplier. Thus a small decision can have profound effects.

Typical special packaging includes attaching parts to paper tapes or strips or placing them in tubes. Some kinds of parts, such as metal

[3] Note, however, the example of cone-point screws in Chap. 3 where the vendors initially charged more but eventually were forced to cut back to prices similar to those of plain point screws.

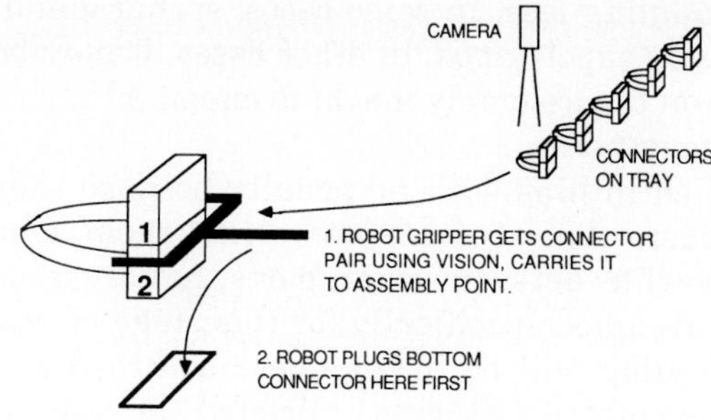

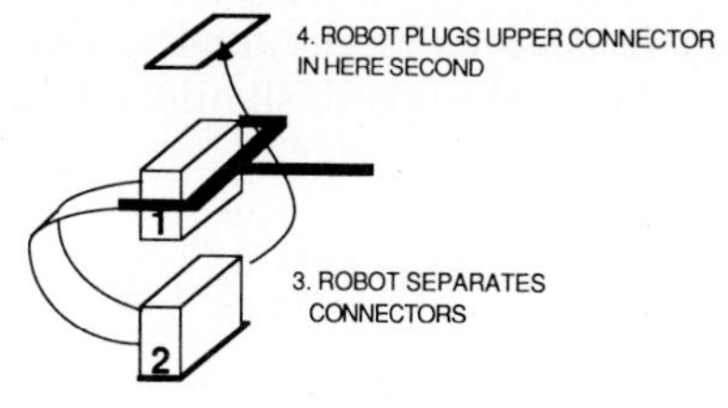

ILLUSTRATION OF INTERLOCKING RIBBON CONNECTOR WHICH ROBOT SEPARATES DURING INSERTION PROCESS

Fig. 9.13 Redesign of a connector to gain control of a ribbon cable. The connectors are shipped plugged together and are put in pallets by the supplier. The robot can grasp the pair and insert one end first. Then it separates the pair and plugs in the second half. The flexibility of the cable is eliminated as a problem. The need for vision resulted from a design compromise regarding the accuracy of the pallet. An inexpensive, disposable pallet was adopted. It is light and adds little to shipping costs, but it is not accurate enough to hold the plugs for a robot to grasp them properly. The vision system is used to remove grasping errors.

connector pins, are made from metal strips and are not separated until the moment of assembly. These techniques are common in the electronics industry where the shape of many parts is independent of their function; thus they may be given standardized outer shapes. Because of that industry's high production rates, special attention has been given to designing parts for easy feeding.

Another example concerns coil springs. It is well known that open end springs, that is, those made from pure sections of helixes, will tangle with each other. Closed end springs, wound so that each end is aclosed circle, are less likely to tangle. It is not so well known that the diameter and pitch of the spring's helix also influence tangling, with larger, more open springs tangling less. In some cases, spring manufacturers will attach springs to paper tapes. In other cases, it may be possible to wind the springs on the assembly machine one at a time as needed, avoiding feeding altogether.

Some parts may be supplied in bins with no penalty because they can be fed by automatic feeders that separate and orient them. One method is to use vibratory bowl feeders. However, parts that are to be fed by such means must be designed specifically for this stage of production or else automatic feeding will be impossible. Boothroyd and Dewhurst (1987) discuss these matters at length. Briefly, the issue is that the feeder needs access to features on the part that are keyed to the position and orientation desired for assembly. Either the part should be symmetric so that its orientation does not matter or else it should be asymmetric in a way that is obvious to the feeder. For example, if the part is a pin with a head, the head should be large enough to be distinguished by a mechanical arm or slot.

Design for part mating

Chapter 5 stated the conditions under which parts would physically mate. These conditions involve the relative lateral and angular error between parts, the relative clearance between them, the coefficient of friction, and the width of chamfers, if any. The theory was stated in terms of round pegs and holes, although similar theories have been developed for rectangular shapes (Sturges, 1988).

These conditions do not indicate whether assembly is easy but rather only if it is possible. Note that assembly may still be possible without the conditions being satisfied, if enough force is used. In fact, actual assemblies include many cases not covered by the specific theory. These include thread mating (for which some theory exists as noted in Chap. 5), push-twist insertions of various degrees of difficulty, snap fits (again, there is some theory as noted in Chaps. 5 and 6), application of adhesives, use of heat or ultrasound to shrink or melt parts together, soldering, welding, crimping, and so on.

A product design may be analyzed with the aim of estimating the ease or difficulty of assembly and the time each mate might take. The Boothroyd method is typical. Its essence is group technology, in which several basic part shapes, feeding methods, and assembly conditions are given in tabular or code form, and the designer must decide which basic types fit the situation at hand.

Each part is identified as to type of shape, using characteristics such as:

- Rotational—disk, short cylinder, or long cylinder
- Nonrotational—flat, long, or cubic

Each type is then further subdivided as to shape details, such as:

- Symmetric features such as projections or grooves
- Asymmetric features
- Features on one side only, or several, or on the end(s)
- Symmetry or asymmetry of the part with respect to ends and/or with respect to principal axis
- Chamfers
- Very large or very small part
- Light, sticky, tangle, etc.

These characteristics are used to estimate manual handling time or automatic feeder cost or to indicate that automatic feeding is probably not feasible. Figure 9.14 shows some examples.

Each part mate is also categorized in such terms as:

- The part is easy to align and position (based on the existence of features as noted above as well as qualitative judgments about how much space for tools or fingers is available around the part during insertion or how easy it is to observe the mate visually).

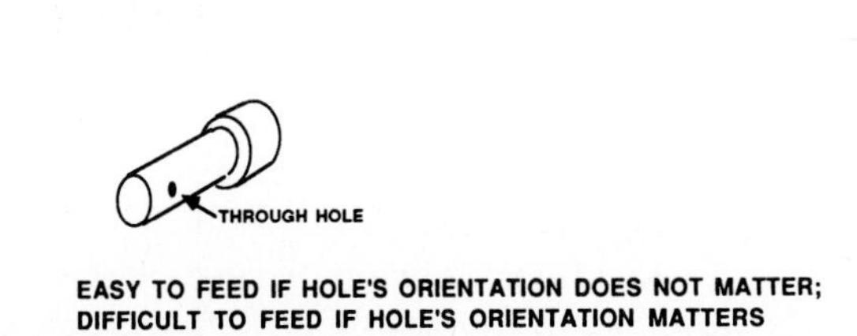

Fig. 9.14 Parts with different degrees of symmetry. Symmetric parts are easy to feed since the feeder does not have to orient them. If orientation with respect to a feature is required, the feature must be accessible to the feeder's orientation-testing mechanism. For mechanical feeders, this requirement usually means that the feature (or a proxy for it) must stick out. If the feeder uses vision to check orientation, the feature need not stick out but must be visible.

- There is resistance to insertion or no resistance (including force fits or the requirement that the part be elastically or plastically deformed in order to achieve the mate).
- The part may be secured immediately or another operation is needed to secure it, including the possibility that a temporary brace is needed.
- Type of securing method (for each method there is a time and cost estimate).

In the Hitachi version of this method, one notes the number of separate motions required to achieve the mate as well as the number of directions or axes along or about which these motions must occur; larger counts result in demerits for the design.

The ultimate judgments consist of estimated assembly time, part feeder cost, and assembly workhead cost. The latter two apply to automatic assembly only. These judgments are arrived at by giving each part or mate a numerical code based on identifying the above characteristics and then finding that code in a table of times and costs. Figure 9.15 is an example table. The time entries in the tables are based on industry standards and specific experiments, plus the judgment of experts. If a part or design has a poor score, the aspects needing redesign are indicated by their large contribution to the score.

This method has several advantages. First, it is specific and systematic, with the results that it can be easily taught to designers and programmed onto a computer. Second, while it is qualitative in some respects and empirical in others, it tells the designer in broad outlines what design alternatives are preferable to others. It also sensitizes designers to a fact which should be obvious but may not be, namely that cost depends on design. In this sense, the method is educational.

The method must be used with caution, however. It does not deal with several of the goals of design cited in Chap. 8 and thus should be used as part of a total design effort rather than being applied after major design is finished or in isolation from other designers. In particular, the redesign aspects of the method, which focus on reducing the number of parts, must be integrated with part fabrication cost estimates, desired functions, and other strategic issues, as described in Chaps. 3 and 8. Fabrication costs almost always exceed assembly costs, and the cost of a part X intended to replace separate parts A and B must be compared to the total costs of A and B. Second, the method also contains economic analyses and estimates of assembly system cost which are not described here. These methods are approximate and are no quicker to apply than the more accurate ones described later in this book.

MANUAL INSERTION—ESTIMATED TIMES (seconds)

Key:

PART ADDED but NOT SECURED

			after assembly no holding down required to maintain orientation and location (3)				holding down required during subsequent processes to maintain orientation or location (3)			
			easy to align and position during assembly (4)		not easy to align or position during assembly		easy to align and position during assembly (4)		not easy to align or position during assembly	
			no resistance to insertion	resistance to insertion (5)	no resistance to insertion	resistance to insertion (5)	no resistance to insertion	resistance to insertion (5)	no resistance to insertion	resistance to insertion (5)
			0	1	2	3	6	7	8	9
addition of any part (1) where neither the part itself nor any other part is finally secured immediately	part and associated tool (including hands) can easily reach the desired location	0	1.5	2.5	2.5	3.5	5.5	6.5	6.5	7.5
	part and associated tool (including hands) cannot easily reach the desired location: due to obstructed access or restricted vision (2)	1	4	5	5	6	8	9	9	10
	part and associated tool (including hands) cannot easily reach the desired location: due to obstructed access and restricted vision (2)	2	5.5	6.5	6.5	7.5	9.5	10.5	10.5	11.5

PART SECURED IMMEDIATELY

			no screwing operation or plastic deformation immediately after insertion (snap/press fits, circlips, spire nuts, etc.)		plastic deformation immediately after insertion							screw tightening immediately after insertion	
					plastic bending or torsion			rivetting or similar operation					
						not easy to align or position during assembly			not easy to align or position during assembly				
			easy to align and position with no resistance to insertion (4)	not easy to align or position during assembly and/or resistance to insertion (5)	easy to align and position during assembly (4)	no resistance to insertion	resistance to insertion (5)	easy to align and position during assembly (4)	no resistance to insertion	resistance to insertion (5)		easy to align and position with no torsional resistance (4)	not easy to align or position and/or torsional resistance (5)
			0	1	2	3	4	5	6	7		8	9
addition of any part (1) where the part itself and/or other parts are being finally secured immediately	part and associated tool (including hands) can easily reach the desired location and the tool can be operated easily	3											
	part and associated tool (including hands) cannot easily reach desired location or tool cannot be operated easily: due to obstructed access or restricted vision (2)	4											
	part and associated tool (including hands) cannot easily reach desired location or tool cannot be operated easily: due to obstructed access and restricted vision (2)	5											

SEPARATE OPERATION

		mechanical fastening processes (part(s) already in place but not secured immediately after insertion)				non-mechanical fastening processes (part(s) already in place but not secured immediately after insertion)				non-fastening processes	
		none or localized plastic deformation				metallurgical processes					
							additional material required				
		bending or similar processes	rivetting or similar processes	screw tightening or other processes	bulk plastic deformation (large proportion of part is plastically deformed during fastening)	no additional material required (e.g. resistance, friction welding, etc.)	soldering processes	weld/braze processes	chemical processes (e.g. adhesive bonding, etc.)	manipulation of parts or sub-assembly (e.g. orienting, fitting or adjustment of part(s), etc.)	other processes (e.g. liquid insertion, etc.)
		0	1	2	3	4	5	6	7	8	9
assembly processes where all solid parts are in place	9										

Fig. 9.15 Sample design for assembly table. (*Boothroyd and Dewhurst, Inc.*)

Example

The Nippondenso meter casing (described in Chap. 3) is a single part that illustrates many of the above points. It serves a triple purpose. It is the "base part" of the assembly, the root of the assembly sequence. It is also the part to which most or all of the others mate, so it provides support and dimensional integrity for the assembly. Finally, it is the carrier or pallet for the assembly while it is passing through the assembly and adjustment processes. In order to provide all these functions, the part had to be designed with dimensioned and toleranced surfaces on the top (for insertion of parts) and on the sides and bottom (for locating it in the conveyor system and each workstation).

Creation and Evaluation of Testing Strategies

The relation between testing and quality control

The "quality" of a product is an important determinant of the product's potential for market success. Quality has many components, some quantifiable, some inherently qualitative, some subjective, others quite objective.

The qualitative and subjective quality components include styling, appearance in a showroom, presentation, certain simple comparisons with competing products, some aspects of fit and finish, and aspects of the buyers' and users' expectations. These matters are vitally important to a product's success but cannot concern us here.

The quantitative and objective components of quality may show up in whole batches or populations of a product or in occasional individual items. The quality of whole batches may be determined by the adequacy of the original design, the materials, or the production processes, whereas a single item's quality is usually due only to production adequacy. Quantitative components include other aspects of fit and finish, whether a product works when it is delivered, how many of a population do not work at various stages of production and what is the distribution of problems, comparisons of performance indicators of finished products with performance standards, how often products must be serviced for other than planned maintenance, and the like. Many of these matters are of concern to us here.

Several ways of obtaining high quality are known. Broadly speaking, they are:

1. *Designing quality in,* that is, choosing materials, dimensions, tolerances, and procedures so that the likelihood of the desired outcome is very high. Often this approach leads to expensive products, but Taguchi (see Chap. 8) has shown that systematic statistical techniques can be used to choose among items or options of similar cost so as to obtain higher quality.
2. *Monitoring production processes* to ensure that they continue to perform as expected. A statistical approach may be taken here as well, by improving the process until no systematic or repeating error re-

mains. The residual nonsystematic error is acknowledged to be purely random and uncontrollable; if it is still too large, a different process must be tried. If it is small enough, occasional sampling is sufficient to detect deviations that require correction. Japanese shipbuilding contains many examples of this approach. It is broadly referred to as statistical quality control.

3. *Testing each product unit* at one or more points during its production. The possibility of testing raises many questions, and the set of answers to these many questions constitutes a test strategy. Matters to be addressed include what faults could occur and what could cause them; what tests are possible, and how many of them to do; where in the assembly sequence various faults become testable, and which of several testable states for each fault to choose; whether to modify an assembly sequence to accommodate or enhance testing; and so on. This section is an introduction to the questions and issues associated with evolving a test strategy.

The consideration of a test strategy is by no means a new issue in production processes. It was interesting to come across an extensive, serial, fixed-automation production-machine about a decade ago which was logically organized on the basis that faults in production did occur and that there was an advantage to be had by expelling faulty subassemblies at test stations spaced along the serial route rather than continuing to add assembly and parts value to a useless entity. The machines, produced by Swanson-Erie Corporation, are named "Synchrobank" and include sufficient buffer after testing sites to accommodate the occasional expulsion of a faulty subassembly. There have also been some theoretical approaches taken. A survey of these may be found in Raz (1986).

Table 9.3 lists and defines important terms used in this section.

Goals of testing

One may cite various goals for testing: prevention of the possibility of faulty products getting into customers' hands, prevention of the possibility of faulty subassemblies continuing on through the assembly process, prevention of extra rework, and so forth. It is convenient to characterize these goals as avoidance of costs, or more precisely, as incurring the predictable costs of testing to avoid less-predictable and presumably larger costs associated with faulty subassemblies passing through factory processes, dealers, and on to customers. This characterization at once both suggests a basis for deciding on a test strategy and reveals a difficulty inherent in deciding a test strategy rationally and completely quantitatively. The basis is minimization of the cost

TABLE 9.3 Definition of Terms and Assumptions in Test Strategy Determination

Faults include unsuitable parts or components, errors in assembly, or damage during assembly. If it could be assumed that components are made to specification, perhaps as determined by parts inspections or by prior tests, faults would include only assembly errors, contamination, or damage.

A fault is *viable* after enough parts or parts and fixtures are assembled for that fault to exist. A fault is associated with that assembly state where it is first viable and with all subsequent states.

Faults are exposed and pinpointed by *tests* and *diagnoses*. Tests are done, and diagnoses are started, on assemblies of parts. Each test is associated with the assembly state where the test can be performed. A diagnosis is associated with not only the assembly state where it can be performed but also with the tests performed on the current and previous assembly states. Thus, there can be a plurality of diagnoses associated with each test, depending on which tests have been performed earlier.

A test is *specific* if it is sensitive to a single fault or if it is self-diagnostic, that is, if it separates and identifies the faults it detects.

Diagnoses are used to determine the fault (or faults) which triggers a nonspecific test. A fault may be specified or localized by a nonspecific test that is preceded by one or several other tests.

Tests are assumed perfect; a test sensitive to a fault will always respond to that fault and never to the absence of that fault.

Sampling is not considered here; if a test is done, it is done on all assemblies. Britney (1972) showed that optimal testing strategies under rather general assumptions involved 100 percent testing and no sampling.

and the difficulty lies in the unpredictability of faults. Fault mechanisms are generally poorly enough known that fault occurrence seems random rather than deterministic, and the statistics of fault occurrence are nonstationary. That is, the occurrence probabilities of various faults depend on so many changeable factors that faults may rise and fall in likelihood, often disappearing for a time and then cropping up again, often being beaten down by the efforts of plant personnel and possibly replaced by others.

Details of test strategy considerations

Testing then serves as one means toward the delivery of a fault-free product. A proper test program screens for common product faults and directs faulty units or subassemblies to rework. Testing also documents the statistics of faults, providing basic data for the establishment or revision of the strategy.

Manufacturing and assembly process improvement, on the other hand, directly reduces the frequencies of fault occurrences. It is a more fundamental means toward quality control and improvement. Taken to the limit, it can preempt various, or even all, parts of a testing strategy. We may distinguish two opportunities for process improvement, namely part fabrication and part assembly. While fabrication issues are crucial, and badly designed or made parts are costlier and occur more often than assembly errors, our focus is on assembly.

We may divide assembly considerations into two classes, those involving single part mates and those covering the entire assembly sequence.

Single part mates are subject to six faults: wrong part, damaged part used anyway, missing part, incorrect assembly action (not tight enough, not fully mated, etc.), dirt or other contamination, or damage caused by the mating action itself. Both manual and automatic assembly are subject to each of these. People tend to make more random errors and rarely make the same error again and again once their training is complete. Automatic assembly tends to behave in the opposite way: A jammed feeder may result in 20 assemblies in a row with the same missing part. The potential for extremely high quality seems better for machines because they "tolerate" the extravagant vigilance that is necessary better than people do. Automation technology can also improve assembly processes by mechanizing assembly steps in which the details of motion, part trajectory, or technique are critical to the success of the step or avoidance of damage. Attention to many details of design for assembly (discussed earlier in this chapter and in Chap. 8) also improve the chances that the correct part will be used and will be inserted properly. All these single mate considerations affect the probabilities of failures and thus affect the scope and shape of the testing strategy.

Beyond single part mates lies the domain of the assembly sequence as a whole. Assembly sequence is a major basis for a choice of test strategy. A test strategy is the list of tests that will be performed, chosen from the generally larger list of all tests which can be performed. A potential fault cannot be tested for until the requisite parts have been mated. Design often constrains the sequence and we have no options. One can choose from many examples: a case must be assembled and closed before it can be tested for leaks, soldering of components must be done before a printed circuit board can be checked for solder bridges and performance of major functions, valve train clearances of a pushrod overhead valve engine cannot be checked until the head is bolted to the specified tightness.

In other situations, there are choices between assembly sequences that offer different test opportunities. One sequence may create a subassembly that can be tested while another will leave out a crucial part until the subassembly has already been mated to the final product; one sequence will permit a likely fault to be detected early in the assembly while another will delay detection.

Summarizing, assembly sequence determines fault viability, viability determines whether a test can exist, and the strategy choice is made from the set of possible tests.

In addition, there are often better and worse assembly sequences in terms of the potential for damage during assembly, directly affecting fault occurrence. One sequence will permit parts to be securely jigged or gripped on well-toleranced surfaces, reducing the likelihood of wedges and jams; another will not. One sequence will permit each mate to involve securely gripped single parts while another will require bulky groups of loosely stacked items to be mated simultaneously.

A major element of test strategy is the question of whether to restrict testing to final assemblies or whether to do testing at subassembly stages. In lieu of a formal and quantitative determination of testing strategy, there are several qualitative circumstances that encourage testing at subassembly stages. These include:

1. Such tests might address faults which occur very often.
2. They might address faults which are substantially cheaper to diagnose or to repair at the subassembly stage than at later stages.
3. No later test for a fault may be available, say because the test points are no longer accessible.
4. No later specific test may be available; that is, later tests may reveal the fault in question only in combination with other faults, requiring additional tests or diagnoses.

Basis for a qualitative test strategy choice

In order to make a qualitative choice of test strategy, one must know:

1. The detailed assembly sequence.
2. A list of faults. Each fault is to be associated with the assembly state or states where the particular fault is viable.
3. The occurrence statistics for each fault, or failing that, a ranking of faults in descending order of likelihood and severity.
4. A list of prospective tests. Each test is to be associated with the assembly state(s) where the test can be performed. For each test, one also needs a list of faults that the test is sensitive to.

The engineer responsible for evolving a test strategy then uses judgment and qualitative knowledge regarding relevant costs to choosethose tests to be done in a way that minimizes total cost. While the basis for optimization is not here, there is the basis for a qualitatively correct informed choice.

Basis for a quantitative test strategy choice

The information needed for a quantitative determination of testing strategy includes all of the information needed for a qualitative judgmental choice and, in addition, quantitative characterizations of relevant costs and details of any constraints which may affect the determination. The costs generally have variable and fixed components and an assignment of the fixed costs to each product unit must be made. Costs include:

1. The costs of testing.
2. The costs of diagnosis. Note that diagnosis costs depend not only on the specificity of the test in question but also on the suite of tests previously completed. That is, prior test results may form a component of the diagnosis following a failure of a current test.
3. The cost of repair. This is a function of the fault and of the state of assembly that exists when the repair is to be made.
4. The costs associated with a customer or user finding each fault.
5. The costs of warranty repair of each fault.

Procedure

With the listed information in hand, the assembly-test engineer is now in a position to choose a testing strategy by quantitative means. Any of several circumstances might prevent the accomplishment: The information may be imprecise or questionable, elements may be sufficiently nonstationary to make determination impractical, or the task of calculating the optimum may be sufficiently daunting to prevent its completion. Notwithstanding, one may proceed as follows:

1. Establish an assembly sequence or a set of candidate sequences. The final determination of assembly sequence may be combined with the determination of test strategy.
2. Prepare a list of faults (F_i).
3. Associate each fault with the assembly state where the fault becomes viable.

4. Devise specific tests (T_i) for each fault F_i. For each nonspecific test, devise a set of diagnoses $D(T_i, T_a \ldots)$ depending on the test and prior tests T_a completed. Associate each specific test, and each nonspecific test and its associated diagnoses, with the assembly state where the test is performed. The hierarchy of faults, tests, and diagnoses are represented in Fig. 9.16.

The first set of faults, represented by the widest and uppermost bracket, is the set of all faults F_i. This set is divided into two sub-

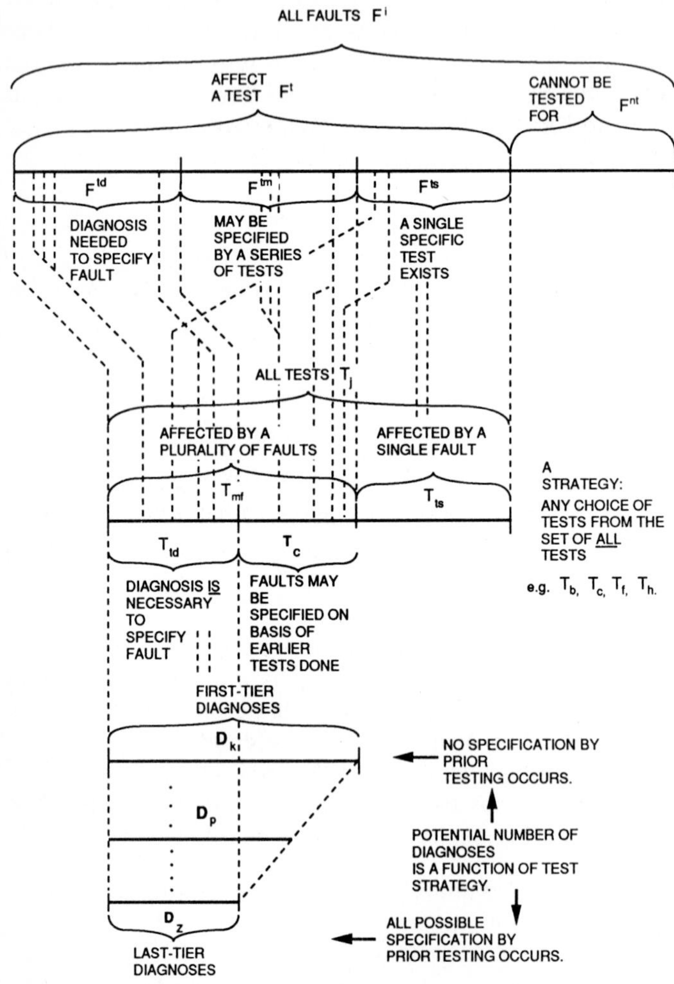

Fig. 9.16 Shown here are certain relations amongst the sets of all the faults which can associate with an assembly, all the tests which can be done to detect existence of faults, and the diagnoses which may be necessary to specify the fault or faults present.

sets, those faults F_t for which there are sensitive tests and those faults F_{nt} for which there are none. (The latter subset F_{nt} may include faults for which there are not any nondestructive tests and faults for which there are tests which will not be considered.) Theformer subset F_t is itself made up of the faults F_{ts} for which a specific test exists and, among the faults for which no specific test exists, the faults F_{tm} which can be specified by a series of tests without disassembly and the faults F_{td} for which diagnosis, possibly including disassembly, is necessary to specify the fault.

The second set of interest is the set of all tests T_j. Subsets include those tests T_{fs} which are sensitive to only a single fault and those tests T_{fm} which are sensitive to a plurality of faults. Note here that the use of a test from the set T_{fm} does not imply that diagnosis is necessary. It is possible that sufficient tests may have been done earlier so that with the positive indication from the current test, the fault is specified unambiguously.

The faults then distribute on all the tests which make up the test strategy. The test strategy does not necessarily include tests from any particular set, so there is not necessarily a correspondence between faults and tests in similar classes, F_{ts} and T_{fs}, say. A particular fault may have a corresponding specific test, but if that test is not part of the test strategy, the fault may go undetected or it may be detected by a nonspecific test sensitive to that and several other faults, to be specified either by subsequent diagnosis or by a fortuitous coincidence of the current nonspecific test and previously completed tests. To the extent that there are faults for which a specific test exists (in the class F_{ts}) covered by corresponding tests (in the class T_{fs}) in the test strategy, no diagnosis is required.

Diagnosis is necessary to specify the fault in the cases where there is no test from the class T_{ts} for a fault from the class F_{ts}; in the case of a fault from the class F_{tm}, the set of tests in the test strategy up to the decision to rework are insufficient to specify the fault; and any fault in the class F_{td}. Diagnoses are tests which are done off the assembly or process line. They may or may not be routinely done on the line. Diagnoses are single tier or multiple tier depending on the number of offline tests needed to specify a fault. This is a function of which fault caused a positive test indication and what the test strategy is or which tests have been run prior to the positive (fault) test indication.

5. Characterize the statistics of fault occurrence. Establishing a probability of occurrence $p(F_i)$ of each fault is a characterization which may be valid for many circumstances.

At this point, the assembly-test engineer faces a branch and may use qualitative and judgmental or some semiquantitative comparisons for deciding on a test strategy; or the engineer may continue consideration of the costs associated with testing or not testing and prepare for a quantitative determination of test strategy. An important indication is the nature of the characterization of the statistics of fault occurrence [$p(F_i)$, for example]. If they are generally quite unstationary, a qualitative test-strategy determination may be the wiser choice. The reasoning is simple; changing statistics lead to changing strategies which imply a different mix of test equipment.

If it is decided that a quantitative determination is in order, move to the next step.

6. Establish and characterize the relevant costs:

   $C(T_i)$ is cost of test i, variable plus unit fixed costs.

   $C[D(T_i, T_a \ldots)]$ is cost of diagnoses associated with test i and the set of previously completed tests a ....

   $CR[F_i, D(T_i, T_a \ldots)]$ is cost to repair fault i after the noted diagnosis.

   $CW(F_i)$ is cost of warranty repair of fault i.

   $CCF(F_i)$ is cost to manufacturer of customer finding fault i.

$CCF(F_i)$ encompasses the costs to the manufacturer that are in addition to the warranty repair cost: loss of good will, reputation, cost of temporary loan equipment or contracted compensation, and the like.

Quantitative determination of a test strategy is now a matter of choosing the strategy (T_a, T_b, ..., T_i) that minimizes the total cost [$C(T) + C(D) + CR + CW + CCF$]. This is done as is, or it is done cognizant of any constraints that are put on the solution. Constraints which have been considered include:

1. Minimize total cost such that a chosen fraction of the possible faults remains at completion
2. Minimize total cost at a given test cost
3. Minimize cost of the customer finding a fault at a chosen test cost
4. Minimize cost of the customer finding a fault when a chosen fraction of faults remains at completion

The foregoing suggests a method for arriving at a test strategy which is in some way optimum, say in the sense that it minimizes certain costs within certain constraints. Such a technique, however, cannot always serve as the basis for arriving at a test strategy, especially if the failure probabilities change over time.

A means different from the strictly rational one outlined above is needed. Such a means may well include solving for an optimal test strategy by strictly rational means with the assumption of reasonable and stationary fault-occurrence statistics; investigating the solution for sensitivity of the solution to changes, even large changes, in the fault-occurrence statistics; and a reasoned synthesis of a test strategy based on the above solution, sensitivity study, and the various qualitative considerations outlined at the beginning of this section.

Restricted example

In lieu of trying to pursue an example of the above procedure in full, we may study a smaller problem, namely that of evaluating the average production cost of a network of process and test stations. We assume as before that we know the process or assembly sequence and have chosen a set of tests. Further, we know the likelihood of each of the faults and the unit cost of each process and test step. Then it is relatively easy to compute the total cost of producing one successful product unit assuming none is scrapped. This formulation can cover the case in which a unit may fail more than one test or may fail a particular test more than once. With the solution method in hand, we may explore the cost benefits of spending more money on a process to reduce the chance of failures or spending more money to improve the specificity of a test. The following analysis is based on the assumption that the process operates on large numbers of product units so that the use of statistical methods and averages is valid.

Consider the production and test process network shown in Fig. 9.17. The process consists of making two major subassemblies. The

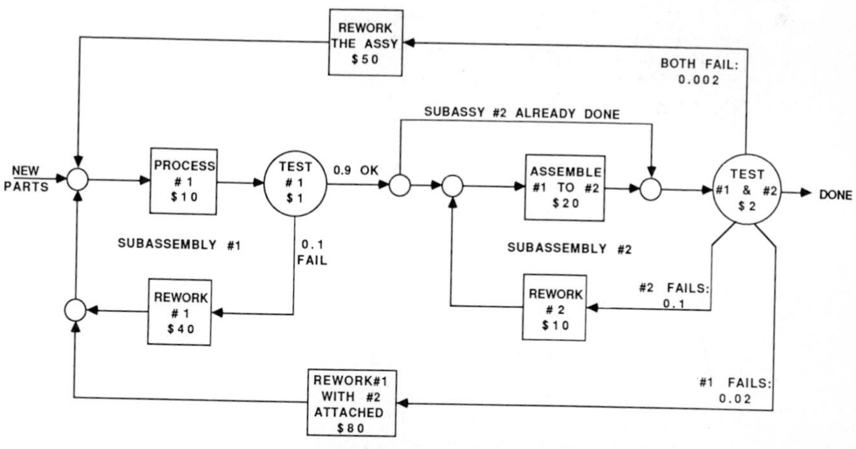

Fig. 9.17 Schematic of a production process with assembly, test, and rework steps. The cost of each step is shown, along with the probability that a single product unit will pass or fail each test.

first is tested and reworked as necessary before being mated to the second. The pair is then tested together. Either or both may then require additional repair. The costs and failure probabilities shown are assumed known. What is unknown is the fraction of products that go around more than once. Equivalently, we want to know the average flow rate of products on each branch of the network if the parts for one product unit per unit time enter from the left. Given these flow rates, we can calculate the rate at which cost builds up and compare it to the cost if no units failed.

The problem of finding the average or steady-state flows in a network is quite easy to solve. One simply writes a conservation of flow equation at every point where branches merge or separate: The sum of all flows in must equal the flow out. If we call each such point a node and label nodes by subscript i, the total flow out of node i may be called y_i. If the probability of going from node i to node j is p_{ij}, the flow from i to j is f_{ij}, which is

$$f_{ij} = y_i p_{ij} \tag{9.22}$$

where we must have

$$\sum_j p_{ij} = 1 \qquad \text{for each } i$$

To conserve flows at node j, we may write

$$y_j = y_j p_{jj} + \sum_{k \neq j} y_k p_{kj} + x_j \tag{9.23}$$

where x_j is the flow entering the node from the outside (say new parts) and p_{jj} is the probability that an item will immediately reenter the node it just left; this we rule out by setting $p_{jj} = 0$. Arranging the p's

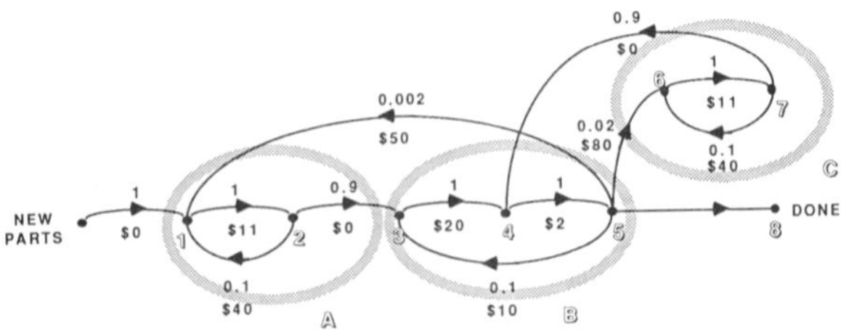

Fig. 9.18 Network equivalent of Fig. 9.17. The arc in Fig. 9.17 marked "subassy #2 already done" is replaced by segment C in the network to permit separate calculation of the flows of assemblies that follow that path.

into a matrix P, the y's into a column vector Y, and the x's into a column vector X, Eq. (9.23) becomes

$$Y = P^T Y + X \tag{9.24}$$

whose solution is

$$Y = [I - P^T]^{-1} X \tag{9.25}$$

```
REM PROGRAM TO EVALUATE EQUILIBRIUM FLOWS AND COSTS
REM IN A SIMPLE PROCESS WITH REWORK
DIM I(8,8),P(8,8),X(8),Y(8),B(8,8),BI(8,8),C(8,8),CO(8),F(8,8), PT(8,8)
MAT I = IDN
REM FLOW PROBABILITIES
MAT P = 0
LET P(1,2) = 1
LET P(2,1)= .1
LET P(2,3) = .9
LET P(3,4) = 1
LET P(4,5) = 1
LET P(5,3) = .1
LET P(5,1) = .002
LET P(5,6) = .02
LET P(5,8) = .878
LET P(6,7) = 1
LET P(7,4) = .9
LET P(7,6) = .1
PRINT "MATRIX P"
MAT PRINT USING " #.###  ":P
MAT PT = TRN(P)
REM INPUT FLOW
MAT X = 0
LET X(1) =1
REM COSTS
MAT C = 0
LET C(1,2) = 11
LET C(2,1) = 40
LET C(3,4) = 20
LET C(4,5) = 2
LET C(5,1) = 50
LET C(5,3) = 10
LET C(5,6) = 80
LET C(6,7) = 11
LET C(7,6) = 40
PRINT "MATRIX C"
MAT PRINT USING " ##.##  ":C
MAT B = I - PT
MAT BI = INV(B)
MAT Y = BI * X
PRINT "EQUILIBRIUM NODE OUTPUTS"
MAT PRINT USING " #.### " :Y
LET COST = 0
REM CALCULATE ARC FLOWS
FOR II = 1 TO 8
FOR JJ = 1 TO 8
LET F(II,JJ) = Y(II) * P(II,JJ)
LET COST = COST + F(II,JJ) * C(II,JJ)
NEXT JJ
NEXT II
PRINT "EQUILIBRIUM ARC FLOWS"
MAT PRINT USING " #.##### ":F
PRINT "COST = "; COST;" COST RATIO = "; COST/(C(1,2)+C(3,4)+C(4,5))
END
```

Listing 9.1 BASIC Program to Evaluate Flows and Costs in the Production Network in Figs. 9.17 and 9.18.

TABLE 9.4 **Output from BASIC Program in Listing 9.1. Equilibrium node outputs are listed as y_1 to y_8 from left to right. Flows F_{ij} are listed with i being the row number and j being the column number.**

```
File  Edit  Search  Format  Run  Fonts
EQUILIBRIUM NODE OUTPUTS
 1.114  1.114  1.116  1.139  1.139   .025   .025  1.000

EQUILIBRIUM ARC FLOWS TO:
       .00000  1.11364   .00000   .00000   .00000   .00000   .00000   .00000
       .11136   .00000  1.00228   .00000   .00000   .00000   .00000   .00000
       .00000   .00000   .00000  1.11617   .00000   .00000   .00000   .00000
  F    .00000   .00000   .00000   .00000  1.13895   .00000   .00000   .00000
  R    .00228   .00000   .11390   .00000   .00000   .02278   .00000  1.00000
  O    .00000   .00000   .00000   .00000   .00000   .00000   .02531   .00000
  M    .00000   .00000   .00000   .02278   .00000   .00253   .00000   .00000
       .00000   .00000   .00000   .00000   .00000   .00000   .00000   .00000

COST =  44.7608  COST RATIO =  1.35639
```

The equilibrium flows may then be found from Eq. (9.22) or equivalently

$$F = Y^T P \tag{9.26}$$

Let c_{ij} be the cost of having one product unit go from node i to node j. Then the total cost is

$$\text{Cost} = \sum_i \sum_j f_{ij} c_{ij} \tag{9.27}$$

Figure 9.18 shows the network equivalent of Fig. 9.17, while Listing 9.1 shows a short program in BASIC that calculates the flows and costs. The output from this program is in Table 9.4. For this set of data, the combined total of test, repair, and rework costs is 35 percent higher than it would be if all units passed their tests the first time.

As an example of the usefulness of this technique, let us explore the benefit of spending 20 percent, or \$2, more per unit to improve the assembly of subassembly 1 so that its failure rate is reduced by half. The result is that the total average cost per unit, including the extra added to subassembly 1, is reduced to \$42.40 from the original \$44.76. On this basis, we may conclude that the extra \$2 was worth it. If, on the other hand, we need to spend \$5 more per unit at subassembly 1 to cut the rework rate in half, we find that the total cost per unit rises to \$45.30, indicating that test and rework is less costly. It is just such a result that causes manufacturers to include tests and adjustments in their processes: in this example, doing it right the first time requires too much precision and is too costly.

Conclusions

In this chapter we have explored in detail several technical aspects of product design that relate to producibility: assembly sequences, tolerances, part feeding and handling, and testing strategies. For each we presented examples and indicated the class of algorithms that is applicable. It should be clear, however, that many problems defy algorithmic solutions either because they are too complex or have not been formulated carefully enough to permit a systematic attack or because there is insufficient data to justify a thorough calculation. Also, there exist many technical aspects of product design that we have omitted. Finally, many of the issues we illustrated for mechanical products have analogies in types of products that we did not treat. In the case of electronic circuit boards, assembly sequence is dominated by part provisioning rather than geometric interferences, part mates are governed by standardized interfaces and tolerances independent of function, and testing prior to completion of assembly is usually impossible. The reader with experience in one industry or another will have to make his or her own extrapolations.

References

Boothroyd, G., and P. Dewhurst: *Product Design for Assembly,* Boothroyd Dewhurst, Inc., Wakefield, RI, 1987.

Bourjault, A.: "Contribution à une Approche Méthodologique de l'Assemblage Automatisé: Elaboration Automatique des Séquences Opératoires," Ph.D. Thesis, l'Université de Franche-Comté, 1984.

Britney, R.: "Optimal Screening Plans for Non-Serial Production Systems," *Mgt. Sci.,* vol. 18, 1972 pp. 550–559.

De Fazio, T. L., and D. E. Whitney: "Simplified Generation of All Mechanical Assembly Sequences," *IEEE J. Robotics and Automation,* vol. RA-3, no. 6, Dec. 1987, pp. 640–658.

——— and ———: "Correction to 'Simplified Generation of All Mechanical Assembly Sequences,' *IEEE J. Robotics and Automation,* vol. RA-4, no. 6, Dec. 1988.

Lui, M. M.: "Generation and Evaluation of Mechanical Assembly Sequences Using the Liaison-Sequence Method," SM Thesis, MIT Mech. Eng. Dept., May 1988.

Nevins, J. L., and D. E. Whitney: "Computer-Controlled Assembly," *Scientific American,* Feb. 1978, pp. 62–74.

——— et al.: "Exploratory Research in Industrial, Modular Assembly Systems," C S Draper Laboratory Report R-1111,(CSDL R-1111) 1977.

Raz, T.: "A Survey of Models for Allocating Inspection Effort in Multistage Production Systems," *J. Quality Technology,* vol. 18, no. 4, Oct. 1986, pp. 239–247.

Sturges, R. H., Jr.: "A Three-Dimensional Assembly Task Quantification with Application to Machine Dexterity," *Int'l J. Robotics Res.,* vol. 7, no. 4, Aug. 1988, pp. 34–78.

SAE Handbook, Society of Automotive Engineers, Warrendale, PA, 1981.

Chapter

10

Basic Issues in Manufacturing System Design

Introduction

This chapter begins a section of the book that deals with system design. It lays out the basic issues, the choices which system designers must make, and some approaches to making these choices systematically. The topics in this chapter are generic to most manufacturing systems, although the emphasis is on assembly. The next few chapters deal in detail with systematic methods of workstation design, fabrication and assembly system design, and economic analysis.

Manufacturing system design is not a science, even though several aspects of it are supported by well-developed computer aids. There is still a great deal that is subject to expert judgment, arbitrary decisions, and lack of information about future conditions that the system may face. No design can cope with all future events and still retain adequate efficiency. No single technology can do all jobs, much less all jobs well.

For these reasons, our approach to system design emphasizes careful specification of the information needed for good design decisions. It also encourages the development of hybrid systems made up of suitable mixes of fixed automation, flexible automation, and people. Finally, it shows how to use the information about processes and the product that is developed during concurrent design so that integrated product, process, and system designs emerge. Even though the book presents the topics in a particular sequence, it should be kept in mind that the actual process is highly iterative.

System Design Procedure

Manufacturing system design can begin when a candidate product design is available along with the requirements for each process step and a candidate assembly sequence. All are subject to change as the design effort proceeds. The process is illustrated schematically in Fig. 10.1. It comprises these steps:

1. Analyze the product and the necessary fabrication and assembly operations. Determine alternative fabrication methods, fabrication and assembly sequences, and candidate subassemblies. Determine fabrication and assembly process requirements. Assess the maturity of these processes and estimate process yield. Identify flexibility requirements such as batch sizes and model mix.
2. Select an assembly sequence for use in assembly system design.
3. Determine the production capacity required of the system, taking yield into account.
4. Tabulate feasible fabrication and assembly techniques (equipment or people) for each operation and estimate the cost and time for each.
5. Using either intuitive techniques or the computerized methods described in Chaps. 13 and 14, select a set of equipment or people that can make the product at the required rate for a reasonable cost.
6. Either make preliminary economic analyses or proceed to detailed workstation designs and then perform economic analyses.

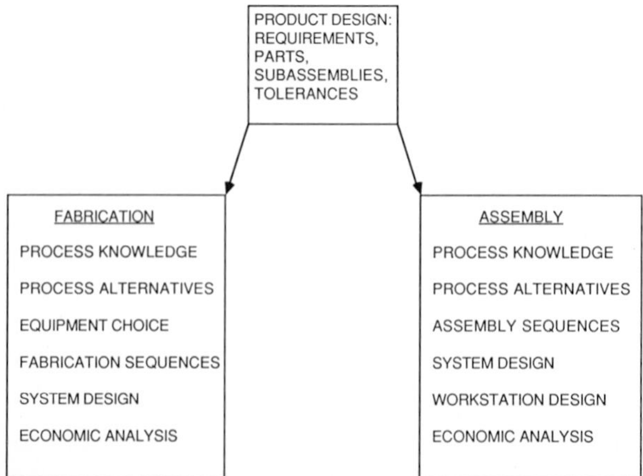

Fig. 10.1 A summary of the steps in manufacturing system design.

At any stage in this process, economic or technical evidence may appear that forces a reconsideration of product design, selection of subassemblies or assembly sequence, timing requirements, and so on. If all of the required information is not available or if system design reveals knowledge gaps, additional product or process design effort, engineering, or experiments may be necessary. The alternative is a system design with less robustness and predictability than desirable. Product quality, delivery, or cost may suffer, or the time to reach full production may be prolonged, as a result.

Even if the analysis is incomplete, performing it has great benefits. Visibility into the lack of robustness of processes or product design gives management the evidence to decide whether a product is ready to be manufactured.

Design Factors

Assuming that at least preliminary information is available, system design deals with the following topics, though not necessarily in this order:

1. *Capacity planning.* Providing the system with the ability to deliver the required number of correct parts or assemblies per hour, day, year, or whatever measure is appropriate. If there are several models, the batch size and changeover frequency are also part of capacity planning information. Required capacity establishes a minimum operating speed for each workstation expressed in time per part or assembly.

2. *Resource choice.* Deciding how each operation should be accomplished. A great deal of judgment is involved here. "Resources" could include people, and the design methods in Chaps. 12 and 14 allow this choice wherever the designers say that it is feasible. Mechanical resources may have to be designed specifically for some steps, making it unlikely that there will ever be a universal equipment database and totally automated system design. Instead, the designers may insert cost and time information about any equipment or processes that they are aware of.

3. *Task assignment.* Deciding which tasks in the system should be done by which resource. Resource choice above may provide several alternatives for each operation, and some kinds of resources—people and flexible automation, for example—may be able to do several operations in a row on each product unit. As long as the available resource options are equally feasible, the matter of choice and task assignment becomes dominated by cost and time. A systematic design procedure must therefore integrate these first three steps, choosing re-

sources and assigning tasks to take advantage of resource versatility so that the operations are done fast enough to meet the capacity specification and the cost meets suitable economic criteria.

It should be clear that making these choices is difficult. It should also be clear that product design and assembly sequence heavily affect system design. A different sequence presents different task assignment opportunities, for example, or may require extra steps like turning a subassembly over, requiring different or extra equipment.

4. *Workstation design.* Detailed design of each station, given the tasks it must perform. The designer must ensure that parts can be reached, tools can move rapidly and accurately enough, and assembly can be done reliably. This is the subject of Chap. 11.

5. *Floor layout.* Arranging the fabrication, assembly, part feeding, and material-handling resources into a compact, efficient, and effective layout on the factory floor. Layout and operation sequences can sometimes affect each other if certain operations must be located at designated places on the floor (painting near ventilation, for example).

6. *Material-handling equipment choice.* Deciding how to convey assemblies and parts within the system. This and floor layout are often determined together with emphasis on meeting the capacity requirements. Transport speed, number of transporters and parts fixtures or pallets, and distances traveled are the important variables. In addition, capacity and efficiency are affected by the number of assemblies, or the number and kind of parts, handled by one transporter or pallet as well as by the space available for queues of pallets in the system.

7. *Part provisioning.* Deciding how parts are to be fed to equipment or people. Options include bulk vibratory feeders, cassettes, or feeder strips for small parts and pallets or kits for large parts. Sometimes these options interact heavily with other aspects of system design; other times part provisioning decisions may be made independently.

8. *Economic analysis.* Deciding if the proposed system design meets economic criteria. Since any system will require an initial investment, typical economic criteria seek to measure whether this is a good investment or not. The basis for judgment is usually a comparison of the required investment and the amount and timing of either (*a*) the savings generated by a *replacement* system compared to the one being replaced or (*b*) the net revenues generated by the sale of a new product made on a *new* system.

Intangibles

In addition to the usual system performance specifications, there are others which are desirable and which may be costly to provide but whose contribution may be difficult to measure. The latter fact does not diminish their importance but may cloud decisions if typical economic criteria are applied. Among the intangibles are flexibility, quality, and responsiveness.

Flexibility means many things to many people. For example:

1. *Product* flexibility is the ability of the system to accommodate minor or major redesigns or new product models.
2. *Production* flexibility is the ability of the system to accommodate changes in demand, deviations of incoming material from specifications, or arbitrarily sized batches for each model.

Product flexibility tends to be long term, with changes occurring over months or years, although the trend is to shorter cycles. Production flexibility tends to be short term, possibly as short as a few minutes.

Each of these kinds of flexibility may be desirable for different reasons and desired by different constituencies within the company. Market uncertainty is a major reason why "flexibility" is needed. Inability to keep machines repaired, keep suppliers under control, or retain employees' cooperation are other "reasons," but solving such problems by demanding more flexibility of the production system may not be a good remedy compared to well-known and directly applicable methods.

In particular, one should avoid providing the flexibility to deal with variations in specifications of incoming parts because this may compromise quality. Too often in the past this kind of flexibility was a major, if hidden, feature of manual production methods. Automated systems usually fail to function on deviant inputs. This feature should not be viewed as a disadvantage of automation or evidence of its inflexibility but instead may be used as an incentive to improve quality.

Flexibility must be looked on with caution not only because it is often sought for the wrong reasons but also because flexibility and efficiency are often at odds. The experienced system designer knows that the most efficient equipment is totally specialized and works on the same task and workpiece type all the time. Flexibility introduces the need to change tools or fixtures, shift attention to other tasks, or to do some other changeover action during which no production is accomplished.

Yet flexibility is rightly seen as the way to accommodate changing circumstances of various kinds. A good way to strike a balance is to separate the possible changes into the predictable and the unpredictable. The predictable ones (future volume increases or possible new models) can be planned for during the design of the product and the assembly system. The others (strikes, technological breakthroughs, changes in laws or market sentiment, etc.) must be looked upon as hazards for which the response in everyday life is to hope they don't happen or to buy insurance. In the case of manufacturing systems, extra flexibility can be designed in at the cost of some efficiency. The extra cost can be thought of as the insurance premium (Fine and Freund, 1986).

Company managers and product and system designers have to carefully define what kinds of and how much flexibility they really need and design products and systems accordingly. When the penalty for being wrong can be calculated, it can be compared to the cost of providing the offsetting flexibility and a decision can be made.

Similar considerations apply in the case of *quality*. This may be defined as the degree to which the product's original specifications are met by each unit. The cost and quality of a product are determined mainly during design and are rarely or slightly improved during production. Workpieces and the processes for making and assembling them are ideally designed to be robust, well understood, and reproducible. The usual procedures of quality control are best used to ensure that the design intentions are still being achieved rather than to correct problems caused by poorly designed products and poorly operated systems.

The above attitude toward quality involves extra expense during design and, possibly, more expensive parts and processing equipment. Justifying such extra expenses was often difficult in the past because the benefits of higher quality are hard to measure quantitatively. As companies and their customers become more conscious of quality, the justifications are becoming easier. One approach is for the company to make quality one of the specifications for the product. Units that fail are reworked or discarded, an action whose cost can be measured. The consequences of different designs for product and system can then be measured, including the quality costs. The company can also view quality as one of its marketing strengths. The cost of lost sales can sometimes be measured and applied as above. This is the basis of the Taguchi Quality Loss Function approach.

The third intangible is *responsiveness* to the market. This may be considered an aspect of flexibility but it uniquely emphasizes speed as well as versatility. Responsiveness could mean the ability to make a customer's order within a specified time, in an arbitrary model mix, or in an arbitrary batch size at a standard cost. Special design efforts are needed to create a system that can be responsive in the short term without being inefficient or requiring lots of inventory of in-process or finished goods. The Nippondenso radiators and panel meters are examples of products designed for responsiveness. The Sony Walkman's early models and production equipment anticipated some of the requirements for later models.

Note that the three intangibles are closely related to the character of the product, a topic that is considered early in product design. If the product has been well thought out, the bases for decisions concerning the intangibles will be available for the system designers.

Assembly Resource Alternatives

Three basic types of assembly resources can be distinguished: people, fixed automation, and flexible automation. These are discussed in terms of assembly but similar considerations apply to fabrication.

Manual assembly—technical aspects

Manual assemblers are the most flexible, adaptable, innovative, dexterous, and responsive to challenging tasks. They are also the least efficient and most variable. These attributes contrast sharply with those of machines, which are relatively more efficient and less variable, adaptable, dexterous, and so on. The above characterizations must be tempered by the fact that the task to be done sets the conditions which must be met. The "same" task may require more or less dexterity, for example, depending on its design, physical layout, variability of incoming parts, or a host of other reasons.

For example, a circuit board "needs" to be assembled manually if some of its components are an odd shape so that no mechanical means of presenting them to an assembly machine is available. A differently shaped component, with the same electrical characteristics or one made by a vendor who will package it in a cassette for easy feeding, could be selected by the designer, permitting machine assembly. This design choice strongly affects the dexterity needed.

People are especially necessary for managing poorly understood processes and for dealing with assembly steps that require tests, adjustments, and decisions about many complex measurements. While it is sometimes possible to redesign the product to tighten tolerances and thus eliminate such adjustments, it is often more economical to make low-tolerance, low-cost parts and adjust the assembly into operation.

In the future, the pressure to increase quality and production speed of complex products will force adjustments to be automated. Figure 10.2 is an example. A major objective of the station shown is to make the adjustment time the same for each unit, something people could not provide. Predictable time allows surrounding stations to be automated with the same cycle time and permits overall capacity to be controlled better (Aoki, 1980).

Manual assembly—economic aspects

To estimate the cost structure of manual assembly, we note that a person operates at a given speed, and if more production is needed, more

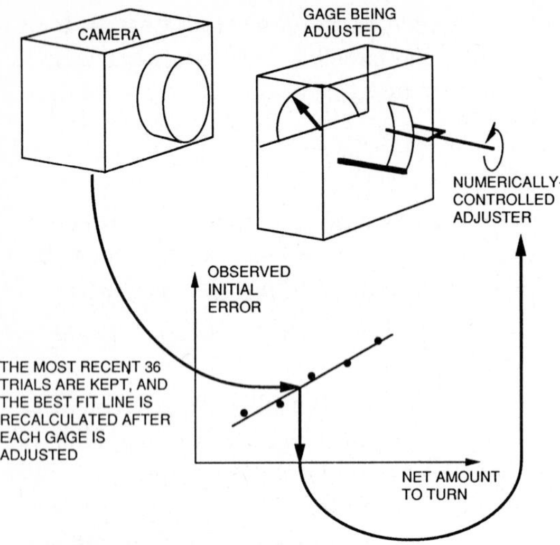

PROCEDURE:

1. OBSERVE GAGE ERROR FOR STANDARD VOLTAGE INPUT
2. REFER TO STRAIGHT LINE FIT
3. SELECT AMOUNT TO TURN, AND TURN ADJUSTMENT THAT MUCH
4. REPEAT 1-3 ONCE
5. NOTE NET AMOUNT TURNED AND INITIAL ERROR
6. ADD THESE RESULTS TO THE DATA SET
7. DELETE OLDEST RESULTS
8. RECALCULATE STRAIGHT LINE FIT.

Fig. 10.2 Automated adjustment of a panel meter gauge. The adjuster shortens search and adjustment time by using results of previous gauges' adjustments to make the first trial adjustment. The adjuster also "learns" about drifts in gauges over time and forgets behavior of old gauges.

people may be employed. If less is needed, they may be employed elsewhere because of their flexibility. Often the tools or fixtures which cannot be redeployed are a small cost component. Since the main cost component, people, is directly proportional to the annual production quantity, the assembly cost per unit is approximately independent of production volume.

Fixed automation—technical aspects

Fixed automation typically describes machines built to do one task without frequent changes or for which changes require a significant amount of reconstruction. As indicated in Chap. 2, fixed automation has been under continuous development for nearly 200 years, with increasing speed, accuracy, and range of task capability being the result. A fixed automation assembly machine reminds one of a diesel engine, with arms, wheels, and levers moving in perfect synchrony, often remarkably slowly. Slow speed is feasible because suitable products usually are small, and good design of product and machine keep mo-

Fig. 10.3 This automatic assembly machine was manufactured by The Bodine Corporation for C & K Components in Clayton, NC. It is being used to assemble toaster switches which are then supplied to a major producer of small household appliances. This machine assembles 45 switches per minute, which is approximately five million assemblies per shift year. (*The Bodine Corporation*).

tion distances small as well, perhaps only a few inches. Each station of such a machine installs or tests just one part. All stations operate simultaneously, so the speed of a station is the speed of the machine. Figure 10.3 illustrates such a machine.

Fixed automation—economic aspects

Consider a machine for assembling automobile cigarette lighters. If its cycle time (time for each station to act and, thus, the time between completed assemblies) is 3 s and if it operates 8 hr a day, 5 days a week for a typical working year of 228 days, it will produce 2,188,800 lighters in a year. If we allow for 20 percent downtime for maintenance and part feeding jams, at most *five* such machines working one shift or *three* working two shifts could make over 9,000,000 lighters per year, enough to satisfy the needs of all the U.S. car manufacturers and still have some capacity left over for the replacement market.

The conclusions to draw from this and other examples are that such machines are often one or few of a kind, can easily produce large quantities of small items, require engineering design to focus their general capability onto a specific product, have one station per part or operation required by the product, and will stand idle if demand for the product falls. Consequently, they are most economical for high-volume products. When demand falls, the machine's cost is spread over fewer units, and the cost per unit rises proportionately. The overall result is that the cost to assemble one unit is approximately proportional to the number of parts in one unit and inversely proportional to annual production volume.

Such machines are made economically by companies that specialize in a limited size range of products and that have created innovative basic machine concepts. These concepts minimize the amount of engineering required to adapt the machine's standard foundation and actuators to a specific product. Modern "fixed" automation assembly machines are also often capable of preplanned production flexibility, based on the ability to switch feeders or skip operations at given stations depending on model mix requirements. However, since these machines usually operate synchronously, it is difficult to include a station whose cycle time may be variable, such as one that makes an adjustment.

Flexible automation—technical aspects

The third type of assembly equipment we take up is flexible automation, commonly thought of as robots. In general, however, flexible automation may be defined as any automation which is reconfigurable to do a range of tasks. Such machines are characterized by movable or controllable degrees of freedom so that different (often arbitrary) shapes, paths, angles, and different (within limits) sizes, forces, directions, and so on can be encompassed. There is strong potential for adaptation of behavior (different path or force, etc.) based on sensor inputs and computed alterations in behavior, although this potential has not been exploited much to date. There may be some setup time penalties, and some people may be needed in attendance. In addition to robots, we may cite knitting, weaving, welding, and bending machines, as well as entire arrays of actuators and welders that make ribbed structures for ships.

Flexible automation—economic aspects

The main economic feature of flexible equipment is its ability to do more than one task. One may interpret this as the ability to be turned to a different application after a period of years, but more frequent and more important is the ability to turn to a different task after a few seconds or minutes. A typical example is an assembly robot. It can assemble two different parts in a row, whereas a fixed automation assembly machine requires two workstations to do the same thing. The cost difference can be large: the cost of a second station compared to the cost of another gripper. (Sometimes even the same gripper can be used.) Like fixed automation and unlike a person, a robot can also work 16 or 24 hr per day. The economic consequences are that the cost of a robot assembly system does not have to grow strictly in proportion either to the required production volume, as manual assembly cost does, or in proportion to the number of parts in the product, as fixed automation does. Instead, one buys as many robots as their cycle time permits and the production rate requires, and at most as many tools as there are assembly operations, and runs the system as many hours as needed. Exactly the same considerations apply when comparing fixed automation fabrication systems (transfer lines with one operation per station) and flexible ones (tool-changing NC machines that do many operations). Figure 11.4 shows Sony assembly robots that each assemble five parts to an assembly at each workstation with a cycle time per part of 2 s.

Simplified economic models

Table 10.1 shows simplified economic models for these three types of equipment. Figure 10.4(*a*) through (*d*) shows the results of using these models to predict unit cost and number of workstations (one person, fixed automation workhead, or robot per station) versus annual production volume. Nominal economic assumptions are shown in the table for the choice of values for the variables in the equations. These values are illustrative only. The systems modeled are homogeneous: (*a*) comprises manual stations with identical cost and speed, (*b*) identical fixed automation stations, and (*c*) identical flexible stations.

Some comment on these graphs is in order. For both manual and flexible automatic assembly, the number of people or robots increases as the production volume grows. At the same time, the number of assembly operations done by each person or robot drops. At the lowest volume, one person or robot has time (but not necessarily the technical capability) to do the entire assembly. To accomplish all these tasks typically requires many tools, tool changing, feeding of many parts, and so on. At the highest volume, each station has time for at most one operation. Only one tool and part are used at each station. This represents the extreme in division of labor, and the system is said to be saturated. If volume exceeds this limit, the assembly system must run a second or third shift or a duplicate assembly system is required.

Naturally, these considerations have a strong influence on task assignment, part feeding, transport, and floor layout, the topics remaining in this chapter.

Note the general trend shown in Fig. 10.4(*d*), indicating that manual assembly is the lowest cost of the three methods until production

TABLE 10.1 Simplified Economic Models of Assembly Alternatives

Manual Assembly

$$C_{\text{unit manual}} = \frac{A\$ \cdot \text{No. people}}{Q}$$

where Q = annual production volume

$$\text{No. people} = \left\lceil \frac{T \cdot N \cdot Q}{2000 \cdot 3600} \right\rceil$$

where T = assembly time per part, seconds

N = number of parts per unit

$A\$$ = annual cost of a person

$$A\$ = \overline{L_H} \cdot 2000$$

where $\overline{L_H}$ = labor cost, \$/hour

[...] = round up to the next larger integer

2000 = number of hours per shift per year

3600 = number of seconds per hour

Fixed automation

$$C_{\text{unit fixed}} = \frac{f_a \cdot N \cdot S\$}{Q}$$

where f_a = fraction of machine cost paid for per year

$S\$$ = cost of one station in the machine

Flexible automation

$$C_{\text{unit flex}} = \frac{f_a \cdot I}{Q} + \frac{L\$}{Q}$$

where I = total investment in machines and tools

$L\$$ = annual cost of workers associated with the system

I = No. machines · \$/machine + No. tools · \$/tool

$$\text{No. machines} = \left\lceil \frac{T \cdot N \cdot Q}{2000 \cdot 3600} \right\rceil$$

where number of parts per unit = n

$$L\$ = w \cdot \text{No. machines} \cdot \overline{L_H} \cdot 2000$$

$$w = \text{number of workers/station}$$

Combining the above yields:

$$C_{\text{unit flex}} = \frac{f_a}{Q}(\text{No. machines} \cdot \$/\text{machine} + \text{No. tools} \cdot \$/\text{tool}) + \frac{L\$}{Q}$$

Assumptions: T = 5 seconds; labor cost $\overline{L_H}$ = \$12/hour; N = 10 parts/unit; f_a = 0.38; $S\$$ = \$50,000 per station = \$/machine; \$/tool = \$10,000; w = 0.25 worker per station

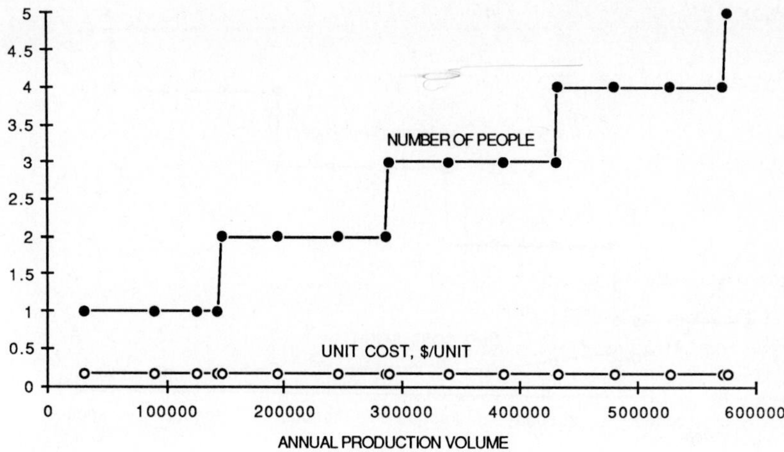

Fig. 10.4(*a*) Simplified economic model of an assembly system containing only manual assembly.

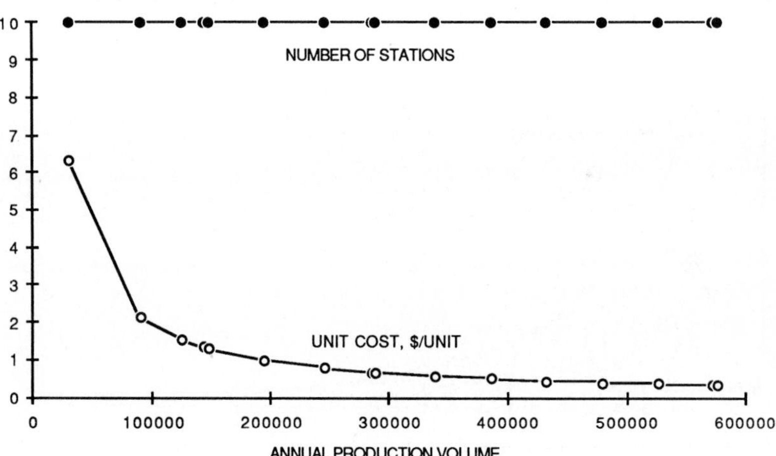

Fig. 10.4(*b*) Simplified economic model of an assembly system containing only fixed automation.

volumes in the range of 750,000 per year are reached and that flexible automation is never the lowest cost. These conclusions are valid only for the numerical values shown in Table 10.1. For other assumptions, such as more expensive labor or faster robots, totally different conclusions may be reached. Flexible assembly may become economical at 200,000 units per year, for example. In order to determine what is best in each case, one must use the detailed models in later chapters. In particular, these models permit design of hybrid systems containing

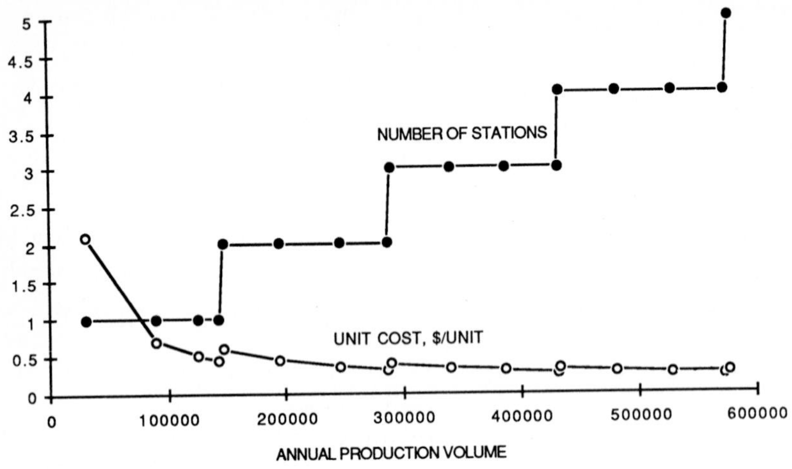

Fig. 10.4(*c*) Simplified economic model of an assembly system containing only flexible automation.

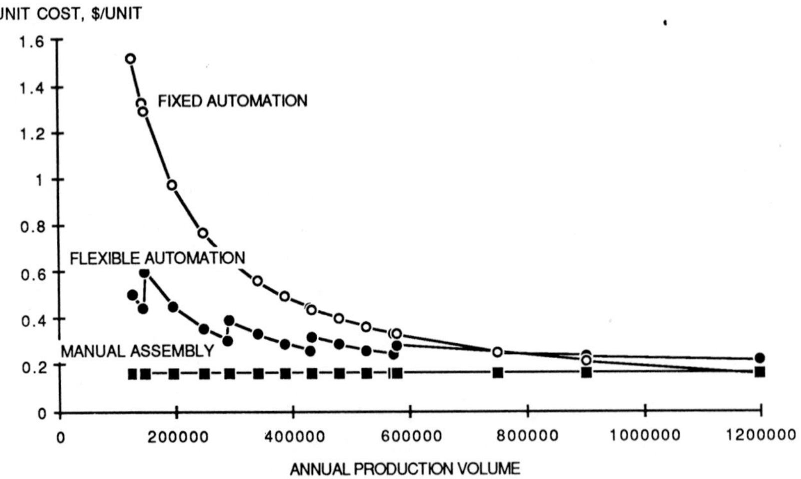

Fig. 10.4(*d*) Combination of unit costs from Fig. 10.4(*a*), (*b*), and (*c*).

the best mix of manual, fixed, and flexible methods. In addition, they take into account several important details, such as tool change time, transport time and cost, and the need for extra shifts or equipment because of system saturation.

Task Assignment

Task assignment is the third interlocking step in the process of defining an assembly system design. This step is traditionally done manually by experts within three constraints, technical, economic, and circumstantial. The technical constraints are the obvious ones such as size, speed, accuracy, and required yield. Economic constraints include cost and speed.

Circumstantial constraints might include the desire to use one kind of equipment for each task, to use that of one manufacturer, or to exclude people entirely, for example. A designer might, by choice, decide that each station must do exactly one operation so as to simplify the design or may wish to design general-purpose stations that can each assemble an entire product and provide enough of these stations to meet the capacity requirements.

Designers who face these choices without computer aids will resolve them as well as their experiences allow, but they may have no idea how good their designs really are. In recognition of these facts, we have developed the systematic approach and computer aids described in later chapters. Nonetheless, human design and judgment will still be required.

Tools and Tool Changing

While there is research directed toward general-purpose hands for robots, it remains true that special tools and grippers are often necessary for assembly tasks. (Even people use tools to hold small parts, exert force or torque, keep parts clean, protect themselves, and so on.) More important, well-designed tools are essential so that an assembly machine of any kind will grip parts in a repeatable way so that part mating will occur reliably. The part-mating error contributed by tools is among those considered in Chap. 11. Figure 10.5 shows the elements of a typical tool changer.

Even though careful design of parts and tools can reduce the number of tools needed, several tools may be required to perform assembly of an entire product. If robots perform part of the assembly, tool changing may still be needed. The need will also depend on the assembly sequence and task assignment, since obviously if work passes to a new station just as a new tool is needed, the new station will hold that tool, and no tool changing is needed. On the other hand, if the work assignment algorithm spreads a series of tasks that need the same tool over two or more stations, duplicate tools must be purchased for each such station. The system design methods in Chap. 14 automatically take tool purchase costs and tool changing time into account.

Part Feeding Alternatives

Part feeding has one obvious purpose, namely to bring parts to the point where they will be assembled. There is at least one not so obvi-

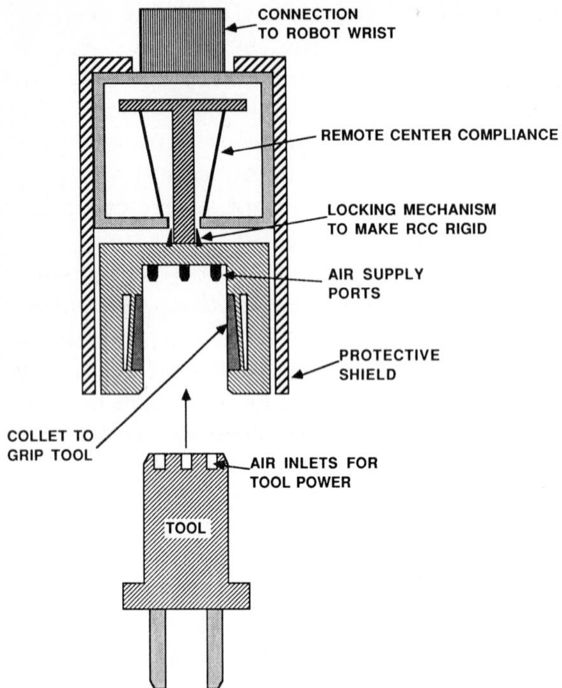

Fig. 10.5 The elements of a typical tool-changing robot wrist.

ous purpose, that is, to keep control over the parts so that they stay intact and clean and so that none get lost or diverted. Choice of feeding method depends on a part's size, shape, and weight. Most of the methods described below do not apply to extremely large parts. However, even manufacturers of cars and tractors have found that nearly all of their parts are smaller than 6 in across and weigh less than 5 lb.

Part feeding methods may be categorized as *bulk* or *individual*. Bulk methods take in several or many disoriented parts at once and, by any of several means, transport them a short distance and, more importantly, orient them correctly and present them individually for assembly. Individual feeding methods present prepackaged, preoriented parts individually. Methods include pallets, cassettes, carrier strips, kits, trays, racks, and other arrays or stacks.

Bulk feeding methods

Examples of bulk feeders include vibratory bowls or hoppers, counterflowing conveyors, and tilting trays. Boothroyd and Redford (1968) contains detailed information on these feeders. Vibratory bowls are the most common. They are suitable for small parts whose outer surface can stand some repeated rubbing and impacts with other parts. (Four such feeders can be seen in Fig. 10.3.) Bowl feeders have the advantages that they work continuously and can be replenished automatically from simple overhead dumpers. On the other hand, they must be designed individually by experts with considerable ingenuity.

A disadvantage of vibratory feeders is that their operation often depends on a subtle combination of geometry and friction. Since the bowls wear under continued use, small changes in their shape or friction properties induced by wear may cause them to suddenly and mysteriously stop working properly. A related problem is that it is often impossible to copy a bowl feeder in order to obtain additional feeding capacity. Instead, a new bowl must be made from scratch. Feeder tracks leading from the bowl's exit to the assembly point are also subject to jamming. Finally, parts with very complex shapes may be impossible to feed this way.

An alternative to bowl feeders with mechanical orienting means are bowls combined with vision systems. Parts and bowl tracks are contrasting colors, and the vision system can see if the part is in the correct orientation. If not, it instructs an air jet to blow the part off the track. This approach is less idiosyncratic than mechanical orienting. Because of the cost of vision systems, the method is not widely used but promises to spread as vision systems become less expensive.

Less structured feeding methods are being tried in several companies. Often this consists of manually placing the parts roughly arrayed on a flat surface, not touching and almost in the correct orientation. A simple vision system can find each part in about 1 s, permitting a robot to pick it up. This approach is well suited to products that are made in smaller quantities, for which it is not economical to build special pallets or bowl feeders, as well as for larger parts that cannot be fed and oriented using bulk means.

The least structured bulk feeding method is a bin or box, with parts mixed in it in arbitrary locations and orientations. While there has been research progress on automatic "bin-picking," it is rarely practiced in industry for several reasons. First, it is slower and more costly than the semistructured vision approach. Second, parts grasped from a bin are in an arbitrary location and orientation in the robot (or other) gripper and must be further analyzed and reoriented. This process takes time and requires additional motion axes, all of which cost money. People are the fastest and cheapest bin pickers and are likely to remain so.

Individual feeding methods

Individual feeding usually implies pallets or kits, although pallets of small parts may be filled by bulk methods. Pallets usually contain one kind of part or assembly. Kits usually comprise enough of each kind of part to make one unit or subassembly. Kits are used when careful control of parts is necessary; reasons include documentation, cleanliness, prior matching or certification, and so on. The choice between kitting and palletizing often depends on the size of the parts. Several examples are shown in Chap. 11.

Combined bulk and individual feeding methods

Bulk methods are often used to load individual feeders with properly oriented parts. Such individual feeders might be pallets or carrier strips. The pallet or strip is then presented to the assembly station. A two-stage feeding system results, with the sometimes troublesome bulk methods accomplished far from the assembly site.

An example of the pallet method is a feeding system for video recorder parts (see Fig. 10.6). Pallets visit one of several pallet loaders, each of which can load several kinds of parts into their respective pallets. Parts are dumped automatically from a hopper onto the pallet, which is vibrated while being held at a slight down slope. Parts which fail to fall into a pocket in the pallet fall off the lower end of the pallet and are recirculated. It may take a minute for a pallet with 100 pockets to fill up. Vibration speed and tilt angle of the pallet are determined experimentally. This technique is less specialized than vibratory bowl feeders and may take less time to get working; however, the pallets are costly since they must be made by accurately molding or NC machining the individual parts pockets.

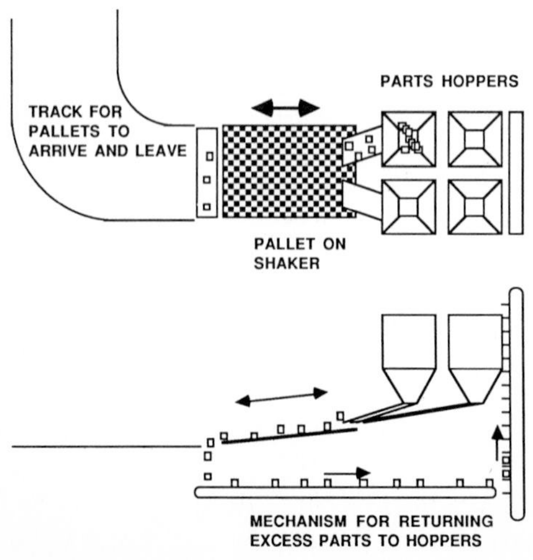

Fig. 10.6 Shaker method of loading pallets with small parts. This shaker station can load any of four part types. Pallets loaded by this method are visible in Fig. 11.4.

An example of the carrier strip method is that of electrical connector pins and sockets. They are made from metal strips by a series of stamping processes and then left in the strip like paper dolls through all subsequent processing (cleaning, plating, and transport) until the instant when they are cut off the strip and pushed into the body of the connector. This process is illustrated in Fig. 10.7.

A third example (Kaneko and Saigo, 1984) concerns Seiko quartz watch assembly, where special attention was given to feeding speed and reliability. As indicated in Fig. 10.8, careful study revealed that there is a direct correlation between the failure rate and the amount of structure applied to the part's manufacturing and feeding method.

The methods Seiko has used include stamping parts from metal strips as in the previous example, plastically molding them into metal carrier strips, or mechanically inserting them into such strips. These actions occur in a separate department where jams or misfeeds cannot interrupt watch assembly. In each case, the strips are conveyed to the assembly stations where parts are removed from the strip at the moment of insertion into the watch. This step is highly reliable, as indicated in Fig. 10.8.

Other alternatives

In addition to the above common feeding methods, one may note traveling magazines, traveling pallets, and roving robots. The first two may be thought of as waiters at a cocktail party, moving from station to station dropping off part of their load at each one. The roving robot (Hitachi, 1981) consists of a robot on a circular track so that it can move from station to station. It performs simple assembly operations on its own work area while moving and drops off or picks up work at specialized press, screw driving, or painting stations.

Table 10.2 summarizes several part feeding options according to part size and logistic requirements.

Feeding, tool changing, and station efficiency

The feeding method can have a profound effect on the efficiency of an assembly station. The ideal situation is one in which the parts are ready, in the correct orientation, the moment the assembly device needs them. No assembly time is wasted. If parts are on a pallet, there may be a loss of time while an empty pallet is moved out of the station and a full one moved in. The actual time lost per assembled unit is less if more parts are on a pallet than the number needed for one product unit, since the in-out time is spread over several units. For large parts, where in-out times could be long, the benefit of even four units per pallet is great. These trade-offs are discussed more fully in Chap. 11.

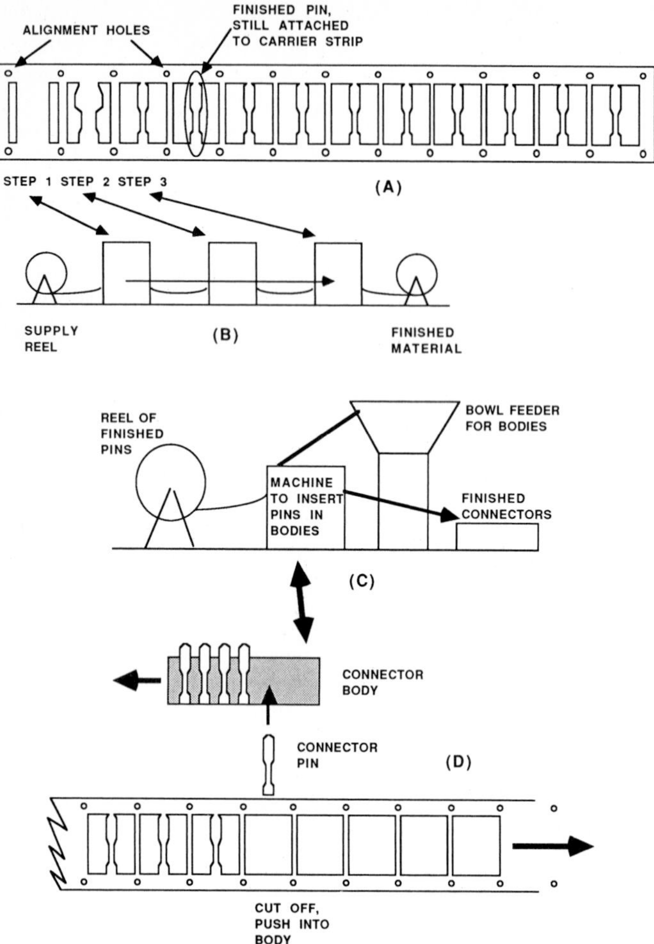

Fig. 10.7 The process of making electrical connectors, showing design of the pins for material handling (A) and (B): Pins are made by successive die stamping operations that gradually create the three-dimensional shape of the pin. A similar process creates sockets. The small holes are punched into the strip first to provide dimensional alignment for the successive stamping stations. Later processes such as cleaning and plating are also performed on the entire strip by passing it from reel to reel. (C) and (D): At final assembly, the strip is passed into an insertion machine that cuts pins or sockets off and pushes them into the connector body. Note that a vibratory bowl feeder is used to feed connector bodies. Since there are 10 to 100 pins per connector, the feed rate needed for pins is too high for bowls. This is an additional reason why the pins are kept attached to the carrier strip until the moment of insertion into the bodies.

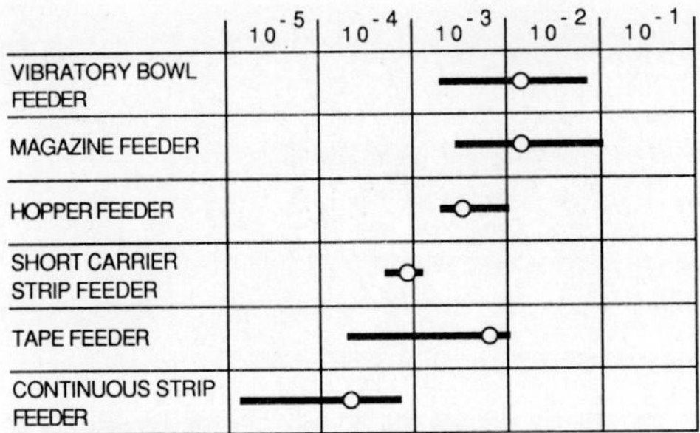

FAILURE RATE OF FEEDERS, FAILURES PER PART FED

(a)

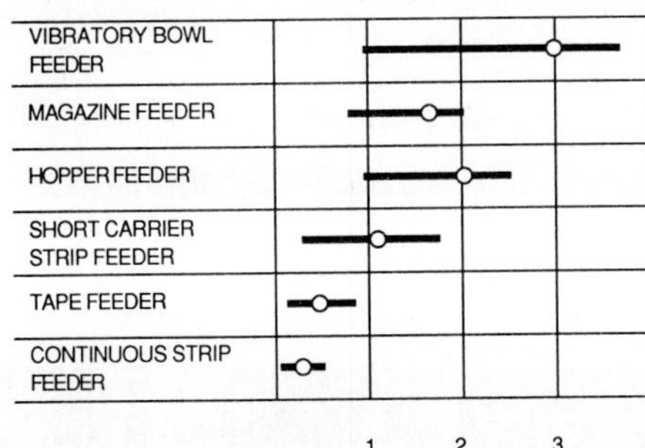

RANGE OF FEEDING TIME PER PART, SEC

(b)

	RELIABILITY	CHANGING TIME	COMMENTS
MAGAZINE FEEDER	99.92%	5 MINUTES	PREPARATION TAKES A LOT OF TIME
SHORT CARRIER STRIP FEEDER	99.93%	7 MINUTES	IT TAKES RELATIVELY MORE TIME TO CHANGE THE PRESS DIE
TAPE FEEDER	99.97%	2 MINUTES	VERY GOOD
SCREWDRIVER	99.96%	4 MINUTES	VERY GOOD

RELIABILITY AND CHANGING TIME OF DIFFERENT KINDS OF FEEDERS

(c)

Fig. 10.8 Comparison of different feeding methods used in quartz watch manufacture. (*a*) Failure rate of different kinds of feeders; (*b*) Range of feeding time per part; (*c*) Reliability and changing time of the most reliable kinds of feeders.

(d)

(e)

Fig. 10.8 (*Continued*) (*d*) Shows typical watch parts in carrier strips; (*e*) Shows a stack of these strips at the rear of an assembly robot ready to be fed in automatically. One strip at a time is taken off the bottom of the stack and fed to the left, where the rear of the assembly robot is visible.

TABLE 10.2 Alternatives for Part Feeding

	FEED SEPARATELY TO EACH STATION	FEED TO MANY STATIONS
SMALL PARTS < 1 INCH	BOWL, HOPPER, MAGAZINE, CARRIER STRIP	TRAVELLING MAGAZINE TRAVELLING PALLET KIT ROVING ROBOT
MEDIUM PARTS < 6 INCHES	ROLLER CONVEYOR STACK MANUAL ORDERED LAYERS IN BIN	KIT OF THE PARTS FOR ONE UNIT PALLET OF IDENTICAL PARTS ROVING ROBOT
LARGE PARTS > 6 INCHES	CONVEYOR RACK ORDERED LAYERS	MAY NOT BE PRACTICAL

Similarly, the need for tool changes has the same effect on productive cycle time, and a similar approach mitigates the effect: if several product units requiring the same tool are within reach of a robot assembler, it can work on all of them before changing tools. The equation below computes the station's net cycle time, consisting of basic assembly time augmented by downtime for repairs, pallet in-out time, and tool change time:

$$\text{Cycle time} = \frac{1}{\epsilon}\left(\text{assy. time} + \frac{\text{in-out time}}{\text{no. units/pallet}} + \frac{\text{tool ch. time} \cdot \text{no. ch./unit}}{\text{no. units/tool change}}\right)$$

where cycle time = average time per assembly
in-out time = time to move one pallet out and another in
tool ch. time = time to put down a tool and pick up another
no. ch./unit = number of tool changes needed to make one unit
no. units/tool change = number of units worked on before tool is changed (cannot be larger than number of units/pallet)
ϵ = station uptime fraction: $0 < \epsilon < 1$

Table 10.3 shows how cycle time varies with some example values of the variables. The system design techniques discussed in Chap. 14 take in-out time loss into account directly when calculating system capacity.

Relation between feeding and production flexibility

Feeding is simplest for large-volume production of identical items, but that situation is really not very common. Instead there is batch production in varying batch sizes in all volume ranges. Assuming that

TABLE 10.3 Illustration of Influence of Tool Changes, In-Out Time, and Number of Items per Pallet on Cycle Time

Line A: Baseline for comparison; line B: effect of increasing number of units per pallet; line C: effect of changing tools efficiently; line D: effect of changing tools inefficiently.

	ASSEMBLY TIME	IN/OUT TIME	TOOL CHANGE TIME	# UNITS PER PALLET	#TOOL CH PER UNIT	#UNITS PER TOOL CHANGE	CYCLE TIME
A	30	2	0	1	0	1	32
		4					34
		6					36
		8					38
B	30	4	0	1	0	1	34
				2			32
				3			31.33
				4			31
C	30	4	6	1	2	1	46
				2		2	38
				3		3	35.33
				4		4	34
D	30	4	6	1	2	1	46
				2			44
				3			43.33
				4			43

the product itself has been designed to support the desired production strategy, feeding methods must be chosen to suit.

Kitting and palletizing can be used effectively in small batch production. Essentially, the pallet or the kit comprises the batch directly. This approach can be inefficient or expensive in feeding small parts such as screws, however, because they usually do not warrant the individual treatment that this kind of feeding demands. A solution is to use the same screws for all items in all batches, a feature that would have to be established during product design. Then efficient bulk feeding could be used for the small parts.

When all the parts are small and bulk feeding methods are appropriate, there are two ways to obtain small batches and model mix even if part standardization cannot be attained. One method may be called *station lockout*, while the other may be called *gated feeders*.

In the station lockout method, the assemblies visit every station, but a station adds a part only if the model in the station needs that part. Otherwise, the station does nothing for one cycle. The station may identify the model by reading a bar code, for example. This technique is especially useful if different models receive different numbers of parts rather than merely different versions of the same parts.

The gated feeder method provides each workstation with several feeders and a controllable feeder track that can connect one feeder at a time to the station. The station always operates, but the identity of the part it picks up depends on which feeder is connected.

Since switching feeders takes time, the gated feeder method is best suited to runs of identical items. By contrast, station lockout can work on a different model during each cycle. However, since each item visits each station regardless of whether work is done on it or not, there is a certain amount of built-in time waste in this method. The two methods can also be combined. Finally, the type of workstation is immaterial; people, robots, or fixed automation could in principle be used with either method.

As an example, the Nippondenso panel meter gauge (see Chap. 3) is assembled in arbitrary batch sizes via the gated feeder method. Product design identified the need for three types of casings or base parts, four terminals, four bimetals, three voltage regulators, one base, and two shafts. This menu defines the number of feeders to be gated at each of the assembly stations. Table 10.4 describes how this machine works.

An extreme of model mix and kitting is the emerging strategy of providing a generalized robot workstation with parts, tools, fixtures, and software in one kit. An automated guided vehicle (AGV) might be suitable for delivering this kit and picking up tools, fixtures, and fin-

TABLE 10.4 Description of Operation of Nippondenso Panel Meter Machine

On the machine's control panel are thumbwheels where the foreman dials in the number of each of up to 40 models needed that day. (The combinatorics of part types permits 288 different models theoretically, but Nippondenso has constructed the machine to support only 40 thus far.) The control computer works through the models, making a solid batch of each before going on to the next. The casing is the pallet and the assembly fixture, so a robot picks up the correct casing and puts it on the conveyor. The control computer signals each station to indicate how to position the feeder tracks. Casings travel through the machine with a cycle time of 0.9 s, receiving parts and tests until assembly is complete.

After the last casing for batch 1 has been loaded onto the conveyor, the control computer instructs the robot to put on a dummy casing with a protrusion that contacts sensor switches at each station. As the dummy reaches each station, the sensor detects it and notifies the control computer, which switches the feeders and disables the assembly action while the dummy is passing through the station. The next casing is the first one in batch 2, and as it arrives, the station is ready for it. Thus the machine automatically changes over from batch 1 to batch 2 in one lost cycle as the dummy reaches each station. Dummies are caught at the end and recycled manually.

ished assemblies. (Actually, the software is sent electronically.) An extension of this extreme includes a separate fixture-building robot that can configure assembly work sites in advance and dispatch them to the assembly robot. The result is a system concept with little or no investment in dedicated items, suitable for making literally one at a time of something whose tools and jig components exist already.

The economic advantages of such an arrangement would likely stem from its ability to run 24 hr per day. The economic disadvantage is that small batches would entail a great deal of setup time in relation to assembly time unless the products were quite complex. Also, the ability to make literally one of something is probably illusory since tools and control software would have to be designed, built, and tested that would be used once and never used again. In practice, what is feasible as well as needed is one-at-a-time assembly of things which are made repeatedly but intermittently with unpredictable demand or made in low volume but requiring complex and lengthy assembly and test.

Material-Handling Alternatives

It should be clear that material-handling choices are fundamentally dependent on flow rate requirements and physical characteristics of the items being transported. In addition, as discussed elsewhere, material handling interacts strongly with interfaces to the rest of the factory and to the logistics that relate the factory to the parts vendors. Typically, the transported items could be unassembled parts, partially completed assemblies, assembly fixtures and tools, and test or repair equipment. Each of these vary in size, weight, required accuracy of final placement, and flow rate, even when associated with the same product.

Technical issues

Material handling is a discipline unto itself. It is taught in departments of industrial engineering and covers types of equipment plus methods for laying out a material-handling system and predicting its capacity (White and Apple, 1988).

Thought is also given to designing products to aid their handling. For example, the Nippondenso panel meter gauge requires no separate assembly pallet; the casing acts directly as the pallet, and it interfaces with the transport fixtures on the assembly machine. As another example, parts are being made with bar codes either applied or built in. Application methods include stick-on labels, paint, and laser etch. Built in includes circuit boards with the code applied like any other conductor stripe. The codes are used to route parts to workstations, count them, record process times and test results, send failed assemblies to repair stations, and so on.

The basic issue in transport system design is meeting the flow capacity requirements. Generally this is accomplished by ensuring that there are enough transporters so that transporters wait for production equipment rather than the reverse. It is also typically true that workpieces and assemblies, too, should wait for production equipment. However, if parts, assemblies, fixtures, and transporters are costly, a thorough economic analysis is required to determine what should wait for what.

A gross determination of the flow capacity of a transport system may be made with elementary algebra, but a detailed and accurate study requires computer simulation. This technique is the subject of Chap. 15.

A major design driver for the transport system is the degree of routing flexibility it must support. The minimum is zero flexibility, for which a continuously moving fixed speed conveyor will suffice. This option well suits mass production with infrequent model change. At the opposite extreme is a set of manually operated carts or fork lifts or an automated guided vehicle (AGV) system that can go from any location to any other. This extreme in flexibility may be needed to support model mix or to permit assemblies to be routed on demand to specialized stations for test or repair based on prior assembly operations or the needs of a particular model.

Like any other taxi system, an AGV network requires a dispatcher, a monitor, and a traffic manager. Delays can occur because of distance, the need to wait at intersections, or the need to detour around unexpected blockages. Thus, comparing the extremes of AGVs and fixed speed in-line conveyors, we find the usual flexibility-efficiency trade-off.

A second driver is the need to identify the *bottleneck stations* and ensure that they always have material to work on. Machines and manual workstations run at different rates because the work they do takes different amounts of time. Only a few machines or stations in any one line or factory are saturated (i.e., running as fast as they can or running 100 percent of the time). These are called the bottlenecks, and every effort is made to keep them running and producing because a lost cycle on a bottleneck machine is lost forever. The other machines can safely stop for limited periods as long as the lost time does not later require them to run faster than their capacity. Leaving an unsaturated machine stopped may baffle a cost accountant but should not bother a manufacturing engineer who knows the system's production requirements.

A subsidiary but important and related design issue concerns queues or waiting lines. These may be of two varieties. First is the type one normally encounters in service environments such as store checkout counters. Items wait until a server arrives. The length of the line is variable and depends on the difference between arrival rates of items and arrival or service rates of servers. In a factory, parts may queue up until a transporter arrives or a machine finishes processing the previous part.

The second type of queue is space deliberately provided in order to accommodate flow fluctuations caused by unpredictable events or to uncouple the operation of one machine from another. For example, when an assembly machine finishes work on one assembly, it should be able to set the finished work aside and start right in on the next. A way to ensure this is to provide a place where incoming work can be left by the transporter and stand ready (an *in-queue*) and a place to leave finished work for the transporter (an *out-queue*). Thus production and transport are decoupled.

Another example involves space provided between in-line or sequential workstations. Such spaces are called buffers and can store a supply of incoming or outgoing work so that a machine can keep working for a while if the machine before or after it breaks. It is not obvious whether such buffers really do much good, however, unless the buffered machine is a bottleneck.

In both types of queues, the design problem is to decide how much space to provide. More uncertainty in arrival rates of transporters or failure rates of machines implies the need for larger space. Typically, the designer makes these determinations with the aid of a simulation, although analytical methods for dealing with these problems are being developed (Suri and Hildebrant, 1984).

A final technical issue is stopping time and stopping accuracy of a transporter. Higher accuracy can imply longer time, lengthening the in-out time. If the transporter cannot stop accurately enough, there are techniques for grasping it or its pallet and locking it into position accurately.

One other characteristic of the transport system is synchrony. A synchronous transporter moves all the work pallets at once, at the same speed, for the same distance. This motion can be continuous or stop and go. A conveyor belt is an example. In an asynchronous system, each pallet essentially is or has its own transporter and can go or stop when it is ready or when it is released. Conveyors with individual powered carts or whose pallets can disconnect themselves from the drive belt are examples. The queues discussed above make sense only in asynchronous systems, where the freedom to move one pallet into or out of a station can be used effectively.

Economic issues

Economic issues in material-handling systems focus on two factors, the physical ability of the equipment to carry and deliver the payloads and the degree of flexibility needed. As with manufacturing systems in general, there are two kinds of flexibility: routing flexibility within the system and reconfigurability of the system for a new product or production strategy.

We present here some simplified economic models for two types of transport systems with similar routing flexibility, namely the monorail conveyor with switches and the AGV. Each model is based on sample bids (1987 prices) supplied by manufacturers of the respective types of transport system and include installation and training costs.

The monorail conveyor is available in various load capacities and usually consists of a rail on the floor, buried in the floor, or suspended overhead. Individual carriers ride the rail and may be self-powered or driven by a chain under the rail. Such systems may contain places where rails cross, branch, or merge, so that a wide variety of flexible routings may be built in. A central controller operates the switches.

A simple cost model of a monorail conveyor with numerous carriers is

$$C = A \times (\text{feet of rail}) + B \times (\text{number of carriers})$$

Element cost A includes installation and could be \$750 per foot. Element cost B could be \$1000 for each passive carrier, or \$5000 for each self-powered one. (In the latter case, A would be less since no drive chain would be needed.) A would be larger if the rail were installed in the floor.

Automated guided vehicles (AGVs) have a similar cost structure but with different element costs:

$$C = A \times (\text{feet of guidepath}) + B \times (\text{number of vehicles}) + S$$

Here, S is a fixed cost that includes system installation (i.e., computers, wiring, power supplies), software, and training. A includes floor installation of guide equipment, and B includes extra equipment such as batteries and battery charging sites. Possible values are \$75 per foot for A and \$79,000 per large-capacity vehicle or \$25,000 for a small one for B.

Clearly, these two types of transport system have very different cost structures. Long trackage and few vehicles favor an AGV system, whereas short trackage and many vehicles would favor a conveyor, if cost were the main criterion. Other factors, such as maintenance, also play a role in the decision. Figure 10.9 shows a comparison between these alternatives for a hypothetical system with 2500 ft of track and

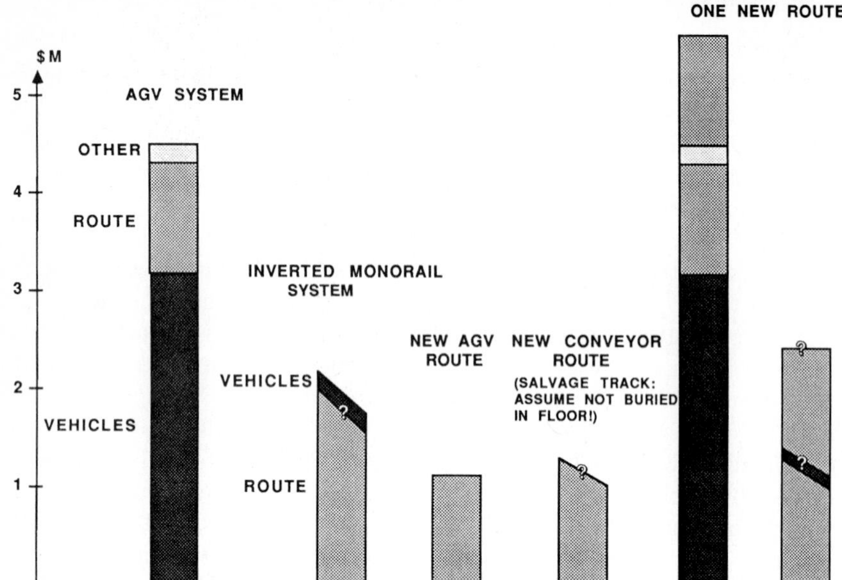

Fig. 10.9 Comparison of AGV and conveyor system costs for a system with many vehicles.

40 vehicles based on the simple model above. The number of vehicles required was determined by simulation. Not only are original installation costs shown, but also the prospective costs of completely rearranging the floor layout later. The assumption is that the vehicles will be reused but the floor installation and system costs must be incurred again. According to this example, the cost gap between AGVs and monorail conveyors will grow if successive total rearrangements of this system are accomplished. For another floor layout, the opposite conclusion might well result. The conveyor might again appear more economical at first, but the AGV might emerge as the better choice if many rearrangements are contemplated.

Floor Layout and System Architecture Alternatives

The history of manufacturing has revolved around the creation of novel production flow arrangements. Tradesmen and craftsmen used to do all the work on an object themselves, so the concept of production flow did not exist. The industrial age created the need to make production more efficient—or perhaps the ability to produce efficiently created the industrial age. In any event, the type of floor layout and system architecture needed depend mainly on the production volume requirements and the amount of variety in the items produced. Very low-volume production can still be satisfied by a single station doing all the work, while mass production is served by lines of stations where each station does one operation. At intermediate volumes are arrangements with several stations, each of which may do one or several operations.

Fabrication systems can be arranged as departments of identical machines, cells devoted to one closed part family, FMSs for an open family, or lines, as described in Chap. 13. In assembly, the architecture options are fewer in practice though not in principle. One could set up assembly departmentally, with one department for driving screws, another for inserting round pegs into holes, another for applying glue, another for making snap fits, and so on. One could also set up a cell with the required equipment or people for each model of the product.

However, cells and departments are not used in assembly for several reasons. Typically assembly task time is very short compared to transport time even if transport distances are a few feet. Department arrangements would make transport time an extremely large fraction of a product's processing time. The result would be large in-process inventory and long overall completion time.

Second, assembly equipment is often much less expensive than fabrication equipment, so there is a smaller penalty associated with having extra equipment at different locations in the factory. By contrast, the fabrication departments concentrate a few costly machines in one place. The work is brought to them and the station times are long.

Third, the various models of one product usually do not differ very much from each other: A few parts may be different or some parts may be omitted from some models. Thus the required operations and equipment for each model are almost the same, justifying merging all potential "cells" for each model into one.

Fourth, the impetus for fabrication departments and cells is low production volume of each part type. There is not enough work on one part to keep one machine busy for a year so machines of one type are grouped together and different parts are brought to them. In assembly, one can operate at low volume by using people and giving them many assembly tasks to do on each product unit. Typical fabricating machines are not versatile enough for this strategy. The exception is the computer-controlled machine tool or composite part layup robot. CNC machines in particular are arranged into FMSs.

Some assembly operations do occur in cells or departments. These are typically toxic or require expensive equipment or special procedures. Soldering, painting, and wire bonding of semiconductor chips are examples. Extreme cleanliness requirements may lead to placing certain types of assembly operations in a separate *clean room* which is supplied with filtered air and populated with workers in gowns and headdresses.

Other than these examples, assembly is typically arranged in lines. Workstations are set up in the order in which the work must be done, with one or more operations, machines, or people at each station. The number of operations per station is based, as discussed above, on the station's speed and versatility and on the required production rate. Other synergies such as team assembly also influence task grouping.

If the speeds of equipment or people differ greatly from one operation to another, it may be necessary to provide two or more identical stations to perform particularly slow operations. In conjunction with this, it may be possible and advantageous to shift work to faster or more lightly loaded stations, with the goal of giving each station about the same amount of work, measured by the time required. The system design algorithms described in Chap. 14 take such matters into account (see Fig. 10.10).

If several stations are needed to perform a series of operations and each station has the technical capability to perform them all, one has the option to arrange them in series or parallel. Both manual and robotic assembly may present this opportunity. In a *series arrangement*, each station is equipped to do one operation and pass the work on to the next. In a *parallel arrangement*, each station is identically equipped to do several operations. Transport is arranged so that each parallel station does all the operations before transport is needed again. Both serial and parallel arrangements have the same production rate.

The parallel arrangement has some attractive features. For people, it provides the opportunity to do a significant amount of work and feel some accomplishment, up to and including the final test. For N robots in parallel, there is some insulation from a mechanical failure because the loss of one robot cuts the production rate by $1/N$. In the serial arrangement, the loss of one station cuts production by 100 percent, assuming no buffers and no significant difference in the amount of saturation from one robot to another. Since more complex, multipurpose stations will likely have lower reliability than simple one-task stations, the decision is not a simple one. The parallel approach will cost more since each station must have all the required tools, feeders, and fixtures. The final decision on whether to set the stations up in series or parallel awaits a detailed analysis that takes the above subtleties into account.

Floor layout is also heavily influenced by product design. If the product is divided into distinct subassemblies, one may set the assembly factory up in separate *subassembly factories* which are each re-

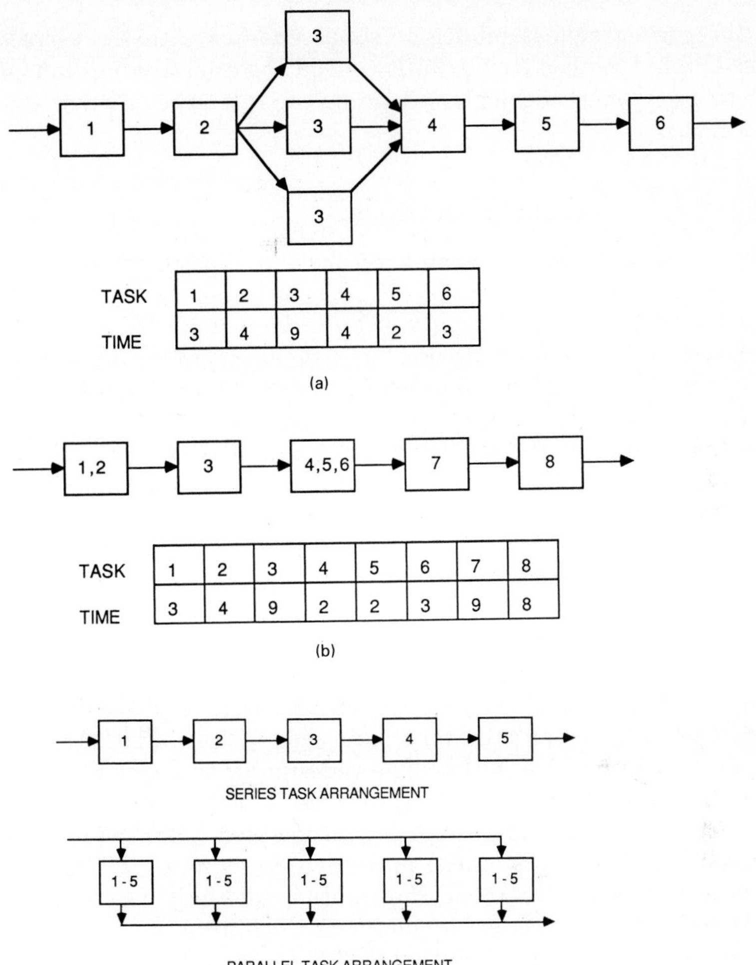

Fig. 10.10 Different ways of arranging workstations. (*a*) Three copies of station 3 are needed because its task takes so long; (*b*) grouping work of stations improves balance of station times; (*c*) in-series and parallel task arrangements. Production rate is the same but task assignment, reliability, transport needs, and tool purchase requirements are different.

sponsible for providing the *final assembly* factory with tested and verified items. The final assembly line may then be rather short. Among the many advantages of this arrangement is the fact that quality problems can be discovered and corrected closer to the point at which they occurred, and the likelihood that the final assembly will be correct is larger. If the product was designed so that model variations are confined to subassemblies, model mix final assembly consists of combining the correct subassemblies or subassemblies with the correct features. Often, the need for flexibility of routing or processing can be isolated to a few areas of the plant, leaving the rest to be efficient single path flows.

System Design and Economic Analysis

Many different systems are technically feasible. Which to choose is usually an economic decision.

A manufacturing system is part of an overall production process that is designed to create a product and make a profit. While this sounds direct, it is not easy to decide either the technical or economic issues. In the case of assembly system design, many factors must be balanced. These include the predicted cost of operation, the percentage of time that the system will be in operating order, and the percentage of finished assemblies that are correctly made and suitable for sale. As stated above, one pays more for a system with greater flexibility, higher reliability, and better quality output. These costs must be compared to the cost of having fewer of these desirable features.

Based on these and other considerations, one may determine not only the cost to assemble each successful unit but all the other costs, including purchase and fabrication of parts. Adding the company's desired profit will result in a minimum sale price. If this exceeds the estimate of what the market will bear, a redesign or strategic rethinking is needed. Perhaps the projected price, while not prohibitive, will result in lesser demand than originally anticipated. Changes in part fabrication and assembly methods may then be required. If the projected price is low, more demand than anticipated may occur, again causing a rethinking of production methods. Such iterations may continue even after the product is introduced to the market.

The economic analyses presented later in this book assume the correctness of the return on investment method and are suitable for two situations: (1) when the company has decided for strategic reasons to introduce a new product, in which case the individual investments may be added up and compared to the revenue stream they will help produce, and (2) when the company has decided to investigate replacing an existing method with a new one, in which case the return will come from cost savings. Great care must be taken to find all the cost saving potential and to design the product and process to reap those savings. Sometimes, labor replacement is the main savings source, but in other cases, process improvement in terms of yield percentage of good assemblies may outweigh labor savings. Indeed, quality, flexibility, yield, percentage of time actually operating, or savings in scrap, energy, or repair may be enough that no labor reduction is needed at all in order to justify the purchase of new equipment.

Summary

This chapter has stated in qualitative terms the various factors that are taken into account during the design of assembly systems. Many of these factors affect fabrication systems as well. The essential feature of the system design process is to determine the production requirements and then to decide how to meet them. The problem is to make a rational choice among the many alternatives as well as to relate these to product design in the hope of making both better. Later chapters will address several system design issues in more detail and will present analytical methods for making the required decisions.

References

Aoki, K.: "High Speed and Flexible Automated Assembly Line—Why Has Automation Successfully Advanced in Japan?" Proceedings, *4th Int'l. Conf. on Production Eng.*, Tokyo, Japan Society of Precision Engineering, 1980, pp 1–6.

Boothroyd, G., and A. H. Redford: *Mechanized Assembly,* McGraw-Hill, New York, 1968.

Fine, C. H., and R. M. Freund: "Economic Analysis of Product-Flexible Manufacturing Systems Investment Decisions," Proceedings, *2nd ORSA/TIMS Conf. on FMS,* Ann Arbor, August 1986, Elsevier, New York, 1986.

Hitachi, *Hitachi Assembleability Evaluation Method, (AEM),* Unpublished description, Hitachi Production Engineering Research Laboratory, Yokohama, Japan, 1981. This material is proprietary to Hitachi but is available for a licensing fee.

Kaneko, K., and T. Saigo: "A Newly Developed Unit Feeder Used in the Analog Quartz Watch Assembly System," Proceedings, *CIC '84,* Besancon, pp. 69–72.

Suri, R., and R. R. Hildebrant: "Modeling Flexible Manufacturing Systems Using Mean Value Analysis," *J. Manuf. Sys.*, vol. 3, no. 1, 1984, pp. 27–38.

White, J. A., and J. M. Apple, "Material Handling," in *The International Encyclopedia of Robotics: Applications and Automation,* S. Y. Nof (ed.), John Wiley, New York, 1988, pp. 873–79.

Chapter

11

Assembly Workstation Design

Introduction

This chapter covers the problem of designing a single assembly workstation. The problem has three major aspects: strategic, technical, and economic. The strategic issues center on choice of method of accomplishing the assembly—manual, robotic, and so on—plus part presentation, flexibility, inspection, and throughput. The technical problems involve detailed technology choice and assurance of proper performance, mainly achieved via an error analysis. Economic analysis is concerned with choosing a good combination of alternative methods of achieving assembly and controlling error.

The information developed during workstation design is used in, and is influenced by, the effort to design an entire assembly system. Thus, while this chapter comes first among the next several, we do not mean to imply by this sequence that stations are designed first, then systems. Quite often, the sequence is reversed or the process is iterative.

Fabrication station design, not discussed here, is entirely analogous. Choices must be made between alternate feeding, processing, and measuring methods so that the desired accuracy is obtained for a reasonable cost. Many of the techniques in this and later chapters apply.

Strategic Issues

Goals of station design

Our objective in designing an assembly workstation is to accomplish one or more assembly operations, in the presence of errors, so as to meet a specification, and to verify the station's performance. The number and identity of the operations to be performed is often tentatively decided during overall system design and may be revised often as station designs are attempted. Typical operations are part mating, application of adhesives, use of tools, application of heat, and measuring. The errors may arise from parts fabrication, assembly equipment, jigs, fixtures, part feeders, and so on. Verification must comprise not only the bare minimum—that the parts have been pushed together—but that the work has been accomplished within prescribed tolerances on interpart forces, accelerations, temperature, pressure, or whatever may be of concern.

Uncertainty reduction

Assembly is a geometric problem and may be looked upon as one of reducing a relatively large uncertainty in a relative location between parts or between a part and a tool to approximately zero. Depending on the error's magnitude, one has the choice of different means for reducing it further. Good design often hinges on recognizing the appropriate choices. Figure 11.1 represents some of these choices schemat-

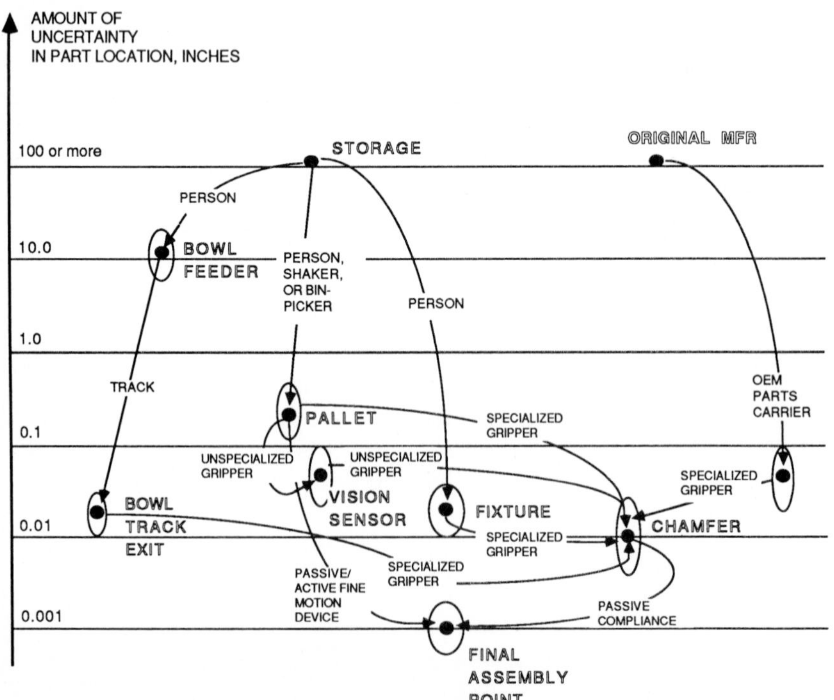

Fig. 11.1 Different error removal strategies that result in parts being assembled successfully.

TABLE 11.1 Pros and Cons of Various Error-Reduction Methods in Assembly

Method	Pro	Con
Vision	100:1 error reduction possible	Can be costly and slow
Chamfers	Inexpensive	Limited to about 10% of hole diameter
Palletizing	Organized bulk feeding	Accuracy is costly
Prefeeding to cassettes or carriers	Isolates assembly from feeding problems	Possible cost penalty

ically and is intended to show that they are very broad, including specification of packaging by vendors of purchased parts.

As the figure shows, it is typical that the error will be reduced in stages, although not every stage is represented in each alternative approach. If the parts have chamfers, then for small parts assembled by simple one-stroke workheads, all the error might be removed in two steps: (1) feeding the parts from a bulk feeder (a vibratory bowl) to an escapement at the end of the feeder track and (2) pushing them together, letting the chamfers and compliance remove the last bit of error. For large parts in pallets, the procedure might take additional steps: (1) the parts are palletized and the pallets located within an inch or so at the workstation, (2) a vision system locates each part to within ±0.125 in, say, (3) this is close enough for a well-designed gripper to capture a part to within ±0.010 in, and (4) this, in turn, is close enough for the chamfers and compliance to take care of the rest. The reader may trace other paths through the figure and catch the spirit of the alternatives. Some of these are listed in Table 11.1 together with pros and cons.

The choice problem

Faced with this array of choices, what should the designer do? Instead of debating pros and cons, this chapter presents an error analysis technique and an economic method for making such choices. Before we can present these techniques, several other topics must be discussed.

Technical Issues

First we take up the technical design issues, beginning with the requirements on a station and ending with a timing analysis. No particular station technology is assumed. The same mathematics can be used for a robot station with many degrees of freedom and tool changing or for a single degree of freedom workhead. Only passing mention will be made of complexities like multiple robots operating in each others' workspace. For such topics, reference will be made to the literature.

Analyzing requirements

The beginning of any design is a listing and analysis of the requirements. These include constraints imposed by the parts themselves because of their weight, size, and manufacturing tolerances. One must consider the part being added to the assembly as well as those to which the part is added; both have location tolerances and uncertainty and may have limits on contact forces they can stand. A major constraint imposed by the system design is the total time available for performing the assembly. Within this time, the following steps, if required, must be done:

1. "Shifting attention to the job" by swinging a tool or robot to it or by moving it into position at the station
2. Fetching the necessary tool
3. Fetching the part (if any)
4. Performing the assembly or operation
5. Performing confirmatory tests
6. Doing any other required tests
7. Releasing the assembly for the next operation
8. Putting away the tool

The requirements will be influenced by decisions which are made in conjunction with system design (see Chap. 14) regarding grouping of tasks and multiple use of the same tool. Each of the above elements takes some time, however small it may seem. In small parts assembly, a total cycle time of 2 s is a typical target, so the time taken by every element must be kept under control.

The following are some typical requirements:

1. *Precision assembly.* Examples are hydraulic valves or computer disk drives. The parts have fine surface finishes and typical clearances are 0.01 mm (0.0004 in). Cleanliness is a prime consideration, and assembly equipment and tools must not generate dirt particles. In addition, contact forces between parts during assembly must be a few grams or less to avoid surface damage or creation of particles. Since contact forces can be hundreds of times larger than insertion forces, parts of this kind must be inserted with great care. Tools with compliance along the insertion direction are often used.

2. *Threaded fasteners.* Each size fastener and material fastened has a recommended tightness, usually expressed in terms of tightening torque. Because of friction under the head of the fastener, plain torque measurements are usually not accurate indicators of tightness. Commercial sensors are available that use a combination of torque and turn angle to measure how far up the stress-strain curve the fastener has been loaded.

3. *Dispensing of liquids.* A typical case is gluing parts together. While accurate automatic dispensers are coming into use, at least two situations can cause trouble. First, the amount dispensed depends critically on the liquid's viscosity, which in turn is very temperature dependent. One company deliberately used a color-contrasting glue and employed a vision system to check the size of each glue dot so that the dispenser could be adjusted before the next operation. Second, the amount of glue needed may depend on an unknown, namely the size of cavity into which it is injected. Cavity size variations may depend on the tolerance to which parts are made, and tightening tolerances is costly. Figure 11.2 shows a solution that uses a low-cost redesign of

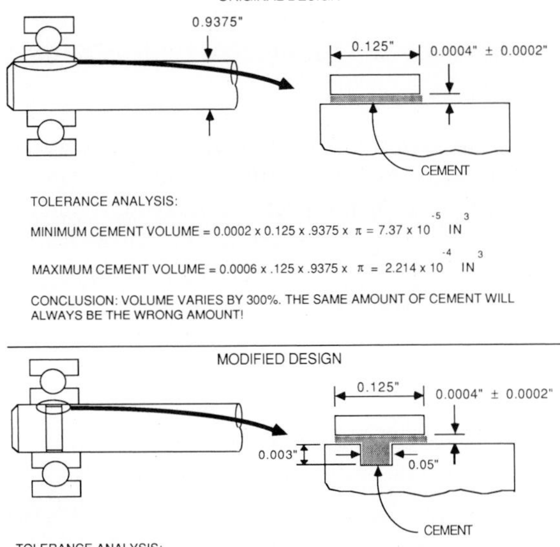

Fig. 11.2 Accurate dispensing of liquids. Initially a workstation design problem, it is solved, after a requirements analysis, by redesigning the parts.

the parts rather than an attempt to dispense more accurately or tighten tolerances on key part surfaces. This example of Taguchi "parameter design" turns an apparent workstation design problem into a parts design problem, resulting in a better situation.

In each case one must be sure that the "requirements" are actually required. Sometimes they are imposed from afar or by rote or without a clear knowledge of the cost or difficulty. Sometimes they are conceived in the context of manual assembly and must be revised if mechanization is being considered. The instruction "Use a small amount of glue" must be replaced by a specific quantity, such as a number of milligrams. Workstation designers must be prepared to identify such ill-formed requirements and obtain quantifications. Consultation with product designers and performance of experiments may be necessary.

Another major pitfall in station design requirements is that parts are not always made to the tolerances on the prints. This may seem incredible to part and product designers but is well-known to manufacturing engineers. Different vendors may make the same part by different means or with varying degrees of success. Some dimensions on parts may seem like unnecessary details and their quality may be allowed to deteriorate. Machines may not be available to make the parts to print, and no one has noticed because manual assemblers have figured out how to assemble them anyway. Ironically, the parts as made may function quite adequately, implying that they were overdesigned.

Regardless of the reasons, if the parts and prints do not agree, the result may be a failed assembly station. As was discussed in Chap. 8, manufacture and assembly depend on functional and nonfunctional surfaces of parts. An integrated product and production system design identifies the critical surfaces and tolerances them accordingly. Proper quality control then assures that the tolerances are met, so that both product and production system will function as intended.

At the end of this phase of station design, the engineers should have a fairly complete if tentative list of required times, tolerances, speeds, forces, and so on, enabling them to make intelligent design decisions. Gaps in the specification must be identified as soon as possible.

Geometric layout

The geometric layout of a workstation is dominated by two factors, accessibility and time. Assembly involves the transfer of parts or tools from one location and orientation to another. There may be obstacles, such as other partly done assemblies, tool storage racks, or other parts in the same assembly. Part size and presentation method play a major role. Total task completion time may depend critically on the location of elements within the station area.

The major items to be located are the work itself, the parts to be assembled, and the tools, if any. Naturally, these should be as close to each other as size and shape permit. Interestingly, however, the relative positions of items visited once per cycle affects only the order in which they are visited but hardly affects total task time.

Relative positions affect task time when tool changing is involved or several of the same part are inserted. Here, the tool storage area or the part feeder is visited more than once and a careful study of locations is required. An example is a circuit board whose assembly sequence is essentially unconstrained (Fisher and Nof, 1984). The same complexity arises if there are multiple robots working on the same assembly (Bedini et al., 1979).

An aspect of accessibility to elements in a workstation is degrees of freedom. A part has 6 degrees of freedom—3 translational and 3 rotational—and all 6 must be brought to the correct values as a result of assembly. One can then think of assembly as the act of reducing the unknown or unspecified degrees of freedom to 0. Part presentation plays a large role, obviously, since several degrees of freedom may be determined by feeding or palletizing. In the simplest of single-stroke workstations, the feeder sets up 5 of the 6, and insertion simply does the sixth.

In other cases, product design, part presentation method, or assembly path may dictate that the assembly device maneuver the part, requiring the device to have several degrees of freedom. Another common cause of multiaxis assembly devices is the need to perform several jobs at one station.

The designer has recourse to several alternatives in such cases. One is to confine the extra degrees of freedom to tools that the assembly device acquires as needed, such as grasping a screwdriver tool. Another choice is to put some degrees of freedom in the workbase or fixture supporting the assembly. This is useful when the assembly must be reoriented.

Naturally, more degrees of freedom or longer reach requirements—whether caused by multiple tasks or product design—can lengthen the time required to do the tasks.

The main design tools used for station layout are static CAD and dynamic or animated station simulation. An example of static CAD is shown in Fig. 11.3. Two robots must work successively on the ends of two product units mounted on a large pallet. The parts are long and the robots have both a maximum and a minimum reach (shown as arcs and circles), which can be derived from manufacturer's specifica-

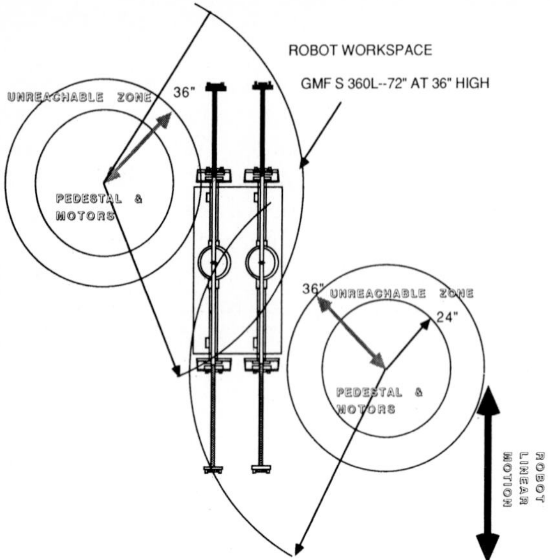

Fig. 11.3 CAD for preliminary robot assembly station layout.

tions as shown. These specifications should be used with caution since they are two-dimensional approximations to the actual maneuverability of a multiaxis machine.

Such CAD is fast, low cost, and preliminary. Detailed animated design is necessary when complex maneuvers, tight space, or limited station time are involved. Several companies offer such computer packages. To date, they are limited in that they do not represent errors of any kind, except as the user may introduce one at a time. Typical, often critical, errors include robot geometric and dynamic repeatability, robot compliance under the weight of parts, and, of course, part and fixture tolerances. These are discussed later in this chapter. When layouts and locations must be time-optimized, shortest path algorithms and traveling salesman techniques are used.

Work, tools, part presentation

Let us consider several typical station design problems. These differ mainly in the size of parts and the impact that part size has on station layout and part presentation. In other respects, the stations all have similar flexibility requirements; several models of the product must be accommodated, and several parts are installed at the station.

First, we take up assembly of parts to a VCR chassis about 20 cm (7 in) square. Each unit has about 100 small springs, stamped metal levers, rivets, screws, rubber belts, circuit boards, and small wires and plugs. Almost all are assembled by SCARA-style robots. Each unit is its own pallet and is locked into position at a station before assembly starts. In-out transfer and locking take about 2 s. Each robot must install five parts in 10 s. Since tool changing typically takes as long as inserting a part, the robot would have to change tools in 1 s and perform assembly of one part in another second in order to meet the time requirement. This is beyond the current state of the art.

To accomplish part feeding, the production system designers separated those parts that are common to all models from those that are model-specific. Additionally, they separated screws and rivets that could be bulk-fed from levers and springs that required palletizing. Pallets are filled at automated stations in which parts are simply poured over the pallet while it is shaken side to side (see Fig. 10.6).

To accomplish batch-size-of-one assembly, the designers bowl-fed the common screws and rivets and pallet-fed the rest. Pallets with 100 parts are about 20 by 40 cm, and some parts are 50 cm or more from the assembly area (see Fig. 11.4).

Each robot has a five-tool turret [see Fig. 11.4(*c*)] similar to that found on a microscope for holding and switching objective lenses. "Tool changing" occurs while the robot is moving to fetch the part. Each tool contains sufficient sensors to determine if a part has been successfully grasped and inserted. The robot controller keeps track of the pallet slots it empties or from which it fails to retrieve a part, and signals the system management computer when it is about to exhaust a pallet. A replacement pallet is then dispatched. When it arrives, the robot exchanges it for the empty one.

The second example involves the same kinds of decisions on a product the size of an automobile engine with much larger parts. One hundred parts per pallet is clearly out of the question. In fact, pallets with even two of the same part may also be impossible, depending on their size and the reach and load capacity of assembly equipment. One alternative employs bulk pallets of small parts and single sets of large ones. The other provides kit pallets containing some or all of the parts for one product unit. In some cases, it may be useful to supply the tools on the parts pallet. Where space is available, it may make sense to kit or palletize the parts directly on the work pallet where the assembly is built. Figure 11.5 shows a concept station layout employing some of these ideas. Space and time optimization of such a station clearly requires considerable effort.

When different pallets hold different numbers of parts per assembly, the pallet transport system must be able to deliver pallets at different frequencies: some once per assembly, some once every two or three assemblies, and so on.

As a final example, let us consider several alternate designs for an automated kitting station. The designer has been asked to consider a robotic station because five different kits must be built at varying production rates, using geometrically similar parts. The parts are disks which are of two types, a and b, of several different diameters. They are purchased from a vendor and arrive in stacks of a's and b's. The kits to be made consist of interleaved stacks of a-b-a-b ... , each of the five types being a different diameter or a different stack height. At

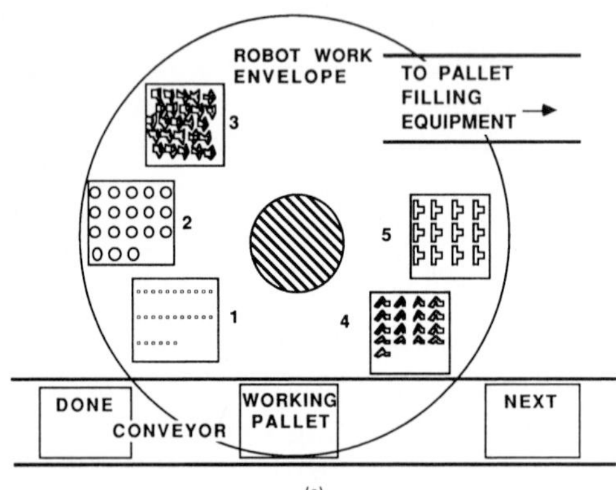

(a)

(b)

Fig. 11.4 (a) Layout of a robot assembly station in the Sony videorecorder head assembly system; (b) overview of Sony VCR head assembly system showing robots with multitool turrets. (*Sony FA*.)

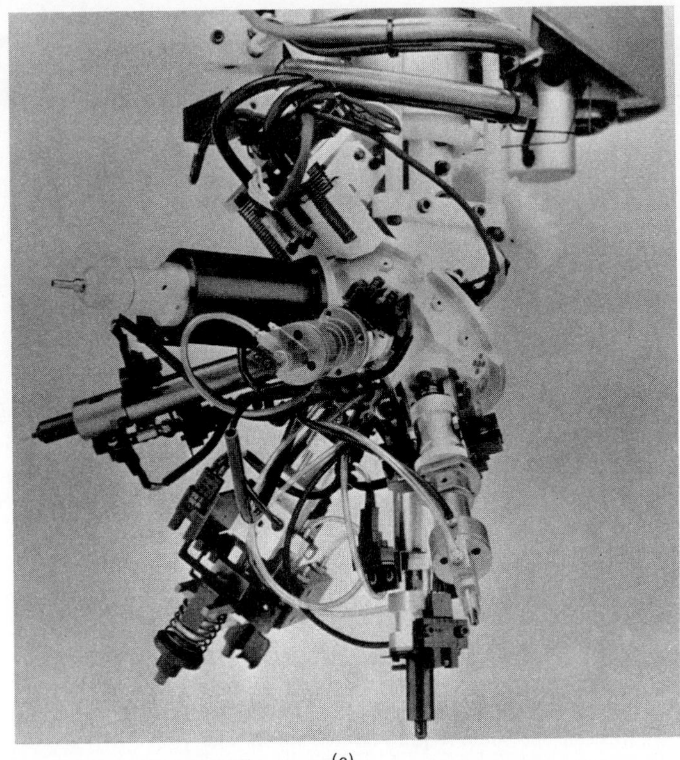

(c)

Fig. 11.4(*c*) Closeup of tool turret. (*Sony FA*)

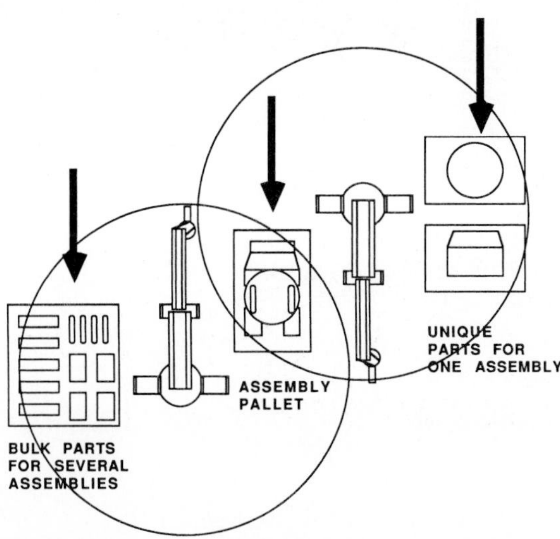

Fig. 11.5 Palletizing options for a large product.

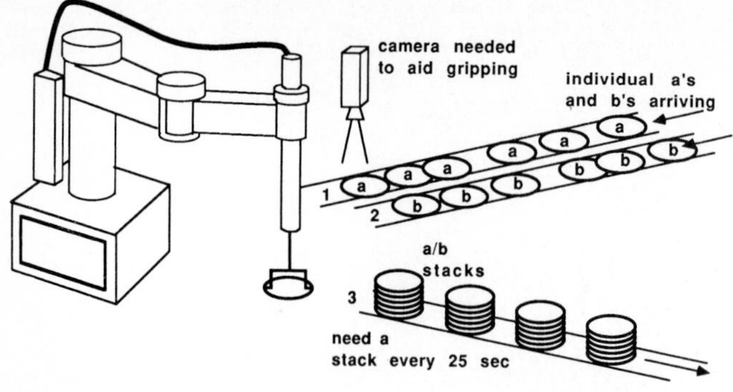

ALTERNATIVE 1: ROBOT GRIPS 1 a AND 1 b

PROGRAM IS 1, 2, 3, 1...
EACH SUBMOVE TAKES T SEC:
1 TO 2, 2 TO 3, 3 TO 1, 5 TIMES.
TIME FOR A STACK OF 5 a's, 5 b's = 15*T SEC
SO T MUST BE 25/15 = 1.67 SEC.

ALTERNATIVE 2: ROBOT CAN GRIP UP TO 5 a's AND 5 b's

PROBRAM IS (2 TO 1) 5 TIMES, (1 TO 2) 4 TIMES PLUS
(3 TO 2) PLUS (1 TO 3).
TIME FOR A STACK OF 10 = 11*T SEC.
SO T MUST BE 25/11 = 2.27 SEC.

SINCE T FOR A ROBOT OF THIS SIZE IS TYPICALLY 5 SEC,
ALT 1 WOULD REQUIRE 4 SUCH STATIONS, WHILE ALT 2
WOULD REQUIRE 3.

Fig. 11.6(*a*) The first concept for creating interleaved stacks. Because of its low speed, this concept would require either three or four identical stations just to make one of the five types of stacks needed.

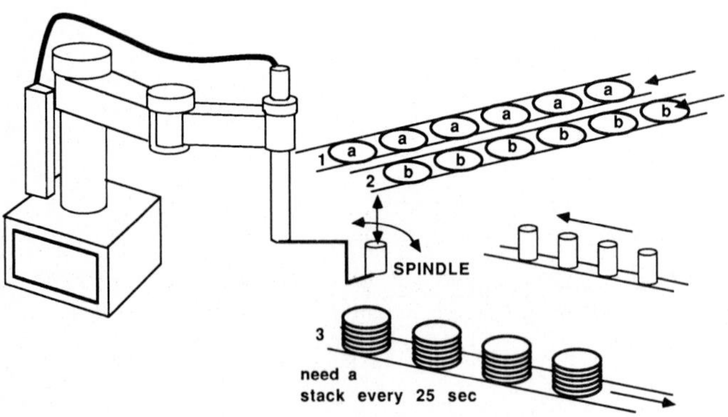

ROBOT PICKS UP SPINDLE IN TIME T.
ROBOT'S TOOL SWINGS SPINDLE FROM 1 TO 2 IN TIME 0.7*T.
ROBOT DEPOSITS STACK WITH SPINDLE IN TIME T.
TOTAL TIME = (9*0.7+2)*T = 8.3*T, SO T MUST BE 3.01 SEC.

ON THIS BASIS, TWO SUCH STATIONS WILL SUFFICE.

Fig. 11.6(*b*) The second stacker concept. Because of its increased speed, only two such stations are needed for each model of stack required.

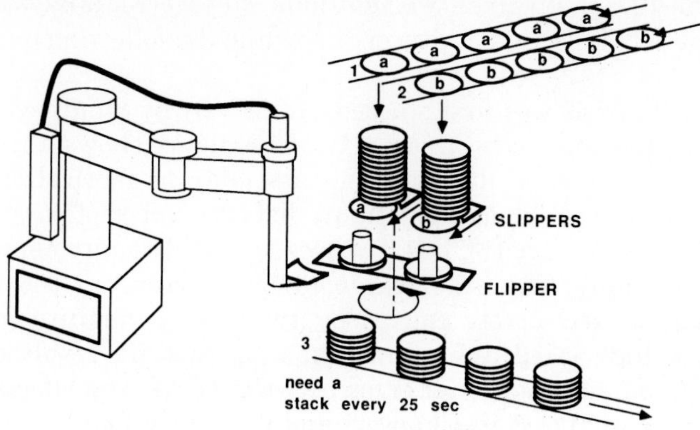

FLIPPER FLIPS EVERY 2 SEC. SLIPPERS SLIDE
A DISK ONTO EACH SPINDLE ON THE FLIPPER.
TWO COMPLETE STACKS ARE DONE IN 10 SEC.
ROBOT TRANSFERS THEM TO CONVEYOR IN 5 SEC.
NET TIME PER STACK = 7.5 SEC

IF THERE ARE N FLIPPER-SLIPPERS, THE ROBOT SERVES
EACH ONE EVERY 5N SEC. SO EACH ONE PRODUCES A
STACK EVERY 2.5N SEC. IF EACH MAKES A STYLE THAT IS
NEEDED ONCE EACH 25 SEC, THEN A ROBOT CAN SERVE 10
FLIPPER-SLIPPERS.

Fig.11.6(*c*) The third robot stacker concept. The robot now merely unloads independent stack makers. This is so efficient that one robot can serve 10 stackers, more than enough to make all the required models.

present, people make these kits by simply taking disks one at a time from an *a* supply and a *b* supply.

Three different station concepts are shown in Fig. 11.6, essentially in the order in which the designer thought them up. Each one is equally flexible, retaining the ability to build a stack of any prescribed height and diameter at the required production rate. But each is an improvement in efficiency over the prior one, achieved by improving the capability of tools and fixtures that work with the robots. At the same time, each later concept has fewer robots, and their role shifts through the concepts from direct stack makers into stack carriers. In this process, the number of degrees of freedom they need is reduced, as is their complexity and speed. While a detailed economic analysis has not been made, it is likely that stations with fewer and simpler robots will cost less to make and keep operating.

Error analysis and error reduction strategies

The above station design examples are simplified concepts or scenarios depicting how the station might operate. Converting such a concept into a reliable design involves two additional steps: error analysis and timing studies. This section covers errors, while the following one covers timing.

Assembly error analysis was first studied extensively by Simunovic (1976). It is stated schematically in Fig. 11.7. This figure shows a robot attempting an assembly, although any assembly or fabrication equipment faces similar problems. The figure lists a number of possible error sources, including parts, jigs, fixtures, assembly equipment, even robot programming. The latter can contribute erroneous robot kinematic models, control errors caused by the robot's inability to move accurately at high speed, and so on. Taken together, the result is relative translational and rotational error between parts. The effects of these errors were analyzed in Chaps. 5 and 6, and we found that error bounds for successfully initiating assembly can be expressed as

$$|\epsilon_0| + L_g|\theta_0| \leq W$$

$$|\theta_0| \leq \frac{c}{\mu} \tag{11.1}$$

Successful completion of assembly can be achieved by using an RCC (see Chap. 7).

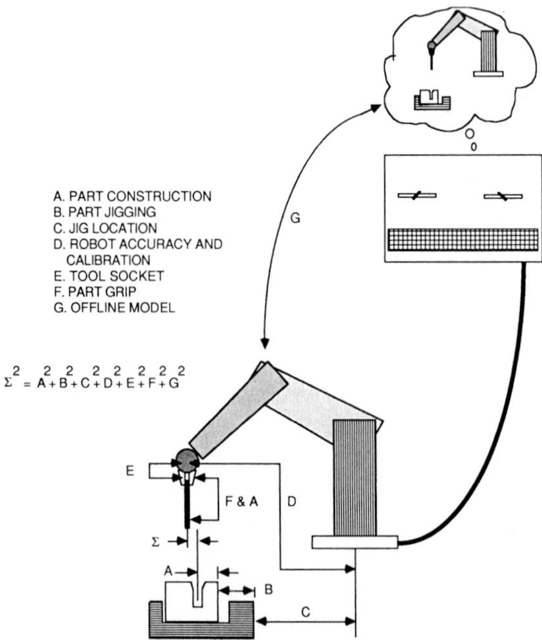

Fig. 11.7 Some of the many sources of error that must be controlled in order to achieve successful assembly.

The remainder of the analysis aims at satisfying Eq. (11.1). We will make use of techniques used for describing the kinematics of robots. A good reference for such information is Paul (1981). The essence of the techniques is the ability to represent the position and orientation of one object with respect to another or to a common base. Also possible and necessary is the ability to represent small changes in position and orientation.

The basic element of the technique is the 4 by 4 matrix called a "transform." This matrix contains a location vector and a rotation matrix and represents the act of first translating an object from a base location to the end point of the vector and then rotating the object by the rotation matrix. This is illustrated schematically in Fig. 11.8. The mathematical form of the transform is

$$\mathbf{T} = \begin{bmatrix} \mathbf{R} & \mathbf{p} \\ \mathbf{0}^T & 1 \end{bmatrix} \tag{11.2}$$

Here, $\mathbf{R}$ is a 3 by 3 rotation matrix, and $\mathbf{p}$ is the translation vector; $\mathbf{0}^T$ is a 1 by 3 row of 0s, and the 1 is a single number. The superscript T denotes a matrix or vector transpose. The matrix product of two $\mathbf{T}$'s has the same form as Eq. (11.2), that is $\mathbf{T}_1 \times \mathbf{T}_2$ is again a $\mathbf{T}$, as illustrated in Fig. 11.9. This figure shows the case where a second object is positioned and oriented with respect to a first object, something we are interested in when analyzing the accumulation of errors during assembly. We may think of object 2 as a part placed on object 1, a jig, for example.

In an analogous way, we may stack up the positions of parts gripped by tools held in tool sockets on the end of robots placed in workstations, a stack of five error sources. The *nominal,* error-free, location of the *part* may be described by T_{np}

$$T_{np} = T_{br} \times T_r \times T_{ts} \times T_t \times T_p \tag{11.3}$$

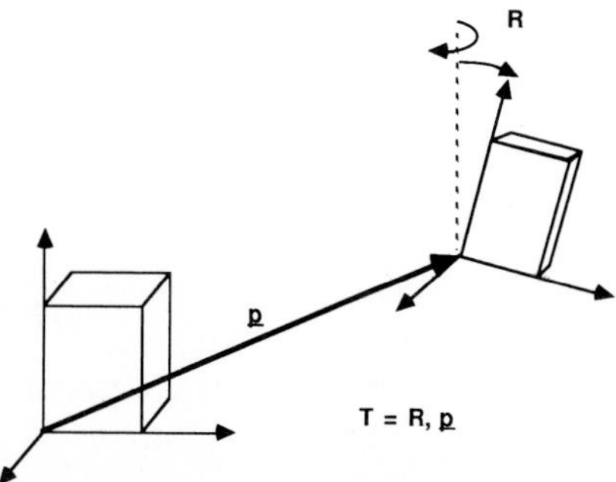

Fig. 11.8 Illustration of a transform as a translation $\mathbf{p}$ followed by a rotation R.

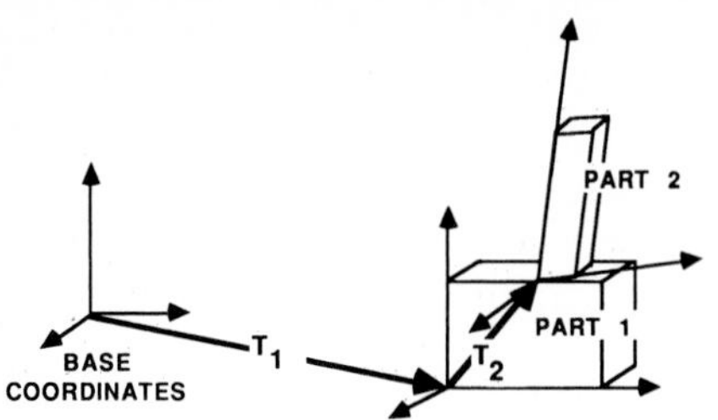

Fig. 11.9 $\mathbf{T}_1 \times \mathbf{T}_2$ locates the second part with respect to the base coordinates.

T_{br} represents the location and orientation of the robot or assembly equipment relative to a reference or base coordinate system, T_r represents the location and orientation of the robot's wrist or tool socket with respect to the robot's base, T_{ts} represents the offsets, if any, between the wrist and the tool socket, T_t represents the same for the tool with respect to the socket, and T_p represents the offset of the tip of the part with respect to the surface where the tool grips it. The insertion axis of the part is assumed to lie along the z axis of the part's coordinate frame. Each of these transformations may be simple in the nominal case but will be more complex when altered to include possible construction, gripping, or programming errors.

The *nominal* location and orientation of the receiving *target* part is T_{nt}

$$T_{nt} = T_{bf} \times T_f \times T_a \tag{11.4}$$

T_{bf} represents the location of the assembly base with respect to the base coordinates, T_f locates the assembly fixture on the assembly base, and T_a locates the partly built assembly (including placement transforms of all previously assembled parts) with respect to the fixture.

Perfect assembly would occur if $T_{np} = T_{nt}$, but this case is too unlikely to consider. There will always be some error, as illustrated schematically in Fig. 11.10. The question is, how big is that error? Thus, we are interested in the "difference" transform Δ between the two *actual* transforms T_{ap} and T_{at}, defined by

$$T_{at} = T_{ap} \times \Delta \tag{11.5}$$

or

$$\Delta = T_{ap}^{-1} \times T_{at} \tag{11.6}$$

The superscript -1 represents transform inverse. The inverse of a transform may be written as

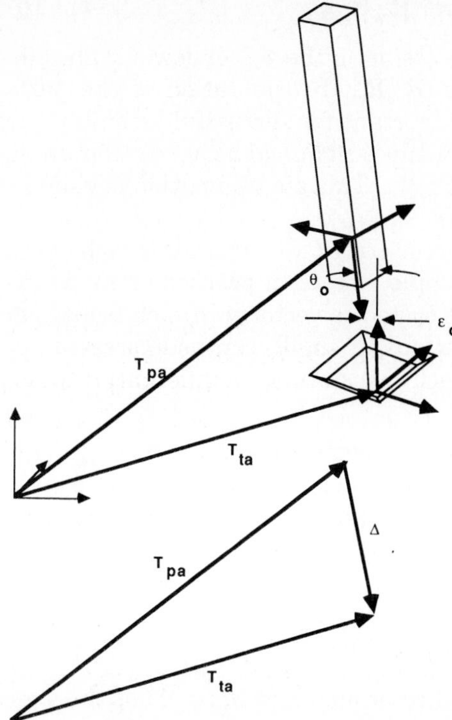

Fig. 11.10 Schematic illustration of assembly error ε_0, θ_0, summarized as transform Δ relating the actual transforms between part and target.

$$\mathbf{T}^{-1} = \begin{bmatrix} \mathbf{R}^T & -\mathbf{p} \\ \mathbf{0}^T & 1 \end{bmatrix} \tag{11.7}$$

which is also a transform. Multiplying out Eq. (11.6) gives us

$$\Delta = \begin{bmatrix} \mathbf{R}_{ap}^T \mathbf{R}_{at} & \mathbf{R}_{ap}^T \mathbf{p}_{at} - \mathbf{p}_{ap} \\ \mathbf{0}^T & 1 \end{bmatrix} \tag{11.8}$$

The product of rotation matrices in the upper left of Eq. (11.8) is a rotation matrix that describes the net rotation required to rotate the z axis of the actual part into the orientation of the z axis of the actual target, while the vector difference in the upper right is the translation, expressed in nominal part coordinates, required to shift the tip of the part into alignment with the target. In terms of Eq. (11.1), we may then write

$$\varepsilon_0 = | \mathbf{R}_{ap}^T \mathbf{p}^{at} - \mathbf{p}_{ap} | \tag{11.9}$$

where | represents vector magnitude, and

$$\theta_0 = \cos^{-1}\left(\mathbf{R}_{ap}^T \mathbf{R}_{at}\right)_{3,3} \tag{11.10}$$

That is, θ_0 is the angle whose cosine is the 3,3 or lower right element of the net rotation matrix $\mathbf{R}_{ap}^T\mathbf{R}_{at}$. If orientation of the parts about the z or insertion axis is important for successful assembly, we may obtain an approximation to this angle, called θ_z, as the angle whose sine is the 1,2 element of $\mathbf{R}_{ap}^T\mathbf{R}_{at}$. This approximation is valid as long as θ_0 is a few degrees or less.

To study the effects of tolerances or errors, we must alter each of the transforms listed above. For example, errors in positions may be expressed by adding small amounts $\delta\mathbf{p}$ to the vector $\mathbf{p}$ in each transform as appropriate. Errors in orientations, if small, can be expressed approximately by premultiplying each transform by a differential transform matrix DT defined as

$$DT = \begin{bmatrix} 1 - \dfrac{\delta\theta_y^2}{2} - \dfrac{\delta\theta_z^2}{2} & -\delta\theta_z & \delta\theta_y & dx \\ \delta\theta_x\delta\theta_y + \delta\theta_z & 1 - \dfrac{\delta\theta_x^2}{2} - \dfrac{\delta\theta_z^2}{2} & -\delta\theta_x & dy \\ -\delta\theta_y + \delta\theta_x\delta\theta_z & \delta\theta_x + \delta\theta_y\,\delta\theta_z & 1 - \dfrac{\delta\theta_x^2}{2} - \dfrac{\delta\theta_y^2}{2} & dz \\ 0 & 0 & 0 & 1 \end{bmatrix}$$

Here, $\delta\theta_x$, $\delta\theta_y$, and $\delta\theta_z$ are small rotations in radians about the axes x, y, and z of the part, fixture, or tool, as the case may be, plus small translations dx, dy, and dz of the origin of those axes.[1]

Then each new transform T_a representing the actual position and orientation may be obtained from the respective nominal T_n by adding $\delta\mathbf{p}$ and/or by calculating

$$T_a = DT \times T_n \tag{11.12}$$

Finally, the overall T_{ap} and T_{at} may be obtained by multiplying out the individual T's as in Eqs. (11.3) and (11.4), and Δ may be found from Eq. (11.5).

This analysis will reveal whether the lateral and angular error requirements for successful assembly are met in a worst-case situation in which every contributing error source is at its maximum. A statistical analysis is beyond the scope of this book. An indication of how to do it is given in Veitschegger and Wu (1986).

However, we can do a simple numerical example. In Fig. 11.11(*a*) shows the coordinate frames and 4 by 4 transforms for a three-link robot whose gripper is holding a part; (*b*) shows the same for an assem-

[1]Rotations occur in the order of x, y, z, with y and z taking place about previously rotated axes.

(A)

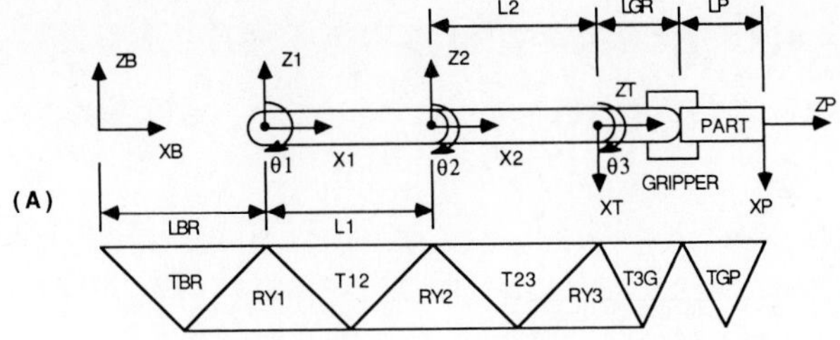

TNP = TBR*RY1*T12*RY2*T23*RY3*T3G*TGP

(B)

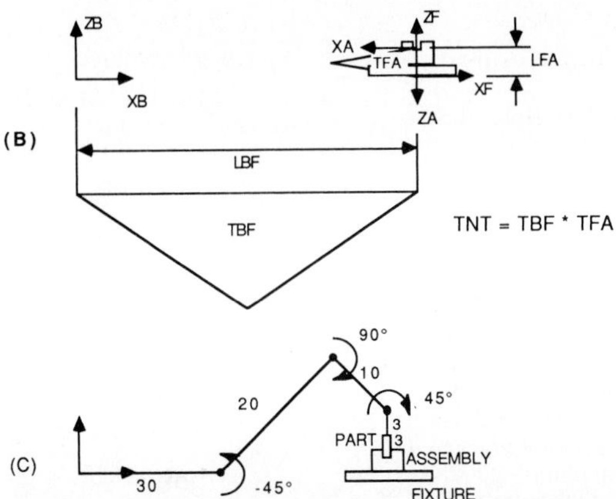

(C)

Fig. 11.11 Coordinates of a robot and an assembly fixture. (A) The model of the robot and the part, referred to the base frame. T_r in Eq. (11.3) expands to RYI × T12 × RY2 × T23 × RY3; $T_{ts} \times T_t$ becomes T3G, while T_p is called TGP. (B) The model of the assembly and its fixture, also referred to the base frame. $T_f \times T_a$ in Eq. (11.4) becomes TFA. (C) The actual nominal configuration of the items in (A) and (B). Along side each link, part, or distance is its length. For example, the robot is 30 units from the base; the gripper is 3 units long, as is the part.

bly (in a fixture) into which the part is to be placed. The nominal transforms are either simple translations, such as TBR, or simple rotations, such as RY2. Part (*c*) shows the nominal configuration of the robot, part, assembly, and fixture at the moment of assembly, assuming no errors. A simple BASIC program computed these transforms. In addition, it used a random number subroutine to generate gaussian random errors with zero mean and standard deviation 0.002 (mm or rad) for the Y coordinate of TBF, the orientation of the robot with respect to the base coordinates about the base's X axis, and the orientation of the part's Y axis with respect to the gripper. The result is a scatter plot of values of ε_0 and θ_0, which is shown in Fig. 11.12. Such

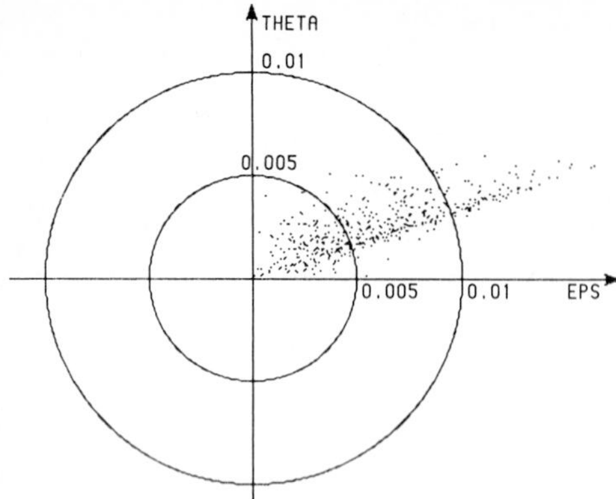

Fig. 11.12 The resulting scatter plot. Note that THETA and EPS are not independent. This is to be expected, since lateral error can be caused by angular error about a distant origin. The largest lateral error independent of angular error is about 0.006, consistent with the fact that the only source of pure lateral error has a standard deviation of 0.002. Further, angular error also seems to have a maximum, consistent with the fact that the two contributors to the total angle are two independent angles perpendicular to each other, each with standard deviations of 0.002. These will add via the pythagorean theorem to give a random variable with a standard deviation of about 0.0028, making total angular errors over 0.006 quite rare.

a plot should be compared to the wedging criteria plot to determine the likelihood of an assembly failure.

Dealing with error

The error analysis method above reveals the consequences of errors but does not show what to do about them. A systematic approach begins by dividing errors into two classes, *systematic* and *random*. Systematic errors are substantially the same, cycle after assembly cycle, or they drift very slowly over many cycles. On the other hand, random errors show little or no correlation from cycle to cycle (see Fig. 11.13).

The distinction between systematic and random errors is fundamental to any error control or quality control process, as described by Taguchi. Systematic errors represent inadequate design, process control, measurement, preparation, modeling, oversight, or discipline. With enough time and effort, they can be found and eliminated. Random errors or "noise" are literally those which remain when all others

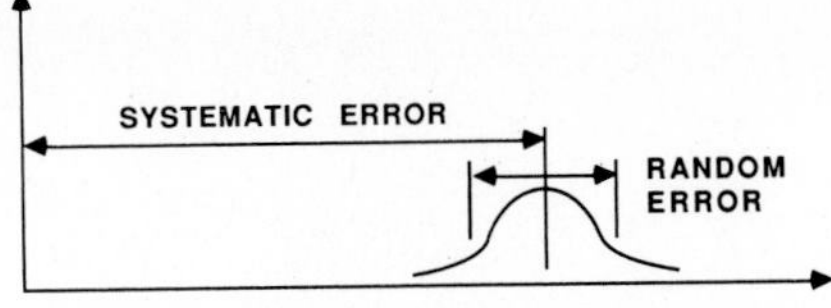

SYSTEMATIC ERRORS ARE THE SAME EVERY CYCLE OR DRIFT SLOWLY OVER MANY CYCLES

RANDOM ERRORS ARE DIFFERENT EVERY CYCLE AND SHOW LITTLE OR NO CORRELATION OVER MANY CYCLES

Fig. 11.13 The distinction between systematic and random errors.

have been removed. They cannot be eliminated and must be blunted by robust design and by monitoring and controlling processes.

A great deal of confusion arises when the distinction between systematic and random errors is not made. In particular, production workers should not be blamed for random errors. This is a basic starting point in gaining the confidence and cooperation of workers when a quality control program is started.

Some examples of systematic and random errors are given in Table 11.2, along with some common remedies.

Timing and cycle time estimation

The last technical issue in workstation design is estimating the time the station will take to complete its tasks. The dynamic simulation software referred to above can be used for this purpose, but a great deal of work and detail are required to obtain the full benefit. During preliminary design, approximate cycle times are needed for many competing station concepts.

The time-consuming activities in an assembly cycle were listed at the beginning of this chapter. Of these, the most difficult to estimate

TABLE 11.2 Types of Errors and Correction Methods

	SYSTEMATIC ERRORS	RANDOM ERRORS
SOURCES	POOR PROCESS MODEL POOR PROCESS CONTROL MECHANICAL WEAR SENSOR OFFSET OR BIAS POOR CONTROL OF INCOMING PARTS OR MATERIALS	POOR PROCESS REPEATABILITY RANDOM DRIFT ENVIRONMENTAL DRIFT SENSOR NOISE PART JIGGING ERRORS
REMEDIES	IMPROVE MODELS AND CALIBRATION MAKE LONG-TERM OBSERVATIONS AND IMPROVE PROCESS CONTROL	USE ROBUST DESIGN MAKE ON-LINE MEASUREMENTS AND TAKE SHORT TERM ACTION USE ERROR-ABSORBING METHODS LIKE COMPLIANT TOOLING

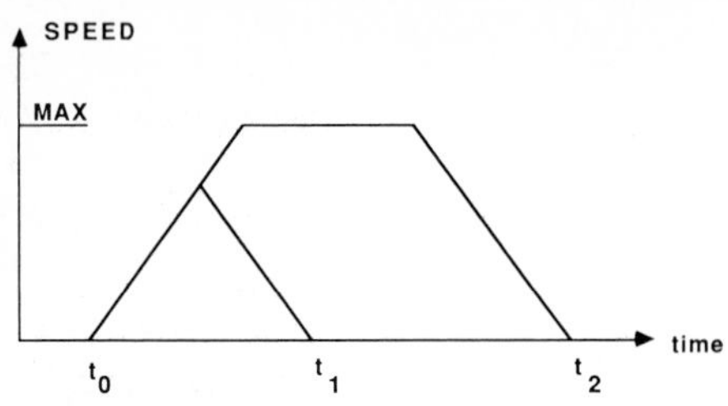

Fig. 11.14 Maximum speed is not reached during a short move.

are robot motions and tool actuation times. Grippers can take from 0.1 to 0.5 s to operate, although larger or smaller figures may apply in particular cases. Occasionally, time may be saved by overlapping the opening of a gripper while the tool is approaching the part.

The timing of other important activities (part transport, tool changing, and arrival or departure of pallets) is governed by mass, acceleration, and force. A surprising amount of time is taken up while actuators, robots, conveyors, or transport vehicles accelerate to or decelerate from full speed. Some robot motions can be so short that full speed is never achieved (see Fig. 11.14). For this reason, one learns little by a simple consideration of quoted top speed and estimated distance. AGVs often "creep" to their final position, improving their stopping accuracy at the cost of time. Robots may oscillate about their final destination if they approach it too fast, negating the intention behind the high approach speed.

Figure 11.15 illustrates the elements of a time estimate for a typical robot assembly action or a typical transport vehicle action. The designer must contact vendors individually to obtain information for

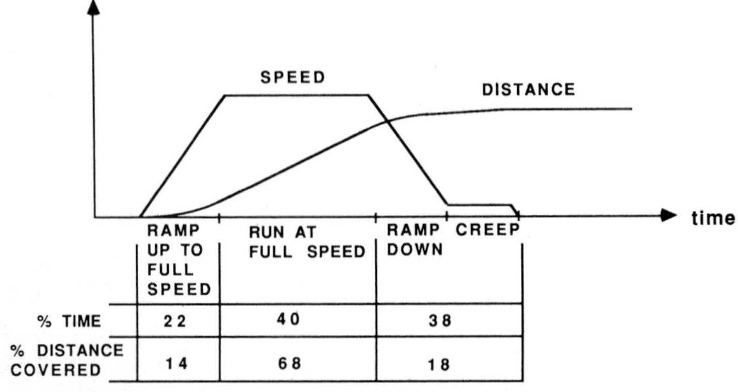

	RAMP UP TO FULL SPEED	RUN AT FULL SPEED	RAMP DOWN CREEP
% TIME	22	40	38
% DISTANCE COVERED	14	68	18

60% OF THE TIME IS SPENT COVERING ONLY 32% OF THE DISTANCE

Fig. 11.15 Typical distribution of time during a robot or AGV move.

TABLE 11.3 **Nominal Values for Cycle Time Analysis**

	SWING 180 DEG	CHANGE TOOLS	ASSY CYCLE
SMALL ROBOT (2 FOOT REACH)	1-2 SEC	2-4 SEC	2-4 SEC
MEDIUM SIZE ROBOT (4 FOOT REACH)	2-4 SEC	4-6 SEC	4-6 SEC
LARGE ROBOT (6 FOOT REACH)	3-5 SEC	10-12 SEC	10-12 SEC

	TIME TO TOP SPEED	TIME TO ENTER OR LEAVE STATION
SMALL AGV (100 # LOAD)	2-4 SEC	5-15 SEC
LARGE AGV (1000 # LOAD)	3-6 SEC	10-30 SEC

NOTE: TIMES SHOWN ARE ILLUSTRATIVE ONLY. CONSULT MANUFACTURERS FOR ACTUAL DATA.

such analyses. Table 11.3 contains approximate values which illustrate the range of possibilities that might occur.

The result of a cycle time analysis is an estimate of the total time needed by a station to accomplish the tasks assigned to it. This can be a crucial element in overall system design, since even a fraction of a second over the allowed cycle time may disrupt the entire design. Designers faced with a slow station may seek faster equipment, more efficient station layout, or redistribution of work to other stations.

Economic Analysis

Equipment cost estimating

It is not possible to give detailed cost estimating procedures or examples in this book. In addition, cost estimates depend for their accuracy on accumulated experience in designing and delivering actual systems. Such experience will be colored by each engineering organization's methods, the skills of its engineers, and the control exerted by its management.

Workstation or system costs can be divided into several categories:

1. Purchased equipment, such as machines, conveyors, and computers
2. Engineered items such as part feeders, grippers, and pallets
3. Skilled work such as concept studies, software, system or station installation, and system or station debugging

The latter two items often cost more than foreseen; success at keeping these costs under control is a measure of the maturity of the design team or of the lack of novelty in the design tasks it faces. In our discussions of economic analysis, cost item 3 is expressed as $(\rho - 1)/\rho$ of total cost. For complex systems, ρ might equal 3 to 5, whereas in simple systems or routine ones, ρ might be as small as 1.2.

An experienced engineering organization will often have reasonably accurate regression models for its costs. For example, a fixed automation assembly machine consists of a base, power train, and a number of stations each having an identical foundation. Experience has shown that the cost of such a machine is well approximated by

$$C = A \times (\text{base and power train}) + B \times (\text{number of stations}) \qquad (11.13)$$

Illustrative values might be about \$40,000 for A and \$25,000 for B. These numbers are strongly dependent on the size of the machine and of the product it is assembling.

Algorithmic approach to equipment selection

Workstation and system design each are complex problems of choosing among many alternatives. In each case, several steps must be accomplished, and there are several methods available for doing each one. Faced with this complexity, designers often pick what they are familiar with or make arbitrary choices. Here we discuss the outlines of a systematic method which uses algorithms developed for the system design problem (Holmes, 1987).

The design approach is termed "economic-technical." That is, an economic choice is to be made among alternatives that have been previously judged to be technically feasible. In keeping with the discussions earlier in this chapter, we are interested in the economic feature of cost and the technical features of speed and error. The choices are made important by the fact that more speed and less error are usually more costly.

It should be kept in mind that workstation and system design are not at present integrated because of their complexity. Instead, the custom is to design them iteratively. System design as discussed in Chap. 14 is capable of suggesting groupings of tasks at each station. Station design starts with the suggested group of tasks and attempts to create a design that can accomplish them within the required time, error, and cost budgets. If this is not possible, a new system design is created, with different groupings of tasks at stations.

Stated formally, the economic-technical design problem for individual stations is as follows. A set of assembly operations has been assigned to the station. We will design the station for each of these operations individually. If the same equipment is selected for more than one operation, fine and well. If different equipment items are selected to accomplish the ensemble of required operations, either all will be purchased, or redundant equipment will be eliminated. Then for each operation, we proceed as follows:

1. An assembly operation has several required phases which together define the operation to be done.
   a. Part presentation (feeders, pallets, etc.).
   b. Acquisition of the part (by gripper or tool).
   c. Transportation of the part to the assembly point (by robot, gripper, actuator, etc.).
   d. Placement or reorientation of the receiving part or assembly (on a jig, say).
   e. Mating of the transported part to the receiving part.
2. For each phase there are different alternate techniques or equipment choices. Each of these has an acquisition and operating cost, an operation time, and a contribution to the final error. The effective operating time could be zero if the operation is overlapped with an adjacent operation. The error contribution could be positive, negative, or zero, although final error cannot be negative. Jigs, grippers, pallets, and robots typically contribute positive error, whereas sensors and chamfers typically reduce error (contribute negative error). Some equipment can do more than one phase, although more cost, time, and error might result.

   In the formulation that follows, phases grouped on one piece of equipment must be adjacent in the sequence, although that is not in general required physically. That is, if an operation requires phases 1, 2, and 3, while operations 1 and 3 might conceivably be assigned to equipment A while phase 2 is assigned to equipment B, our formulation will not do so. However, operations 1 and 2 may be assigned to equipment A.

   Cost and error are related inversely for each type of equipment. That is, given two pieces of equipment capable of doing the same task, the one that reduces error more or increases it less will cost more.
3. To design the workstation to do an operation, we must select equipment so that:
   a. Each required phase of the operation is done.
   b. Total cost is minimized.
   c. Total error does not exceed a specified maximum.
   d. Total time does not exceed a specified maximum.

Formally, the problem is described as follows:

Given M phases to be done and N alternate equipment choices for each phase, where each equipment choice has a cost c_{ij}, a time t_{ij}, and an error contribution e_{ij}, choose equipment for each phase such that we obtain minimum total cost C:

$$\min C = \sum_{i=1}^{N} \sum_{j=1}^{M} c_{ij} x_{ij} \tag{11.14}$$

where x_{ij} = 1 if equipment type i is chosen to do phase j
x_{ij} = 0 otherwise

subject to

$$\sum_{i=1}^{N} \sum_{j=1}^{M} e_{ij} x_{ij} \leq E \tag{11.15}$$

(keeps total error less than E)

$$\sum_{i=1}^{N} \sum_{j=1}^{M} t_{ij} x_{ij} \leq T \tag{11.16}$$

(keeps total time less than T)

$$\sum_{i=1}^{N} \sum_{j=1}^{M} x_{ij} = M \tag{11.17}$$

(makes sure each phase gets done)

$$\sum_{i=1}^{N} x_{ij} = 1 \qquad \text{for each } j \tag{11.18}$$

(makes sure one and only one piece of equipment is chosen for each phase).

This is a typical problem statement in the management sciences and falls within the class of problems solved by integer programming. The algorithms in this class operate to choose which of the x_{ij} to set equal to 1 and which to set equal to 0, thereby selecting which equipment will do which operation(s) so that the cost is minimized and the constraints are satisfied. Usually such problems are easier to pose than to solve.

The solution procedure proposed here is a variant of an existing solution to a similar problem. That problem is the system design problem, and the solution described below was published in Holmes (1987). (A different algorithm for system design is described in Chap. 14.) Briefly, the Holmes algorithm is as follows:

1. The list of M required phases is partitioned into every possible grouping and subgrouping.
2. From the list of N possible equipment choices for each phase, each possible assignment of equipment choices to phases or groups of sequen-

tial phases is made, subject to the limitation that the total time required to perform each phase or group of phases cannot exceed the cycle time available for performing the whole operation. (In the system design problem, several groups—stations—can operate simultaneously, so each must obey the cycle time restraint. In the station design problem, there is only one cycle available and the phases or groups of phases must be executed in succession, so not only must each feasible group take less than one cycle, but the total time taken by all groups must be checked separately to ensure that their total time, and total error, do not exceed

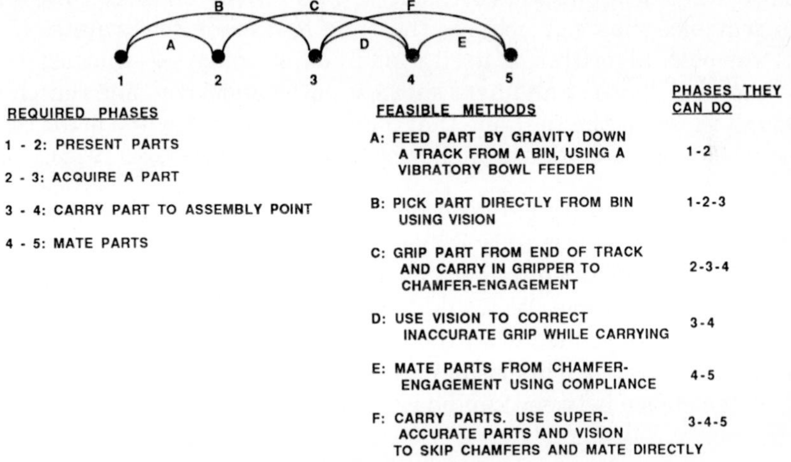

METHOD	COST	TIME	TRANSLATIONAL ERROR
A	$10000	OVERLAPPED	0.02"
B	$35000	6 SEC	0.04"
C	$15000	4 SEC	0.015"
D	$15000	OVERLAPPED WITH B	- 80% OF PRIOR ERROR
E	$9000	0.2 SEC	- ALL PRIOR ERROR IF LESS THAN 0.04"
F	$15000	3 SEC	- ALL PRIOR ERROR EXCEPT 0.005"

NOTE: COSTS, TIMES, AND ERRORS ARE ILLUSTRATIVE ONLY.

COMPARISON:	COST	TIME	ERROR
PATH A-C-E	10+15+9 = $34K	4.2 S	0.035" (ABSORBED BY CHAMFER)
PATH B-D-E	35+15+9 = $59K	6.2 S	0.008" (ABSORBED)
PATH B-F	35+15 = $50K	9.0 S	0.005"

FIGURE 11.16 NEVINS

Fig. 11.16 Illustration of algorithmic workstation design.

the limits imposed.) If more than one candidate equipment exists for each phase, the lowest-cost candidate is chosen.

3. The various lowest-cost equipment choices are arranged into a network, where each pair of nodes in the network is a phase and each arc or leg of the network is an equipment choice that does one phase or a group of phases. This is illustrated in Fig. 11.16. (The technique by which this network is built is an important feature of the Holmes method, but it need not concern us here.)

4. A shortest path algorithm is used to find a sequence of equipment choices of minimum cost that will do all the phases. However, this sequence may not achieve the time and error constraints. If a shortest path algorithm is used that finds not only the shortest but also the next shortest and next shortest paths and so on, one searches through these for the first one that meets both the time and error constraints. Many such algorithms exist (Dreyfus, 1969; Fox, 1978).

This approach will yield good but not necessarily optimal designs. The reason for nonoptimality is the arbitrary way we decided between competing candidate equipment choices for each group, in which we took the least-cost one. We could have taken the least-error or least-time one, having no idea what the impact of such a choice would be on the overall outcome. This issue may be moot in any particular example, or the choice between candidates may be obvious to the designer.

Summary

This chapter introduced the problem of assembly workstation design. While many of the examples concerned robotic workstations, the principles of conceptualization, error analysis, and economic analysis apply equally well to other kinds of technology. The reader should be aware of the ways in which product design influences station design and the degree to which station design can be kept independent. As a designer, the reader should also be wary of seizing upon the first station concept that comes to mind and should generate many alternatives with different characteristics. This process will enrich one's understanding of what features to consider and how to rank them so that a good design choice may be made.

References

Bedini, R., et al.: "Optimal Programming of Working Cycles for Industrial Robots," *ASME J. Mech Des.*, vol. 101, Apr. 1979, pp. 250–257.

Dreyfus, S. E.: "An Appraisal of Some Shortest Path Algorithms," *Operations Research*, vol. 17, 1969, pp. 395–412.

Fisher, E. L., and S. Y. Nof: "FADES: Knowledge-Based Facility Design," Proceedings, *1984 Annual International Industrial Engineering Conference,* Institute of Industrial Engineers, 1984, pp. 74–82.

Fox, B. L.: "Data Structures and Computer Science Techniques in Operations Research," *Operations Research,* vol. 26, 1978, pp. 686–717.

Holmes, C. A.: "Equipment Selection and Task Assignment for Multiproduct Asssembly System Design," Master of Science Thesis, MIT Operations Research Center, Jan. 1987.

Paul, R. P.: *Robot Manipulators,* MIT Press, Cambridge, 1981.

Simunovic, S. N.: "Task Descriptors for Automatic Assembly," MIT Mech Eng Dept SM Thesis, Jan. 1976.

Veitschegger, W. K., and C. H. Wu, "Robot Accuracy Analysis Based on Kinematics," *IEEE J. Robotics and Automation,* vol. RA-2, no. 3, Sept. 1986, pp. 171–179.

Chapter

12

Economic Analysis of Systems

Introduction

Economic analysis of manufacturing systems consists of:

- Identifying alternative ways of making or assembling something
- Determining the manufacturing or assembly cost (or cost per unit made) by each alternative
- Determining the up-front investment required to acquire and install each alternative
- Deciding which investment makes the most economic sense in terms of the identified costs and other strategic benefits

This chapter discusses the types of costs and methods for evaluating "economic sense." Naturally, economic sense must be weighed in the overall strategy for making and selling the product rather than being the only criterion.

Types of Manufacturing Cost

Manufacturing system costs are divided into four fundamental categories:

1. *Fixed cost.* Based on annualizing the initial investment
2. *Variable cost.* Based on loaded labor rate, number of workers required, operating or maintenance rate, and the usable system cycle

time (cycle time less downtime and time effectively lost because a bad part or assembly was made)

3. *Materials cost.* Based on cost of parts at the beginning of assembly or materials at the beginning of fabrication (accounting for scrap and rework)
4. *Institutional cost.* Based on all other cost factors (general and administrative, sales, service, debt repayment, dividends, etc.)

Fixed cost occurs regardless of production volume or equipment usage. It is a financial cost that includes the price of capital equipment and all of the cost for engineering, design, implementation, software, and debugging prior to production that is required to create a working system. *Variable cost* is incurred only when a system is actually operating. Typical variable cost categories are labor, maintenance, and wear and tear. While implementation of an automated system usually increases the *materials cost* (better parts are needed), it can be argued that improved materials will eventually be required to meet the necessary quality goals anyway. Thus intense study of the relation between product and system design is needed. The last category (*institutional cost*) is normally eliminated from system comparisons since it can be assumed constant; we shall not consider institutional cost again but emphasize that it may be a significant cost factor.

The total cost of a manufacturing system is then

$$\text{Total cost} = \text{fixed cost} + \text{variable cost} + \text{material cost} \tag{12.1}$$

For predominantly manual systems, variable cost is much larger than fixed cost, while the reverse is true for mostly automated systems.

Equation (12.1) applies to the entire life of a product (or group of similar products). However, it is necessary to allocate the cost to each unit produced. This is called the "unit cost." Variable cost per unit is assumed to occur as each unit is being made, so it may be calculated simply as the total variable cost divided by the number of units produced. However, fixed cost is spent before any units are produced, so it must be allocated to the individual units in a more complex way. We need a method for annualizing such costs since businesses work on a fiscal year basis.

A company decides to invest in a system (or cell or factory) using various criteria to compare that investment to alternatives. Whatever the criterion, the investment must be paid back at a specified rate of return so that investing can be compared to, say, simply putting the funds in a bank. This is analogous to repaying a loan with constant payments over several years. Spreading a fixed cost over a given number of years in this way is called "capital recovery" and/or "annualized cost." The *yearly* cost to the company to produce the product(s) can then be found as the sum of the financial or annualized fixed cost and the actual operating or variable cost. This is the basis on which the costs of competing systems are compared in Chap. 14.

The money for recovering the investment arises either because the investment buys a less costly replacement for an older method, or because it buys a new system that builds a new product that generates sales revenues. More savings or revenue for a given investment implies a larger rate of return, but an investment will not be made, even if there is an apparent cost saving, unless its rate of return is large enough and other criteria are satisfied. While the traditional evaluation method (Grant et al., 1984) is to specify an investment and calculate the rate of return or the net present value of the savings stream, this chapter shows how to determine the allowable investment for a specified rate of return assuming zero present value of a specified savings stream. There are two fundamental questions:

1. How much can be invested for every dollar earned or saved?
2. How much can the company actually spend on a system (or cell or factory)?

Unfortunately, no single evaluation criterion is universally accepted as *the* condition which must be met. As we shall see in later sections, many factors have mutual influence; the problem is analogous to a product or system design which is to fit within numerous, sometimes conflicting, constraints.

Useful general references for engineering economy and discounted cash flow analysis are Canada and White (1980), Thuesen et al. (1977), and Grant et al. (1984). Specific manufacturing applications can be found in Canada and Edwards (1985), Lutz (1982), Boothroyd et al. (1982), and Gustavson (1981, 1983).

Table 12.1 is a list of the nomenclature that the reader will find useful.

Pro-Forma Cash Flow

In this chapter we will study the case where an investment is made to improve an existing process, with the hope of generating savings. These savings will accumulate over a period of years. Thus, to evaluate the investment we must predict the future in some way. The future is envisioned by means of the "pro-forma cash flow statement." Figure 12.1 is an example. At least 10 significant parameters are involved (the numbers in Fig. 12.1 correspond to the following descriptions):

1. *Savings stream.* When compared to a base system, it is hoped that an alternative will fabricate or assemble the product at a lower

TABLE 12.1 Nomenclature

C	Actual unit cost for a system with rework (m.u./unit)
D_i	Amount of depreciation in year i (m.u.)
H	Investment horizon (yr)
I_A	Allowable investment (m.u.)
i	Subscript denoting year within the cash flow model.
IRoR	Internal rate of return (percent)
m	Average value of w, the number of units reworked
M	Material unit cost (m.u./unit)
MACRS	Modified accelerated capital recovery system as defined by the 1986 U.S. tax laws
m.u.	Monetary unit used (e.g., $)
N_i	Net income in year i (m.u.)
P	Processing unit cost (m.u./unit)
q	Quantity in production batch
r	Internal rate of return (percent / 100 percent)
R	Recycling unit cost (m.u./unit)
S_i	Savings or net revenue in year i (m.u.): total revenue less expenses
w	Number of units reworked (random variable)
y	Actual yield of a single-level process (percent / 100 percent)
δ_i	Depreciation rate in year i (percent / 100 percent)
η_i	Discounted net income in year i (m.u.)
ν_H	Residual (undepreciated) value at end of year H
ρ	Rho—ratio of system cost (hardware cost plus engineering, software, debugging, etc.) to hardware cost
τ_i	Tax rate in year i (percent/100 percent)

cost. Contributing factors are variable cost and materials costs such as improved process yield, higher quality (less rework and warranty problems), lower direct and indirect labor cost, and higher throughput. These savings can significantly change from year to year. Figure 12.2 exhibits typical data (S) for a commercial product. Savings are calculated as net revenue (total revenue minus expenses). In Fig. 12.1, the Income column under Pro-Forma Cash Flow shows negative income in year 0 because of the investment, savings income during years 1 through 3, and both savings and salvage value income in year 4.

2. *Investment horizon.* The number of years savings are assumed to accumulate for purposes of economic analysis. The longer the horizon, the larger the total income. The horizon strongly affects the allowable investment and the internal rate of return; 4 years are used in Figs. 12.1 and 12.2.

3. *Depreciation plan.* When a company spends money (has expenses), it normally deducts those expenses from income before calculating its taxes. However, the large expenditures associated with in-

Parabolic Income Example

ZERO PRESENT WORTH CASH FLOW ANALYSIS 12-29-1987

7 YEARS OF ECONOMIC LIFE, SALVAGE VALUE 0 % OF COST

	EXPENSE FORECAST			INCOME FORECAST			
YEAR	RATIO	TAX RATE	DEPRECIABLE	SAVINGS	DEPRECIATION	TAX RATE	CREDIT
				①	③	④	
0	100.00%	34.0%	66.7%				
1	⑧	⑨	⑨	100.000	14.29%	34.0%	0.0%
2				181.427	24.49%	34.0%	
3				198.094	17.49%	34.0%	
4 } ②				150.000	12.49%	34.0%	
4*				SALVAGE VALUE	31.24%		

TOTAL INVESTMENT = 400.000

DEPRECIABLE INVESTMENT = 266.667 ⑨

INTERNAL RATE OF RETURN = 18.42% ⑥

PRO-FORMA CASH FLOW

YEAR	INCOME	DEPRECIATION	TAXES	CREDITS	NET ⑤	DISC. NET ⑦
0	-400.000	0.000	-45.333	0.000	-354.667	-354.667
1	100.000	38.095	21.048	0.000	78.952	66.674
2	181.427	65.306	39.481	0.000	141.946	101.228
3	198.094	46.647	51.492	0.000	146.602	88.290
4	150.000	33.319	39.671	0.000	110.329	56.111
4*	83.299	0.000	0.000	0.000	83.299	42.364
INCOME TOTALS	712.820	183.368	151.692	0.000	561.128	354.666
NET TOTALS	312.820	183.368	106.359	0.000	206.461	-0.000

NOMINAL CAPITAL RECOVERY = 134.024 ⑩

PAYBACK IN APPROXIMATELY 2.91 YEARS

Fig. 12.1 Specific cash flow data for a typical commercial product exhibiting the various evaluation parameters that may be used.

vestments cannot be deducted all in 1 year but must be spread over several years. The amount of the investment deducted each year is called depreciation. Taxes are paid on income minus depreciation. Under the 1986 U.S. tax law, manufacturing equipment must be depreciated according to the 7-year modified accelerated capital recovery system (MACRS): year 1, 14.29 percent; year 2, 24.49 percent; year 3, 17.49 percent; year 4, 12.49 percent; years 5 to 7, 8.92 percent, and year 8, 4.46 percent. If the horizon is less than 8 years, the equipment is assumed to have a *salvage value* equal to the unused depreciation. In Fig. 12.1, the depreciation amounts for years 1 through 4 appear in

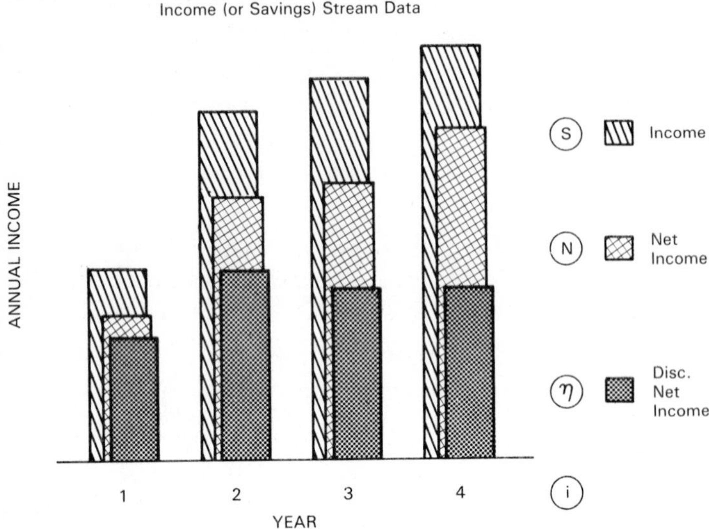

Fig. 12.2 Income characteristics for a typical commercial product.

the Depreciation column under Pro-Forma Cash Flow. [Note that some costs associated with an investment are deducted as expenses ("expensed") in the year of the investment and are not depreciated; see nos. 5 and 9 below.]

4. *Tax rate.* Income for businesses is taxed at a prescribed rate. For most U.S. companies, the effective rate used in pro-forma cash flow models is the federal rate (34 percent, 1986 tax law).

5. *Net income.* The amount remaining in year i after taxes have been subtracted from the income reduced by the depreciation. Net income equals 1 minus the tax rate times the savings plus the tax rate times the depreciation:

$$N_i = (1 - \tau_i)S_i + \tau_i D_i \tag{12.2}$$

In Fig. 12.1, the Taxes column shows taxes calculated as 34 percent of income except in year 0, where there is a tax deduction of 34 percent of the portion of the total investment that is expensed rather than depreciated. Figure 12.2 displays the portion of income that is net income (N) for each year. Note that it is not constant even if τ is constant since depreciation varies from year to year.

6. *Internal rate of return.* The compound interest (or discount) rate which is applied to future net incomes out to the investment horizon such that the total discounted net income (see no. 7 below) equals the

net initial investment. This is the rate at which the investment is deemed to be paid back, based on zero present worth.

7. *Discounted net income.* Net income in a future year i must be reduced using the internal rate of return (or discount rate) according to

$$\eta_i = \frac{N_i}{(1 + r)^i} \tag{12.3}$$

Internal rate of return is sometimes called the "discount rate"; a monetary unit (m.u.) earned or spent in the future must be discounted to establish its value today. The value today, if compounded at the rate of return for a period of years, will equal the final value. The larger i is, the smaller η_i will be for given N_i (see Fig. 12.2). Figure 12.3 plots the sums of the Net and Disc. Net columns from Fig. 12.1, including the initial investment. Note that cumulative discounted cash flow is 0 (i.e., has 0 present worth) while net profit is positive 206.461. The point at which total nondiscounted or actual net income equals 0 is the break-even point (sometimes called the payback period).

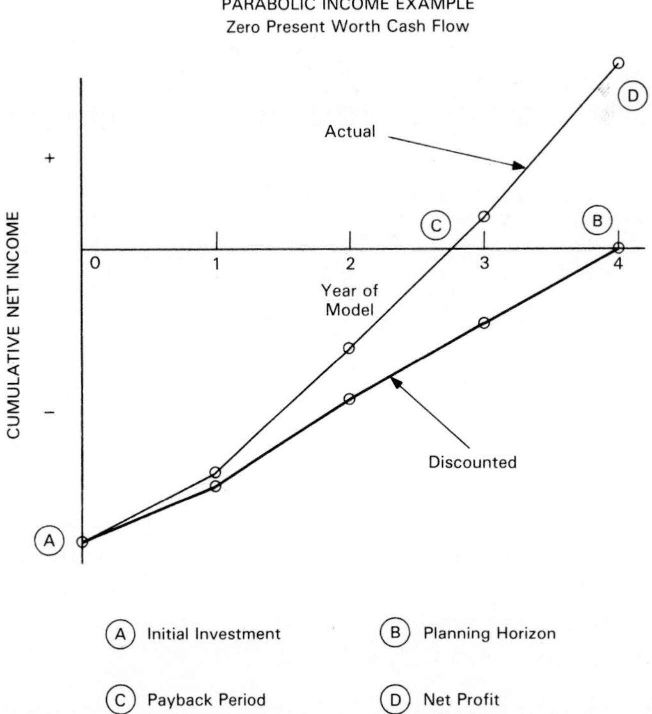

Fig. 12.3 Income characteristics for a typical commercial product illustrating payback period and net profit.

8. *Investment scheme.* While the most likely condition is that 100 percent of the investment is made in year 0, some costs can occur before year 0 (site clearing, building construction, etc.). Or the investment might be spread over a year or two after time 0 if a buildup in production capability is required or it is deemed financially advantageous.

9. *Depreciable investment.* The portion of the initial investment that is depreciated over years 1 through H. If this is less than 100 percent of the investment, the difference is taken as tax-deductible expenses in year 0, the year when the expenses are assumed to occur. Typical nondepreciable expenses are engineering, software, and debugging costs paid by the company to its own employees. If a company buys a "turn-key" system whose supplier does the engineering, the entire purchase price is depreciable. The total system cost (hardware plus engineering, software, debugging, etc.) divided by the hardware cost is called "rho" (ρ). A fraction $1/\rho$ of the initial investment is depreciable. A "turn-key" system has ρ of 1. Companies that want in-house expertise will incur nondepreciable engineering, software, and debugging expense; ρ can then be from 1.2 to 5 depending upon the complexity and/or uniqueness of the system. For some cash flow situations, there is an inversion point IRoR: Below that IRoR the allowable investment is maximized if $\rho = 1$; above that IRoR the largest ρ maximizes the allowable investment.

10. *Capital recovery.* If the total investment is recovered over a specified number of years, it is said to have an equal annual amount returned each year. This is analogous to a mortgage with only one payment per year (capital recovery or annualized cost). It is important to realize that this is the annualized fixed cost for any system. The formula for capital recovery is in Chap. 14.

All of the parameters described above appear in Fig. 12.1. The savings stream was arbitrarily specified to simulate behavior of a 4-year product life with initial sales, maximum sales at some point, and declining sales toward the end. Depreciation and tax rates conform to the 1986 law. The depreciable portion and total investment specified are arbitrary. The internal rate of return is found iteratively [as described in Thuesen (1977)].

Thus far, we have determined the rate of return for a prescribed investment. In the next section, we shall do the reverse, providing useful budget information to the system designer.

Determining Allowable Investment

Specification of the savings stream, planning horizon, depreciation plan, tax rates, and investment scheme can be illustrated in a table format setup similar to Fig. 12.1. Three parameters must still be established. We will specify the internal rate of return and rho factor and then calculate directly the (year 0 only) allowable total investment from Gustavson (1981):

$$I_A = \frac{\displaystyle\sum_{i=1}^{H} \frac{S_i(1-\tau_i)}{(1+r)^i}}{\left(1 - \tau_0 + \dfrac{\tau_0}{\rho}\right) - \dfrac{1}{\rho}\displaystyle\sum_{i=1}^{H} \frac{\delta_i \tau_i}{(1+r)^i} - \dfrac{\upsilon_H}{\rho(1+r)^H}} \tag{12.4}$$

Equation (12.4) is obtained by writing out the sum of discounted cash flows, using Eq. (12.2) and (12.3) and the details of the depreciation plan, and solving for the initial investment. This is a far easier computation than finding the rate of return for a specified investment since no iteration is required. Figure 12.4 exhibits a typical result for a specified IRoR of 20 percent when the investment is totally depreciable (i.e., $\rho = 1$). Let's compare this with a 50 percent depreciable year 0 investment ($\rho = 2$) in Fig. 12.5. The allowable investment is 2.7 percent higher, total depreciation is much less, and the net profit is 18 percent lower. Capital recovery and payback period are similar. Figure 12.5 displays the inversion point IRoR of 15.75 percent.

Now that we have looked at some specific cases, let's investigate the situation over a range of values. First, varying the IRoR for prescribed ρ causes the characteristic behavior seen in Fig. 12.6. The specific case of 20 percent IRoR agrees with Figs. 12.4 and 12.5. In general, the lower the expected IRoR, the larger the allowable investment. Figure 12.6 displays allowable investment data divided by the first year savings. This can be extremely useful at the beginning of a project, since (given the financial planning criteria) we can find how much every monetary unit saved (from whatever source) is worth in terms of the investment allowed. This answers the first financial question we posed.

Next we investigate varying ρ for prescribed IRoR. Figure 12.7 exhibits the general characteristics. Specific cases of $\rho = 1$ and $\rho = 2$ can be compared to Figs. 12.4 and 12.5, respectively. A 10 percent IRoR shows decreasing allowable investment (with accompanying decreasing payback period, decreasing capital recovery, and significantly decreasing net profit) as ρ increases. A 20 percent IRoR reveals increasing allowable investment as ρ increases. Note that the inversion point IRoR is 15.75 percent for this data set.

How Are Alternative Investments Evaluated?

The financial officials of a company decide what parameters are most important although many nonfinancial factors are also evaluated.

SAMPLE CASH FLOW

ZERO PRESENT WORTH CASH FLOW ANALYSIS 12-29-1987

7 YEARS OF ECONOMIC LIFE, SALVAGE VALUE 0 % OF COST

	EXPENSE FORECAST			INCOME FORECAST			
YEAR	RATIO	TAX RATE	DEPRECIABLE	SAVINGS	DEPRECIATION	TAX RATE	CREDIT
0	100.00%	0.0%	100.0%				
1				100.000	14.29%	34.0%	0.0%
2				110.000	24.49%	34.0%	
3				121.000	17.49%	34.0%	
4				133.100	12.49%	34.0%	
4*				SALVAGE VALUE	31.24%		

ALLOWABLE TOTAL INVESTMENT = 278.668

DEPRECIABLE INVESTMENT = 278.668

INTERNAL RATE OF RETURN = 20.00%

PRO-FORMA CASH FLOW

YEAR	INCOME	DEPRECIATION	TAXES	CREDITS	NET	DISC. NET
0	-278.668	0.000	0.000	0.000	-278.668	-278.668
1	100.000	39.810	20.465	0.000	79.535	66.279
2	110.000	68.245	14.197	0.000	95.803	66.530
3	121.000	48.747	24.566	0.000	96.434	55.807
4	133.100	34.819	33.416	0.000	99.684	48.073
4*	87.048	0.000	0.000	0.000	87.048	41.979
INCOME TOTALS	551.148	191.621	92.643	0.000	458.505	278.668
NET TOTALS	272.479	191.621	92.643	0.000	179.836	0.000

NOMINAL CAPITAL RECOVERY = 91.431

PAYBACK IN APPROXIMATELY 3.07 YEARS

Fig. 12.4 Specific cash flow data for a typical commercial product with no tax benefit at time 0.

There is a surprisingly large number of possibilities which are interestingly interrelated. While any one of them could be deemed most important, it usually cannot be viewed by itself. Commonly used factors are:

1. *Return on investment.* The only consistent definition calls it "internal rate of return" (see prior discussion) because it treats all future cash flows with respect to time 0 in a closed form way. Sometimes, a minimum attractive rate of return (MARR) is specified against which the actual internal rate of return can be compared.

SAMPLE CASH FLOW

ZERO PRESENT WORTH CASH FLOW ANALYSIS 12-29-1987

7 YEARS OF ECONOMIC LIFE, SALVAGE VALUE 0 % OF COST

	EXPENSE FORECAST			INCOME FORECAST			
YEAR	RATIO	TAX RATE	DEPRECIABLE	SAVINGS	DEPRECIATION	TAX RATE	CREDIT
0	100.00%	34.0%	50.0%				
1				100.000	14.29%	34.0%	0.0%
2				110.000	24.49%	34.0%	
3				121.000	17.49%	34.0%	
4				133.100	12.49%	34.0%	
4*				SALVAGE VALUE	31.24%		

ALLOWABLE TOTAL INVESTMENT = 286.097

DEPRECIABLE INVESTMENT = 143.049

INTERNAL RATE OF RETURN = 20.00%

PRO-FORMA CASH FLOW

YEAR	INCOME	DEPRECIATION	TAXES	CREDITS	NET	DISC. NET
0	-286.097	0.000	-48.637	0.000	-237.461	-237.461
1	100.000	20.436	27.052	0.000	72.948	60.790
2	110.000	35.032	25.489	0.000	84.511	58.688
3	121.000	25.023	32.632	0.000	88.368	51.139
4	133.100	17.874	39.177	0.000	93.923	45.295
4*	44.684	0.000	0.000	0.000	44.684	21.549
INCOME TOTALS	508.784	98.365	124.350	0.000	384.434	237.461
NET TOTALS	222.687	98.365	75.714	0.000	146.973	0.000

NOMINAL CAPITAL RECOVERY = 102.192

PAYBACK IN APPROXIMATELY 2.91 YEARS

INVERSION POINT IRoR = 15.75%

Fig. 12.5 Specific cash flow data for a typical commercial product with tax benefit at time 0.

2. *Payback period.* The time at which the aggregate undiscounted income equals the initial net investment. This is also known as the cross-over point since the cumulative undiscounted cash flow goes from negative to positive.

3. *Net profit.* The amount that the aggregate undiscounted net income exceeds the net initial investment over the life of the planning model. To some long-range thinking companies this parameter is much more important than the payback period.

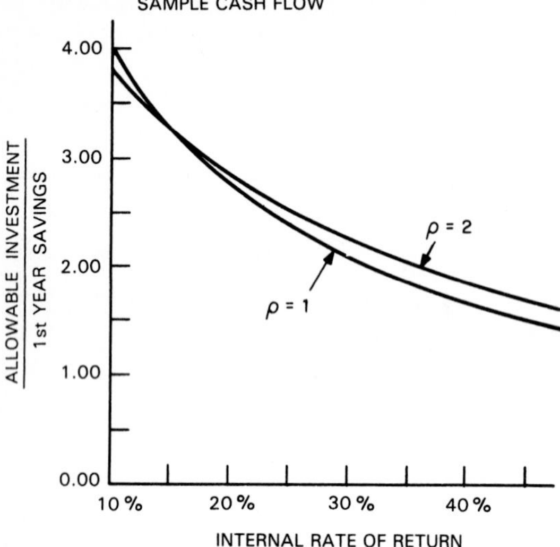

Fig. 12.6 Allowable investment versus internal rate of return for varying rho factor.

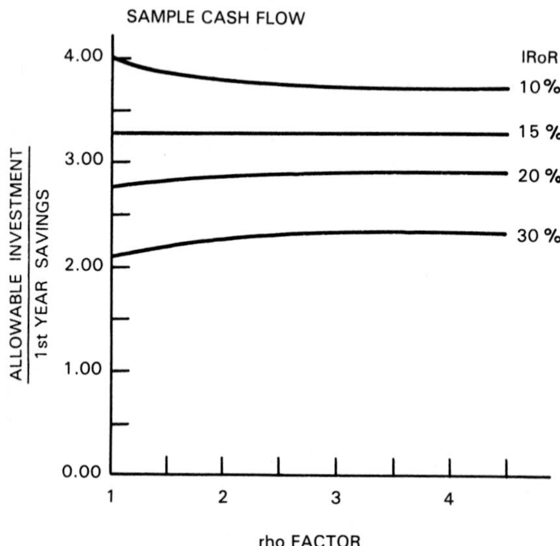

Fig. 12.7 Allowable investment versus rho factor for varying internal rate of return.

4. *Maximum investment funds available.* Most companies must give serious consideration to where their funds are invested and therefore often put a ceiling on how much any department may spend in a given fiscal year.
5. *Reduction in rework and warranty costs.* While usually difficult to put numbers on, these two factors are becoming increasingly important. They require a global view of the company and allow justification of investments that would not be likely to occur within one department.

All of these factors are represented in a cash flow model which allows the prediction of what may happen over the life of that model.

Sensitivity Analysis

We are now ready to investigate the influence of various parameters on the allowable investment, plotted against IRoR. The data shown in Fig. 12.5 will be the basis for comparison. The results will be presented in terms of the nondimensionalized format (allowable investment divided by first-year savings).

First look at changes in income over a 4-year planning horizon. Figure 12.8 shows that the larger the (constant) rate of change in income, the higher the allowable investment for given IRoR. Note that nega-

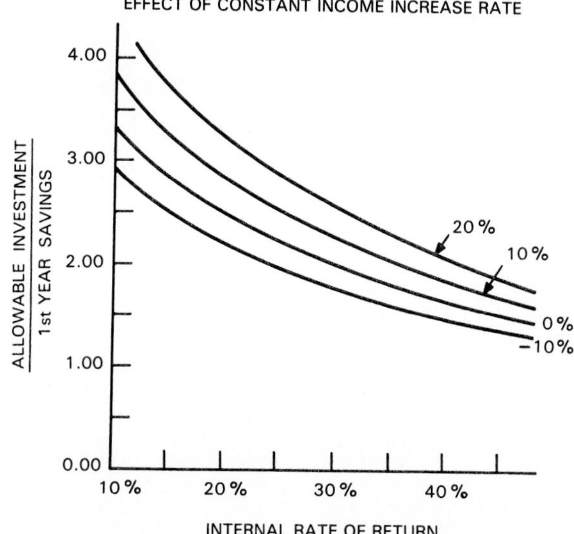

Fig. 12.8 Effect of constant rate of increase in income on allowable investment.

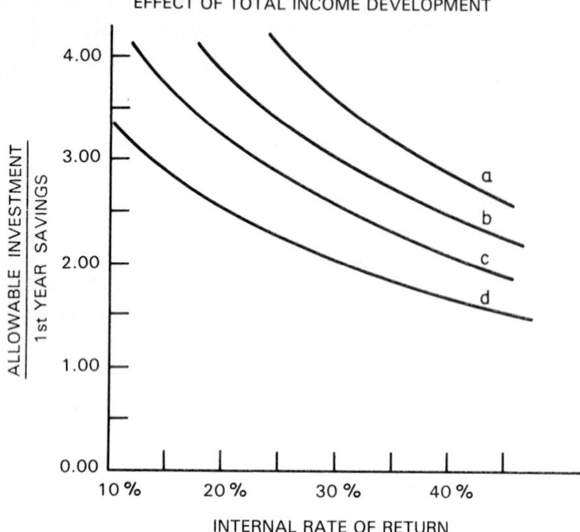

Fig. 12.9 Effect of total income characteristic on allowable investment. Curve (*a*) 50% constant rate of increase in income, (*b*) parabolic increase in income, (*c*) 2% constant rate of increase in income, (*d*) 0% increase (constant income).

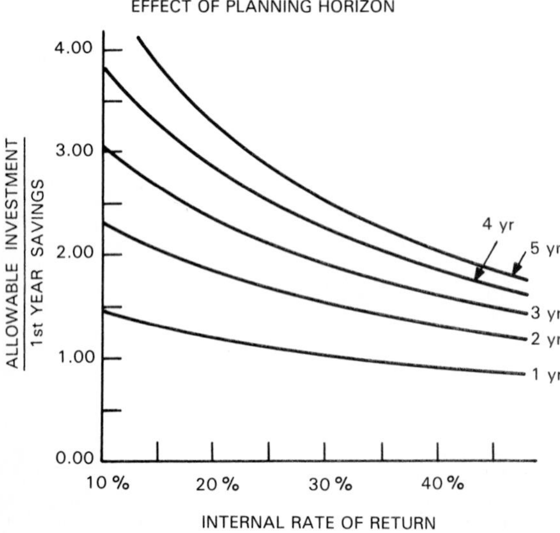

Fig. 12.10 Effect of planning horizon years on allowable investment.

tive rate is also usable data. Most products exhibit roughly parabolic income behavior (there is a maximum somewhere between the first and final year of the model); this characteristic approximates that for 35 percent constant rate increase as seen in Fig. 12.9. Any income data may be analyzed this way. In general, the greater the income, the larger the allowable investment.

If we fix the rate of increase in income at 10 percent and vary the planning horizon, we find in Fig. 12.10 the significant differences which result. Obviously, the longer the planning period in years, the more savings accumulate and the larger the investment allowed. This effect is much more pronounced for an IRoR of less than 25 percent. One year is, by far, the least desirable since each m.u. saved in year 1 will allow only about one m.u. of investment.

Now let's look at tax rates. First let all tax rates be constant. Figure 12.11 shows that paying no tax allows slightly higher investment. When the effective tax rate in year 0 can be applied to the nondepreciable portion of the investment to generate a deduction, we obtain the desirable result shown in Fig. 12.12.

What happens when the investment is not made just in year 0? Figure 12.13 displays some arbitrarily chosen investment ratios which show that the effect is small.

The other important part of the investment strategy is the ρ factor.

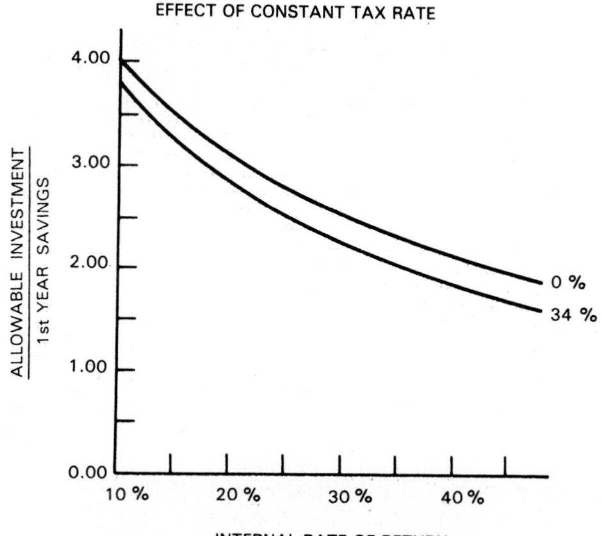

Fig. 12.11 Effect of (constant value) tax rate on allowable investment.

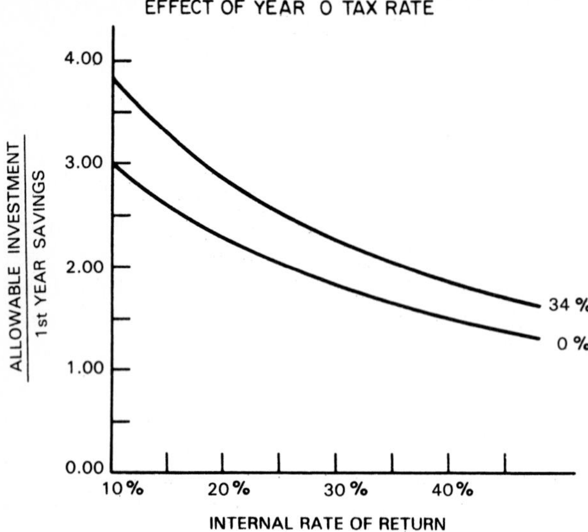

Fig. 12.12 Effect of tax benefit in year 0 on allowable investment.

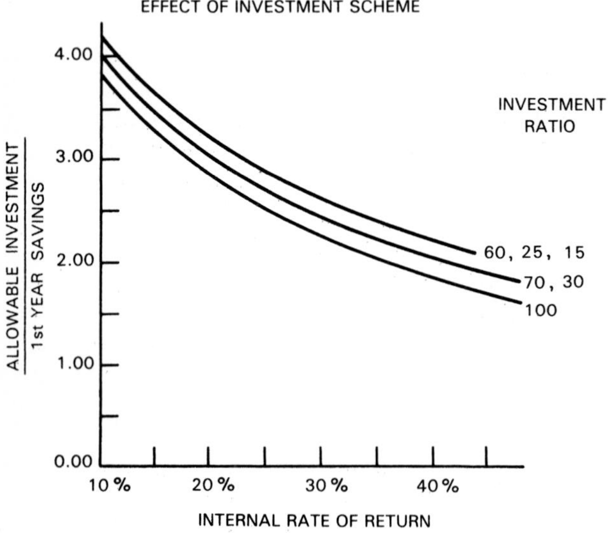

Fig. 12.13 Effect of timed investments on allowable investment. A portion of the investment is made in each of a specific number of years.

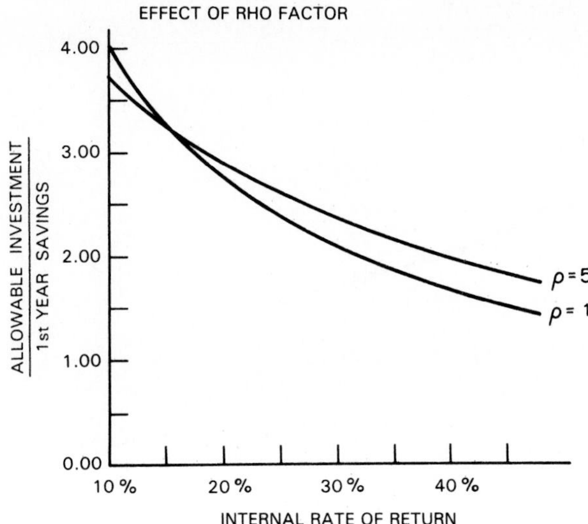

Fig. 12.14 Effect of the total cost divided by hardware cost on allowable investment (rho factor).

Figure 12.14 reveals only small differences in investment allowed, but we also note the inversion point where the curves cross.

Finally, we want to know what effect various depreciation plans have on investment allowed. It turns out (see Fig. 12.15) that there is little difference between 5-year ACRS, 7-year MACRS and 8-year straight line. The latter is better below about 20 percent IRoR but not by enough to challenge corporate or government approved depreciation plans.

All of the above discussion concerned changes in allowable investment which occurred while altering one parameter at a time. The same conclusions can be drawn with respect to internal rate of return for a prescribed investment. The amount of income (including method, rate, and planning horizon) is the significant contributor. No other parameters have much effect.

Effect of Recycling and Rework

The goal of every manufacturing process is to produce at minimum cost. Unfortunately, many factors prevent the ideal from occurring in the real manufacturing world; they include parts that do not meet specifications, improper product or process specifications, asking resources (including people) to perform beyond their capability, misalignment of components or equipment, random resource failure or breakdown, and impurities in the environment. A goal of modern manufacturing is to improve the yield of every device, cell, system,

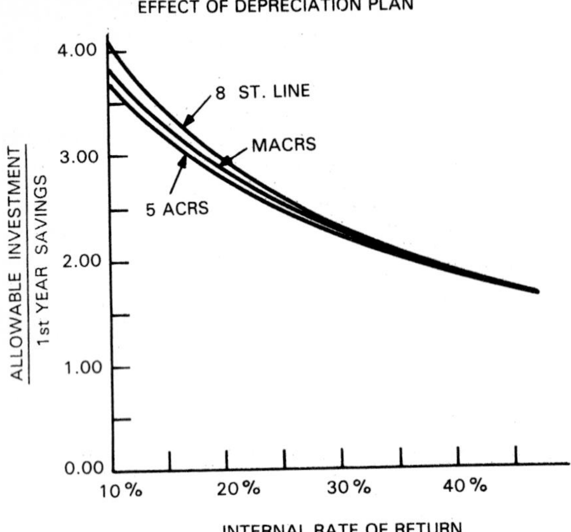

Fig. 12.15 Effect of the type of depreciation used on allowable investments.

factory, or company. The way to do this is to create a certifiable, reproducible, documentable process. It will not be free, but the potentially significant increase in yield and quality can be translated into lower unit cost which will more than justify the expense.

Let's look at a single-level process as shown in Fig. 12.16. The system must produce q items. To start, q sets of materials each costing M are introduced. They all get processed and tested for cost P each. A certain number w fail and must be recycled (which usually includes rework and/or material replacement) at cost R each. Elementary flow balance shows that $u = q + w$. We assume that binomial random variable statistics apply; such a scheme is widely used when there are only two possible outcomes, pass or fail. The probability of success is called y, the fractional yield of the process. Using the definition of binomial statistics, we can solve for the mean value m of w and express y in

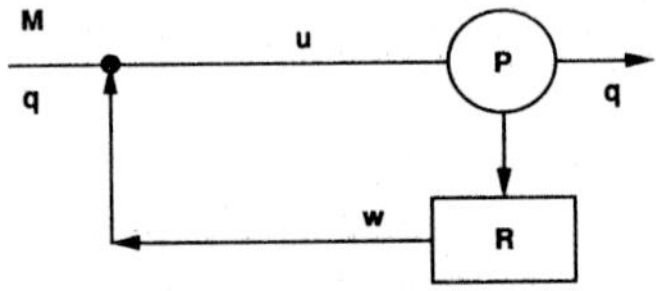

q = number of units to be made
M = unit material cost
u = number of units which must be processed
P = unit processing and test cost
w = number of units which must be reworked
R = unit rework cost (can include replacing materials)

Fig. 12.16 Single-level rework analysis model.

terms of m and q as:

$$y = \frac{q + 1}{q + m + 1} \tag{12.5}$$

The larger m is, the lower the yield; when $m = 0$, we have a perfect system. Total cost to produce will be

$$C_p = (M + P)q + (R + P)m \tag{12.6}$$

Recognizing that $(M + P)q$ is the theoretical cost, we can rearrange Eq. (12.6) to find the ratio of actual cost to theoretical cost:

$$C_R = 1 + \frac{(1 + R/P)m}{(1 + M/P)q} \tag{12.7}$$

Rearranging the yield Eq. (12.5) and substituting into Eq. (12.7) gives

$$C_R = 1 + \frac{(1 + R/P)}{(1 + M/P)}\left(\frac{1}{y} - 1\right)\left(1 + \frac{1}{q}\right) \tag{12.8}$$

If desired, the material unit cost can be set to zero so that only the assembly (fabrication, etc.) cost will be evaluated. Note that when the system is perfect ($y = 1$), the cost ratio is 1 and as y decreases the right-most term becomes more important to system cost. Figure 12.17(a) displays the cost ratios for particular M/P and R/P ratios. Corresponding numerical data is exhibited in Fig. 12.17(b).

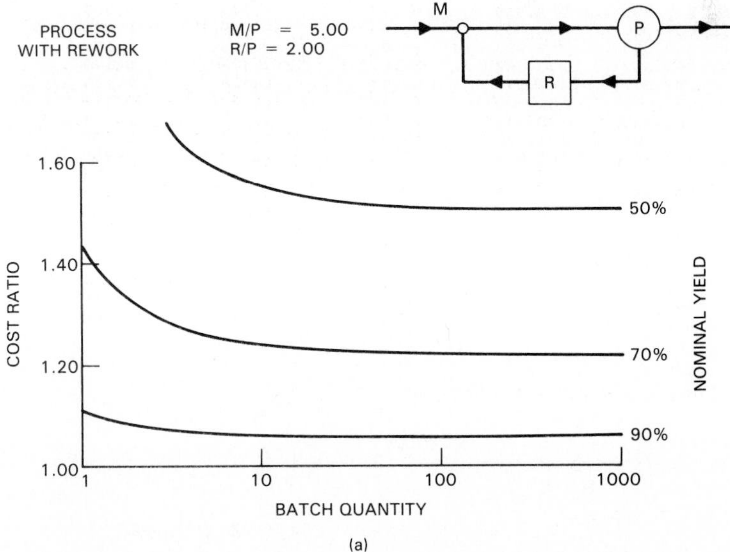

(a)

Fig. 12.17(a) Cost versus batch size characteristics for prescribed material, process, and rework costs (expressed as ratios).

SINGLE LEVEL PROCESS

BINOMIAL RANDOM VARIABLE STATISTICS

M/P = 5.00 R/P = 2.00

PRODUCTION BATCH : 16 UNITS

NOMINAL YIELD	UNITS PROCESSED	UNITS RECYCLED	RECYCLES STD. DEV.	COST RATIO	COST STD. DEV.
0.050	339.000	323.000	80.374	11.094	2.512
0.100	169.000	153.000	39.115	5.781	1.222
0.150	112.333	96.333	25.342	4.010	0.792
0.200	84.000	68.000	18.439	3.125	0.576
0.250	67.000	51.000	14.283	2.594	0.446
0.300	55.667	39.667	11.499	2.240	0.359
0.350	47.571	31.571	9.498	1.987	0.297
0.400	41.500	25.500	7.984	1.797	0.250
0.450	36.778	20.778	6.795	1.649	0.212
0.500	33.000	17.000	5.831	1.531	0.182
0.550	29.909	13.909	5.029	1.435	0.157
0.600	27.333	11.333	4.346	1.354	0.136
0.650	25.154	9.154	3.753	1.286	0.117
0.700	23.286	7.286	3.226	1.228	0.101
0.750	21.667	5.667	2.749	1.177	0.086
0.800	20.250	4.250	2.305	1.133	0.072
0.850	19.000	3.000	1.879	1.094	0.059
0.900	17.889	1.889	1.449	1.059	0.045
0.950	16.895	0.895	0.970	1.028	0.030
0.990	16.172	0.172	0.416	1.005	0.013

PRODUCTION BATCH : 100 UNITS

NOMINAL YIELD	UNITS PROCESSED	UNITS RECYCLED	RECYCLES STD. DEV.	COST RATIO	COST STD. DEV.
0.050	2019.000	1919.000	195.908	10.595	0.980
0.100	1009.000	909.000	95.341	5.545	0.477
0.150	672.333	572.333	61.770	3.862	0.309
0.200	504.000	404.000	44.944	3.020	0.225
0.250	403.000	303.000	34.814	2.515	0.174
0.300	335.667	235.667	28.028	2.178	0.140
0.350	287.571	187.571	23.150	1.938	0.116
0.400	251.500	151.500	19.462	1.757	0.097
0.450	223.444	123.444	16.563	1.617	0.083
0.500	201.000	101.000	14.213	1.505	0.071
0.550	182.636	82.636	12.258	1.413	0.061
0.600	167.333	67.333	10.593	1.337	0.053
0.650	154.385	54.385	9.147	1.272	0.046
0.700	143.286	43.286	7.864	1.216	0.039
0.750	133.667	33.667	6.700	1.168	0.033
0.800	125.250	25.250	5.618	1.126	0.028
0.850	117.824	17.824	4.579	1.089	0.023
0.900	111.222	11.222	3.531	1.056	0.018
0.950	105.316	5.316	2.365	1.027	0.012
0.990	101.020	1.020	1.015	1.005	0.005

(b)

Fig. 12.17(*b*) Rework costs expressed as ratios.

Let's apply this behavior to individual tasks that are to be performed in a system. For that purpose, there is no input material cost (M), thus Eq. (12.8) reduces to

$$C_R = 1 + \left(1 + \frac{R}{P}\right)\left(\frac{1}{y} - 1\right)\left(1 + \frac{1}{q}\right) \tag{12.9}$$

We are actually interested in the components R/P and y; the resulting cost ratio will influence total system cost. Each workstation has an expected uptime which should be de-rated by y. The minimum possible task time must be divided by the expected yield to obtain realistic task time; this directly affects the number of stations that will be needed, hence the total investment or number of manual workers. The rework cost for an automated station contains other factors that are not easy to capture; as a reasonable approximation, we can multiply the tool hardware cost by $1 + R/P$ assuming that R/P can be adequately specified. Or we can invest in rework facilities or personnel.

Alternative System Justification

Previous sections (along with Chap. 14) show how the various aspects of system cost and performance can be determined. Now, we need to combine them in a comprehensive way. Unit cost and cash flow can be united to totally evaluate economically an alternative system compared to a base system.

Figure 12.18(*a*) exhibits comparison data for two competing systems. Material cost and space allocation cost are not considered at first; they will be assumed to be the same for both systems. The base system is predominantly manual while the alternative system is hybrid. Recall that the difference in the sum of variable and material costs produces the savings seen at the bottom of Fig. 12.18(*a*). Depreciation and tax rates are the same as those used earlier.

Using the variable cost savings as a basis and specifying the percentage of the total cost that is depreciable (100 percent / ρ), we can determine the allowable investment for various values of IRoR. The complete unit cost is the sum of fixed unit cost (annualized investment cost divided by production volume) plus variable unit cost (labor plus operating and maintenance cost). A table of the alternative system's unit costs is shown in Fig. 12.18(*b*). Comparison of the base system's complete unit cost and that of the alternative system provides the (hoped for) unit cost improvement. An example is plotted in Fig. 12.18(*b*) for each of the 3 years of the model. For example, we read from the figure:

IRoR	Total investment	Unit cost improvement		
		Year 1	Year 2	Year 3
18 percent	2.25M m.u.	0.005m.u.	0.30 m.u.	0.56 m.u.
28 percent	1.80M m.u.	0.17m.u.	0.44 m.u.	0.70 m.u.

A general view of first-year cost improvement versus allowable investment can be seen in Fig. 12.19. Specific ρ (1, 2, 4) and internal rate of return (10 percent, 20 percent, 30 percent) curves are exhibited which help lead to the general conclusions:

EXAMPLE DATA 34 (rho = 2)

MANUFACTURING COSTS 12-29-1987

240 WORKING DAYS PER YEAR
2.0 SHIFTS AVAILABLE
10.0 % ANNUAL INCREASE IN PRODUCTION
5.0 % ANNUAL COST INCREASE
3 YEAR RECOVERY OF CAPITAL EXPENSES
34.0 % TAX RATE IN YEAR 0 FOR EXPENSED INVESTMENT

50.0 % OF TOTAL COST IS DEPRECIABLE

COMPETING SYSTEM SPECIFICATIONS

	BASE	ALTERNATIVE
WORKERS REQUIRED PER SHIFT	22.00	5.00
AVERAGE LOADED LABOR RATE ($/HR)	17.00	19.00
OPERATING/MAINTENANCE RATE ($/HR)	3.00	11.00
IDEAL SYSTEM CYCLE TIME (SEC)	22.0	21.0
EXPECTED UP-TIME	85.0%	90.0%
MATERIAL COST ($/UNIT)	0.00	0.00
EXPECTED MATERIAL REJECT RATE	0.0%	0.0%
YEARLY SPACE ALLOCATION COST ($)	0	0
TOTAL SYSTEM COST ($)	250000	?
YEAR 1 VARIABLE COST ($/UNIT)	2.710	0.687
MATERIAL COST ($/UNIT)	0.000	0.000
TOTAL	2.710	0.687
YEAR 2 VARIABLE COST ($/UNIT)	2.846	0.721
MATERIAL COST ($/UNIT)	0.000	0.000
TOTAL	2.846	0.721
YEAR 3 VARIABLE COST ($/UNIT)	2.988	0.757
MATERIAL COST ($/UNIT)	0.000	0.000
TOTAL	2.988	0.757

1 YEAR NET COST SAVINGS REQUIRED

CASH FLOW PARAMETERS

YEAR	UNITS	SAVINGS	DEPRECIATION	TAX RATE	TAX CREDIT
1	425000	859954	14.29%	34.0%	0.0%
2	467500	993246	24.49%	34.0%	
3	514250	1147200	17.49%	34.0%	
3*	SALVAGE VALUE		43.73%		

(a)

Fig. 12.18 Total cost comparison between a base system and an alternative system; allows direct evaluation of the economic viability of the alternative.

RATE of RETURN	ALLOWABLE INVESTMENT	APPROX. PAYBACK	ANNUAL COST	ALTERNATIVE SYSTEM - UNIT COST YEAR 1 425000	YEAR 2 467500	YEAR 3 514250
18%	2248183	2.60	965190	2.958	2.786	2.634
20%	2144677	2.51	953716	2.931	2.761	2.612
22%	2049535	2.42	943148	2.906	2.739	2.591
24%	1961811	2.34	933384	2.883	2.718	2.572
26%	1880691	2.26	924335	2.862	2.699	2.555
28%	1805478	2.19	915927	2.842	2.681	2.539
30%	1735567	2.13	908094	2.824	2.664	2.523
32%	1670435	2.07	900778	2.807	2.648	2.509
34%	1609621	2.01	893930	2.790	2.634	2.496
36%	1552723	1.95	887507	2.775	2.620	2.483
38%	1499387	1.89	881470	2.761	2.607	2.472
40%	1449299	1.84	875786	2.748	2.595	2.460
42%	1402182	1.79	870424	2.735	2.583	2.450
44%	1357786	1.74	865358	2.723	2.572	2.440

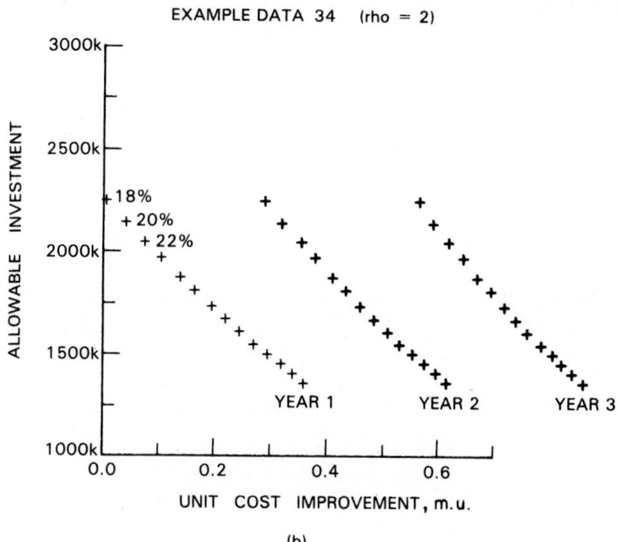

(b)

Fig. 12.18 *(Continued)*

1. For a prescribed investment, the higher the ρ, the lower the unit cost improvement.
2. The lower the IRoR, the higher the allowable investment (for any ρ).
3. For a prescribed ρ, the larger the IRoR, the greater the unit cost improvement but the lower the allowable investment.
4. Allowable investment does not vary significantly with changes in ρ for typical prescribed IRoR (20 percent or more). This statement holds when the nondepreciable part of the investment provides a tax benefit in year 0; see Fig. 12.20 for a specific case where ρ = 2.

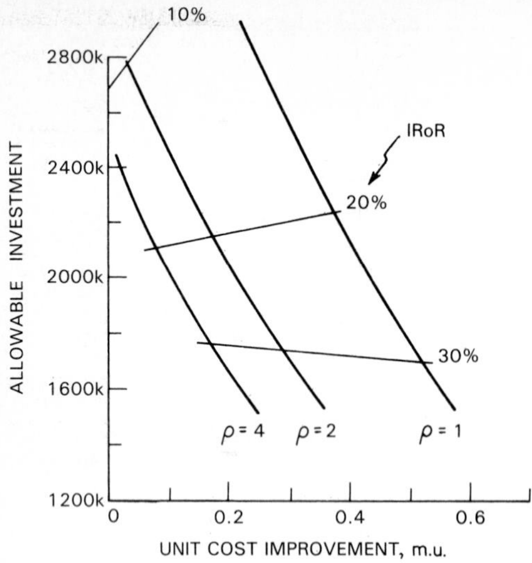

Fig. 12.19 General characteristics for the cost comparison between a base system and an alternative system.

EXAMPLE DATA 34

ZERO PRESENT WORTH CASH FLOW ANALYSIS 06-16-1987

7 YEARS OF ECONOMIC LIFE, SALVAGE VALUE 0 % OF COST

	EXPENSE FORECAST			INCOME FORECAST			
YEAR	RATIO	TAX RATE	DEPRECIABLE	SAVINGS	DEPRECIATION	TAX RATE	CREDIT
0	100.00%	34.0%	50.0%				
1				859.954	14.29%	34.0%	0.0%
2				993.247	24.49%	34.0%	
3				1147.200	17.49%	34.0%	
3*				SALVAGE VALUE	43.73%		

ALLOWABLE TOTAL INVESTMENT = 1961.811
DEPRECIABLE INVESTMENT = 980.906
INTERNAL RATE OF RETURN = 24.00%

PRO-FORMA CASH FLOW

YEAR	INCOME	DEPRECIATION	TAXES	CREDITS	NET	DISC. NET
0	-1961.811	0.000	-333.508	0.000	-1628.303	-1628.303
1	859.954	140.129	244.740	0.000	615.214	496.140
2	993.247	240.222	256.029	0.000	737.218	479.460
3	1147.200	171.587	331.708	0.000	815.492	427.715
3*	428.968	0.000	0.000	0.000	428.968	224.988
INCOME TOTALS	3429.368	551.938	832.477	0.000	2596.891	1628.303
NET TOTALS	1467.557	551.938	498.970	0.000	968.588	0.000

NOMINAL CAPITAL RECOVERY = 763.051
PAYBACK IN APPROXIMATELY 2.34 YEARS
INVERSION POINT IRoR = 25.90%

Fig. 12.20 Specific case of Fig. 12.19.

EXAMPLE DATA 34 (with Materials)

MANUFACTURING COSTS 06-16-1987

240 WORKING DAYS PER YEAR
2.0 SHIFTS AVAILABLE
10.0 % ANNUAL INCREASE IN PRODUCTION
5.0 % ANNUAL COST INCREASE
3 YEAR RECOVERY OF CAPITAL EXPENSES
34.0 % TAX RATE IN YEAR 0 FOR EXPENSED INVESTMENT

COMPETING SYSTEM SPECIFICATIONS

	BASE	ALTERNATIVE
WORKERS REQUIRED PER SHIFT	22.00	5.00
AVERAGE LOADED LABOR RATE ($/HR)	17.00	19.00
OPERATING/MAINTENANCE RATE ($/HR)	3.00	11.00
IDEAL SYSTEM CYCLE TIME (SEC)	22.0	21.0
EXPECTED UP-TIME	85.0%	90.0%
MATERIAL COST ($/UNIT)	4.43	4.61
EXPECTED MATERIAL REJECT RATE	1.0%	4.0%
YEARLY SPACE ALLOCATION COST ($)	0	0
TOTAL SYSTEM COST ($)	250000	?
SYSTEM SATURATION OCCURS (YR)	3.40	4.49
YEAR 1 VARIABLE COST ($/UNIT)	2.710	0.687
MATERIAL COST ($/UNIT)	4.474	4.794
TOTAL	7.185	5.481
YEAR 2 VARIABLE COST ($/UNIT)	2.846	0.721
MATERIAL COST ($/UNIT)	4.698	5.034
TOTAL	7.544	5.756
YEAR 3 VARIABLE COST ($/UNIT)	2.988	0.757
MATERIAL COST ($/UNIT)	4.933	5.286
TOTAL	7.921	6.043

1 YEAR NET COST SAVINGS REQUIRED

CASH FLOW PARAMETERS

YEAR	UNITS	SAVINGS	DEPRECIATION	TAX RATE	TAX CREDIT
1	425000	723911	14.29%	34.0%	0.0%
2	467500	836117	24.49%	34.0%	
3	514250	965716	17.49%	34.0%	
3*	SALVAGE VALUE		43.73%		

Fig. 12.21 General cost comparison between a base system and an alternative system when material costs are considered.

Before concluding this chapter, let's look at the effect of material cost for both systems. We shall arbitrarily assign a reject rate as well as an anticipated base material cost. Usually, a manual system has lower values for both parameters since people (with their brain and dexterity) can overcome many material and part difficulties. Automated systems usually require toleranced grip surfaces which normally add cost unless the product design originally included them. However, automated systems often have better reproducibility and thus lower reject rates. Specific cases must be evaluated carefully.

Figure 12.21 exhibits the conditions which often occur when a design is "thrown over the wall." Some of the production cost savings are lost because of material cost increases [compare data to Fig. 12.18(*a*)]. Care must be taken during concurrent design to prevent this.

Summary

This chapter has described various methods for economically analyzing manufacturing systems. Cash flow methods, yield analysis, and a combination of the cash flow and unit cost procedures provide useful information for budgeting investments and determining if an investment is economically viable. In the next two chapters, this information is used to formulate methods for designing manufacturing and assembly systems.

References:

Boothroyd, G., et al.: *Automatic Assembly,* Marcel Dekker, New York, 1982.

Canada J. R., and R. L. Edwards: *Should We Automate Now?* North Carolina State University, Raleigh, NC, 1985.

———, and J. A. White: *Capital Investment Decision Analysis for Management and Engineering,* Prentice-Hall, Englewood Cliffs, NJ, 1980.

Grant, E. W., et al.: *Principles of Engineering Economy,* 7th ed., John Wiley, New York, 1984.

Gustavson, R. E.: "Choosing a Manufacturing System Based on Unit Cost," *Proceedings of the 13th ISIR/Robots 7 Conference,* Chicago, IL, Apr. 1983.

———: "Engineering Economics Applied to Investments in Automation," *Proceedings of the 2d Assembly Automation Conference,* Brighton, U.K., May 1981.

Lutz, R. P.: "Discounted Cash Flow Techniques," in *Handbook of Industrial Engineering,* G. Salvendy, (ed.), John Wiley, New York, 1982.

Thuesen, H. G., et al.: *Engineering Economy,* 5th ed., Prentice-Hall, Englewood Cliffs, NJ, 1977.

Chapter

13

Design of Automated Fabrication Systems

Introduction

This chapter discusses the design of automated flexible fabrication systems. While most such systems today make metal parts from castings or formed stock by means of metal cutting processes, the principles given in this chapter are applicable to many other kinds of processes, such as sheet metal forming, circuit board manufacturing, and composite layup. An example problem in metal cutting is used as a case study throughout this chapter.

There is no single definition of a fabrication system. Depending on the part spectrum and the production volumes of those parts, the most appropriate "system" could be a:

1. Manually controlled machine
2. Unattended machine
3. Cell comprising several machines and a fixed process sequence for a part family
4. Flexible machining system (FMS) with several machines and arbitrary routings for several part families
5. Flow or transfer line with synchronous transport and one routing for one part

Table 13.1 exhibits the characteristics of these systems.

Objectives of Modern Fabrication System Design

Even in markets commonly considered the domain of dedicated, high-volume fabrication equipment, such as automobiles and appliances,

TABLE 13.1 Characteristics of Different Processing Alternatives

	Manually Controlled Machine	"Unmanned" Machine	Fabrication Cell	Flexible Machining System	Transfer Line
Example	Milling Machine	CNC Machining Center	Group Technology Cell	FMS	Engine Block Machining
Tool Storage	Small	Large	Limited	Large	Replacements Only
Workpiece Changing	Manual	Automatic	Automatic	Fast, due to special pallets and fixtures	Can be complex
Inspection	Off-line	In-process gauging	Can be part of system	Part of System	Can be part of system
Control Method	Human	Workstation Computer	Cell Computer	System Computer	Programmable Controller
Process Time / In/Out Time	Small	Large	Very Large	Very Large	About Equal
Part Variety	Large	Limited by tool type & storage capacity	Small	Limited by available processes	One to Three
Comments			Common Tools & Fixtures	Automated Material Handling	Stable Production Environment

product differentiation, customization, and shortened life cycles are driving component fabrication to increased levels of variety and responsiveness. Typical manufacturing systems and factories strive to achieve a balance between the following objectives:

1. *Throughput.* The ability to produce the number of parts needed
2. *Flexibility.* The ability to produce the variety of parts needed and/or to accommodate changes in part design or mix of variety
3. *Quality.* The ability to produce parts conforming to design requirements
4. *Flow time.* The ability to produce parts needed in as short a time as possible
5. *Utilization.* The ability to keep system resources producing products as much of the available time as possible

6. *Inventory.* The ability to minimize the work-in-process and finished goods inventory levels while still allowing the system to function smoothly
7. *Economic efficiency.* The ability to produce the mix and volume of parts required at the lowest total cost per part

Unfortunately, the objectives described above often conflict, especially as the variety of parts to be produced increases. A fabrication system design methodology must accommodate these conflicting needs.

Minimization of setup

A key to providing the high throughput, high utilization, low inventories, and low flow times necessary to survive in an environment of increasing part variety is to minimize the impact of providing the flexibility necessary to produce a given variety of parts. The amount of time required to adapt equipment to produce a new part or parts is called "setup time."

Three design approaches for reducing the impact of flexibility on a fabrication system's efficiency are:

1. Minimize the need for setup by grouping parts together that require similar processing techniques and tooling and developing systems that address each of these groups
2. Minimize the time required to change equipment over from producing one part type to producing another by moving setup offline, selecting machines with large automatic tool storage systems, and standardizing the tools used to produce parts in the system wherever possible
3. Minimize the need for setup by incorporating inherently flexible equipment into the system, allowing the consolidation of operations currently performed on numerous dedicated, single-function machines into one or two operations on a flexible machine (a four-axis, horizontal spindle machining center is a good example)

Item 3 is discussed below. Items 1 and 2 are continuing themes throughout the chapter.

Process consolidation

A primary objective in system design is to define and select equipment that allows consolidation of necessary manufacturing operations into as few processing steps as possible. Although this tends to require more complex equipment, the advantages of the consolidation include:

1. Reduced refixturing and part movement and significantly improved part accuracy. More features are produced in a single fixturing, relying on the accuracy of the machine for feature-to-feature relational accuracy rather than on a number of machines and the skill of many setup personnel and operators.
2. Reduced fixture design, fabrication, storage, and maintenance costs because of the reduction in different fixtures needed.
3. Reduced number of individual operations required, reducing interprocess material handling.
4. Reduced number of part loads and unloads, increasing available capacity of that equipment.
5. Reduced manufacturing lead times because of the reduction in individual operations and machines needed.
6. Reduced work-in-process inventory because of the reduction in production lead times afforded by process consolidation.

The following equipment typically provides a significant opportunity for process consolidation. Any or all of these types of machines could appear in a flexible fabrication system.

Metal removal machines

1. *Turning centers.* Five-axis computer numerically controlled (CNC) lathes capable of light milling and cross-hole/off-axis drilling, enabling many parts normally requiring separate turning, milling, and drilling operations (and machines) to be completed in one setup on the turning center. Turning centers are commonly used in small cells in combination with another lathe and a grinder to completely fabricate entire part families.
2. *Machining centers.* Four- and five-axis CNC machining centers can perform complex milling, boring, drilling, and tapping operations without necessitating part refixturing, combining the operations often performed on a series of milling machines, drill presses, and other specialized machines. Machining centers are commonly used in cellular and flexible manufacturing systems.
3. *Grinding centers.* CNC grinding machines capable of automatic wheel control and dressing, wheel changing, and sophisticated in-process gauging for feature size control. Some versions are capable of performing both inside diameter (ID) and outside diameter (OD) grinding to demanding concentricity requirements. Work holding consists simply of chucks or chuck and tailstock combinations, and

usually little or no setup is required. Grinding centers are just emerging as stand-alone work centers and cellular system components, combining operations often performed in sequence on a number of different manual grinding machines.

4. *Creep feed grinding.* A grinding process used to grind a complete feature into the part in one pass, often combining several milling and grinding operations into one. This is extremely useful when the final part must be in a hardened state; the blank can be hardened first and then ground, rather than machining the part to a semifinished size, heat treating, and finishing the part.

5. *Electrical discharge and electrochemical machining.* CNC controlled machines which remove material through the use of electrical spark erosion or through electrically enhanced chemical attack. This equipment can generate extremely accurate and complex three-dimensional features in a wide variety of metals. Now being equipped with automatic electrode changing and multiple part fixturing. Usually used as stand-alone equipment because of process and environment considerations.

Sheet metal working

1. *Turret punch presses.* CNC punch presses capable of using a large number of individual punches stored in the machine to perforate metal into complex shapes. Often incorporated into metal forming cells with automatic sheet feeding, press brakes, and welding equipment.

2. *Forming machines.* CNC combinations of turret punch presses and press brakes which can both cut out sheet metal blanks and bend the metal into the required shapes, such as equipment covers, etc., in one operation. This is another emerging technology.

3. *Laser presses.* CNC laser capable of cutting exotic material or normal sheet metal rapidly into intricate shapes. Often coupled with automatic sheet feeding and press brakes in sheet metal systems.

4. *Quick change die-press systems.* An extension to large presses of the pallet shuttle concept used for machining centers, enabling the complete exchange of one die set for the next in less than 5 min. Provides dramatic increases in stamping system throughput, especially for very large die presses, such as those in the automotive industry.

Printed circuit board assembly

1. *High-speed insertion machines.* CNC machines capable of selecting the correct component from a large number of storage reels internal to the machine, testing the component, forming and trimming its leads, inserting it into the printed circuit board, and crimping the leads for wave soldering. Typical placement rates can range as high as 15,000 components per hour. Usually combined with other insertion, wave soldering, and in-circuit test equipment for assembly of boards with through-hole components.
2. *High-speed on-sertion equipment.* Equipment analogous to the insertion equipment discussed above but used to assemble boards with surface-mounted components.

Composites fabrication

1. *Tape laying machines.* CNC multiaxis machines capable of orienting and laying plies of composite material in the uncured state. Laying machines can accommodate a wide variety of components of reasonably simple shapes.
2. *Ply-cutter.* A CNC machine used to cut intricate shapes out of composite pre-impregnated sheets, for hand or robotic assembly into complex structures, such as aircraft components. The machine control software is often capable of "nesting" different patterns to be cut from the same sheet to maximize usage of that sheet of composite.

System Design Methodology

Fabrication system design methodology currently consists of the following steps:

1. Perform preliminary system feasibility analysis
2. Perform detailed work content analysis
3. Define alternative fabrication system configurations, considering:
   a. Process technology alternatives
   b. Material-handling alternatives
   c. Process control alternatives
   d. System control alternatives
   e. Human resource roles
4. Evaluate the technical performance of each alternative solution
5. Evaluate the economic performance of each alternative solution
6. Select the best performing alternative and develop an implementation plan for its installation

Each of these steps is described in detail in the following sections of this chapter. The design of a flexible manufacturing system to fabricate spare parts for military vehicles (called the "job shop example") is used as an example to clarify the concepts and procedures introduced in each section.

Preliminary System Feasibility Analysis

The objective of this preliminary analysis is to determine the general feasibility of applying fabrication system technology cost effectively to the parts manufactured by the company. This high-level evaluation will define specific groups of parts and types of equipment that appear likely to be usable.

Establish a fabrication strategy

A key to successfully implementing advanced manufacturing technologies rests in firmly establishing the plantwide scope and refining the future vision of the manufacturing strategy. A fabrication strategy must translate the critical success factors and product definitions into integrated objectives (see Chap. 8) for the fabrication systems. The translation of the fabrication strategy into operating policies requires that management evaluate and resolve the following types of questions:

1. *Capacity planning.* How are long- to medium-term variations in demand caused by business cycles and other causes to be handled?
2. *Operating hours.* As part of the design and development effort, the number of hours to operate the system must be investigated.
3. *Batch sizes.* How will production be divided into batches? Is lot-size-of-one capability necessary or desirable? How will this need be integrated with purchases, deliveries, forecasts, and orders?
4. *Just-in-time manufacturing.* Dramatic reductions in manufacturing lead time should be expected from the implementation of advanced manufacturing systems. However, without reductions in vendor and in-house lead times for operations not included in the new system(s), overall production lead time could still remain high (see Chap. 3).
5. *Quality policies.* Significant opportunities exist for modernizing approaches to quality assurance. In general, quality assurance functions will be shifted from post process to real-time in-process, from manual to automated, and toward more effective forms of adaptive sampling.

While the fabrication strategy guides the enterprise as a whole, its impact on individual systems can vary widely. Some systems may need to produce a variety of components in low volumes, while others may produce a large volume of a single component for the same product.

The success of the Job Shop depended on meeting these strategic criteria:

1. Rapid response to customer demand for a wide variety of parts in small quantities
2. Very high-quality interchangeable parts
3. Low part cost
4. Surge capacity, the ability to accommodate rapid increases in part mix and volume on short notice

Perform candidate part and machine selection

The objective in this task is to define combinations of parts and machines that appear to have production improvement potential and sufficient longevity to:

1. Justify the reorganization of existing equipment into systems
2. Justify the purchase of new equipment
3. Justify investigation of automating material handling and control of the system

This is accomplished by defining part families via group technology and determining approximately how many machines are needed.

Part family definition. The definition of part families simplifies the overall productivity improvement problem, partitioning the total part set into smaller groups of parts that share (to some extent) the same or similar processing requirements. These families can often provide sufficient aggregate production volumes to allow the application of a more automated production solution than would be practical for individual parts in those families. All parts currently produced should be considered during the part family analysis.

Group technology. The principles of group technology (GT) can be used to create candidate part families to which to apply advanced manufacturing strategies and techniques. Numerous GT systems exist, and the elements of group technology theory and application can be understood by review of any of a number of texts on the subject

(Ham, 1984). Traditional group technology applications have focused on the classification and coding of physical attributes of the candidate parts, such as:

- Part geometry
- Part size
- Part material or materials
- Feature tolerances
- Surface finishes

These approaches can be combined with a second emphasis on the production techniques currently used to produce the parts, creating families of:

- Turned parts in various size ranges
- Turned and milled parts
- Turned, milled, and ground parts
- Machining center parts, etc.

The second criterion for part grouping can be very helpful in reducing the amount of time necessary to understand the processing requirements for these parts, as well as reducing the amount of time required to generate possible processing alternatives. An example of a GT classification and coding system that combines geometric and processing data is the Opitz system, illustrated in Fig. 13.1.

Part family generation. Two types of part families can typically be defined:

1. Closed families, consisting of parts sharing a single part geometry that vary primarily in the size of, or the inclusion or exclusion of, a special feature. Parts in a closed family usually share the same manufacturing processes and routing through those processes. An example of a closed family of parts is illustrated in Fig. 13.2(*a*). Cellular manufacturing systems are typically the most appropriate for closed families. If production volumes are great and part variety is very small, transfer lines can also be applied effectively.

2. Open families, consisting of multiple part types that share a need for some or all of the same manufacturing processes but do not necessarily follow the same routings through those processes. An example of an open part family is presented in Fig. 13.2(*b*). Unattended machines and FMS technologies are usually the most effective for producing open part families.

1st Digit

Component Class		
0	rotational parts	L/D ≤ 0.5
1	rotational parts	0.5 < L/D < 3
2	rotational parts	L/D ≥ 3
3	rotational parts	
4	rotational parts	
5	rotational parts	
6	non-rotational parts	
7	non-rotational parts	
8	non-rotational parts	
9	non-rotational parts	

2nd Digit

External shape, external shape elements			
0			smooth, no shape elements
1	stepped to one end		no shape elements
2	stepped to one end	or smooth	thread
3	stepped to one end	or smooth	functional groove
4	stepped to both ends		no shape elements
5	stepped to both ends		threads
6	stepped to both ends		functional groove
7			functional cone
8			operating thread
9			all others

3rd Digit

Internal shape, internal shape elements		
0		no hole, no breakthrough
1	smooth or stepped to one end	no shape elements
2	smooth or stepped to one end	thread
3	smooth or stepped to one end	functional groove
4	stepped to both ends	no shape elements
5	stepped to both ends	thread
6	stepped to both ends	functional groove
7		functional cone
8		operating thread
9		all others

4th Digit

Surface machining	
0	no surface machining
1	surface plane and/or curved in one direction, external
2	external plane surface related by graduation around a circle
3	external groove and/or slot
4	external spline (polygon)
5	external plane surface and/or slot, external spline
6	internal plane surface and/or slot
7	internal spline (polygon)
8	internal and external polygon, groove and/or slot
9	all others

5th Digit

Auxiliary holes and gear teeth		
0	no gear teeth	no auxiliary hole
1	no gear teeth	axial, not on pitch circle diameter
2	no gear teeth	axial on pitch circle diameter
3	no gear teeth	radial, not on pitch circle diameter
4	no gear teeth	axial and/or radial and/or other direction
5	no gear teeth	axial and/or radial on PCD and/or other directions
6	with gear teeth	spur gear teeth
7	with gear teeth	bevel gear teeth
8	with gear teeth	other gear teeth
9	with gear teeth	all others

Main Code

6th Digit		7th Digit		8th Digit		9th Digit	
Diameter D or length of edge A (mm)		Material		Initial shape		Accuracy in coding digit	
0	< 20	0	grey cast iron	0	round bar	0	no accuracy specified
1	> 20 ≤ 50	1	nodular graphitic cast iron and malleable cast iron	1	bright drawn round bar	1	2
2	> 50 ≤ 100	2	steel ≤ 42 kg/mm^2 (St - steel)	2	triangular, square, hexagonal or other bar	2	3
3	> 100 ≤ 160	3	steel ≤ 42kg/mm^2 (C and Ck steel)	3	tubing	3	4
4	> 160 ≤ 250	4	steel 2 + 3 heat-treated	4	angle, U-, T - and similar sections	4	5
5	> 250 ≤ 400	5	alloy steel	5	sheet	5	2 + 3
6	> 400 ≤ 600	6	alloy steel heat-treated	6	plates and slabs	6	2 + 4
7	> 600 ≤ 1000	7	non-ferrous metal	7	cast or forged component	7	2 + 5
8	> 1000 ≤ 2000	8	light alloy	8	welded group	8	3 + 4
9	> 2000	9	other materials	9	pre-machined component	9	(2 + 3) + 4 + 5

Supplementary Code

Fig. 13.1 Opitz classification chart.

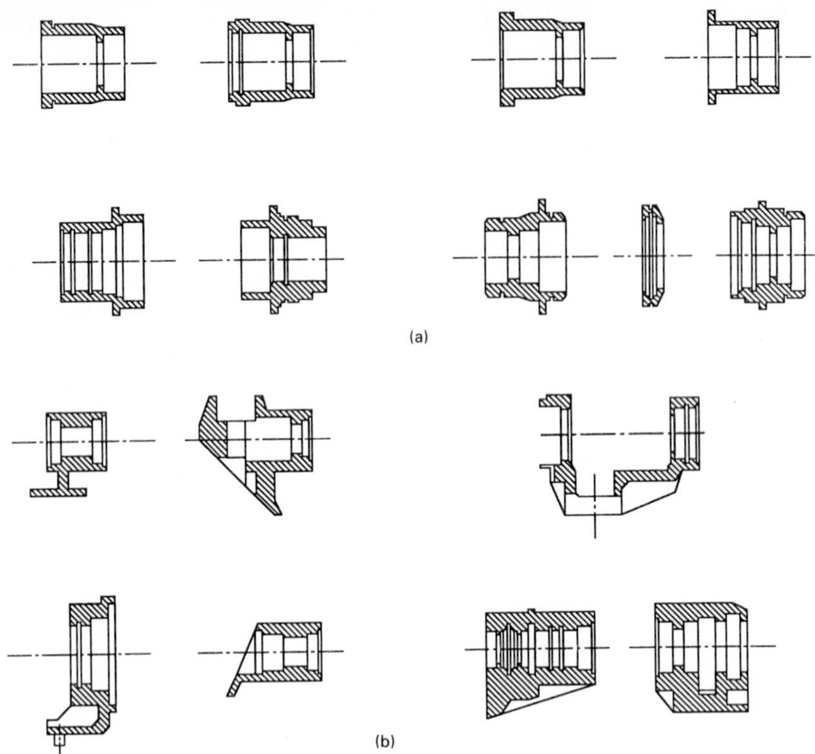

Fig. 13.2 (*a*) Closed part family, consisting of parts that differ only in feature dimensions; (*b*) open part family, consisting of parts that have different features.

For the Job Shop example, 2740 parts were reviewed with the following results:

1. Part envelope—6-in cube to 36-in cube.
2. Materials—aluminum and steel only.
3. Tolerances—0.003-in true position.
4. Machined components comprised the vast majority of parts to be made.
5. No shafts made within system because of current external capability.
6. Only parts requiring at least 200 processing hours per year were to be considered.

These constraints reduced the part set count to 192. No closed families could be defined, so one large open family was used.

Machine selection. Machine selection for the feasibility analysis consists of identifying classes of machines for each part family that:

1. Can perform the fabrication operations necessary
2. May be integrated into a system

The selected machines should be able to collectively complete as much of the work content of each part family as possible to minimize the need for additional processing outside of the system. The number of each type of machine can be determined using:

1. The current cycle time per operation per part to produce the parts in each family and an adjustment factor established by the design team to approximate the cycle times in the new system or
2. An estimated cycle time per operation per part for the new system and
3. The expected production volume for each part for the next 5 years (or longer) and
4. The operating hours and utilization factors defined in the manufacturing strategy from

$$M_C = \frac{\sum_P \sum_O T_o V}{H_C U_C}$$

M_C = machines in class C
T_o = time per operation done by machine class C on part type i
V = production volume of part type i
H_C = hours available per machine in class C
U_C = utilization of machine(s) in class C
P = number of parts
O = number of operations

The Job Shop's 192 selected parts can be produced with 10 FMS machine classes; 240 working days of two 8-hr shifts (3840 hr per year) are available. Machine utilization is expected to be 75 percent.

Preliminary evaluation procedure

The evaluation process is illustrated in the flow chart presented in Fig. 13.3. The following information is necessary to perform the preliminary economic evaluation required for this task:

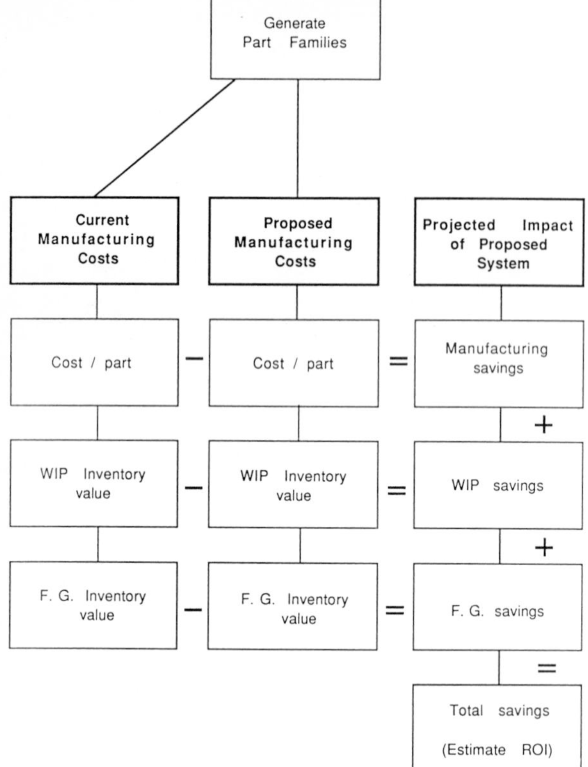

Fig. 13.3 Fabrication system evaluation process.

1. For each candidate part:
   a. Annual production volume
   b. Current fabrication cost (including quality costs)
   c. Current procurement cost (if a purchased part)
   d. Current average work-in-process (WIP) inventory value
   e. Current average finished goods (FG) inventory value
   f. Estimated cycle time per machine in the proposed system
   g. Estimated fabrication cost, based on full system costs and time in the system
   h. Estimated work-in-process and finished goods inventory values, if any, resulting from the new processing techniques
2. For each proposed system:
   a. Cost of the proposed machines in the system
   b. Cost of support equipment, such as material-handling systems, computer hardware and software, tooling and fixturing, etc., expected to be used to support the proposed system
   c. Cost of personnel associated with the system

Material costs can be excluded as long as no significant changes are implied by the proposed system. To estimate the cost to produce each part in the proposed system, an operating cost per hour must be defined. The operating cost can be approximated by adding together estimates of the following:

1. The cost per year to operate and maintain each machine in the system—the cost of utilities, maintenance, programming, operator training, and any other applicable fabrication shop overhead
2. The cost per year to operate and maintain the support systems, such as material-handling equipment and computer hardware and software
3. The costs of personnel necessary to operate the system
4. The costs of any anticipated scrap or acceptable yield other than 100 percent

These costs can then be divided by the total number of machine hours provided by the system; this will define the process cost per hour a part is in the system. The average work-in-process and finished goods inventory values anticipated to result from processing in the system can also be estimated and should be added to the estimated processing cost to represent the fabrication cost of the parts in the proposed system.

The estimated cost of fabricating each part in the proposed system can be subtracted from the current fabrication costs for that part. The differences for all parts are added together to define the cash flows resulting from the installation of the proposed system. These cash flows are then compared to the anticipated total cost of implementing the proposed system, using techniques described in Chap. 12. If the proposed system provides a return on investment greater than the minimum acceptable to the company, more detailed design and evaluation of the system and its associated part family is justified.

An automated procedure can be used to match parts and machines on an economic basis. Draper Laboratory has developed a large-scale linear program called PAMS (part and machine selection) that attempts to optimize the return on investment in a system given a specific part spectrum. The data needed by PAMS (or any linear optimization approach) has been defined in the previous section.

Two advantages of using PAMS rather than the step-by-step economic evaluation outlined above are described below:

1. PAMS combines part and machine selection and justification processes into a single step and performs that step automatically. PAMS will continue to match parts with machines until a user-

TABLE 13.2(*a*) Worst-Case Condition Results of Preliminary Machine Selection
They are 100% cycle times, two fixtures required for each part, 75% FMS efficiency.

Number of Machines		4		5		6		7		8		9	
		2 class	3 class	2 class	3 class	2 class	3 class	2 class	3 class	2 class	3 class	2 class	3 class
Machines in each class	Small	1	0	2	1	2	1	1		2		2	
	Medium	3	3	3	3	4	4	4		6		7	
	Large		1		1		1	2					
Total Investment (M$)		2.67	2.97	2.94	3.26	3.33	3.65	4.25		4.11		4.50	
Number of parts with potential savings		55	93	55	93	55	93	55	93	55	93	55	93
Number of parts chosen		9	10	16	18	16	20	16		20		23	
Annual Savings (M$)		0.69	0.68	0.81	0.84	0.91	0.98	1.12		1.30		1.44	
Before taxes ROI (%)		26	23	28	26	27	27	26		32		32	

A blank indicates that no machines were chosen or that combination was not investigated.
Maximum size FMS: 9 machines for 2-class, 7 machines for 3-class

TABLE 13.2(*b*) Better-Case Condition Results of Preliminary Machine Selection
They are 75%, one fixture required for each part, 80% FMS efficiency.

Number of Machines		4		5		6		7		8		9		13
		2 class	3 class	2 class	3 class	2 class	3 class	2 class	3 class	2 class	3 class	2 class	3 class	3 class
Machines in each class	Small	1	1	1	1	1	1	2	1	2	1	2	1	2
	Medium	3	2	4	3	5	4	6	4	6	4	7	4	5
	Large		1		1		1		3		3		4	6
Total Investment (M$)		2.66	2.97	3.05	3.26	3.44	3.86	3.83	4.25	4.11	4.85	4.50	5.45	7.32
Number of parts with potential savings		91	129	91	129	91	129	91	129	91	129	91	129	129
Number of parts chosen		12	24	17	33	20	19	33	33	52	37	72	40	83
Annual Savings (M$)		1.18	1.11	1.58	1.46	1.78	1.83	2.01	2.06	2.22	2.37	2.41	2.66	3.55
Before taxes ROI (%)		45	38	50	45	52	47	53	49	54	49	54	49	49

A blank indicates that no machines were chosen or that combination was not investigated.
Maximum size FMS: 9 machines for 2-class, 13 machines for 3-class

specified maximum investment level is reached or until no further part and machine assignments are justifiable.

2. If the part spectrum is small (less than 500 part types), part family definition is not necessary. PAMS will match parts to machines until no additional machines are justifiable. Individual families can then be defined from the part and machine combinations rather than the entire part set.

PAMS is described in detail in C. S. Draper (1982*a*). A typical PAMS output is shown in Table 13.2. Table 13.2(*b*) is representative of a series of evaluations in which one or more planning assumptions were altered to determine the sensitivity of the analyses to those data. In this case, a system of four to nine machines could be implemented cost-effectively, so a further detailed FMS system design and evaluation should be undertaken.

System implementation feasibility

Determining the capability of the company to successfully implement and maintain fabrication systems is equally as important as determining the economic feasibility of those systems. One must objectively examine the staff's ability to:

1. Design fabrication systems rather than select individual machine tools
2. Program and maintain complex, often computer-controlled machines and material-handling equipment
3. Program and operate computerized system controls
4. Understand the impact the system(s) will have on part flow, response time, and interaction with the rest of the shop

The overall direction provided by the manufacturing strategy should be very useful in determining if the system helps the company achieve the objectives established by management and should help prevent improper implementation of advanced technology.

Performed Detailed Work Content Analysis

The feasibility analysis described above typically results in the definition of one or more candidate systems for detailed design and evaluation. The first step in the detailed design process is to determine the work content of each part in the candidate families.

The objective of work content analysis, usually called "process planning," is to describe the elemental operations necessary to completely fabricate each part. A key aspect of process planning is that it results in an estimate of the time and number of tools required to complete each fabrication operation. Part cycle times will be used to determine the number of workstations necessary in the system to achieve a specific production volume for a specific mix of parts. These times will also be used to determine the maximum allowable service or delivery rate and time available for the material-handling system.

The definition of a process plan for a part is based on:

1. A thorough understanding of processing techniques, precedences, and constraints
2. The material and tolerances of the part
3. Proper definition of machinability data
4. Proper work-holding design
5. Proper tool selection
6. The capability of the equipment selected

The definition of the elemental process plan is very dependent on the work-holding concepts selected which are constrained to some extent by equipment options. These three topics *must* be considered concurrently for successful equipment selection and system design. Machinability data, work holding, and tool selection are discussed here with respect to their impact on fabrication system design and cost. Machine selection affects configuration design as much as it does process planning.

Machinability data

The cycle times defined in the process plan for each operation are the sum of the cycle times for each tool used during that operation. The process planner determines the amount of time a tool is in cut based on:

1. The form of the raw material
2. The dimensions and surface finish of the final form of a specific feature
3. The tools necessary to generate that feature
4. The cutting speed and feed relationship based on the tool selected and the material to be cut (metal forming is governed by an analogous set of forming speed rules)
5. The capabilities of the machine(s)

A principal cause of poor performance in existing systems is the incorrect choice of cutting speed and feed for the parts in the system. The process planner should start with standard machinability data for the specific tools and part materials to be processed in the system. These data can be adjusted for experience with the material, cutting thin or weak sections in the parts, long tool extensions, and other potential problems in the cutting process. The same machinability data should be used by all process planners associated with the system to assure consistency between the process plans and time estimates. The *Machining Data Handbook* is an excellent source for basic machinability data (Machinability Data Center, 1980).

Work-holding alternatives

Proper conception and design of work-holding devices (usually called "fixtures" in metal cutting systems) are critical to the successful fabrication (and subsequent assembly) of any product. The system designer's objective with respect to fixture definition is to minimize the number of fixtures required throughout the system to fabricate each component, while assuring proper control and orientation of the component. Adequate support and clamping force must be designed into every fixture. Additionally, the fixture's design should prevent the loading of incorrect parts into the fixture as well as improper orientation of the correct part in the fixture.

Part orientation in the fixture should be selected to maximize access for processing by the equipment in the system. The designer should also consider fixture and clamping arrangements that allow access to more than one side of the part without reclamping the part. A "window frame" fixture (see Fig. 13.4) uses clamping points around the periphery of the part to clamp and support it while providing access to both sides without obstruction. If material and rigidity constraints permit, fixture "lugs" can be designed into the raw material to permit the use of window frame and other multiple-axis access fixturing. The surfaces chosen as fixturing surfaces also have the potential for use as jigging surfaces during assembly. Assembly sequence design and machining process planning should be coordinated to take advantage of this.

Clamping is usually accomplished using standard clamping components mounted on a base plate or "tombstone" (a four-sided vertical fixture plate commonly used with horizontal machining centers). Traditionally, each clamping device was actuated manually, requiring manual attention every time a part was loaded and unloaded, and relied on the skill of the attendant to adequately load and clamp the part without error or distortion during clamping. Modern fixtures

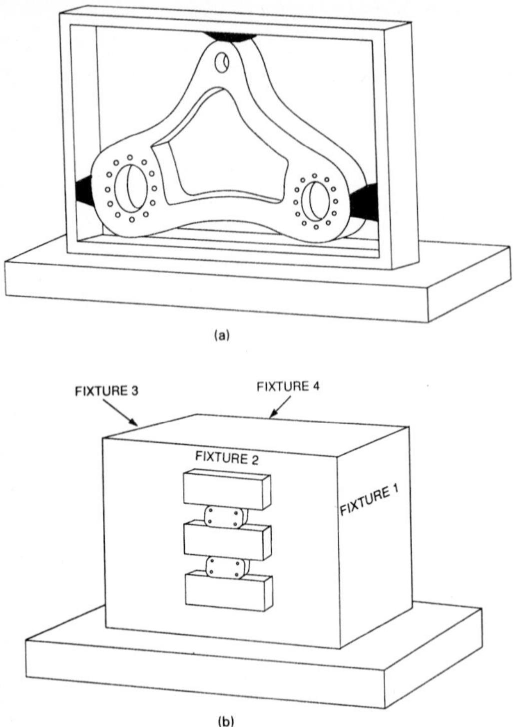

Fig. 13.4 (*a*) Window frame fixture and (*b*) tombstone fixture.

take advantage of hydraulically actuated mechanical clamping and support devices. This type of clamping approach is very important to fabrication system designers in that it minimizes both the time the fixture (and part) spends in the load or unload station and the opportunity for part distortion during clamping.

Tool selection

The process planner attempts to satisfy the following objectives when selecting tools for processing parts in a fabrication system:

1. Accurately generate each feature as quickly as possible
2. Provide sufficient tool longevity to avoid an unnecessary amount of tool replacement (and machine downtime waiting for tools)
3. Minimize the number of tools per part
4. Maximize the commonality of tools among parts

Cutting time and tool life are inversely related; the faster a tool cuts the shorter its useful life (between resharpenings). The process planner must balance the speed at which parts are produced with the downtime on the equipment to replenish tools because of wear. Almost all equipment in a fabrication system will change tools automatically to minimize the direct labor necessary to produce a part. Tool changing machines have a limited capability to store tools, often only 40 to 60 tools.

The fewer tools required by each part, the greater the number of parts a machine can accommodate between tool exchanges. Using the same tools where appropriate on as many parts as possible also addresses this problem; as more parts share a greater number of tools, the total number of unique tools needed in the system is reduced. This allows more parts to be produced with less interruption of productive machine time. Additional benefits derived from tool standardization and consolidation include reduced tool storage space and inventory tracking requirements, higher-quantity purchases, and less potential for tool unavailability. Scheduling and part routing are also simplified: A part does not have to visit a particular machine just because a unique tool is stored there. Instead, it may visit any available machine that has the common tools it needs.

Computer-aided process planning

Computerized process planning aids based on spread-sheet-like computer programs can be used to significantly reduce the time required to generate individual process plans. An example of these programs is CTIME (cycle time), developed at Draper Laboratory. This program uses three databases to calculate the cycle time for each part as well as the number of tools used per part, the number of unique tools per part set, and the total time in cut per tool type. The first database includes the elemental operation description: the operation number, the type of material, the tool diameter and number of cutting teeth, and the length of cut. The second database contains the machinability data for normal combinations of tools and materials used by the process planner. The third database contains machine parameters for the machines used by the company. The process planner supplies the part data required by the first database for each part, and CTIME generates the process plan and cycle time. Changes in machinability data, machine data, materials, or tools can be made quickly and automatically for the entire part set simply by altering the appropriate database. The process planner does not have to perform any calculations, and adjustments in cutting length or tool selection can be simply performed. A sample of the three input databases is presented in Fig.

13.5. Examples for the Job Shop elemental process plan and the process planning summary are displayed in Fig. 13.6. CTIME is discussed in detail in C. S. Draper (1984).

Define Alternative Fabrication Configurations

The creation of alternative fabrication system designs or "configurations" involves the concurrent definition of the most appropriate process and material-handling equipment, process control strategy, and fabrication system control strategy. Individual configurations can then be modified and improved iteratively based on physical and economic performance evaluations. Key considerations for equipment selection and process control strategies from a fabrication system design viewpoint are discussed below.

Process and equipment selection

The work content analysis for each family describes the necessary processes, the desired processing sequence, the work-holding concepts, and the number and variety of tools necessary to fabricate each part in the candidate part family(ies). The process planner also decides the number of machine axes necessary to perform each operation. Machine workspace or "envelope" is defined by the largest and smallest parts in the family(ies). Required equipment accuracy is determined by the dimensional tolerances on features of the parts (in combination with overall processing requirements at each processing step), as well as the proposed equipment operating strategy: attended, partially attended, or unattended fabrication. As the human is removed from the process, the accuracy of the parts processed by the system relies to a greater extent on the inherent process capability of the equipment in the system and on the in-process and post-process feedback given to that equipment. The system designer must use all of these data, as well as other processing and operational constraints, as potential equipment is reviewed and evaluated.

Machines selected for the job shop system

The PAMS analyses indicated that small, medium, and large machining centers could be applied cost-effectively to the selected parts. To provide maximum process and product flexibility for the future, only "large" (36-in machining cube) four-axis horizontal machining centers were to be used in the system, given that small and medium-size parts could be produced on large machines. Each of the machines would be

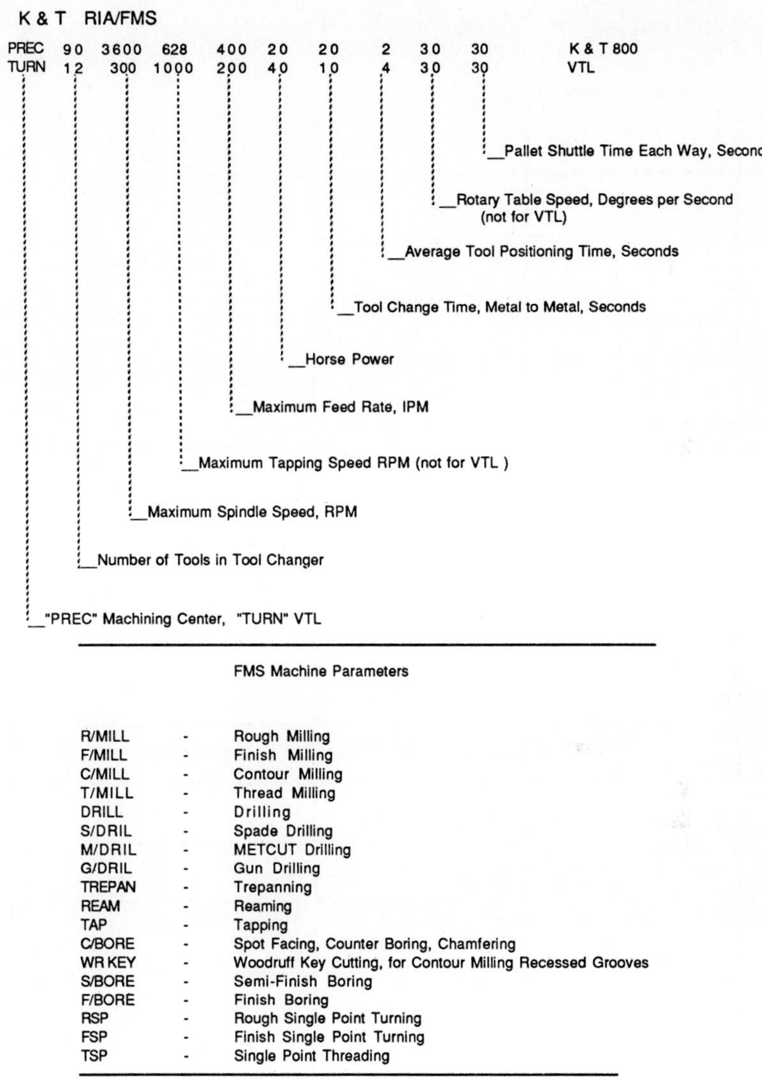

R/MILL	-	Rough Milling
F/MILL	-	Finish Milling
C/MILL	-	Contour Milling
T/MILL	-	Thread Milling
DRILL	-	Drilling
S/DRIL	-	Spade Drilling
M/DRIL	-	METCUT Drilling
G/DRIL	-	Gun Drilling
TREPAN	-	Trepanning
REAM	-	Reaming
TAP	-	Tapping
C/BORE	-	Spot Facing, Counter Boring, Chamfering
WR KEY	-	Woodruff Key Cutting, for Contour Milling Recessed Grooves
S/BORE	-	Semi-Finish Boring
F/BORE	-	Finish Boring
RSP	-	Rough Single Point Turning
FSP	-	Finish Single Point Turning
TSP	-	Single Point Threading

Tool Codes for Machinabililty Data

(a)

Fig. 13.5(a) Machinability data code.

COMPANY XYZ MACHINABILITY DATA

	MATL	R/MILL	F/MILL	C/MILL	T/MILL	DRILL	S/DRIL	M/DRIL	G/DRIL	TREPAN	REAM	TAP	C/BORE	WR KEY	S/BORE	F/BORE	RSP	FSP	TSP
Surface Speeds	G120	300	450	235	60	45	40	140	165	300	35	18	55	300	230	345	320	390	150
	4130	350	475	275	70	55	30	140	200	300	35	25	60	300	240	385	320	410	150
	1020	440	525	350	80	65	55	175	350	350	40	50	75	300	260	490	375	565	150
	G105	300	400	235	60	45	40	140	165	300	35	18	55	300	230	345	320	390	150
	ALUM	1800	1800	1000	1000	275	600	800	650	500	200	75	750	1500	1800	1800	1800	2000	250
	6535	300	400	235	60	45	40	140	165	300	35	18	55	300	230	345	320	390	150
	COPPR	600	750	400	300	140	70	300	400	225	80	55	150	440	400	650	500	650	250
	BRASS	600	750	400	300	140	70	300	400	225	80	55	150	440	400	650	500	650	250
	SS416	265	355	200	70	50	40	140	250	200	35	16	60	300	175	265	245	300	100
Feed per Tooth or Revolution	G120	8	6	5	1	12	4	8	1	6	8	0	4	16	12	3	15	7	0
	4130	8	6	5	1	15	5	8	1	6	8	0	5	16	10	3	15	7	0
	1020	10	7	7	1	15	6	8	1	7	12	0	6	16	15	3	15	7	0
	G105	8	6	5	1	12	4	8	1	6	8	0	4	16	12	3	15	7	0
	ALUM	10	8	6	4	15	4	20	2	3	8	0	8	30	15	6	20	10	0
	6535	8	6	5	1	12	4	8	1	6	8	0	4	16	12	3	15	7	0
	COPPR	12	8	5	4	16	6	16	2	5	20	0	6	25	15	3	20	7	0
	BRASS	12	8	5	4	16	6	16	2	5	20	0	6	25	15	3	20	7	0
	SS416	7	5	3	1	12	5	8	1	4	6	0	4	16	12	3	15	7	0
Power Factors	G120	1.5	1.5	1.5	1.5	1.3	1.3	1.3	1.3	1.3	0	0	0	1.4	1.4	1.4	1.4	1.4	1.4
	4130	1.5	1.5	1.5	1.5	1.3	1.3	1.3	1.3	1.3	0	0	0	1.4	1.4	1.4	1.4	1.4	1.4
	1020	1.5	1.5	1.5	1.5	1.3	1.3	1.3	1.3	1.3	0	0	0	1.4	1.4	1.4	1.4	1.4	1.4
	G105	1.5	1.5	1.5	1.5	1.3	1.3	1.3	1.3	1.3	0	0	0	1.4	1.4	1.4	1.4	1.4	1.4
	ALUM	.38	.32	.38	.38	.18	.18	.18	.18	.18	0	0	0	.28	.28	.28	.28	.28	.28
	6535	1.5	1.5	1.5	1.5	1.3	1.3	1.3	1.3	1.3	0	0	0	1.4	1.4	1.4	1.4	1.4	1.4
	COPPR	.60	.55	.60	.60	.25	.25	.25	.25	.25	0	0	0	.55	.55	.55	.55	.55	.55
	BRASS	.60	.55	.60	.60	.25	.25	.25	.25	.25	0	0	0	.55	.55	.55	.55	.55	.55
	SS416	1.5	1.5	1.5	1.5	1.3	1.3	1.3	1.3	1.3	0	0	0	1.4	1.4	1.4	1.4	1.4	1.4

9 material types   18 tool types   54 different part numbers

(b)

Fig. 13.5(b) Typical machinability data.

R1 K & T RIA/FMS
PREC 68 3600. 628 . 400. 20. 20. 2. 30. 30.
TURN 12 300. 1000. 200. 40. 10. 4. 30. 30.

SUMMARY - PROCESS PLANNING CHART

			CYCLE TIME	DISTRIBUTION OF CYCLE TIME									
				R/MILL	F/MILL	C/MILL	T/MILL	DRILL	S/DRIL	M/DRIL	G/DRIL	TREPAN	REAM
1)	PART	10930330	69.51	25.40	6.17	22.55	0.00	3.14	0.00	0.00	0.00	0.00	0.00
2)	PART	11590764	21.35	1.69	1.62	3.47	0.00	2.28	0.00	0.00	0.00	0.00	3.02
3)	PART	10891945	50.95	10.84	11.90	9.14	0.00	8.34	0.00	0.00	0.00	0.00	0.00
4)	PART	10882028	86.08	4.72	5.27	2.28	0.00	12.13	32.32	0.00	0.00	0.00	0.00
5)	PART	8432887	114.48	4.63	8.26	13.24	41.96	2.88	0.00	0.00	0.00	0.00	0.00
6)	PART	10923025	9.86	0.25	0.29	0.04	0..00	1.11	0.00	0.00	0.00	0.00	2.51
7)	PART	8433724	10.57	0.40	0.50	0.00	0.00	1.30	0.00	0.00	0.00	0.00	0.00
8)	PART	10933932	27.27	3.14	3.06	5.23	0.00	2.18	0.00	0.00	0.00	0.00	4.30
9)	PART	10895627	19.10	0.78	1.88	3.01	0.00	2.34	0.00	0.00	0.00	0.00	0.00
10)	PART	10895673	27.53	4.30	4.30	0.00	0.00	5.17	0.00	0.00	0.00	0.00	1.85
11)	PART	10895694	6.39	0.97	1.22	0.42	0.00	1.28	0.00	0.00	0.00	0.00	0.00
12)	PART	10895695	15.24	0.00	0.00	0.00	0.00	0.00	0.00	0.00	0.00	0.00	0.00
13)	PART	10895696	15.24	0.00	0.00	0.00	0.00	0.00	0.00	0.00	0.00	0.00	0.00
14)	PART	12007723	316.66	50.74	19.79	5.74	39.27	17.23	32.45	0.00	0.00	0.00	0.00
15)	PART	12012132	16.12	0.75	0.00	4.47	0.00	3.19	0.00	0.00	0.00	0.00	0.00
16)	PART	8432870	127.76	0.89	2.33	2.47	42.60	5.21	0.00	0.00	0.00	0.00	0.00
17)	PART	8433535	26.45	0.56	1.70	3.08	0..00	0.84	6.37	0.00	0.00	0.00	0.00
18)	PART	8433536	28.91	1.29	2.58	3.08	0.00	1.29	6.37	0.00	0.00	0.00	0.00
19)	PART	8433634	29.30	0.95	0.93	0.00	0.00	4.82	0.00	0.00	0.00	0.00	0.00
20)	PART	8433635	30.27	0.95	0.93	0.00	0.00	4.82	0.00	0.00	0.00	0.00	0.00
21)	PART	8433797	14.98	0.23	0.50	0.00	0.00	1.04	0.00	0.00	0.00	0.00	0.00
22)	PART	12274291	59.09	5.14	7.11	7.98	0.00	12.72	0.00	0.00	0.00	0.00	7.83
23)	PART	12274293	40.30	4.78	6.64	9..94	0.00	6.87	0.00	0.00	0.00	0.00	2.38
24)	PART	12274331	21.13	1.78	0.53	1.73	0.00	2.86	4.91	0.00	0.00	0.00	0.00
25)	PART	10895603	22.78	0.00	0.00	0.00	0.00	3.13	2.52	0.00	0.00	0.00	0.00
26)	PART	6505782	89.13	15.64	13.87	17.13	0.00	5.33	0.00	0.00	0.00	0.00	0.00
27)	PART	6505788	85.30	15.12	13.34	17.13	0.00	3.72	0.00	0.00	0.00	0.00	0.00
28)	PART	12007725	14.69	0.78	0.69	0.00	0.00	5.26	0.00	0.00	0.00	0.00	0.00
29)	PART	1200765	46.02	0.19	0.00	7.14	0.00	3.46	0.00	0.00	0.00	0.00	0.00
30)	PART	8430397	44.34	1.78	0.91	1.75	0.00	1.89	10.91	0.00	3.93	0.00	0.00
31)	PART	8432888	33.36	7.42	1.49	0.72	0.00	2.98	0.00	0.00	0.00	0.00	0.00
32)	PART	8432951	12.17	0.17	0.20	0.00	0.00	0.97	0.41	0.00	0.00	0.00	0.00
33)	PART	8432977	12.01	0.58	0.69	0.19	0.00	0.97	0.00	0.00	0.00	0.00	1.77
34)	PART	10922978	2.34	0.61	0.11	0.61	0.00	0.00	0.00	0.00	0.00	0.00	0.00
35)	PART	8433716	26.36	2.93	1.57	2.29	0.00	3.00	0.00	0.00	0.00	0.00	1.98
36)	PART	10884271	11.29	1.98	1.47	1.64	0.00	1.00	0.00	0.00	0.00	0.00	0.00
37)	PART	12274327	14.84	2.56	2.08	3.33	0.00	1.46	0.00	0.00	0.00	0.00	0.00
38)	PART	6105074	26.37	0.00	0.00	5.09	0.00	1.32	0.00	0.52	0.00	0.00	0.00
39)	PART	6536154	119.54	0.05	0.00	0.55	35.53	2.08	37.50	0.41	2.99	0.00	0.00
40)	PART	6507039	261.81	34.97	1.61	8.55	101.97	0.42	22.76	0.00	0.00	35.11	0.68

Fig. 13.6 Process planning summary example.

capable of automatically exchanging palletized fixtures in less than 45 s, and each machine would be equipped to store 90 tools in an automatic tool changer mounted on the machine. Vertical turning machines, equipped with pallet changers and 24 tool-changing systems, would also be included in the system.

In addition to the machining centers and lathes, the system would incorporate coordinate measurement machines to provide accurate part measurement data as soon as possible after the parts have been machined. These machines would also be equipped with pallet changers.

All of the machines in the system would be computer numerically controlled (CNC) machines and would be linked to a distributed numerical control (DNC) system for automatic downloading of production part programs and uploading of optimized part programs, as well as measurement data and machine status. The use of a DNC eliminates the need to manually load and unload program tapes and minimizes the possibility of using the wrong tape at the machine. The metal cutting machines would also be equipped with part measurement probes for fixture and part offset generation and in-process part measurement when necessary for part accuracy.

Material-handling equipment selection

In parallel with the definition of process equipment, the system designer must determine the most appropriate material-handling techniques to use for the transfer of parts from machine to machine for each family. This includes the selection of storage devices appropriate for raw, work-in-process, and finished goods inventory as well as fixtures, gauges, and tooling. The material-handling equipment may be very different for each family, depending on part size and weight, aggregate production volume, part quality considerations during transfer, and the ease of loading and unloading the candidate machines. Different material-handling approaches may also be appropriate within individual fabrication systems.

A range of material-handling techniques should be investigated, from manual operators and inspectors to pick and place mechanisms, robots, wire-guided vehicles, and conveyors. Storage techniques may range from shelves and tables to flow racks and automated storage and retrieval systems. Additionally, a cell or FMS may have a combination of these approaches. Material-handling concepts and equipment alternatives must be developed in four distinct areas: containerization, machine and material-handling system interfaces, transportation systems, and storage systems.

Typical part-handling and transport techniques are discussed in Chap. 10.

Job shop material-handling selection

The Job Shop required a very flexible material-handling system of relatively low capacity—about 60 to 80 moves per hour. Conveyors were ruled out based on the small number of moves, large size of the system, and degree of route flexibility required. The distance between machines was too large to use robots. Tow-chain carts were rejected as being too difficult to alter or expand the route, leaving AGVs as the preferred method.

Process quality assurance

A quality assurance philosophy must be developed that emphasizes process control as the means to assure part conformance rather than emphasizing the detection of part nonconformance as a means of detecting processes out of control. The success of any fabrication process is based on rigid work-holding accurately referenced to the machine, accurate tool sizing, and tool position control. The basic way to determine if these three factors are functioning together acceptably is to measure a feature they produce as they produce it or as soon as possible after that feature is machined. The primary objective of this measurement is to determine that the combination is working within acceptable limits [statistical process control, see Taguchi and Wu (1980)]; the fact that the part feature is in conformance to print is a by-product of a process that is in control. This concept is key to eliminating the waiting time typically incurred for first piece setup; process quality assurance establishes a level of capability for each combination of machine, tool, and fixture. If feature tolerance is within that capability, the fact that that combination is being used to machine two different features on two different parts will not inhibit the ability of the machine to successfully produce those features on both parts. Extend this concept to measuring every combination, and total machine capability will be determined and can be maintained.

The statistical quality approach provides the long-term data necessary to determine the normal process capability of the equipment so that feature requirements can be matched to those capabilities and not exceed them. Frequency of measurement depends on the number of features produced by a specific tool and machine combination and the level of confidence desired in the process. These frequencies have to be determined as part of the implementation of the statistical process control procedure.

The first step in the drive to improve quality while reducing the impact of inspection on machine use is to consolidate manufacturing operations. As long as the part is maintained in the fixture or chuck, feature-to-feature accuracy is significantly enhanced over that possible from multiple fixture processing.

Process quality maps should be prepared jointly by the manufacturing and quality engineers, and they should work backward from the part print and specification highlighting each operation that is critical for part conformance. A complete process quality map is very similar to a CPM project management chart (the "critical" path for conformance is clearly defined as are the dependencies from one process to the next). Through this procedure, process requirements and tolerance limits for each operation can be developed, and the features that should be measured can be determined. This up-front planning effort can significantly reduce the number of features included in the statistical analysis and, most importantly, define the tolerance limits for acceptable process control. These tolerance limits can then be used to match processing needs to machine capability, and they serve as the control chart limits for the statistical analyses.

Configuration Design and Layout

We are now ready to match the machines and workstations defined for each family with the selected material-handling techniques to develop candidate manufacturing system configurations. These configurations may include:

1. A single machine with multiple part processing capability
2. Groups of stand-alone equipment located in close proximity to each other, with manual material handling and inspection
3. Production cells with machines organized into a "production line" with manual part handling, automated part handling, or both
4. Flexible machining systems with automated material handling
5. Transfer lines

The wide variety of parts in the open family for the Job Shop example and relatively low production volumes expected suggest that a flexible machining system would be most appropriate.

System size

The number of machines in each configuration will be based on the cycle time estimates generated from the process planning effort, the available operating hours, and the system's expected utilization. The material-handling and storage systems will be sized to assure timely service for each workstation. Block floor layouts should then be developed to estimate floor space and to generate material-handling time estimates for system performance evaluation.

Experience from numerous CNC shop and flexible machining system evaluations indicates that a reasonable level of machine utilization to strive for is between 75 and 80 percent. The following illustrates the typical causes of lost utilization in a CNC or FMS environment:

Equipment or controller downtime	7 percent
Preventive maintenance	5 percent
Scheduling conflicts	2 percent
Material-handling conflicts	3 percent
Perishable supply and tool replenishment	3 percent

Supervisory computer downtime	1 percent
Other miscellaneous inefficiencies	4 percent

Job shop machine load estimates

The process planning effort resulted in the following load estimates, by machine type:

Machine type	Time, hr/yr
Machining centers	9678.60
Turning machines	1817.70
Measuring machines	1299.80
Load and unload time	4164.80

The number of expected operating hours per year is based on the total available time and the expected utilization of the equipment. Two shifts 240 days per year at an anticipated utilization rate of 75 percent allows 2880 hours per machine. Therefore, the number of each type of machine needed in the system is

$$\text{Machining centers} = 9678.6/2880 = 3.3 \text{ or } 4 \text{ machines}$$

$$\text{Turning machine} = 1817.7/2880 = 0.63 \text{ or } 1 \text{ machine}$$

$$\text{Measuring machines} = 1299.8/2880 = 0.45 \text{ or } 1 \text{ machine}$$

$$\text{Load/unload stations} = 4164.8/2880 = 1.5 \text{ or } 2 \text{ stations}$$

The low production volumes for these parts enables the system to produce them without the need for duplicate fixtures.

Human Resource Considerations

We have observed that an organization's strategies for highly automated systems and the role for workers in these systems are generally based on one of two distinct philosophical approaches. One approach views workers within the plant as the greatest source of error. This approach uses computer integrated manufacturing (CIM) technology to limit workers' ability to influence the manufacturing process. The second approach uses CIM technology to help the workers make the best product possible for the marketplace. It implies that workers use the technology to control variance, detect and correct error, and adapt to a changing marketplace.

The best approach is to maximize the attributes of mature, committed employees using the factory to produce products in response to customer demand. This viewpoint fosters a feeling in the employees that they are in control of the system rather than serving it. There is also a feeling of pride of ownership in that the employees are capable and willing to use the system as a tool to achieve production goals.

Job shop human resources

The FMS will not have any personnel operating the machines. The system will be controlled by a system manager, whose skills include not only production management and manufacturing engineering but also computer system experience. Two people will be required to load and unload parts from the palletized fixtures, and a third person will set tools, clear machine jams, and so on. These people should rotate these jobs among themselves to prevent boredom and to increase their overall skills base. A full-time maintenance technician, with both mechanical and electrical troubleshooting skills, completes the personnel requirements per shift. A part programmer and a quality assurance person will be required at least part time on the first shift.

Evaluate Technical Performance of Solution

The anticipated performance of the alternative system configurations developed above must be evaluated. There are three levels of model complexity that can be applied to system evaluation:

1. Average throughput models
2. Queuing or networking models
3. Simulation models

Before these models can be applied, the parts and their tools must be assigned to specific equipment (or sets of equipment) to allow accurate modeling of the system. This allocation effort is often called "batching and balancing."

Batching and balancing

Production batching, the division of production into subgroups or lots, is necessary when tool storage capacity limitations do not allow all the desired parts to be fabricated in the system at one time (very often the case). Occasionally, balancing the workload on the equipment in the system may be so difficult that batching is required.

Balancing the workload on each machine attempts to maximize machine use as well as relieve or avoid potential bottlenecks in the system, with the intent of maximizing system throughput. Often, however, it will not be possible to balance everything. This is especially true in systems with different types of equipment. Balancing can also be difficult when a large number of tools is needed for certain parts. The division of work content and tool-changer storage limitations is crucial.

As a result of the batching and balancing exercise, specific parts and tools will have been allocated to specific machines in the system. This allocation process is in reality iterative; the allocation provides realistic information for the system modeling effort, and the modeling results indicate the "goodness" of the allocation and may suggest modifications in the allocation or the design of the system, which can then be remodeled.

Job shop system batching and balancing example

The number of unique tools (607) required by the parts selected for the system necessitates division of the parts into at least two subgroups or batches for production. An advantage of using CTIME to generate the cycle times for each part is that it also generates a unique tool list for each operation for each part. The cycle time and unique tool list for each part was then used as input for a third Draper Laboratory system software tool, BATCHBAL. BATCHBAL is an acronym for batching and balancing of workload, a program that attempts to allocate parts and tools to specific machines and balance the time on each machine. If insufficient tool storage is available on the equipment, BATCHBAL will divide the work content among the machines so as to maintain the best balance of machining time among the machines. It will only attempt to balance times within a batch—batch-to-batch times may vary substantially because of the tool restrictions involved in defining each batch. BATCHBAL performs the tool and part allocation in minutes instead of the hours necessary to perform the same task manually. The program divided the parts into two batches, allocated by machine as shown in Fig. 13.7.

Average throughput models

Average throughput models provide a rough estimate of expected system throughput and utilization based on averages of cycle times, transportation times, availability of resources, production rates, product mix, etc. These models are usually sufficient to locate potential bottlenecks, as well as to assess general system capacity and resource utilization. Average throughput models are inexpensive and can be simply modified as system concepts change. They are most appropriate for preliminary system design, where parameters are likely to

Parts Group #1 Summary

Mach#	Total Time	Total Tools
1	107307	83
2	109938	78
3	103421	88
4	107143	86

0.973 Average machine utilization

0.931 Average tool utilization

335 Total tools required

Parts Group #2 Summary

Mach#	Total Time	Total Tools
1	42092	80
2	41986	83
3	42815	78
4	42918	73

0.989 Average machine utilization

0.872 Average tool utilization

314 Total tools required

Parts grouping strategies based on tool magazine capacities

Tool Chain Size	Number of Machines	Number of Parts Groups	Production Time required (minutes)
68	4	3	156,963
90	4	2	152,855
110	4	2	150,379
136	4	2	150,557
136	3	2	202,435

Production time available at 75% utilization: 172,800 minutes

Production time available at 85% utilization: 195,840 minutes

Fig. 13.7 Results of running BATCHBAL on the Job Shop example.

change significantly from design iteration to design iteration, and the level of detail necessary in the model and the evaluation of the results is relatively low.

Queuing models

Queuing models are mathematical representations of systems based on the assumption that the systems can be modeled as a network of queues. This is a valid assumption for most fabricating and nonsynchronous assembly systems. These models provide more detail than average throughput models but less than a simulation model. Queuing models are moderately expensive to develop, run, and modify and are best suited to exploring production bottlenecks highlighted by the average throughput models. Queuing model analysis should be performed where necessary during the system design process to rectify bottlenecks that cannot be resolved through the use of average throughput analysis.

Job shop system queuing model

The system design evolving for the Job Shop example can be evaluated using a queuing model to determine the most appropriate number of AGVs in the material-handling system and to verify that the number of each class of machine was calculated correctly. Queuing models also indicate when machine use is likely to be affected by machine blockage caused by poorly conceived material-handling systems or marginally sufficient numbers of machines. A computer program developed at Draper Laboratory called MVAQ (Mean Value Analysis of Queues) was used in this analysis, (Suri and Hildebrant, 1984). The MVAQ model indicates that two AGVs are sufficient to maintain the desired level of system utilization and that 19 to 20 parts should be the maximum allowed in the system at any one time. The MVAQ results are shown in Fig. 13.8.

Simulation

Simulation can provide detailed, moment by moment information regarding the reaction of a specific system or factory design to specific operating parameters and loads. Simulations are, in general, expensive to develop, run, and modify but provide much more detail and accuracy than can be derived from queuing models. Simulation is most appropriate for detailed material-handling system design, especially at the FMS level, and for modeling alternative operating strategies after the system design has been finalized. An additional task required to facilitate accurate simulations is the definition of realistic scheduling algorithms and dispatching rules for each system. These allow parts to enter and leave the system in the proper sequence at the proper time.

Job shop system simulation

Using a scale layout describing the exact location and relationship of all components in the system provides the detailed material-handling system distance information necessary to perform accurate simulation. The simulation model helps to determine the exact number of fixtures necessary for each operation for each part and the number of AGVs given the actual travel distances in the system and to evaluate various system scheduling approaches. The simulation indicated that the system could produce the parts in 75 percent of the available time and that one part required two duplicate fixtures for each operation to

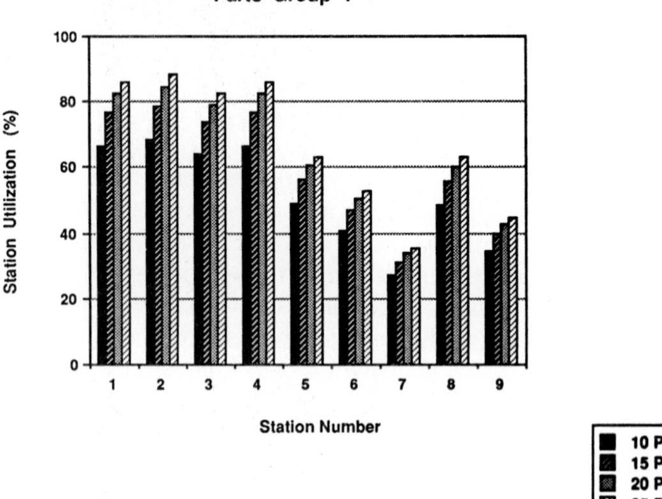

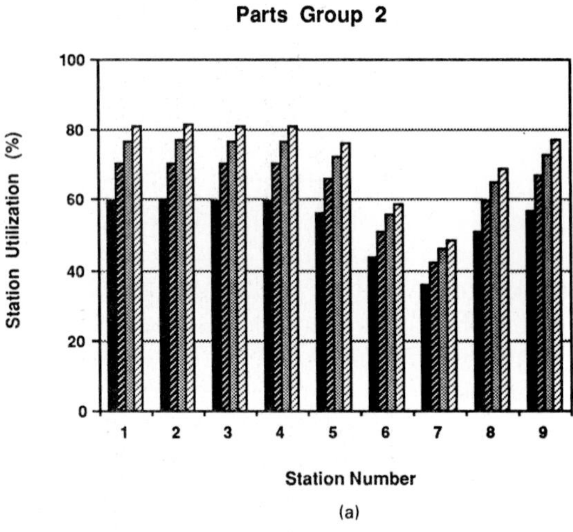

(a)

Fig. 13.8 Results of running MVAQ on Job Shop example. (*a*) Effect of different numbers of parts with two transport carts and 90 tool slots per machine.

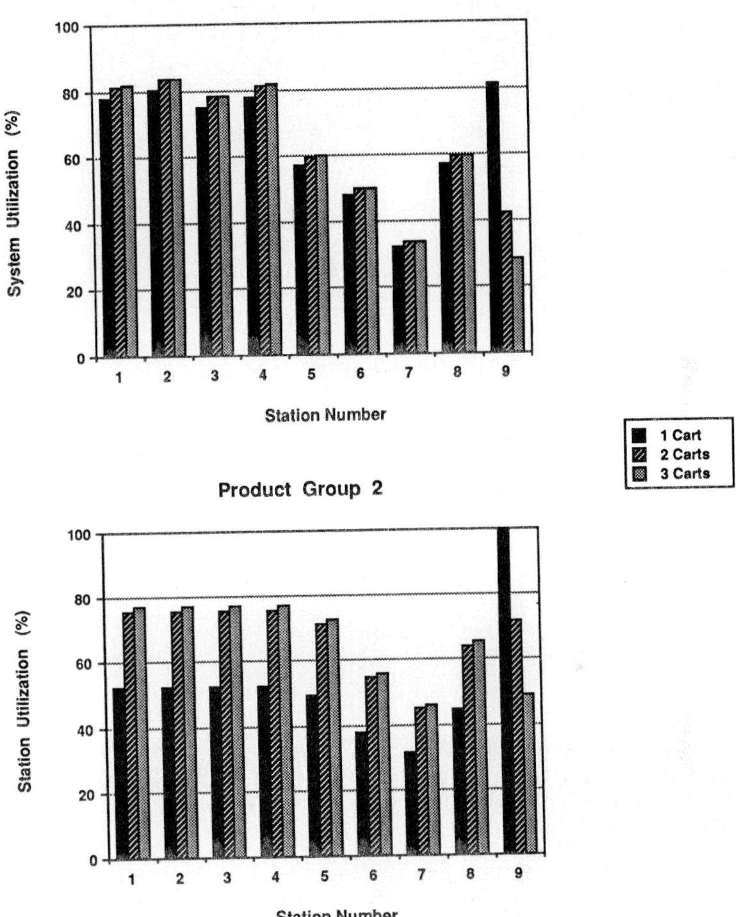

(b)

Fig. 13.8(b) Effect of different number of carts with 19 parts in the system and 90 tool slots per machine.

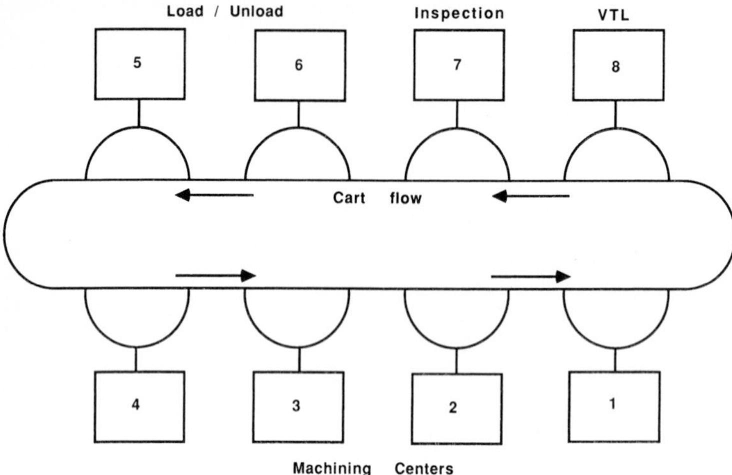

Fig. 13.9 Floor plan of simulated Job Shop FMS.

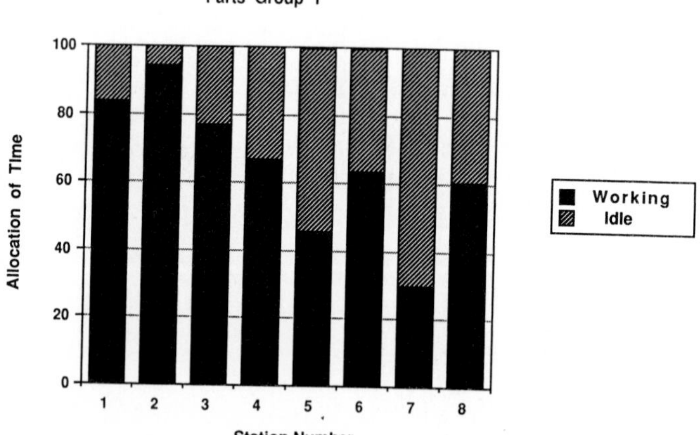

Fig. 13.10 Job Shop FMS simulation results: utilization of stations with part group 1.

achieve the desired production volume for that part. The final system layout is illustrated schematically in Fig. 13.9. The output of the simulation is presented in Figs. 13.10 and 13.11. Actual production rates from the queuing model and simulation are exhibited in Table 13.3.

Sensitivity analysis

A sensitivity analysis should be performed to reduce the estimation uncertainty of the data used in any of the modeling techniques to a minimum and to quantify the amount of associated technical and financial risks. Perturbations within system parameters can be introduced into any of the modeling techniques to estimate upper and lower bounds on subsystem and total system performance.

Evaluate Economic Performance

There are three basic categories of economic analysis for advanced manufacturing technology:

1. Replacement
2. Capacity expansion
3. Displacement

In each of these categories, the annualized acquisition, implementation, and operating costs of a specific recommended productivity im-

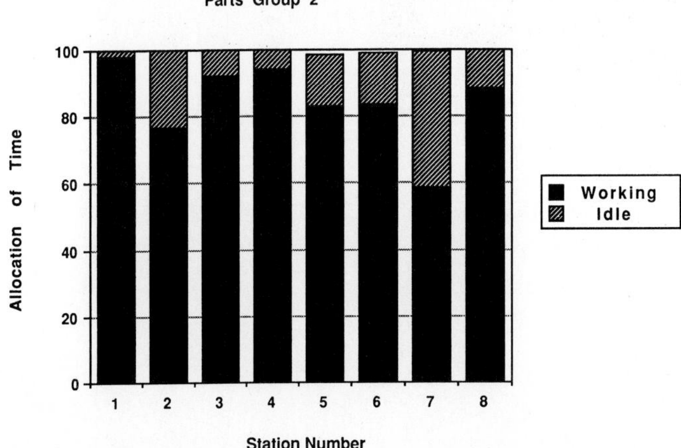

Fig. 13.11 Job Shop FMS simulation results: utilization of stations with part group 2.

TABLE 13.3 Production Rates Obtainable in Job Shop Example

No.	Part Number	Name	End Item	Required Annual Quantity	Projected Quantity	Simulation Projected Quantity
1	10884271	BRACKET	M140	399	432	528
2	10891945	GEAR, GUN ELEVATING (MACH)	M174	106	126	132
3	10892028	HOUSING (MACH-CAST)	M174	100	110	108
4	10895603	FOLLOWER FRONT	M178	1134	1325	1188
5	10895627	HOUSING (MACH)	M178	599	718	612
6	10895673	HOUSING (MACH)	M178	599	718	612
7	10895694	COVER (MACHINING)	M178	567	663	576
8	10895695	BEARING SLEEVE (MACHINING)	M178	599	718	936
9	10895696	BEARING SLEEVE (MACHINING)	M178	599	718	936
10	10909285	KEY, TORQUE (MACHINING)	M178	567	664	624
11	10922978	BRACKET CAM MOUNTING (MACH)	M178	599	680	864
12	10923025	LEVER CAM (MACH)	M178	567	647	576
13	10930330	CAM BREECH OPERATING	M178	567	663	624
14	10933932	BRACKET	M140	378	431	440
15	11590764		M1	254	291	297
16	11636292	MANIFOLD REPL. SYS	M178	567	663	900
17	12007690	ADAPTOR (MACH)	M45	252	291	308
18	12007719	YOKE MIDDLE ASSEMBLY	M45	252	303	396
19	12007721	BODY	M45	252	303	360
20	12007723	YOKE REAR (MACH)	M45	252	303	360
21	12007725	BRACKET (MACH)	M45	252	291	352
22	12007765	END	M45	252	291	341
23	12007772	CLAMP (MACH)	M45	756	860	1100
24	12012132	COVER TUBING	M178	567	636	770
25	12274291		M1	254	303	396
26	12274293		M1	254	303	396
27	12274327		M1	504	540	770
28	12274331		M1	268	313	374
29	5507255	GUIDE (MACH)	M174	201	216	286
30	5509262	TRUNNION LEFT HAND	M174	106	129	154
31	5509263	TRUNNION RIGHT HAND	M174	106	129	154
32	5568984	HEAD	M174	201	216	275
33	6105074	BRACKET	M174	212	237	297
34	6505782	CAP TRUNNION LEFT (MACH)	M174	100	110	144
35	6505788	CAP TRUNNION RIGHT (MACH)	M174	100	110	144
36	6507039	YOKE	M174	100	110	144
37	6536154	BODY REGULATOR	M174	100	118	132
38	8430397	HEAD	M174	201	216	231
39	8432870	YOKE ASSY FRONT (MACHINING)	M102	126	151	154
40	8432887	YOKE REAR	M102	126	151	154
41	8432888	YOKE CENTER (MACHINING)	M102	126	151	154
42	8432977	BRACKET ASSEMBLY	M102	126	151	154
43	8433535	BRACKET	M102	126	138	144
44	8433536	BRACKET RIGHT	M102	126	138	144
45	8433634	SUPPORT ASSEMBLY R.H. (MACH)	M102	126	151	154
46	8433635	SUPPORT ASSEMBLY L.H. (MACH)	M102	126	151	154
47	8433716	YOKE (MACHINING)	M102	126	151	154
48	8433724	HOUSING (MACH)	M102	133	151	165
49	8433797	HOUSING GEAR	M102	252	303	252
50	8447496	HOUSING	M102	133	151	165
51	8449308	BRACKET SUPPORT (MACHINING)	M140	378	442	396
52	8449309	BRACKET TORQUE (MACHINING)	M140	378	442	396
53	8432951	HOUSING UPPER		250	291	297

Note: No part failed to meet production targets in either MVAQ or SIM scenarios.

provement (often referred to as the "life cycle" costs) can be compared to the process benchmark as well as other alternatives based on the differences in production costs and the capital invested. Chapter 12 provides methods for the economic evaluation.

Job shop system economic analyses

The expected economic characteristics of the FMS in two situations (capacity expansion and incremental replacement of existing stand-alone equipment) was evaluated. The cost of the necessary components for the FMS is presented in Fig. 13.12, accompanied by the cost of stand-alone technology to provide the same additional capacity for the Job Shop. The economic comparison is summarized in Fig. 13.13. Since both the investment and the manufacturing cost for the parts would be lower if an FMS is installed, it is wise to implement an FMS. Suppose instead that the company wanted to first install the stand-alone system for a few years and then replace it with an FMS. Some components could be used for both systems, while the replaced machines would be sold to help buy the FMS equipment. Figure 13.14 shows the analysis for this case. Assuming that the equipment replaced by the FMS is sold for its salvage value, and that the savings from these changes will last 5 years, the FMS provides a return on investment of 25.5 percent after taxes (see Fig. 13.15). The conclusion is that under either scenario (capacity expansion or replacement), the FMS is a good investment.

Evaluation of intangible costs and benefits

Only a portion of the benefits of an integrated system can be evaluated on the basis of traditional tangible values. A secondary evaluation of each configuration should be performed based on projected benefits which, because they are more difficult to precisely quantify, are often considered "intangible." One way of evaluating these intangibles is to ask management to assign an "equivalent dollar value" to each one based on their intuitive estimate of the cost or value of each intangible to the company. Another approach is to develop an evaluation matrix, similar to those used to evaluate individual proposals for equipment, projects, etc. A sample form is illustrated in Fig. 13.16. Listed across the top are the completed configurations. Down the left-hand column are the intangibles, and the number next to each intangible is a mutually agreed upon "weighting factor" which quantifies the perceived importance of a specific intangible to the company. The diagonal in each box on the right-hand side separates the rating of the configuration with respect to an intangible from the "score" for that

FMS Investment

4	4-Axis Machining Centers, 90-tool storage $580,000 each (20 HP) (includes 8 pallets, chip conveyor, flood coolant)	$2,320,000
1	Bullard or Gray VTL, 12-tool changer $900,000 each	900,000
1	Material Handling Systems, wire-guided vehicles (2)	680,000
1	Automatic Storage/Retrieval System store up to 150 pallets	450,000 Installed
1	DEA Bravo Inspection Robot	150,000 Installed
1	Computer Control	650,000
1	Master Alignment Pallet	9,000
90	Pallets, $8,000 each	720,000
101	Fixtures, $20,000 each	2,020,000
1080	Tool Holders, $150 each (3 sets)	162,000
1	Computer Room	30,000
	Installation, $25,000/machine	125,000
	Total	$8,216,000

Stand-Alone Machine Tool Investment

8	NC Machine Centers, same as those in FMS $580,000 each, with pallets, changer	$4,640,000
2	VTL's $900,000 each	1,800,000
1	Inspection Robot	150,000
79	Pallets, $8,000 each	632,000
101	Fixtures, $20,000 each	2,020,000
2160	Tool Holders, $150 each (3 sets)	324,000
	Installation $25,000 per machine	250,000
	Total	$9,816,000

Fig. 13.12 FMS investment analysis: capacity expansion.

Total Annual Manufacturing Costs -Stand Alone:

Direct Labor	=	$ 709,450.22
Variable Overhead	=	495,293.18
Fixed Overhead	=	1,409,819.90
		$2,614,563.30

FMS - Total Annual Manufacturing Costs:

Direct Labor	=	$ 303,052.80
Variable Overhead	=	210,048.00
Fixed Overhead	=	629,413.73
		$1,142,514.53

Capacity Expansion Study Summary

	FMS	Stand-Alone
Total Investments	$8,216.000.00	$9,816,000.00
Total Annual Manufacturing Cost	$1,142,514.53	$2,614,563.30

- Material costs are assumed to be equal, although an FMS usually has lower scrap rate than similar stand-alone machines.
- Rework costs are assumed to be buried in overhead for both alternatives although an FMS rework rate is usually 50% of that for stand-alone machines.
- Since the FMS is both the smaller investment and less costly manufacturing method, it should be installed instead of the equivalent number of stand-alone CNC machine tools required.

Fig. 13.13 FMS investment analysis, continued: capacity expansion.

Incremental FMS Investment

Investment required for replacement of the current stand-alone system is calculated by using data from Figure 13.12, omitting cost of fixtures, pallets, and tool holders, which would have to be purchased for both the FMS and stand-alone alternatives and therefore exist already. The resulting FMS investment is:

FMS Investment = $5,314,000.00

Cost Savings Due to FMS Implementation

- In year 1

Stand-Alone Manufacturing Cost (from Fig 13.13)	=	$2,614,563.30
FMS Manufacturing Cost (from Fig 13.13)	=	$1,142,514.53
Net Savings Due to FMS Implementation	=	$1,472,048.77

- Assume the annual manufacturing costs for both alternatives will increase at the rate of inflation, 7%.
- Assume these manufacturing costs are representative of the costs for both alternatives for the first five years.
- If all of the stand-alone CNC machines could be sold for one quarter their original price to offset the price of the FMS:

  Machine tool sales, year 0 = 0.25 x 6,440,000 = $1,610,000.

- Annual cash flow from FMS (five-year period):

Year	Cash Flow
0	-$5,314,000.00 + 1,610,000 = $3,704,000
1	1,472,048.77
2	1,575,092.18
3	1,685,348.63
4	1,803,323.04
5	1,929,555.64

- Since the FMS has a return on investment better than inflation in all cases, it should be installed to replace the current CNC machine tools.

Fig. 13.14 FMS investment analysis, continued: incremental replacement of stand-alone equipment by FMS .

INCREMENTAL FMS INVESTMENT
CASH FLOW ANALYSIS

Zero Present Worth Cash Flow Analysis 06-20-1988

7 Years of Economic Life, Salvage value 0 % of cost

	Expense Forecast			Income Forecast			
Year	Ratio	Tax Rate	Depreciable	Savings	Depreciation	Tax Rate	Credit
0	100.00	0.0%	100.0%				
1				1472.049	14.29%	34.0%	0.0%
2				1575.092	24.49%	34.0%	
3				1685.349	17.49%	34.0%	
4				1803.324	12.49%	34.0%	
5				1929.556	8.92%	34.0%	
5 *				Salvage value	22.31%		

Rate of Return	Allowable Investment	Depreciable Investment	Approx. Brk-even	Capital Recovery	Net Profit
15.0	5211.176	5211.176	3.77	1382.125	2915.165
16.0	5022.937	5022.937	3.67	1371.089	3011.683
17.0	4846.430	4846.430	3.57	1360.659	3102.185
18.0	4680.630	4680.630	3.48	1350.785	3187.197
19.0	4524.626	4524.626	3.39	1341.422	3267.187
20.0	4377.606	4377.606	3.30	1332.529	3342.570
21.0	4238.842	4238.842	3.22	1324.069	3413.720
22.0	4107.685	4107.685	3.15	1316.009	3480.969
23.0	3983.551	3983.551	3.07	1308.321	3544.618
24.0	3865.912	3865.912	3.00	1300.977	3604.936
25.0	3754.292	3754.292	2.93	1293.955	3662.168
26.0	3648.260	3648.260	2.87	1287.231	3716.535
27.0	3547.425	3547.425	2.81	1280.787	3768.237
28.0	3451.429	3451.429	2.75	1274.604	3817.458
29.0	3359.949	3359.949	2.69	1268.666	3864.364
30.0	3272.686	3272.686	2.64	1262.958	3909.106
31.0	3189.369	3189.369	2.58	1257.465	3951.827
32.0	3109.748	3109.748	2.53	1252.176	3992.651
33.0	3033.594	3033.594	2.48	1247.078	4031.699
34.0	2960.696	2960.696	2.43	1242.161	4069.076
35.0	2890.860	2890.860	2.39	1237.415	4104.884

Fig. 13.15 FMS investment analysis, continued: incremental replacement of stand-alone equipment by FMS.

SUGGESTED INTANGIBLES AND STUDY FORM
(WEIGHTING/RATING SCHEME SHOULD BE DEVELOPED BY
THE PARTICIPANTS TO BE MUTUALLY AGREEABLE)

FACTOR/CONSIDERATION	WT.	RATINGS AND WEIGHTED RATINGS					COMMENTS
		A	B	C	D	E	
1. MINIMIZE FUTURE TOOLING AND FIXTURE INVESTMENT							
2. REACT TO MARKET CHANGES							
3. MINIMIZE INDIRECT LABOR							
4. REACT TO ENGINEERING CHANGES							
5. MINIMIZE LEADTIME							
6. MINIMIZE WIP INVENTORY							
7. MINIMIZE SPINDLE TOOLING DESIGN							
8. MINIMIZE SOFTWARE REQUIREMENTS							
9. COMMONALITY OF MACHINE TYPE							
10. PART DEBUG TIME							
11. PART SELECTION FLEXIBILITY							
12. MINIMIZE EFFECT OF MACHINE DOWN TIME							
13.							
14.							
TOTALS							

NOTES

Fig. 13.16 Evaluation matrix for intangibles.

intangible. The rating is a relative value from 1 to 5, conveying the relative performance of the configuration for that intangible (5 indicating the greatest performance or expected value). The "score" equals the rating multiplied by the weighting value for each intangible.

Summary

A procedure for designing flexible machining systems has been described. Note that there are more parameters required than are needed for the design of an assembly system (see Chap. 14). The combination of part families, machine families, and material handling must all be considered concurrently. Since there is no known way to directly optimize the solution, several iterations of trial solutions are required. Computer programs significantly expedite the process.

References

Amstead, B. H., et al.: *Manufacturing Processes,* 8th ed., John Wiley, New York, 1987.

C. S. Draper Laboratory, "Decision Support Software Guides," in *Flexible Manufacturing System Handbook,* vol. 5-A, C. S. Draper Laboratory Report R-1599, 1982(*a*), pp. 3–52.

———: "Software Packages," in *Flexible Manufacturing System Handbook,* vol. 5, C. S. Draper Laboratory Report R-1599, 1982(*b*), pp. 25–86.

———: *Users' Guide for the Cycle Time Calculation Software Package,* rev. 1, December 1984.

Committee on the Effective Implementation of Advanced Manufacturing Technology of the Manufacturing Studies Board: *Human Resource Practices for Implementing Advanced Manufacturing Technology,* Commission on Engineering and Technical Systems, National Academy Press, Washington, 1986.

DeGarmo. E. P., and R. A. Kosher: *Materials and Processes in Manufacturing,* 6th ed., Macmillan, New York, 1984.

Greene, James H.: *Operations Management: Productivity and Profit,* Reston, Englewood Cliffs, NJ, 1984.

Ham, I.: *Group Technology: Applications to Production Technology,* Kluwer-Nijhoff, Norwell, MA, 1984.

Hirschorn, L.: *Beyond Mechanization: Work and Technology in a Post-Industrial Age,* MIT Press, Cambridge, 1986.

Machinability Data Center, *Machining Data Handbook,* 3rd ed., Metcut Research Assoc., Cincinnati, 1980.

Mayer, R.: *Production and Operations Management,* 4th ed., McGraw-Hill, New York, 1982.

Suri, R., and R. R. Hildebrant: "Modeling Flexible Manufacturing Systems Using Mean Value Analysis," *J. Manuf. Sys.,* vol. 3, no. 1, 1984, pp. 27–38.

Taguchi, G., and Y. Wu: *Introduction to Off-Line Quality Control,* American Supplier Institute, Romulus, MI., 1980.

Chapter

14

Economic-Technical Synthesis of Systems

Introduction

Creation of a manufacturing system usually occurs using a "bottom-up" approach. The manufacturing or industrial engineer draws on a store of knowledge about what really works for the various operations that need to be performed in order to assemble a product. While this is likely to be a useful solution to the system design problem, there is little guarantee that the result is the most cost effective.

Various "top-down" methods for combining economics with technology have been proposed. The intent is to create least-cost systems. Graves and Whitney (1979) used linear programming techniques which were extended by Lamar and Graves (1983). Although the cost was optimized (for the exact data set only), the resulting systems were often not easy to operate because work sometimes had to return to a station after leaving it. This led to heuristic schemes by Gustavson (1984) which form the basis for this chapter. Holmes (1987) has created an optimum solution for certain cases using the shortest path through a network algorithm. Both the Holmes and Gustavson methods can be restricted to create systems in which work proceeds from station to station without returning.

These methods can all be categorized as *synthesis* since a computer creates systems subject to various constraints. In the bottom-up approach, people create systems which they *analyze* using computer simulation.

Only one other method for designing assembly systems has thus far been published. Daschenko (1986) uses a building block approach with step optimization of process structure variants. The technique requires analysis of experimental graphs constructed on the results of over 1500 variants of the system with various structures.

In order to create usable systems that are cost effective, a combination of the bottom-up and top-down approaches will be used in this chapter. Every system must perform a number of tasks. Each task normally has alternative technological means (resources) for its accomplishment. Once the resources' cost and performance characteristics have been established, a cost-effective system can be computer synthesized using techniques outlined in this chapter. The optimum system will be the one that minimizes the complete unit cost as defined in Chap. 12. While it is possible to use the methods described here at any point in the product creation process, they are best used during concurrent design. (See Table 14.1 for nomenclature used in this chapter.)

Before describing the solution method, we must understand the ways that costs are allocated. A unit cost model will be described followed by an explanation of methods for evaluating annual cost factor.

Unit Cost Equation

While total cost (see Chap. 12) is obviously important to the company, most system comparisons are made on a unit cost basis. We can express unit cost to assemble (handle, fabricate) as a combination of fixed cost and variable cost. To simplify matters, we will define the total system fixed cost as the sum of all resource and tool costs multiplied by a scale factor, ρ, which accounts for the expensed investment:

$$C_s = \sum_{\sigma} \rho(P_R + N_T P_T) \tag{14.1}$$

We define the variable cost rate to be the sum of the operating or maintenance rate and the number of workers multiplied by the loaded labor rate:

$$V_R = O_H + wL_H \tag{14.2}$$

The unit cost is defined as the annualized fixed cost divided by yearly production plus the variable cost rate multiplied by the actual cycle time:

$$C_u = \frac{f_{AC} C_s}{Q_B} + \left(\frac{(T + t_m)/\epsilon}{3600} \right) V_R \tag{14.3}$$

Production capacity Q_C is that quantity which, when multiplied by the actual cycle time, equals the total time available in which to do work. It is the throughput capability of the system:

TABLE 14.1 Nomenclature

A	Annual cost charged for an investment (m.u.)
App	Symbol for the apparent (or minimum chargeable) cost
C_i	Tool change time for resource i (s)
C_s	Total system fixed cost (m.u.)
C_{si}	Complete cost of one station
C_u	System unit cost (m.u./unit)
D_B	Number of working days per batch period (usually, per year)
f_{AC}	Annualized cost factor (1/yr)
f_{AVL}	Availability factor indicating how much of a resource's time should be committed per cycle: $0 \le f_{\mathrm{AVL}} \le 1$
H	Capital recovery period or investment horizon (yr)
i	Resource designator
I_0	Initial total investment (m.u.)
IRoR	Internal rate of return (percent)
j	Task number designator
L_H	Average loaded labor rate (m.u./hr; wages + benefits + overtime premiums)
MACRS	Modified accelerated capital recovery system (1986 U.S. tax law)
m.u.	Monetary unit being used (e.g., $)
N_i	Number of tasks that resource i can perform
N_T	Number of tools required for a particular resource
O_H	Operating or maintenance rate (m.u./hr; costs directly attributable to running a system)
O_{ij}	Operation time for resource i on task j (s)
P_R	Hardware price for a resource (m.u.)
P_T	Hardware price for each tool (m.u.)
Q_B	Production batch required (units/period)
Q_C	Production capacity of the system (units/period)
r	IRoR (internal rate of return; percent / 100 percent)
S	Number of shifts available per work day
S_{Wi}	Number of stations of resource type i per worker
T	Theoretical system cycle time (s/unit)
t_m	Station-to-station move time (s)
t_s	Time required for tasks assigned to a station
UC_{si}	Complete unit cost for a resource
V_R	Variable cost rate (m.u./hr)
w	Number of workers in the system (direct + indirect)
α_{ij}	Equals 0 or 1, depending whether a tool change is needed to perform task j at resource i
ϵ	Uptime expected (percent / 100 percent) equals the fraction of the production period when the station or system is operating
η	Number of tool changes required
ρ_i	Total cost / hardware cost of resource i
σ	Number of stations in the system
ν_H	Retained value (usually undepreciated remainder) at the end of year H (percent / 100 percent)
3600	Seconds per hour
28,800	Seconds per 8-hr shift

$$Q_C(T + t_m)/\epsilon = 28{,}800SD_B \tag{14.4a}$$

Also, we define

$$\text{Utilization} = Q_B/Q_C \tag{14.4b}$$

Equation (14.3) can be applied to any production batch size Q_B less than or equal to the capacity Q_C. The portion of total time that any system requires to produce at less than capacity is often called utilization. Generally, the higher the utilization, the better (especially for predominantly manual systems) since fewer resources will be required. We shall see later in this chapter, however, that least-cost hybrid systems often have considerably less than 100 percent utilization but they still make the best use of the necessary resources.

SAMPLE UNIT COST

UNIT ASSEMBLY COST 06-04-1987

240 WORKING DAYS PER YEAR
2.0 SHIFTS AVAILABLE

ANNUALIZED COST FACTOR = 0.3500

$ 250000 TOTAL SYSTEM COST
85.0 % SYSTEM UP-TIME
22.00 SECONDS SYSTEM CYCLE TIME
17.00 $/HR LOADED LABOR RATE
22.0 WORKERS IN THIS SYSTEM
3.00 $/HR OPERATING/MAINTENANCE RATE

534109 UNITS PRODUCTION CAPACITY
2.874 $ UNIT COST AT CAPACITY

PRODUCTION VOLUME	TOTAL COST	UTILIZATION	UNIT COST FIXED	UNIT COST VARIABLE	UNIT COST TOTAL
25000	155261	0.047	3.500	2.710	6.210
50000	223023	0.094	1.750	2.710	4.460
75000	290784	0.140	1.167	2.710	3.877
100000	358546	0.187	0.875	2.710	3.585
125000	426307	0.234	0.700	2.710	3.410
150000	494069	0.281	0.583	2.710	3.294
175000	561830	0.328	0.500	2.710	3.210
200000	629592	0.374	0.438	2.710	3.148
225000	697353	0.421	0.389	2.710	3.099
250000	765114	0.468	0.350	2.710	3.060
275000	832876	0.515	0.318	2.710	3.029
300000	900637	0.562	0.292	2.710	3.002
325000	968399	0.608	0.269	2.710	2.980
350000	1036160	0.655	0.250	2.710	2.960
375000	1103922	0.702	0.233	2.710	2.944
400000	1171683	0.749	0.219	2.710	2.929
425000	1239445	0.796	0.206	2.710	2.916
450000	1307206	0.843	0.194	2.710	2.905
475000	1374967	0.889	0.184	2.710	2.895
500000	1442729	0.936	0.175	2.710	2.885
525000	1510490	0.983	0.167	2.710	2.877

(a)

Fig. 14.1 Typical manual system unit cost characteristics as a function of production volume and system utilization.

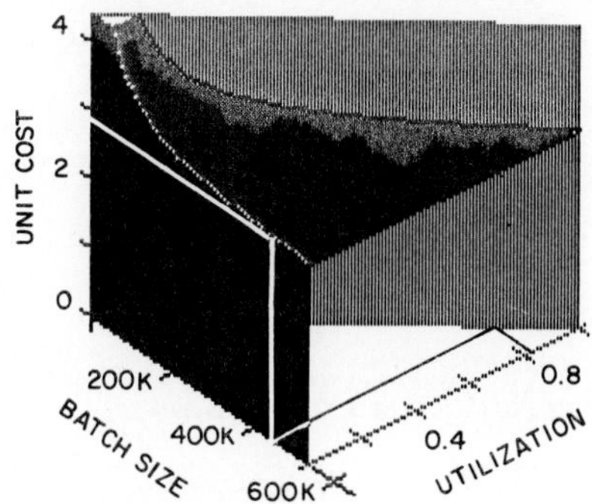

Fig. 14.1 *(Continued)*

We are now ready to investigate unit cost as a function of batch size. Figure 14.1(*a*) exhibits tabular data for a mostly manual system. Production volume increment was arbitrarily chosen. Note that the fixed unit cost decreases with increasing production volume, but the variable unit cost is constant. Total cost comes from multiplying production volume by the corresponding total unit cost. These data are typical for a manual system: Fixed unit cost is usually much less than variable unit cost and the total unit cost "levels off" for large Q_B as seen in Fig. 14.1(*b*). A second curve exhibits system utilization. For example, the condition at 450,000 units is highlighted; the unit cost is 2.905 with 84.3 percent utilization.

Let's now look at data for a hybrid system with significant automation. Figure 14.2(*a*) shows that the system costs 8 times that of Fig. 14.1(*a*) and that it will operate slightly faster with fewer (but more expensive) people and higher operating or maintenance expense. In this case, the fixed unit cost is always much higher than the constant variable unit cost. A plot of the data [see Fig. 14.2(*b*)] shows no "leveling-off" characteristic. Comparison of the 450,000-unit condition with Fig. 14.1(*b*) reveals a lower unit cost (2.143) at a lesser utilization (66.9 percent).

The cost of any number of systems can be compared in exactly the same manner. When these two example systems are compared, Fig. 14.3 shows their characteristics and that the cross-over point occurs at 288,441 units. If these were the only two choices available, S-1 (see

Fig. 14.1) should be used for production less than 288,441 per year and S-2 (see Fig. 14.2) for anything higher. If we define a base (B) and an alternative (A) system, the cross-over point is found by dividing the difference in system fixed costs by the difference in system variable costs:

$$Q_{co} = \frac{f_{AC}(3600)(C_{sA} - C_{sB})}{(T/\epsilon)_B V_{RB} - (T/\epsilon)_A V_{RA}} \tag{14.5}$$

The relationships between fixed and variable costs within a system as

SAMPLE UNIT COST

UNIT ASSEMBLY COST 06-04-1987

240 WORKING DAYS PER YEAR
2.0 SHIFTS AVAILABLE

ANNUALIZED COST FACTOR = 0.3500

$ 2000000 TOTAL SYSTEM COST
90.0 % SYSTEM UP-TIME
18.50 SECONDS SYSTEM CYCLE TIME
18.36 $/HR LOADED LABOR RATE
5.0 WORKERS IN THIS SYSTEM
11.00 $/HR OPERATING/MAINTENANCE RATE

672519 UNITS PRODUCTION CAPACITY
1.628 $ UNIT COST AT CAPACITY

PRODUCTION VOLUME	TOTAL COST	UTILIZATION	UNIT COST FIXED	UNIT COST VARIABLE	UNIT COST TOTAL
25000	714674	0.037	28.000	0.587	28.587
50000	729349	0.074	14.000	0.587	14.587
75000	744023	0.112	9.333	0.587	9.920
100000	758698	0.149	7.000	0.587	7.587
125000	773372	0.186	5.600	0.587	6.187
150000	788046	0.223	4.667	0.587	5.254
175000	802721	0.260	4.000	0.587	4.587
200000	817395	0.297	3.500	0.587	4.087
225000	832069	0.335	3.111	0.587	3.698
250000	846744	0.372	2.800	0.587	3.387
275000	861418	0.409	2.545	0.587	3.132
300000	876093	0.446	2.333	0.587	2.920
325000	890767	0.483	2.154	0.587	2.741
350000	905441	0.520	2.000	0.587	2.587
375000	920116	0.558	1.867	0.587	2.454
400000	934790	0.595	1.750	0.587	2.337
425000	949465	0.632	1.647	0.587	2.234
450000	964139	0.669	1.556	0.587	2.143
475000	978813	0.706	1.474	0.587	2.061
500000	993488	0.743	1.400	0.587	1.987
525000	1008162	0.781	1.333	0.587	1.920
550000	1022836	0.818	1.273	0.587	1.860
575000	1037511	0.855	1.217	0.587	1.804
600000	1052185	0.892	1.167	0.587	1.754
625000	1066860	0.929	1.120	0.587	1.707
650000	1081534	0.967	1.077	0.587	1.664

(a)

Fig. 14.2 Typical automated system unit cost characteristics as a function of production volume and utilization.

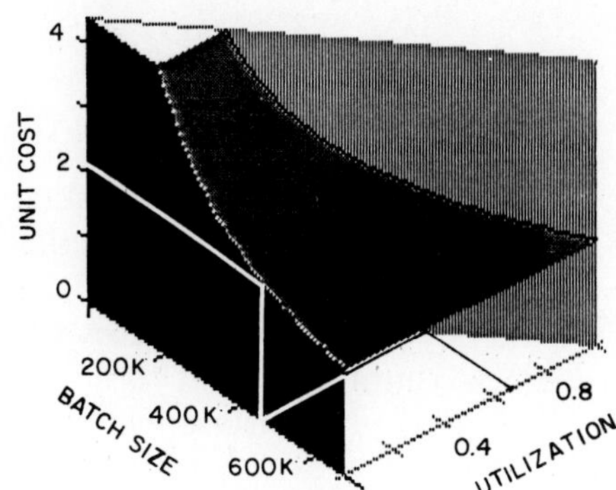

Fig. 14.2 *(Continued)*

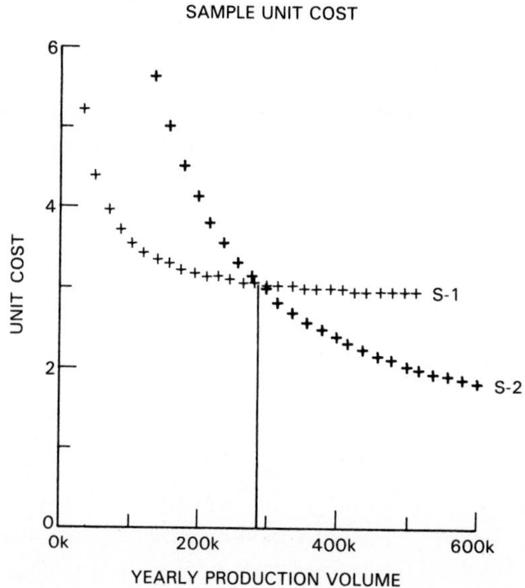

Fig. 14.3 Unit cost comparison for two competing systems showing a condition when each is most desirable.

well as among various systems become very important when creating least-cost systems. Synthesis of a system requires comparison on a task-by-task basis but follows the same general scheme described here. Before reaching that stage, we must have some understanding of annual cost factor and of process yield and quality. The latter has been described in Chap. 12.

Annualized Cost Factor

In order to rationally compare fixed cost to variable cost, we must have some appropriate method. Total variable cost for a work year can be likened to the total fixed cost, once the latter is annualized. Although a system is typically paid for in 1 year, that cost (from an accounting standpoint) must be paid out over a capital recovery period at some prescribed rate of return; accountants want to be sure that this investment is better than potential alternatives, as discussed in Chap. 12.

Spreading the investment cost over a number of years is analogous to the central accounting department taking a mortgage on the cost of the equipment and all other initial expenses related to the product(s) which will be repaid yearly with a prescribed interest rate. Capital recovery and annualized cost are the two names given to this process. The yearly cost is usually written:

$$A = I_0 \left[1 - \frac{\upsilon_H}{\rho(1 + r)^H} \right] \left[\frac{r(1 + r)^H}{(1 + r)^H - 1} \right] \tag{14.6}$$

The retained value υ_H is often considered to be the not-yet-depreciated part of the depreciable portion of the investment. When υ_H goes to zero (i.e., H is larger than the years used for depreciation), Eq. (14.6) reduces to the familiar period payment equation. Dividing both sides of Eq. (14.6) by I_0 leads to the annualized cost factor relationship:

$$f_{AC} = \frac{A}{I_0} = \left[1 - \frac{\upsilon_H}{\rho(1 + r)^H} \right] \left[\frac{r(1 + r)^H}{(1 + r)^H - 1} \right] \tag{14.7}$$

Figure 14.4 exhibits a range of values for Eq. (14.7) with $\rho = 2$. As might be expected, the higher the required IRoR, the larger the annualized cost factor. Many simple cost models assume that the fixed cost per year is merely the total cost divided by the number of recovery years (Graves and Whitney, 1979). This data is shown in Fig. 14.4(*b*) by the (1/*y*) curve. Suppose that a 4-year recovery period is specified; the (1/*y*) cost factor is 0.25, which corresponds to a 6 percent IRoR for the data in Fig. 14.4. Other examples can be found using the same approach.

ANNUAL COST FACTOR

7 YEAR M.A.C.R.S. DEPRECIATION

2.00 rho FACTOR

RATE OF RETURN	CAPITAL RECOVERY YEARS 1	2	3	4	5
10%	0.6714	0.4304	0.3361	0.2818	0.2455
11%	0.6814	0.4389	0.3438	0.2892	0.2527
12%	0.6914	0.4473	0.3516	0.2966	0.2598
13%	0.7014	0.4558	0.3593	0.3040	0.2671
14%	0.7114	0.4642	0.3672	0.3115	0.2744
15%	0.7214	0.4727	0.3750	0.3190	0.2818
16%	0.7314	0.4812	0.3829	0.3265	0.2892
17%	0.7414	0.4898	0.3908	0.3342	0.2967
18%	0.7514	0.4983	0.3987	0.3418	0.3042
19%	0.7614	0.5068	0.4067	0.3495	0.3118
20%	0.7714	0.5154	0.4147	0.3572	0.3194
21%	0.7814	0.5240	0.4227	0.3650	0.3271
22%	0.7914	0.5326	0.4307	0.3727	0.3348
23%	0.8014	0.5412	0.4388	0.3806	0.3426
24%	0.8114	0.5498	0.4468	0.3884	0.3504
25%	0.8214	0.5584	0.4549	0.3964	0.3583
26%	0.8314	0.5670	0.4631	0.4043	0.3662
27%	0.8414	0.5757	0.4712	0.4123	0.3741
28%	0.8514	0.5843	0.4794	0.4203	0.3821
29%	0.8614	0.5930	0.4876	0.4283	0.3902
30%	0.8714	0.6017	0.4958	0.4364	0.3982

RATE OF RETURN	CAPITAL RECOVERY YEARS 6	7	8	9	10
10%	0.2209	0.2031	0.1874	0.1736	0.1627
11%	0.2279	0.2099	0.1943	0.1806	0.1698
12%	0.2350	0.2169	0.2013	0.1877	0.1770
13%	0.2421	0.2240	0.2084	0.1949	0.1843
14%	0.2493	0.2311	0.2156	0.2022	0.1917
15%	0.2566	0.2383	0.2229	0.2096	0.1993
16%	0.2639	0.2457	0.2302	0.2171	0.2069
17%	0.2713	0.2531	0.2377	0.2247	0.2147
18%	0.2788	0.2605	0.2452	0.2324	0.2225
19%	0.2864	0.2681	0.2529	0.2402	0.2305
20%	0.2940	0.2757	0.2606	0.2481	0.2385
21%	0.3016	0.2834	0.2684	0.2561	0.2467
22%	0.3094	0.2912	0.2763	0.2641	0.2549
23%	0.3171	0.2990	0.2843	0.2722	0.2632
24%	0.3250	0.3069	0.2923	0.2805	0.2716
25%	0.3329	0.3149	0.3004	0.2888	0.2801
26%	0.3408	0.3229	0.3086	0.2971	0.2886
27%	0.3488	0.3310	0.3168	0.3056	0.2972
28%	0.3569	0.3391	0.3251	0.3140	0.3059
29%	0.3650	0.3473	0.3335	0.3226	0.3147
30%	0.3731	0.3556	0.3419	0.3312	0.3235

(a)

Fig. 14.4 Annual cost factors to be used for various capital recovery periods and specific rates of return.

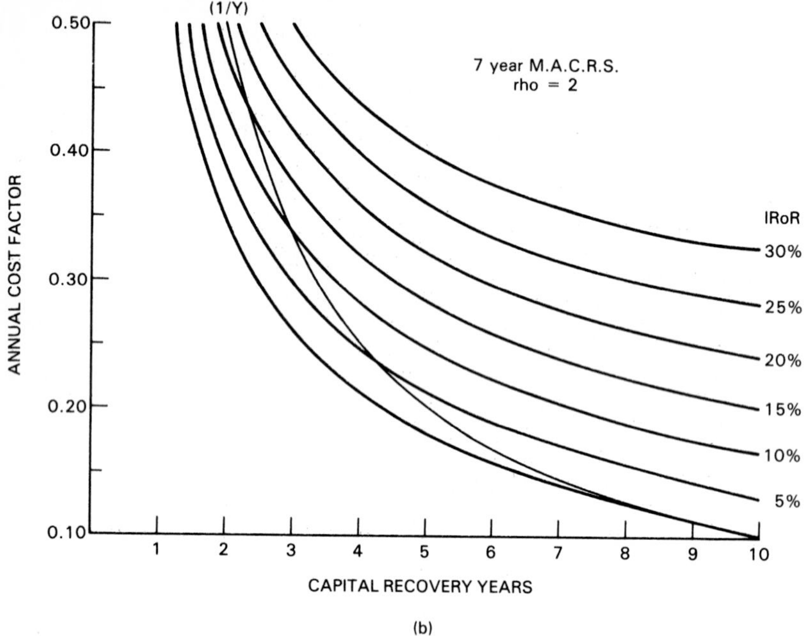

Fig. 14.4 *(Continued)*

Figure 14.5 displays f_{AC} when the IRoR is constant at 20 percent and ρ varies from 1 to 3. For this data set, increasing ρ from 1 to 2 when capital recovery period (H) = 4 creates an 8.9 percent increase in f_{AC} but only a 2.4 percent increase when H = 6. Both values are probably within the accuracy of the numbers used to predict future events.

We now have a method for determining the annualized fixed cost of the investment in a system. That will allow us to determine total product cost so that various methods of manufacture (assembly, material handling, fabrication) can be correctly compared.

Preliminary System Estimation

The rest of this chapter describes the creation of assembly systems. The techniques used are also applicable to material handling and short cycle time fabrication. What we will do is to create system solutions for a fixed sequence set of tasks by selecting methods from a set of applicable resources. The goal is to create a system that can meet a specified production rate for a minimum complete unit cost.

As a preliminary step, we can construct some homogeneous systems, that is, systems with only one resource type, each resource of a type identical to all the others. The goal is to see if some resource

ANNUAL COST FACTOR

7 YEAR M.A.C.R.S. DEPRECIATION

20.0% INTERNAL RATE-OF-RETURN

rho FACTOR	CAPITAL RECOVERY YEARS 1	2	3	4	5
1.00	0.3429	0.3763	0.3546	0.3281	0.3044
1.10	0.4208	0.4016	0.3655	0.3334	0.3071
1.20	0.4857	0.4227	0.3746	0.3378	0.3094
1.30	0.5407	0.4405	0.3823	0.3415	0.3113
1.40	0.5878	0.4558	0.3889	0.3447	0.3130
1.50	0.6286	0.4690	0.3946	0.3475	0.3144
1.60	0.6643	0.4806	0.3996	0.3499	0.3156
1.70	0.6958	0.4909	0.4041	0.3521	0.3167
1.80	0.7238	0.4999	0.4080	0.3540	0.3177
1.90	0.7489	0.5081	0.4115	0.3557	0.3186
2.00	0.7714	0.5154	0.4147	0.3572	0.3194
2.10	0.7919	0.5220	0.4175	0.3586	0.3201
2.20	0.8104	0.5281	0.4201	0.3598	0.3207
2.30	0.8273	0.5336	0.4225	0.3610	0.3213
2.40	0.8429	0.5386	0.4247	0.3620	0.3219
2.50	0.8572	0.5432	0.4267	0.3630	0.3224
2.60	0.8703	0.5475	0.4285	0.3639	0.3228
2.70	0.8826	0.5515	0.4302	0.3647	0.3233
2.80	0.8939	0.5552	0.4318	0.3655	0.3237
2.90	0.9044	0.5586	0.4333	0.3662	0.3240
3.00	0.9143	0.5618	0.4347	0.3669	0.3244

rho FACTOR	CAPITAL RECOVERY YEARS 6	7	8	9	10
1.00	0.2872	0.2740	0.2606	0.2481	0.2385
1.10	0.2884	0.2743	0.2606	0.2481	0.2385
1.20	0.2895	0.2745	0.2606	0.2481	0.2385
1.30	0.2903	0.2748	0.2606	0.2481	0.2385
1.40	0.2911	0.2750	0.2606	0.2481	0.2385
1.50	0.2917	0.2751	0.2606	0.2481	0.2385
1.60	0.2923	0.2753	0.2606	0.2481	0.2385
1.70	0.2928	0.2754	0.2606	0.2481	0.2385
1.80	0.2932	0.2755	0.2606	0.2481	0.2385
1.90	0.2936	0.2756	0.2606	0.2481	0.2385
2.00	0.2940	0.2757	0.2606	0.2481	0.2385
2.10	0.2943	0.2758	0.2606	0.2481	0.2385
2.20	0.2946	0.2759	0.2606	0.2481	0.2385
2.30	0.2948	0.2759	0.2606	0.2481	0.2385
2.40	0.2951	0.2760	0.2606	0.2481	0.2385
2.50	0.2953	0.2760	0.2606	0.2481	0.2385
2.60	0.2955	0.2761	0.2606	0.2481	0.2385
2.70	0.2957	0.2761	0.2606	0.2481	0.2385
2.80	0.2959	0.2762	0.2606	0.2481	0.2385
2.90	0.2961	0.2762	0.2606	0.2481	0.2385
3.00	0.2962	0.2763	0.2606	0.2481	0.2385

(a)

Fig. 14.5 Annual cost factors to be used for various capital recovery periods and specific rho factors

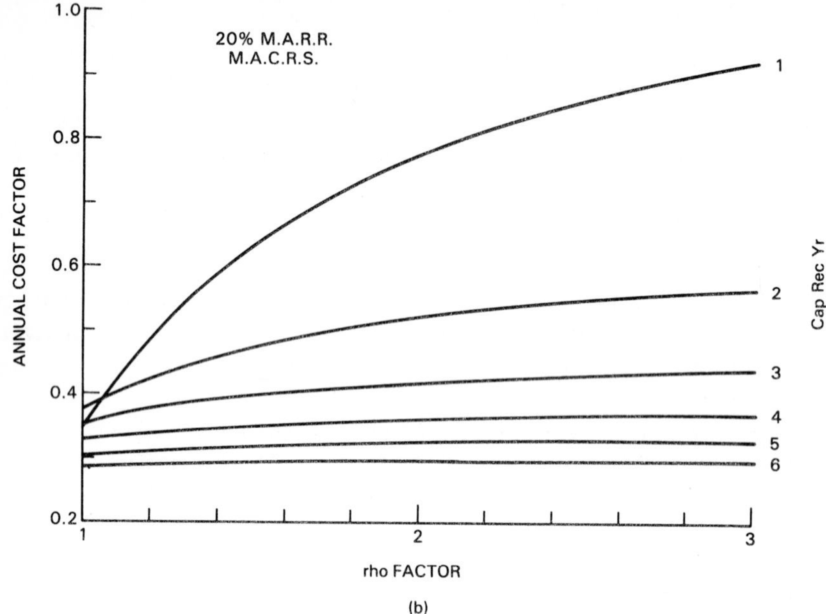

Fig. 14.5 *(Continued)*

types are clearly uneconomical. Equation (14.3) will be used to make the comparisons. What must be defined for every resource is as follows:

1. *Resource price.* The purchase price of the resource. For a manual resource, the price of the workbench, chair, etc. For a robot station, the price of the robot. For fixed automation, zero (see 2, below).
2. *Tool and material-handling price per part.* For manual and robotic stations, this is a task-specific cost in addition to the resource price. For fixed automation stations, the entire price is considered to be task specific, so it is included here, and the "resource price" of fixed stations is set to zero.
3. *Uptime expected.* Allowance for downtime caused by preventive maintenance, part failure, resource failure, etc. (Occurs within available clock time.)
4. *Minimum expected task cycle time.* This time is both task- and resource-specific but for preliminary analysis is taken to be an average value for a given resource type.
5. *Tool change time.* Charged when more than one task is performed at a station and requires a different tool. Fixed automation usually has zero time unless a cell requires shuttling between workheads.

6. *Operating and maintenance rate.* Charge for actual usage of the system.
7. *Maximum stations per worker.* The way that indirect labor gets charged to the system cost. This parameter may also be used to increase the cost of direct labor when higher skills are required for a particular task.
8. *Total cost / hardware cost* = ρ.

Typical resource characteristics are listed in Table 14.2. Since we are seeking general characteristics at this point, we shall define the average tool and material-handling cost, average task time, and nominal loaded labor rate.

Figure 14.6(*a*) displays input data for three resource types applicable to a particular product: 1 is manual, 2 is fixed automation, 3 is programmable automation. The number of tool or material-handling units required is an estimate except for fixed automation (resource 2, in this case) which requires one station per part. The principal assumption made is that each of these resource types has average costs and can perform all tasks; that is unfortunately not generally true but provides a useful first approximation. Another important assumption is that the work can be equally divided among σ resources since task times for each resource are assumed identical.

We have chosen 240 work days, 2 shifts, 0.3682 annual cost factor, 18 $/hr loaded labor rate, and 5-s station-to-station move time as fundamental parameters. Unit costs versus production batch size for three homogeneous systems are shown for a 12-part assembly in Fig. 14.6(*b*). System 1 is totally manual; the numbers 1 through 6 indicate the number of direct workers required to produce up to the production volume specified by the vertical lines. System 2 is composed of 12 fixed automation stations. System 3 contains from 1 to 6 totally programmable devices; the more pronounced "sawtooth" is caused by additional capital expenditure as each new robot is added and the work reassigned.

The significance of this estimate is that the resource types likely to comprise the system for a particular production volume are readily apparent. From Fig. 14.6(*b*) we can estimate the following:

Production volume	Likely system composition
$Q < 60{,}000$	1 M (manual)
$60{,}000 < Q < 250{,}000$	1 P to 3 P (programmable)
$Q > 250{,}000$	12 F (fixed)

TABLE 14.2

ASSEMBLY SYSTEM OPTIONS
GENERAL TECHNOLOGY DATA

Type	Symbolic Name	Average Resource Price	Average Tool & Material Handling Price (per part)	System Up-Time Expected	Minimum Expected Task Cycle Time* (seconds)	Average Loaded Labor Rate ($/hour)	Oper./Maint. Rate for Each Resource Used ($/hour)	Maximum Number of Stations per Worker	(Total Cost) / (Hardware Cost)
		$\bar{P}_R$	$\bar{P}_T$	E	$\bar{t}$	$\bar{L}_H$	O_H	m_s	ρ
Manual	M05	$ 200	$ 2000	85%	5	5	0.5	0.833	1.2
	M10					10			
	M15					15			
	M20					20			
Programmable	P07	$ 7500	$ 3500	85%	2	$\bar{L}_H$	1	8	2.0
	P15	$ 15000	$ 5000		2		1.5	7	2.5
	P29	$ 29000	$ 6500		3		2.0	6	3.0
	P45	$ 45000	$ 8500		4		2.5	5	3.5
	P70	$ 70000	$12000		7		3	4	4.0
	P85	$ 85000	$14000		7		3	4	4.0
	P120	$120000	$18000		10		4	3	5.0
Fixed Automation	F30	0	$30000	90%	1.5	$\bar{L}_H$	1	6	1.5
	F60		$60000		5.0		2	4	
	F90		$90000		10.0		3	2	

*Includes tool change, where applicable.

Note that two of the resource types have nearly the same nominal unit cost between about 50,000 and 150,000 units and two others have similar costs between 200,000 and 350,000. If the actual tool costs and task times for a data set are similar to the estimates, the optimum synthesized systems might include some very interesting hybrid systems in those production batch ranges.

This preliminary estimation step will usually not be necessary once the product becomes well defined. It can be invaluable at early design stages when actual data are generally very fluid. We are now ready, in any case, to synthesize systems.

```
Preliminary   System   Evaluation


                 RESOURCE NUMBER  1

$    200 AVERAGE RESOURCE COST
$   2000 AVERAGE TOOL/MATL.HDLG. COST
       7 TOOL/MATL.HDLG. UNITS REQUIRED
    1.20 (TOTAL COST)/(HARDWARE COST) = RHO FACTOR
    80.0 %  SYSTEM UP-TIME EXPECTED
   10.00 seconds  NOMINAL TASK TIME
    0.83 MAXIMUM STATIONS PER WORKER
    0.50 $/hr  OPERATING/MAINTENANCE RATE

                  COLOR NUMBER 1


                 RESOURCE NUMBER  2

$      0 AVERAGE RESOURCE COST
$  30000 AVERAGE TOOL/MATL.HDLG. COST
      12 TOOL/MATL.HDLG. UNITS REQUIRED
    1.50 (TOTAL COST)/(HARDWARE COST) = RHO FACTOR
    90.0 %  SYSTEM UP-TIME EXPECTED
    4.00 seconds  NOMINAL TASK TIME
    5.00 MAXIMUM STATIONS PER WORKER
    1.50 $/hr  OPERATING/MAINTENANCE RATE

                  COLOR NUMBER 3


                 RESOURCE NUMBER  3

$  29000 AVERAGE RESOURCE COST
$   6500 AVERAGE TOOL/MATL.HDLG. COST
       5 TOOL/MATL.HDLG. UNITS REQUIRED
    3.50 (TOTAL COST)/(HARDWARE COST) = RHO FACTOR
    85.0 %  SYSTEM UP-TIME EXPECTED
    8.00 seconds  NOMINAL TASK TIME
    4.00 MAXIMUM STATIONS PER WORKER
    2.00 $/hr  OPERATING/MAINTENANCE RATE

                  COLOR NUMBER 2
```

(a)

Fig. 14.6 Results of a preliminary system evaluation for typical resources from Table 14.2 exhibiting when each type is cost effective. (*a*) Input data. (*b*) Resulting unit cost versus batch size.

Preliminary System Evaluation

240 WORKING DAYS PER YEAR
2.0 SHIFTS AVAILABLE

18.00 $/hr LOADED LABOR RATE

ANNUALIZED COST FACTOR = 0.3682

5.0 seconds MINIMUM STATION-TO-STATION MOVE TIME

12 TASKS TO BE PERFORMED

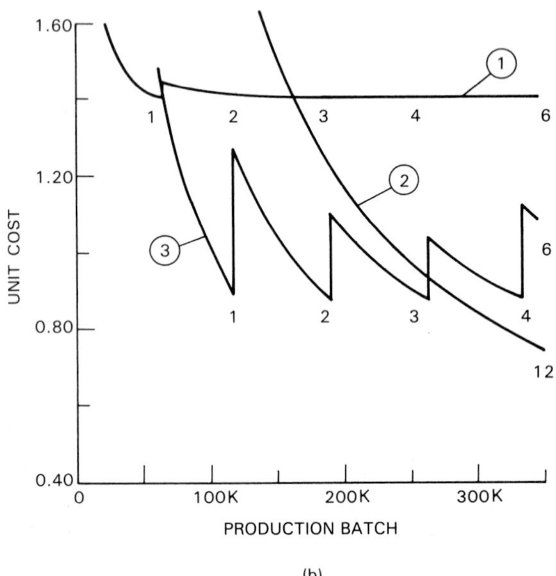

Fig. 14.6 *(Continued)*

Assembly System Synthesis

Once the specific tasks that must be performed are defined, we can create the resource and task matrix for input to a computer program. A convenient format for starting the process can be seen in Fig. 14.7. In that chart, the engineer prescribes what each task requires. Here, a task is defined as the total activity (for assembly) from rest to obtaining a component to making it part of the assembly and back to rest. The individual moves, described by such techniques as MTM (methods time measurement; Maynard et al., 1948), are combined into one task operation. In order to perform that task, certain characteristics must be established:

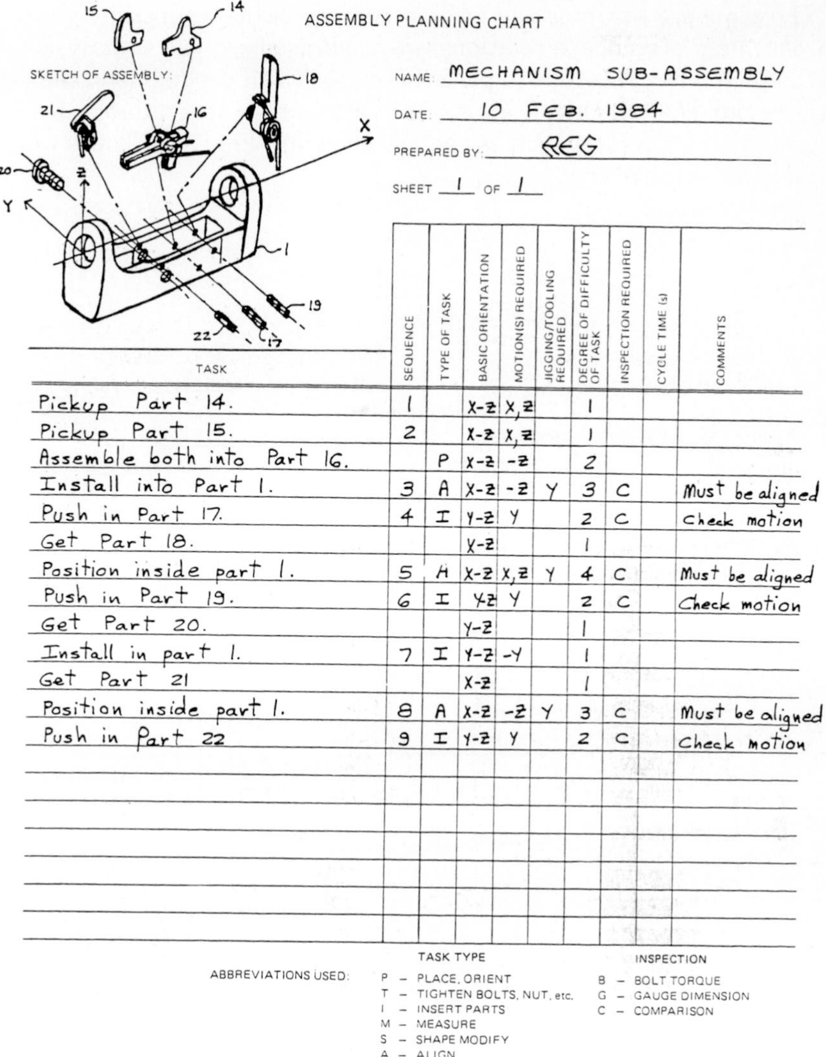

ASSEMBLY PLANNING CHART

SKETCH OF ASSEMBLY:

NAME: MECHANISM SUB-ASSEMBLY

DATE: 10 FEB. 1984

PREPARED BY: REG

SHEET 1 OF 1

TASK	SEQUENCE	TYPE OF TASK	BASIC ORIENTATION	MOTION(S) REQUIRED	JIGGING/TOOLING REQUIRED	DEGREE OF DIFFICULTY OF TASK	INSPECTION REQUIRED	CYCLE TIME (s)	COMMENTS
Pickup Part 14.	1		X-Z	X,Z		1			
Pickup Part 15.	2		X-Z	X,Z		1			
Assemble both into Part 16.		P	X-Z	-Z		2			
Install into Part 1.	3	A	X-Z	-Z	Y	3	C		Must be aligned
Push in Part 17.	4	I	Y-Z	Y		2	C		Check motion
Get Part 18.			X-Z			1			
Position inside part 1.	5	A	X-Z	X,Z	Y	4	C		Must be aligned
Push in Part 19.	6	I	Y-Z	Y		2	C		Check motion
Get Part 20.			Y-Z			1			
Install in part 1.	7	I	Y-Z	-Y		1			
Get Part 21			X-Z			1			
Position inside part 1.	8	A	X-Z	-Z	Y	3	C		Must be aligned
Push in Part 22	9	I	Y-Z	Y		2	C		Check motion

ABBREVIATIONS USED:

TASK TYPE
P – PLACE, ORIENT
T – TIGHTEN BOLTS, NUT, etc.
I – INSERT PARTS
M – MEASURE
S – SHAPE MODIFY
A – ALIGN

INSPECTION
B – BOLT TORQUE
G – GAUGE DIMENSION
C – COMPARISON

Fig. 14.7 One useful method of describing the requirements for an assembly system.

1. Type of task.
2. Basic orientation.
3. Motion(s) required to accomplish the task.
4. Is special tooling, jigging required?
5. Is inspection required?
6. How difficult is the task?

The sequence in which the tasks occur can be determined by physical reasoning, precedence relationships, or liaison sequence analysis (see Chap. 9). The cycle time to perform the task will depend upon the type of resource(s) which can do it. Once a sequence is available, we can enter data on a form such as the one shown in Fig. 14.8. There we see familiar parameters:

APPLICABLE TECHNOLOGY CHART

TITLE MECHANISM SUB-ASSEMBLY DATE 10 FEB. 1984

228 WORKING DAYS PER YEAR .3682 ANNUALIZED COST FACTOR

1 or 3 SHIFTS AVAILABLE 13 AVERAGE LOADED LABOR RATE ($/h)

2 s STATION-TO-STATION MOVE TIME

RESOURCE DATA SET NAME: RES14 TASK DATA SET NAME: RECB1

FOR EACH RESOURCE:

- C HARDWARE COST ($)
- ρ INSTALLED COST/HARDWARE COST
- ϵ UP-TIME EXPECTED (%)
- v OPERATING/MAINTENANCE RATE ($/h)
- t_c SECONDS TOOL CHANGE TIME
- m_s MAXIMUM STATIONS PER WORKER

WHEN A RESOURCE CAN BE USED ON A TASK: OPERATION TIME (s) | TOOL NUMBER / HARDWARE COST ($)

TASK NUMBER \ RESOURCE	M13	P29	F30	F60
	C: 200 ρ: 1.5 ε: 80 v: .88 t_c: 2 m_s: .833	C: 25000 ρ: 3.5 ε: 80 v: .75 t_c: 3 m_s: 6	C: 0 ρ: 1.5 ε: 80 v: .60 t_c: 0 m_s: 6	C: 0 ρ: 1.5 ε: 80 v: .60 t_c: 0 m_s: 4
1. Part 14	5 | 111 2000	4 | 211 7000	3 | 311 15000	2 | 411 60000
2. Part 15	5 | 111 2000	4 | 211 7000	3 | 311 15000	2 | 411 60000
3. Part 16	30 | 112 4000	20 | 212 10000	15 | 312 40000	10 | 411 60000
4. Part 17	10 | 113 1500	6 | 213 5000	4 | 312 40000	2 | 411 60000
5. Part 18	60 | 114 8000	X	X	20 | 412 60000
6. Part 19	10 | 113 1500	6 | 213 5000	4 | 313 15000	2 | 412 60000
7. Part 20	10 | 111 2000	6 | 211 7000	4 | 314 15000	2 | 413 60000
8. Part 21	25 | 112 4000	15 | 212 10000	12 | 315 30000	10 | 413 60000
9. Part 22	10 | 113 1500	6 | 213 5000	4 | 315 30000	2 | 413 60000

	UNITS	DAYS
PRODUCTION	60000	228
BATCH	180000	228
DATA	600000	228

Fig. 14.8 Specification of cost / performance for the technology that can perform the required tasks shown in Fig. 14.7.

1. Resource cost and task performance data (the task data set is shown below)
2. Working days per year
3. Shifts available
4. Annualized cost factor
5. Average loaded labor rate
6. Station-to-station move time (the "dead" time for in and out moves when no work can take place)

For each task, we must decide which resources are applicable; at least one resource must be able to perform each task since they all must be completed. Three parameters are necessary for the task data set:

1. *Operation time* O_{ij}. The time required to make all the necessary moves and do all the necessary operations. Note that the minimum time can be significantly increased if the yield (success) of the resource type attempting to perform a particular task is low.
2. *Hardware cost.* The price paid for task-specific tooling, part presentation, and/or inspection equipment. This price may be increased by a rework cost factor. It must always be multiplied by the resource's ρ factor.
3. *Tool identification number.* Often a unique number, it allows the possibility of the same tool (e.g., gripper) being used for more than one task, assuming that time is available. Each different tool assigned to a resource implies a tool change.

If the resource is deemed unsuitable for the task, that cell is crossed out.

It is possible that the production batch takes fewer days to produce than are available in a year; this fact may be entered on Fig. 14.8. Another possibility is that different production batches will be required at various times. Once the resource and task data sets exist, we can investigate a range of production volumes. The hybrid systems which usually result are normally compatible; the components of the best one for a small batch size are part of the best one for a larger batch size (not merely because of replication). Tasks are often assigned to the same resource type for a wide range of production volumes, but there is no guarantee that this will occur.

The first parameter that the synthesis algorithm determines is the actual operation time available for each resource type. Rearranging Eq. (14.4) results in

$$T_{\mathrm{AVL},i} \leq \left(\frac{28{,}800SD_B}{Q_B}\right)\epsilon_i - t_m \tag{14.8}$$

(Subscript i denotes resource type i.) The term inside the parentheses will be the same for each resource type while the uptime expected (ϵ) may be different.

We also define an estimated task time based on the tasks which can be performed and the tool changes which would be required:

$$E_i = \frac{1}{N_i}\left(\sum_{N_i} O_{ij} + \eta C_i\right) \tag{14.9}$$

If we divide the available time [Eq. (14.8)] by the estimated task time [Eq. (14.9)], the result is a measure of the versatility of the resource:

$$V_i = \frac{T_{\mathrm{AVL},i}}{E_i} \tag{14.10}$$

This can be considered a first approximation to the number of tasks that might be performed by each workstation of that resource type. This parameter is very important to the heuristic system synthesis method (Gustavson, 1984) but is irrelevant to those algorithms which actually investigate all possible combinations (Graves and Whitney, 1979; Lamar and Graves, 1983; Holmes, 1987).

The variable cost rate, which will be applied to each station, can be found from

$$V_{Ri} = \frac{L_H/S_{Wi} + O_{Hi}}{3600\,\epsilon_i} \tag{14.11}$$

When V_{Ri} is multiplied by the station time (which must be $\leq T_{\mathrm{AVL}}$), the workstation variable unit cost is established. Three station time values are potentially applicable: the actual time used (minimum condition denoted App, since it defines an apparent cost), the time available (maximum condition denoted Max), and the system cycle time (actual condition denoted Act).

The heuristic system synthesis algorithm operates by choosing candidate resources according to their versatility and trying to put as much work as possible onto each without exceeding a given fraction of the available time. This fraction is called the availability factor f_{AUL} and can vary between 0 and 1. (The reason for including the availability factor is discussed below.) A station's complete unit cost is

$$UC_{si} = \frac{(P_{Ri} + \Sigma P_{Ti})\rho_i f_{AC}}{Q_B} + V_{Ri}t_s \tag{14.12}$$

where $$t_s = \sum_{\text{tasks}}(O_{ij} + \alpha_{ij}C_i) \leq f_{\mathrm{AVL}}T_{\mathrm{AVL},i} \tag{14.13}$$

Each workstation has a resource cost and specific tool costs which are multiplied by the resource's ρ factor. The total station fixed cost is multiplied by f_{AC} and divided by the yearly production volume; t_s is the assigned task time for this station, consisting of the operation times of the assigned operations plus time for tool change(s) if any. Adding this to the product of variable cost rate and assigned task time results in the station unit cost. Except for very special cases, the assigned task time at the various stations will not be the same. Once the synthesis is complete, we can determine which station has the longest actual time requirement. That is the system cycle time. All other stations must then be charged with idle time.

Usually, the ideal system is one whose stations have nearly the same time requirements. In effect, we seek the best line balance. This ideal can often be achieved with manual systems. Hybrid systems contain mixes of resources with very different speeds. We have found that least-complete-cost hybrid systems often do not have 100 percent utilization. That is, their cycle time is less than the maximum available time T_{AVL}. To date, there is no one-step way of finding the least-cost cycle time. The procedure used by the heuristic algorithm is to multiply the maximum time by the availability factor to produce a reduced value for time available (equivalently asking for higher capacity). Running the algorithm repeatedly for a range of availability factors ≤ 1 produces numerous possible systems, each being least cost for its available time. One of these has the best combination of line balance, resource speeds, and costs and thus overall the lowest complete cost.

Figure 14.9(*a*) exhibits such results for a moderate production example. Behavior of unit cost for the three time allocations (App, Max, Act) is readily seen. Note that apparent cost (using only time required for operations) in this case is minimum when the availability factor approaches 1. For maximum and actual times, the lowest unit cost occurs in the availability range 0.830 to 0.865. The precise data are better established in Fig. 14.9(*b*) where the input data as well as the resources actually used in the various systems are defined. Note that the cost difference between the App line and the Act line represents the cost of imperfect line balance.

Suppose that criteria other than (or, in addition to) minimum cost are to be applied. What if the number of direct workers is to be minimized? A scan of Fig. 14.9(*b*) shows that no systems have zero direct workers (M30 category) but that three have only one. The least-cost configuration shows a 15.465 unit cost (which is 15.5 percent higher than the true minimum). What if the number of robots is to be maximized? Figure 14.9(*b*) exhibits a system with five P70 (robots) which has unit cost of 17.048 (27.3 percent higher than minimum). Neither of these particular systems could be acceptable from a least-cost standpoint.

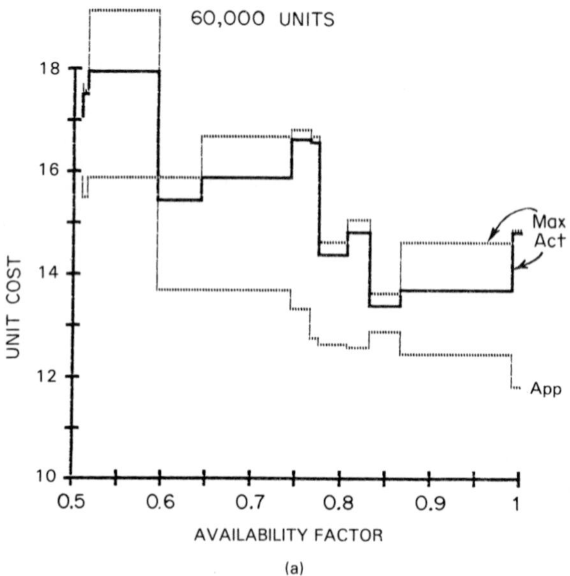

Fig. 14.9 A collection of least-cost assembly systems which have different task allocations and production capacities.

Let's take a closer look at the least-cost system. Figure 14.10 displays all the cost and time allocations. We can see that a P70 resource performs tasks 1 through 6, and its resource cost gets charged only at task 1. Since tasks 3 and 4 can use the same tool, the cost is charged only once and there is no tool change time at task 4. For this data set, the station-to-station move time is 20 s so the tool change for the first assigned task can be performed during that time leaving a net of zero. In the resource(s) used summary, near the bottom of Fig. 14.10, we can observe that the maximum station times are similar. Note that indirect workers are charged (in the workers column) and that variable cost is much higher than fixed cost for the manual (M30) resources while the reverse is true for the programmable (P70) devices. Summary performance and cost data appear at the top of Fig. 14.11, which also displays a schematic of the synthesized system. Each "station" exhibits the task(s) allocated, the actual time required, and the type of resource assigned. Note that the work times are quite well balanced. That was not necessarily our goal, but the least-cost system

Moderate Production Example

ASSEMBLY SYSTEM DESIGN 07-17-1987

0.4021 ANNUALIZED COST FACTOR
26.00 AVERAGE LOADED LABOR RATE ($/HR)
240 WORKING DAYS PER YEAR
100.0 % OF WORK YEAR REQUIRED
3.00 SHIFTS AVAILABLE
20.00 seconds STATION-TO-STATION MOVE TIME

RESOURCE DATA SET NAME : MDTRES
TASK DATA SET NAME : MDTFTSK

60000 UNITS IN PRODUCTION BATCH

240 DAYS, 3.0 SHIFTS AVAILABLE

AVAIL. FACTOR	APPARENT UNIT COST	MAXIMUM UNIT COST	ACTUAL UNIT COST	RESOURCES USED: M30	P70	P99	F90
1.0000	11.843 ←	14.875	14.827	2	2	0	0
0.9900	12.461	14.645	13.677	2	2	0	0
0.8650	12.865	13.653 ←	13.390 ←	2	2	0	0
0.8300	12.575	15.052	14.832	2	2	0	1
0.8050	12.597	14.614	14.355	2	2	0	1
0.7750	12.765	16.700	16.586	3	2	0	1
0.7650	13.331	16.793	16.626	2	3	0	1
0.7450	13.703	16.695	15.886	1	4	0	1
0.6450	13.703	15.871	15.465	1	4	0	1
0.5950	15.865	19.149	17.939	3	4	0	1
0.5150	15.528	17.569	17.513	2	4	0	2
0.5100	15.895	17.666	17.048	1	5	0	2

(b)

Fig. 14.9 *(Continued)*

invariably presents the best possible timing combinations. Many systems will not be as evenly matched as this example but still will provide minimum cost.

The techniques discussed in this chapter may be used not only to design single systems but also to compare different systems or different conditions. For example, it is sometimes necessary to determine the cost sensitivity as the production batch varies around that specified. Figure 14.12 shows that for a ±10 percent shift in batch size, the unit cost shifts by 10 percent. Note that the system needs to run at 83.2 percent of capacity; in this case, only 2.5 shifts would be needed.

Suppose we wanted a totally manual system. Figure 14.13 exhibits the required six direct person system, which should be compared to Fig. 14.11. Note that even when only one resource type is prescribed, the least-cost combination does not necessarily occur at 100 percent utilization. Here it is only 78 percent. The unit cost is 32 percent higher than that for the hybrid system of Fig. 14.11. Such large differences do not always occur.

Moderate Production Example

60000 UNITS IN PRODUCTION BATCH

UNUSED RESOURCE AVAILABLE TIME SCALE FACTOR 0.862

206.9 DAYS FOR 3.0 SHIFTS; 240 DAYS FOR 2.59 SHIFTS

RESOURCES

	*	M30	P70	P99	F90
AVLTIME	*	218.3	233.2	233.2	248.1
NSTA	*	5.0	3.0	3.0	1.0
WRKR	*	6.0	0.8	1.5	0.5
VRATE	*	0.0088	0.0026	0.0047	0.0044
ESTTIME	*	61.47	38.93	31.33	19.80
VRSTLTY	*	3.0	5.0	7.0	1.0

SYNTHESIZED SYSTEM

TASK	RESOURCE USED	RESOURCE COST	VARIABLE COST	OPERATION TIME	TOOL CHANGE	TOOL NUMBER	STATION COST
1	P70- 1	84441	3725	20.0	0.0	201	12063
2	P70- 1	0	5588	25.0	5.0	202	12063
3	P70- 1	0	10245	50.0	5.0	203	18095
4	P70- 1	0	9314	50.0	0.0	203	0
5	P70- 1	0	8382	40.0	5.0	204	30158
6	P70- 1	0	3167	12.0	5.0	205	12063
7	M30- 1	121	53042	80.0	0.0	107	9047
8	M30- 1	0	16576	20.0	5.0	106	3016
9	M30- 1	0	43097	60.0	5.0	108	24126
10	P70- 2	84441	9314	50.0	0.0	1203	18095
11	P70- 2	0	8382	45.0	0.0	1203	0
12	P70- 2	0	6520	30.0	5.0	1207	18095
13	P70- 2	0	7451	35.0	5.0	1208	18095
14	P70- 2	0	6520	30.0	5.0	1207	0
15	M30- 2	121	26521	40.0	0.0	1113	12063
16	M30- 2	0	56357	80.0	5.0	1114	15079
17	M30- 2	0	56357	80.0	5.0	1115	36189

APPARENT SYSTEM COST = $ 771898

RESOURCE	TOTAL COST	NUMBER USED	TIME USED	UNIT COST FIXED	UNIT COST VARIABLE	NUMBER OF TASKS	NUMBER OF TOOLS	NUMBER OF WORKERS
M30	404754	2	287.5	1.663	5.083	6	6	2.41
P70	398648	2	278.8	5.127	1.517	11	8	0.50

12.52 UNITS PER HOUR
287.5 seconds CYCLE TIME EXPECTED
80.00 % BOTTLENECK STATION UP-TIME EXPECTED
72125 units PRODUCTION CAPACITY OF THIS SYSTEM
7.00 $/hr SYSTEM OPERATING/MAINTENANCE RATE

803402 COST ($) TO PRODUCE 60000 UNITS, WITH UNIT COST ($) 13.390
1013100 ($) TOTAL INVESTMENT REQUIRED
420400 ($) FOR REQUIRED HARDWARE

Fig. 14.10 Actual allocation of times and costs for a specific synthesized assembly system.

What would happen if the production requirement doubled? Certainly a new system would be required. Following the procedure above, we can find the result shown in Fig. 14.14. Comparison with Fig. 14.11 is very enlightening. Tasks 1 through 6 are still performed by P70 robots but now three are required. Tasks 7 and 8 are also performed by the third robot while task 9 requires fixed automation

Moderate Production Example

```
                287.50 seconds  USABLE CYCLE TIME
80.0 %  BOTTLENECK UP-TIME          12.52  UNITS/HR EXPECTED
           72125 units  ACTUAL CAPACITY OF THIS SYSTEM

     1013100 ($)  TOTAL INVESTMENT,  RHO FACTOR =  2.41
            2.91 WORKERS AT  26.00 $/hr REQUIRED
          7.00 $/hr  SYSTEM OPERATING/MAINTENANCE RATE

          0.832 YEAR REQUIRED FOR 3.0 SHIFT OPERATION
           240 DAYS REQUIRED FOR 2.50 SHIFT OPERATION
```

60000 Units $ 13.390 Each 240 Days

287.5s Cycle Time 3.0 Shifts 0.862 AF

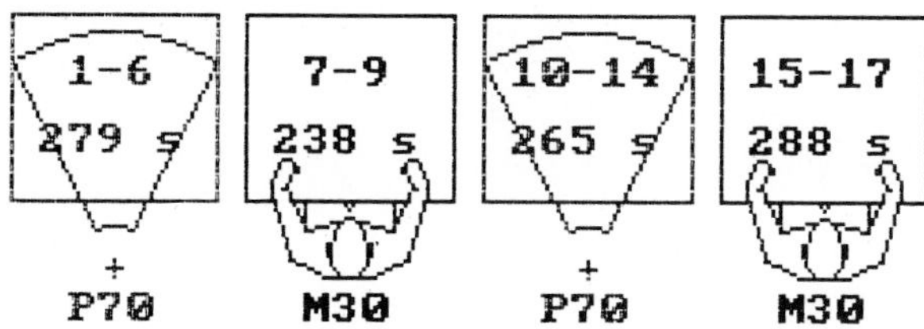

Fig. 14.11 Schematic diagram and system cost / performance characteristics for Fig. 14.10.

(F90). Tasks 10 to 14 are now done by two P70 robots. Not only are more workstations required, but also no direct workers are involved. Automated stations have become totally cost effective at this production volume; the two robots used for 60,000 units are part of the 120,000-unit system.

Let's try one more example. A totally different product requires 605,000 units to be produced in a year. Figure 14.15(*a*) exhibits a very interesting condition; for all throughput time categories, least cost occurs for 95 percent utilization. Another system has slightly lower actual unit cost but requires more equipment and about 64 percent utilization [see Fig. 14.15(*b*)]; it would probably not be selected (unless only two shifts were desirable]. Systems with nearly the same unit cost do occur as solutions to the design problem occasionally. Choice is obviously then made using other criteria: maximum (or minimum) of a resource type, utilization, total investment cost, market flexibility needs, etc.

Specific details for the least-cost system are shown in Fig. 14.16. Comparing it to Fig. 14.10 displays differences caused by the presence of automation: All the fixed automation (FXD) cost is in the station

```
Moderate     Production     Example

60000 UNITS IN PRODUCTION BATCH        UNIT COST ($)   13.390

       287.50 seconds  USABLE CYCLE TIME
 80.0 %  BOTTLENECK UP-TIME         12.52  UNITS/HR EXPECTED
       72125 units  ACTUAL CAPACITY OF THIS SYSTEM

   1013100 ($)   TOTAL INVESTMENT,   RHO FACTOR =   2.41
        2.91 WORKERS AT   26.00 $/hr REQUIRED
     7.00 $/hr   SYSTEM OPERATING/MAINTENANCE RATE

      0.832 YEAR REQUIRED FOR 3.0 SHIFT OPERATION
       240 DAYS REQUIRED FOR 2.50 SHIFT OPERATION
```

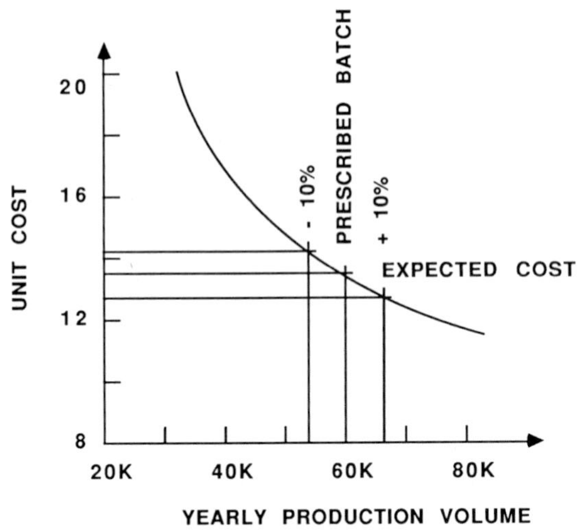

Fig. 14.12 Cost versus batch size sensitivity for the synthesized system of Fig. 14.10.

itself, and there is normally no tool change specified for FXD resources. Because station-to-station move time is only 3 s rather than 20, net tool change time for the first task assigned to a station is 4 − 3 = 1 compared to 0 in Fig. 14.10. Since two fixed automation cells (see Fig. 14.17) have been synthesized, the engineer must decide whether all of the tasks can really be performed without moving the assembly in that cell. If so, the solution in Fig. 14.17 is acceptable. If not, a shuttle time must be used in place of the tool change time for FXD in the resource data set and a new solution found. Of course,

Moderate Production (Manual) Example

```
            268.75 seconds  USABLE CYCLE TIME
80.0 %  BOTTLENECK UP-TIME          13.40  UNITS/HR EXPECTED
          77157 units  ACTUAL CAPACITY OF THIS SYSTEM

    519300 ($)  TOTAL INVESTMENT,  RHO FACTOR =  1.50
          7.23 WORKERS AT  26.00 $/hr REQUIRED
      3.00 $/hr  SYSTEM OPERATING/MAINTENANCE RATE

      0.778 YEAR REQUIRED FOR 3.0 SHIFT OPERATION
       240 DAYS REQUIRED FOR 2.33 SHIFT OPERATION
```

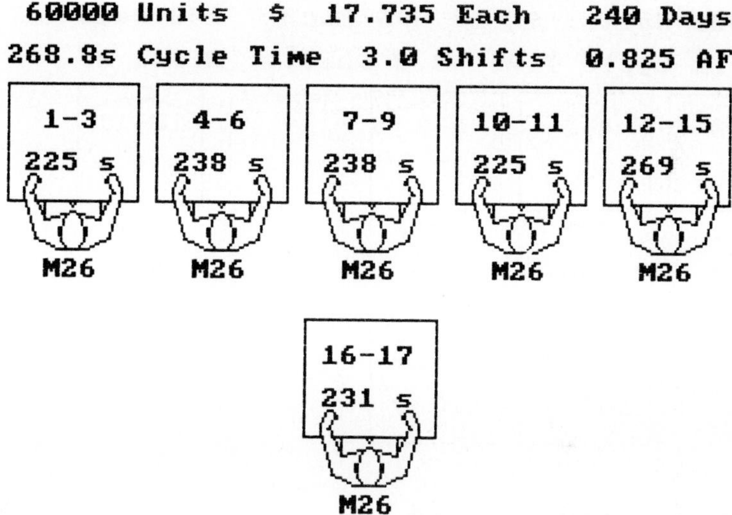

Fig. 14.13 The best totally manual assembly system. Compare properties with the hybrid system in Fig. 14.11 and the totally automated system in Fig. 14.14.

there is no guarantee that it will be the same system (with only additional variable cost).

The corresponding least-cost manual system (see Fig. 14.18) has 14 direct workers. Ten are required to perform two tasks each while four perform only one. The unit cost is 37 percent higher than that for the hybrid system (see Fig. 14.17).

Summary

A procedure for synthesizing a system that meets technological and economic criteria has been described. Cost accounting procedures used to establish the least-cost system were shown. Examples of preliminary system estimation as well as assembly system synthesis were shown and characterized.

Moderate Production Example

147.06 seconds USABLE CYCLE TIME
85.0 % BOTTLENECK UP-TIME 24.48 UNITS/HR EXPECTED
141005 units ACTUAL CAPACITY OF THIS SYSTEM

2047500 ($) TOTAL INVESTMENT, RHO FACTOR = 2.66
2.50 WORKERS AT 26.00 $/hr REQUIRED
24.00 $/hr SYSTEM OPERATING/MAINTENANCE RATE

0.851 YEAR REQUIRED FOR 3.0 SHIFT OPERATION
240 DAYS REQUIRED FOR 2.55 SHIFT OPERATION

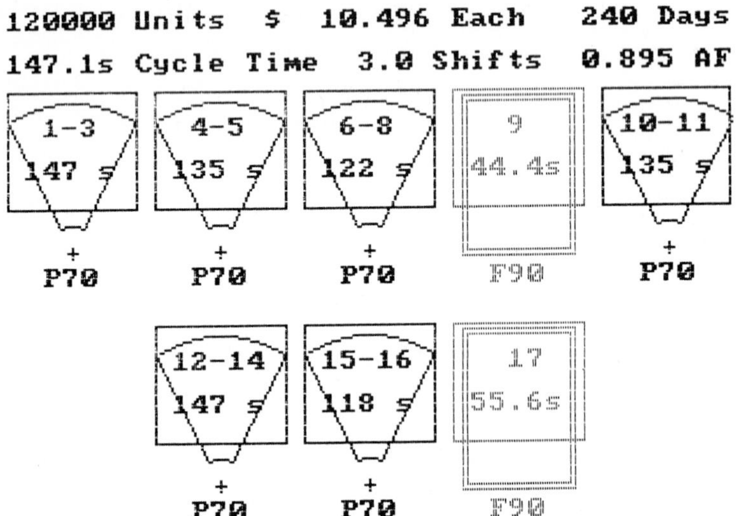

Fig. 14.14 A totally automated system for higher production requirements.

To complete the picture, any system created should be seriously analyzed by simulation (see Chap. 15) for performance and for economic viability (see Chap. 12). It may be necessary to resynthesize a system if the economic justification criteria or the performance requirements are not well-enough satisfied. Figure 14.19 exhibits a schematic diagram for the information contained in Chaps. 12, 13, and 14. The system synthesis technique highlights the interaction between technology and economics, providing the visibility management and/or engineering needs to make decisions. It is no longer necessary to use "back-of-the-envelope" methods to design or justify manufacturing systems.

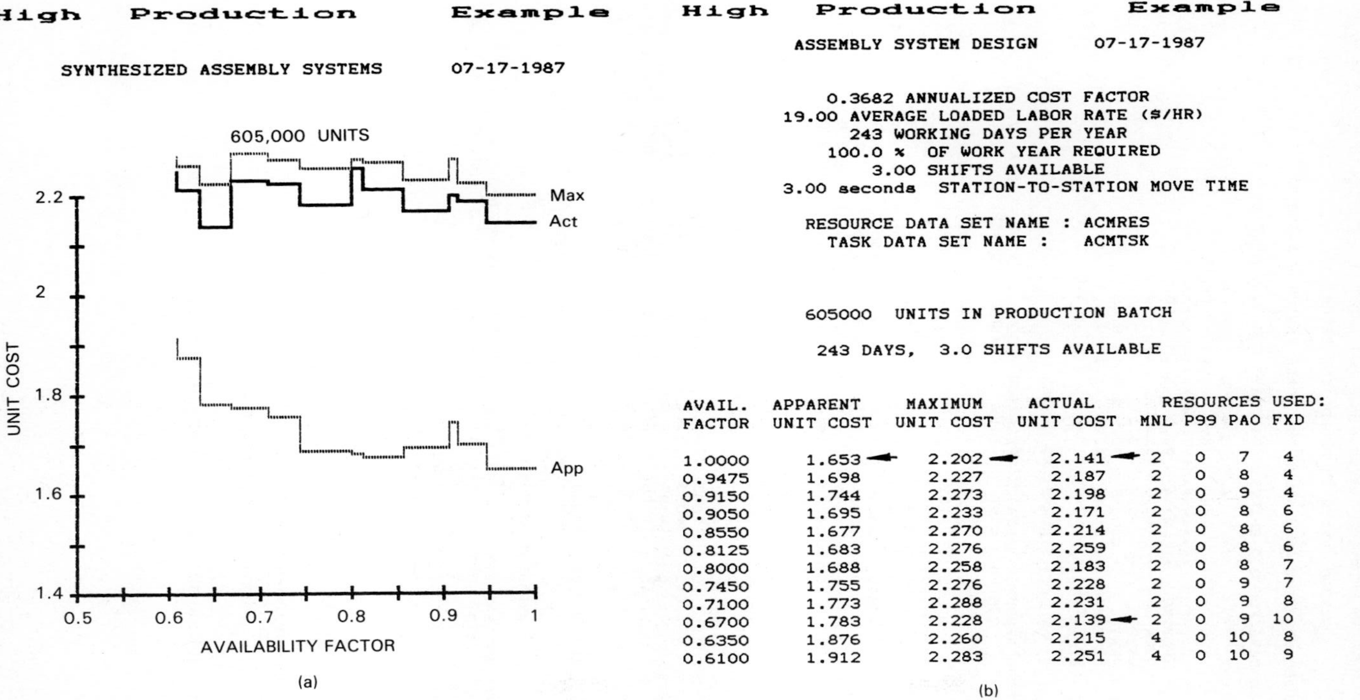

(a)

High Production Example

ASSEMBLY SYSTEM DESIGN 07-17-1987

0.3682 ANNUALIZED COST FACTOR
19.00 AVERAGE LOADED LABOR RATE ($/HR)
243 WORKING DAYS PER YEAR
100.0 % OF WORK YEAR REQUIRED
3.00 SHIFTS AVAILABLE
3.00 seconds STATION-TO-STATION MOVE TIME

RESOURCE DATA SET NAME : ACMRES
TASK DATA SET NAME : ACMTSK

605000 UNITS IN PRODUCTION BATCH

243 DAYS, 3.0 SHIFTS AVAILABLE

AVAIL. FACTOR	APPARENT UNIT COST	MAXIMUM UNIT COST	ACTUAL UNIT COST	RESOURCES USED: MNL	P99	PAO	FXD
1.0000	1.653 ←	2.202 ←	2.141 ←	2	0	7	4
0.9475	1.698	2.227	2.187	2	0	8	4
0.9150	1.744	2.273	2.198	2	0	9	4
0.9050	1.695	2.233	2.171	2	0	8	6
0.8550	1.677	2.270	2.214	2	0	8	6
0.8125	1.683	2.276	2.259	2	0	8	6
0.8000	1.688	2.258	2.183	2	0	8	7
0.7450	1.755	2.276	2.228	2	0	9	7
0.7100	1.773	2.288	2.231	2	0	9	8
0.6700	1.783	2.228	2.139 ←	2	0	9	10
0.6350	1.876	2.260	2.215	4	0	10	8
0.6100	1.912	2.283	2.251	4	0	10	9

(b)

Fig. 14.15 Systems with different capacities capable of producing a product with high-volume requirements.

High Production Example

605000 UNITS IN PRODUCTION BATCH

UNUSED RESOURCE AVAILABLE TIME SCALE FACTOR 1.000

243.0 DAYS FOR 3.0 SHIFTS; 243 DAYS FOR 3.00 SHIFTS

	RESOURCES			
	MNL	P99	PAO	FXD
AVLTIME	27.4	26.5	26.5	28.2
NSTA	10.0	11.0	8.0	3.0
WRKR	12.0	2.2	1.6	0.8
VRATE	0.0065	0.0013	0.0013	0.0015
ESTTIME	11.87	12.23	11.88	4.94
VRSTLTY	2.0	2.0	2.0	1.0

SYNTHESIZED SYSTEM

TASK	RESOURCE USED	RESOURCE COST	VARIABLE COST	OPERATION TIME	TOOL CHANGE	TOOL NUMBER	STATION COST
1	FXD- 1	0	4145	4.0	0.0	401	33138
2	PAO- 1	27615	8185	8.0	1.0	301	7364
3	PAO- 1	0	9095	6.0	4.0	302	1841
4	MNL- 1	0	53912	12.0	0.0	104	203
5	MNL- 1	0	49419	10.0	1.0	101	41
6	PAO- 2	27615	10004	10.0	1.0	1303	4603
7	PAO- 2	0	10004	7.0	4.0	1304	2762
8	FXD- 2	0	4145	4.0	0.0	1406	16569
9	FXD- 2	0	14509	14.0	0.0	1407	165690
10	FXD- 2	0	4145	4.0	0.0	1408	13808
11	PAO- 3	27615	8185	8.0	1.0	2305	4603
12	PAO- 3	0	14552	12.0	4.0	2306	9205
13	PAO- 4	27615	9095	9.0	1.0	3307	4603
14	PAO- 4	0	12733	10.0	4.0	3308	9205
15	PAO- 5	27615	8185	8.0	1.0	4308	9205
16	PAO- 5	0	9095	10.0	0.0	4308	0
17	PAO- 6	27615	9095	10.0	0.0	5305	4603
18	FXD- 3	0	4145	4.0	0.0	2411	16569
19	PAO- 7	27615	8185	8.0	1.0	6307	4603
20	PAO- 7	0	5457	6.0	0.0	6307	0
21	FXD- 4	0	3109	3.0	0.0	3413	55230
22	FXD- 4	0	3109	3.0	0.0	3413	0
23	FXD- 4	0	12436	12.0	0.0	3414	55230
24	MNL- 2	0	53912	12.0	0.0	1114	41

APPARENT SYSTEM COST = $ 999766

RESOURCE	TOTAL COST	NUMBER USED	TIME USED	UNIT COST FIXED	UNIT COST VARIABLE	NUMBER OF TASKS	NUMBER OF TOOLS	NUMBER OF WORKERS
MNL	259273	2	29.7	0.000	0.428	3	3	2.41
PAO	434157	7	32.9	0.423	0.295	13	11	1.40
FXD	602030	4	27.8	0.589	0.406	8	7	2.00

109.29 UNITS PER HOUR
32.9 seconds CYCLE TIME EXPECTED
85.00 % BOTTLENECK STATION UP-TIME EXPECTED
637354 units PRODUCTION CAPACITY OF THIS SYSTEM
13.00 $/hr SYSTEM OPERATING/MAINTENANCE RATE

1295460 COST ($) TO PRODUCE 605000 UNITS, WITH UNIT COST ($) 2.141
1663272 ($) TOTAL INVESTMENT REQUIRED
923702 ($) FOR REQUIRED HARDWARE

Fig. 14.16 Actual time and cost allocations for a specific assembly system.

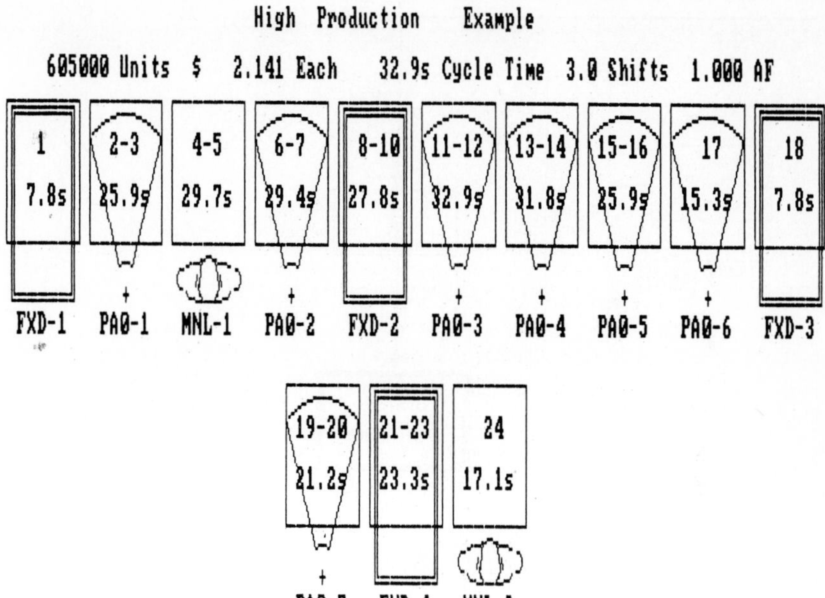

Fig. 14.17 Schematic diagram of the system in Fig. 14.16.

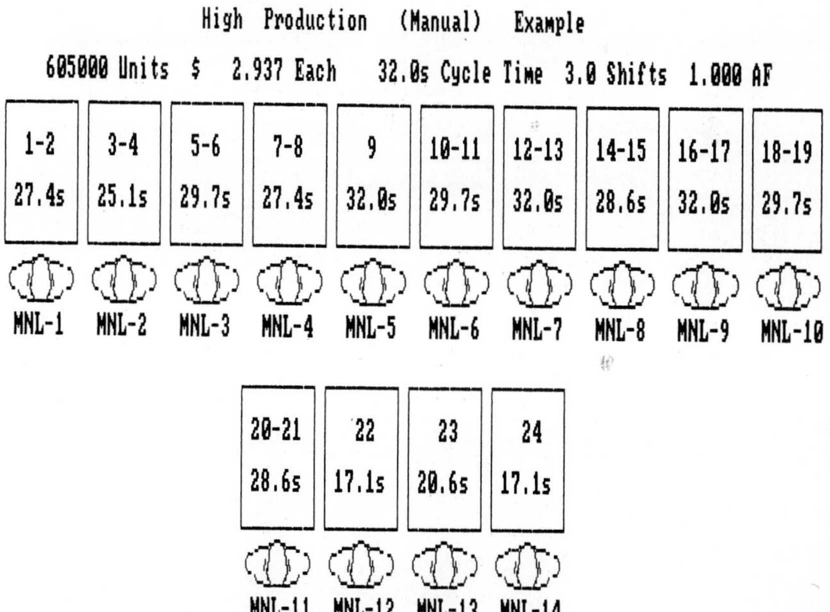

Fig. 14.18 The best totally manual system corresponding to the mostly automated system in Fig. 14.17.

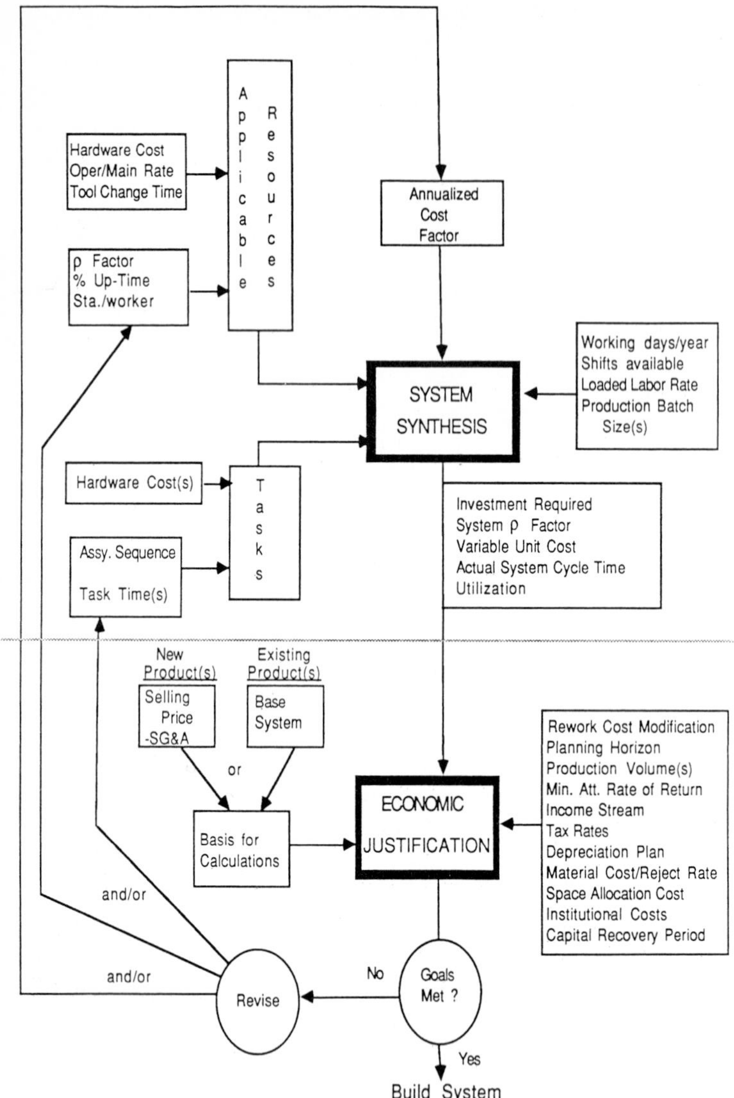

Fig. 14.19 Logic diagram for the creation of cost-effective systems.

References

Daschenko, A. I.: "Optimization Synthesis for Building Block Assembly Systems," *Int. Jour. Adv. Manuf. Technology,* vol. 1, no. 5, Nov. 1986, pp. 75–88.

Graves, S.C., and D. E. Whitney: "A Mathematical Programming Procedure for Equipment Selection and System Evaluation in Programmable Assembly," Proceedings, *1979 IEEE Decision and Control Conference,* Ft. Lauderdale, FL, December 1979.

Gustavson, R. E.: "Computer-Aided Synthesis of Least-Cost Assembly Systems," Proceedings, *14th ISIR,* Gothenburg, Sweden, October 1984.

Holmes, C. A.: "Equipment Selection and Task Assignment for Multiproduct Assembly System," MIT Operations Research Center SM Thesis, Cambridge, MA, Jan. 1987.

Lamar, B. W., and S. C. Graves: "An Integer Programming Procedure for Assembly System Design Problems," *Operations Research,* vol. 31, no. 3, May-June. 1983.

Maynard, H. B., et al.: *Methods Time Measurement,* McGraw-Hill, New York, 1948.

Chapter

15

System Simulation

Introduction

An important step in the design of many manufacturing systems is the simulation of system operation. Simulation may be incorporated in the design process for specifying system characteristics or it may be used to verify the performance of a proposed system after the specification process is complete. Simulation of the type described here, called "discrete event simulation," is a very powerful tool in operations research and is widely used for such problems as route and equipment scheduling for transportation systems. Consequently, numerous software tools and languages exist for system simulation. It is beyond the scope of this book to cover any particular simulation software package in depth or even to list all the available packages. Rather, the purpose of this chapter is to describe, in a general sense, how and when simulation may be effectively applied to the design of manufacturing systems. For a more detailed description of simulation and the available tools, the reader is referred to the references.

Simulation is the operation of computer models of systems for the purpose of studying phenomena expected to occur during their operation. Simulation is instrumental in the design process because it allows the engineer or analyst to:

1. Study the performance of systems without building them
2. Study the impact of different operational strategies without implementing them
3. Study the impact of major external uncontrollable events such as component failures without requiring them to occur
4. Expand or compress time to study phenomena otherwise too fast or too slow to observe

The key to any simulation effort is the formulation of a model of the system under study. The results obtained through simulation can be only as accurate as the underlying model. The model is an abstract representation of a system or part of a system. The model describes, in some convenient way, how the system will behave under all conditions that it is likely to experience. The model may be based on fundamental physical laws which govern the behavior and operation of the system or it may be based on a functional, heuristic description of observed behavior of the system. In most practical applications, the model is a combination of both of these elements.

The most important aspect of any model is its *scope*. No model can include all levels of detail in the operation of a system. Furthermore, simplification to aid in understanding is one of the goals of modeling and simulation. The scope of the model should be restricted to include only the phenomena that are of interest to the system designer and the simulation engineer but must be broad enough that it will accurately respond to all events and conditions that will affect these phenomena. The type and scope of the model will determine the type of simulation to be performed. In the design of an aircraft, a simulation might be performed to study in detail the effect of aerodynamic forces on the motion of the aircraft. In the design and integration of manufacturing systems, one seldom explicitly models the forces which govern the motion of physical bodies in the system but is interested only in discrete state changes that occur as a result of such motions.

The concept of *state* is very important in modeling and simulation; the state is a complete description of the condition and tendencies of the system at any instant in time. The motion of the aircraft is described by a continuously varying state; the operation of the manufacturing system is described by discrete state changes, or *events*. Simulation of such discrete state change systems is called "discrete event simulation."

All discrete event simulation tools share a common modeling viewpoint—that of entities, activities, and queues. *Entities* are objects that flow through the system or resources that reside in the system. Examples of entities are workers, robots, machine tools, and production parts. *Activities* are the productive elements of system behavior and require the participation of one or more entities in order to occur. Examples of activities are the machining of a part or the replacement of a machine's cutting tool. The machining activity requires the participation of a machine tool and a production part. The tool replacement activity requires the participation of the machine and a maintenance worker. An important feature of an activity is its duration because it is the notion of time consumption by activities that makes simulation useful. The start and finish of activities are the state-change events on which the simulation operates. Finally, *queues* are places where entities collect when not participating in any activity. Queues may represent real aspects of the system such as inventories of materials or idle machines, or they may represent fictitious quantities such as raw materials that have not yet entered the system. In some cases, the behavior of queues may be of specific interest because the size of an inventory queue or time that machines are present in an idle queue are important aspects of system performance. The model is a network of activities and queues through which the entities flow. The essence of constructing the model is to specify the network and the logic that governs the flow of entities.

The concepts of entities, activities, and queues are illustrated by a simplified model shown in Fig. 15.1. This figure, an *activity cycle diagram*, depicts the various activities as rectangles, the queues as circles, and the "flow" of entities as connecting lines. The flow of entities along the connecting lines is instantaneous; at all times, every entity must be either involved in an activity or waiting in a queue. The connecting lines represent the possible state changes for each class of entity. Two classes of entities are included; pallets and a machine tool. The pallets can move between the activities and queues defined by the network paths shown by solid lines. The machine tool is constrained to the network paths shown in dashed lines. The process that this model simulates can be described as follows:

- A blank is loaded onto an empty pallet (activity 1).
- The blank is machined (activity 2).

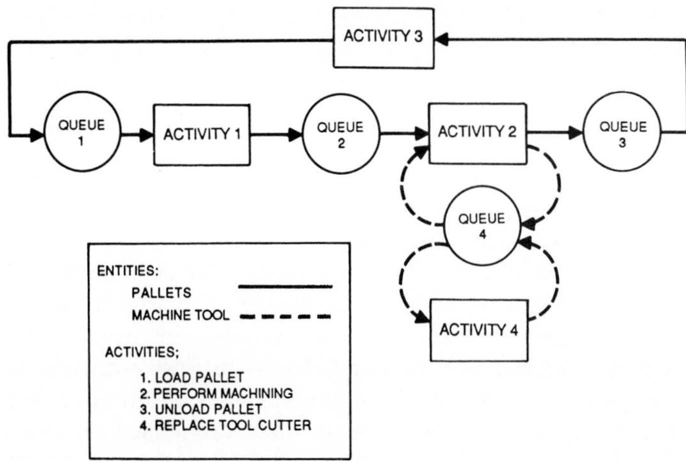

Fig. 15.1 Simplified simulation model.

- The finished part is removed from the pallet (activity 3).
- Provision has been made for the tool cutter to be replaced when worn or broken (activity 4).

Two features illustrated in the figure are especially important to discrete event simulation: cooperation and branching. Activity 2, machining, cannot occur without the cooperation of a pallet and the machine tool. The machine tool may branch from queue 4 to either activity 2 or activity 4. The model must specify some logic for determining which branch to follow. This model could be used to study how in-process storage requirements change when activity durations and tool replacement strategies are varied.

Beyond the common modeling viewpoint, the various discrete event simulation tools are very different. All require different methods for describing and diagramming the system model. Furthermore, there can be several different algorithms used to drive the simulation. The next section describes the application of discrete event simulation, in a generic sense, to the design of manufacturing systems. Then "Discrete Event Simulation Tools" briefly describes the types of simulation languages and lists some of the available tools. The section "An Example Simulation" presents an example of such a simulation.

Simulation as an Alternative to Analysis

The performance of a proposed system can often be predicted by purely analytical means such as those described in previous chapters. Simulation should not be considered as a substitute for proper analysis. However, many phenomena occurring in complex systems may not be amenable to a practical analysis. In such cases, simulation may provide a tractable means to investigate these phenomena or to validate results obtained by an analysis based on unproven simplifying assumptions. The point of this section is to describe what types of system behavior will warrant the use of simulation. It must be recognized that a rough-cut analysis is always a prerequisite for building a simulation model. The analysis involved in building the model may reveal that the simulation is unnecessary.

If a system is deterministic, i.e., not subject to random behavior, or if its random behavior can be adequately described using statistics, analysis may be sufficient. It is common, for example, to rate the production capacity of a machine by its expected downtime, a statistical parameter. If machine failures are independent of each other, a production line can be specified and properly balanced based on these rated capacities. If the production line is a serial arrangement of several machines, other statistical parameters, such as mean time between failures (MTBF) and mean time to repair (MTTR), can be used to size buffers between machines to ensure that the failure of a particular machine does not force other machines into an idle, nonproductive state. All this can be done without the need for simulation.

Consider now the maintenance of the machines on this hypothetical production line. One can compute, based on the MTBF and MTTR statistics, how much repair effort can be expected. It may be concluded, for example, that if the expected total repair effort is less than 8 hr per shift, one repair worker per shift will be sufficient to maintain all the machines. However, these statistics do not reflect the possibility of simultaneous failures. If the repair worker is busy repairing one machine when another fails, one of the machines must sit idle, awaiting repair. The time lost while the machine is neither operating nor being repaired was not accounted for in the line balance and the system's production will be less than that predicted by analysis. Such a phenomenon is easily studied using simulation by including the repair activity in the system model. The simulation may reveal that such occurrences are limiting the production capacity of the system and that additional repair workers are necessary to achieve full production rate. Furthermore, simulation may be used to investigate the effects of different operating strategies such as scheduling the repair worker to give priority to certain machines in case of simultaneous failures.

The above example, a case of *resource sharing and contention*, is one of several types of system behavior that is not easily analyzed and may justify the use of discrete event simulation. The repair worker, a system resource entity, must be shared by several competing activities—the repair of several different machines. In general, any system with complex interaction between entities may encounter such resource contention and may be a viable candidate for simulation. Another aspect of the above example is the occurrence of *asynchronous events*. The repair activity is an asynchronous event because its occurrence and perhaps its duration are unpredictable and independent of the status of other activities in the system. Another example of an asynchronous event is the irregular arrival of raw materials to the system. The delivery of materials within a system by automated guided vehicle (AGV) may be an asynchronous activity if the transit duration is variable.

Once it has been determined that there are elements of system behavior that are worthy of a simulation effort, one must establish *what is to be learned by the simulation*. This will determine the scope and construction of the model as well as what data must be recorded by the simulation program. The program can record such parameters as the time that an entity spends in each queue, the number of entities in each queue, the durations of each activity, and the number of occurrences of each activity. Commonly, simulation is used to do the following:

1. *Determine resource utilizations.* This will identify bottlenecks in system performance and fine-tune the line balance. In the above example, simulation would have shown that machine utilization was less than expected because of the idle time.
2. *Investigate scheduling strategies.* System performance is often affected by changing the scheduling and priority of activities. For example, simulation would have shown that system throughput could be improved by giving highest priority to the repair of the machines with the highest utilization.
3. *Determine inventory levels.* These may be inventory levels or queue sizes that result from operation of the system in a prescribed manner or the inventory or queue sizes required to achieve system performance unconstrained by the effects of finite queue size.
4. *Investigate the impact of different batching strategies for batch-process systems.*

The usefulness of the simulation to the system designer relies on the use of other tools such as economic models. Without proper interpretation of its results, simulation would be merely a trial and error process. Simulation will yield the characteristics of a single point in design space; it is the responsibility of the designer, using other methods such as those described in Chap. 14, to optimize the system within the design space.

Discrete Event Simulation Tools

Properties of discrete event models and languages.

A discrete event simulation computer program could be written in any general-purpose language such as FORTRAN or BASIC. However, a substantial effort would be required to develop a code structure for defining entities and events and a timing mechanism to drive the simulation. The timing mechanism, a fundamental feature of discrete event simulation, must advance the simulated time from one event to the next, since the system state cannot change between events, and must be responsible for executing events in their proper sequence. Fortunately, numerous specialized computer languages exist for performing discrete event simulation. These languages can be based on several methods for constructing and specifying discrete event models. These methods each take a different perspective on the system and, as a result, differ both in their program syntax and sequence of execution. The major types of modeling perspective are as follows:

1. *Event oriented.* The event-oriented model specifies and schedules all system state changes (events). Events may be conditional, i.e., their occurrence depends on the system state, or they may be unconditional. Unconditional events are specified to occur at prescheduled or random times. The task of the programmer is to define the possible events, the times or statistical properties of unconditional events, and the logic associated with conditional events. The programmer is not strictly concerned with defining activities, only with the state changes that occur as the result of an activity starting or ending. This method is the most general but also the most complicated to program.

2. *Process oriented.* A process is a sequence of activities and queues through which a particular entity can flow. The process-oriented model specifies cycles of state changes which every entity in the system undergoes. The cycles may incorporate branching based on the system state or on random occurrences. The algorithms required to schedule the events and drive the simulation are built into the language. This is easier to program but less flexible than the event-oriented approach.

3. *Activity oriented.* The activity-oriented model is a description of the prerequisite system states to start every activity. The program timekeeper executes an activity scan and starts all possible activities at each change of state. This approach is conceptually simple and easy to program but is inefficient in execution. It is useful, however, when activity durations are state dependent and therefore cannot be scheduled a priori.

While the basic structure of the different simulation languages can be very different, they all have several features in common: the capability of generating random occurrences, the capability of assigning *attributes* to entities, and a method for recording information as the simulation executes. Random occurrences can be generated according to a statistical model supplied by the programmer. Randomly distributed entity arrivals or machine failures are easily incorporated into most simulations. An attribute is a variable associated with an entity which specifies additional information such as its location, size, or position in a queue. The recording mechanism is the means by which the simulation generates usable information. Some data may be recorded automatically by the language. Other data must be recorded by writing program statements into the simulation. The programmer must give careful consideration to what data must be recorded since, after the simulation has executed, all information not recorded is lost.

Many simulation languages allow the user to develop a model using a graphic block diagram structure in which the various type of blocks (sometimes called "nodes") correspond to program statements and functions. The block diagram delineates the flow of entities through the activities and processes of the system and defines all possible branching. The programmer may then write the simulation program by inspection of the block diagram.

Executing and interpreting the simulation

In addition to formulating and coding a system model, the simulation engineer must give careful attention to how the simulation is to be run. The simulation engineer must specify the initial state of the system and the duration of the simulation. As in any dynamic system, there will be a transient response of the system from the initial state. Sometimes the nature of the transient response is important. For example, the performance of a manufacturing plant during start-up may be of interest. In this case, the initial state of the simulation model should accurately reflect the starting conditions of the plant. In fact, one may wish to investigate the effect of different starting conditions on performance. In other cases, only the steady-state performance of the system is of interest, and the transient response is not important. In these cases, the initial state can be any state that will permit activities to commence. The simulation engineer must then ensure that the duration of the simulation is sufficient to allow the transient response to subside before recording any data.

Data recorded during the simulation will represent a *sample* of the system's performance. The term sample means that the data are based on a finite set of observations which may not reflect all possible occurrences. Statistical parameters estimated from these data, such as average queue sizes or the average time an entity has spent in a queue, are accurate only to the degree that the sample is representative. Increasing the duration of the simulation and performing several replications each serve to increase the statistical accuracy of the parameter estimates. The simulation engineer must determine the minimum duration and number of replications required to obtain reliable results. For a more thorough treatment of probability and statistics necessary for simulation, the reader is referred to the references.

Commonly used simulation languages

1. *ECSL.* The Extended Control and Simulation Language (ECSL) was developed by A. T. Clementson at the University of Birmingham (Clementson, 1966). Its predecessor, the Control and Simulation Language (CSL) was conceived as a format for specifying simulation models to FORTRAN programmers (Buxton, 1966; Buxton and Laski, 1962). Thus, the language has a very readable, plain-

English style. ECSL is an activity-oriented language. An ECSL program consists primarily of a declaration of all entities and the queues associated with them and a procedural description of each possible activity. The activity description defines what conditions are necessary to start the activity, what state changes will occur when the activity is started, the duration of the activity, and what state changes will occur when the activity ends. In execution, the list of activities is scanned, all possible activities are started, and time is advanced to the next state change. The state of the ECSL model is completely described by the location of all entities (i.e., the queue or activity in which they are involved), the time remaining for all entities involved in activities, and the values of all attributes.

An ECSL program can be written directly from an activity cycle diagram such as that shown in Fig. 15.1. An extension to ECSL, Computer-Aided Programming of Simulations (CAPS), allows the user to write an ECSL program by describing all of the cycles in the diagram as an alternating sequence of queues and activities through which the entities flow (University of Birmingham, 1980). CAPS then creates the necessary activity descriptions. ECSL/CAPS allows a more process-oriented modeling approach.

2. *GPSS.* The General Purpose Simulation System (GPSS) is one of the most widely used simulation languages (Greenberg, 1972; Reitman, 1971). It was originally introduced by IBM in 1961 and has undergone many revisions since. GPSS takes a process-oriented approach to modeling which concentrates on the flow of *transactions* through processes. GPSS transactions are temporary entities that can be created according to some predefined periodic or random arrival pattern. Permanent entities, or resources, are called "facilities" and "storages." Facilities and storages are associated with processes and their flow through the system is not explicitly modeled as it is in ECSL. The GPSS program executes by "pushing" transactions through the system. At each time step, all possible transactions are processed, i.e., moved through the system, as far as possible. When the movement of a transaction is impeded, because it is engaged in an activity or delayed in a queue for example, the transaction and the time at which it will be available for further processing are listed in a *future events chain*. Time then advances to the time of the earliest transaction in the future events chain.

GPSS has a comprehensive block-diagramming format with over 40 different types of blocks, each of which corresponds directly to a program statement. All necessary parameters and operands to the program statements appear with the blocks on the diagram. Thus the block diagram is easily translated to a simulation program.

3. *SIMSCRIPT II.* SIMSCRIPT II is a widely used event-oriented simulation language originally developed by the Rand Corporation

(Kiviat et al., 1969, 1973). A SIMSCRIPT II program consists of a *preamble*, in which all entities of the system are defined, a *main program*, which initializes and starts the simulation, and a group of *event subroutines*. The event subroutines describe the state changes that occur as a result of each event and may also include data recording statements. The system timekeeper invokes the event subroutines in the proper sequence. SIMSCRIPT II has a very English-like syntax; thus, programs are easy to read and interpret.

4. *SLAM*. The Simulation Language for Alternative Modeling (SLAM) is a relatively new language (Pritsker and Pegden, 1979). SLAM can perform continuous system as well as discrete event simulation. The discrete event capabilities of SLAM allow for activity-oriented and process-oriented model implementations, although the primary modeling perspective is event oriented. Because of these alternative perspectives and the capability to incorporate FORTRAN subroutines in the simulation program, SLAM is a very powerful language.

A process-oriented SLAM model can be defined in a block diagram form similar to that of GPSS. This is referred to as a "network model" in SLAM because it comprises a network of nodes and branches. An event-oriented SLAM model is programmed as a group of FORTRAN subroutines—one for every possible event. The SLAM processor performs the timekeeping function and properly sequences and invokes the event subroutines. Numerous built-in subroutines allow the generation of random numbers and the recording of data.

Specialized tools for the simulation of manufacturing systems

In addition to the many general discrete event simulation languages available, there are numerous software packages available specifically for the simulation of various types of manufacturing systems. Some of these tools are essentially limited simulation languages; others are generalized system models. Because of their limited scope, they are often less expensive than general-purpose simulators and can be run on less powerful computers. Many of these packages allow graphical model building and provide an animated graphical display of the system operation.

An Example Simulation

Purpose of the simulation

The following is an example of the application of simulation to a manufacturing system. The system described here is complex, with 18 asynchronous activities and 12 different classes of entities. Many of the activities have variable state-dependent durations; thus the system is most easily modeled using an activity-oriented approach. The model is illustrated by an activity cycle diagram and has been simulated using ECSL.

Figure 15.2 illustrates the example, an assembly line with a combination parallel and serial arrangement of work cells served by an automated guided vehicle (AGV) material-handling system. Pallets are transported around the system, carrying parts from one work cell to the next and eventually to an unloading station. After unloading, the pallets are returned to a loading area and reused. The arrangement and number of work cells have been balanced to achieve the desired production rate. However, one goal of the simulation is to verify that this arrangement will operate as predicted. The station times (duration of assembly operations at the work cells) are fixed, but the operational characteristics of the AGVs and the transportation times are variable. The system has been designed so that the AGVs can operate in a "taxi" mode whereby, after delivering a pallet of production parts to a work cell, they are available to pick up and deliver another pallet elsewhere in the system. It has been assumed that there are sufficient routes in the system to allow completely flexible dispatching without regard to traffic interference. Operated in this mode, a single AGV would be sufficient to run the system but at a greatly reduced production rate because other resources in the system must sit idle while waiting for AGV service. The task of the analyst and the purpose of the simulation, then, is to determine the characteristics of the AGV system necessary to achieve full production and thus maximize the utilization of the work cell facilities. Since the AGV system also represents a capital expenditure, it is desired to maximize the utilization of the vehicles as well.

Specifically, the simulation of this system will be used to determine the following:

1. How many AGVs are necessary to achieve the desired production rate.
2. How many pallets of parts must be in the system to achieve the desired production rate.
3. What scheduling and dispatching strategy results in the most efficient use of the AGVs.
4. The identity of any impediments to efficient operation of the material-handling system. These impediments might be associated with the physical layout of the work cells or with the distribution of tasks between them.

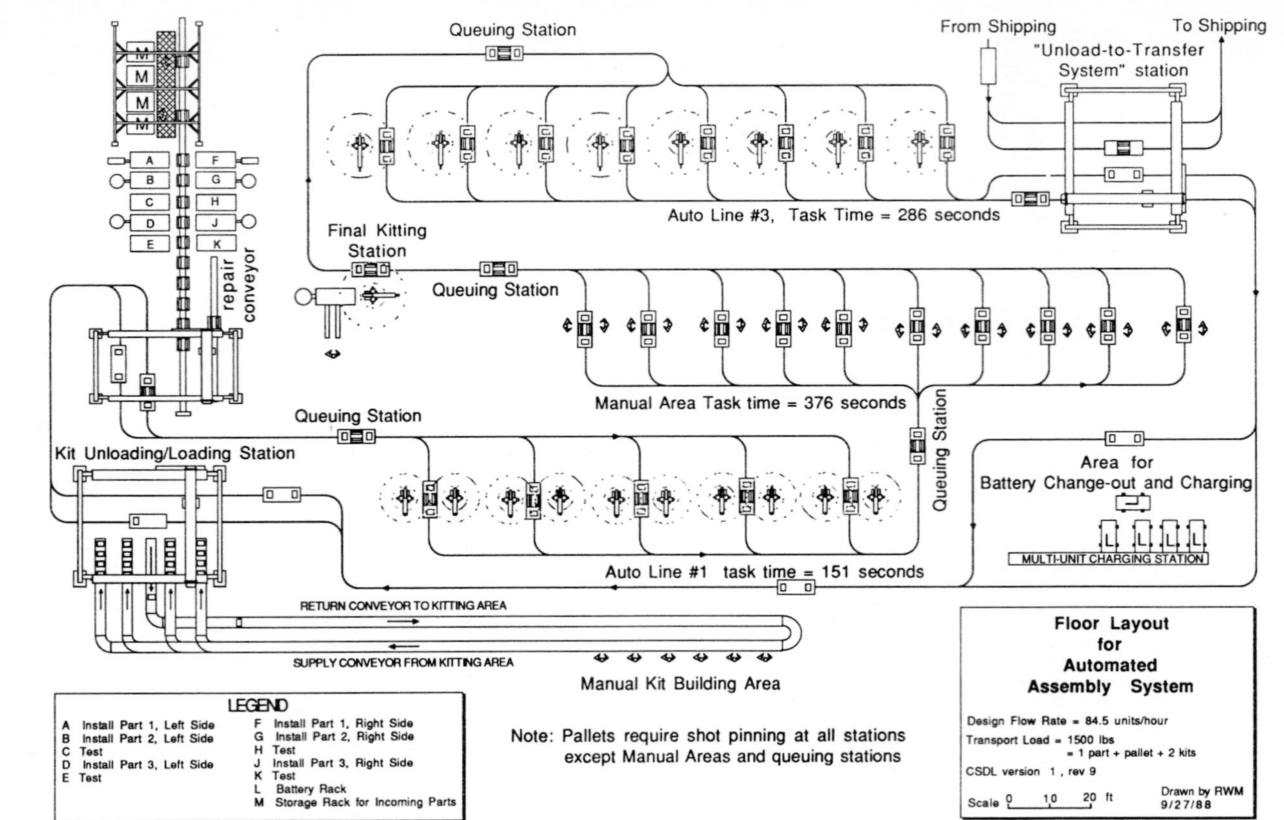

Fig. 15.2 Factory floor layout to be simulated.

The latter item is of special interest because it calls for somewhat qualitative conclusions to be drawn from the simulation. Furthermore, it exemplifies the far-reaching consequences of system design and the need for interaction of simulation and system design.

Constructing the model

The complete model of the assembly line has 12 *classes* of entities. The flow entities (those that would be transactions in a GPSS-type model) are pallets and AGVs. The remaining entity classes are resource entities such as several types of robots, manual workstations, and entities known generally as "tickets" or "tokens." This last type of entity may have no physical significance but is a fictional entity useful for controlling the execution of activities and the flow of other entities in the system. For example, the number of transactions accumulating in a given queue can be limited by defining a ticket entity that is required to move a transaction into the queue. If the activity that removes transactions from the queue releases the ticket, the number of transactions in the queue will be limited to the number of tickets in existence. This system makes use of this type of entity for controlling the flow of AGVs. Entities of the AGV class have an attribute called LOCATION associated with them. The LOCATION attribute will be used in this model for finding available AGVs and for determining transport times.

There are 18 activities in the model. Most activities involve either processing pallets at the work cells or transporting pallets between work cells. All work cell activity durations are fixed, but the duration of transport activities is dependent on the location of an available AGV and the distance of the move. Figure 15.3 shows an activity cycle diagram of a segment of the model incorporating both transport and processing. The figure shows three activities involving four entity classes: pallets, AGVs, robots, and tickets. The figure represents an entire work cell consisting of several robots, such as Auto Line #1 in Fig. 15.2.

As an example in activity modeling, consider the activity, TRANSPORT TO WORK CELL. To start this activity, the following system state is prerequisite: There must be a pallet in the NEW PALLETS queue, a TICKET in the AVAILABLE TICKETS queue, and an AGV in the IDLE AGVS queue. The duration of this activity will be the time required to fetch the AGV, based on its LOCATION attribute, plus the time required to move the pallet into the work cell (which could be a variable based on an attribute of the TICKET). At the completion of this activity, the pallet is in the READY queue, the TICKET is in the TICKET HELD queue, and the AGV is returned, after setting

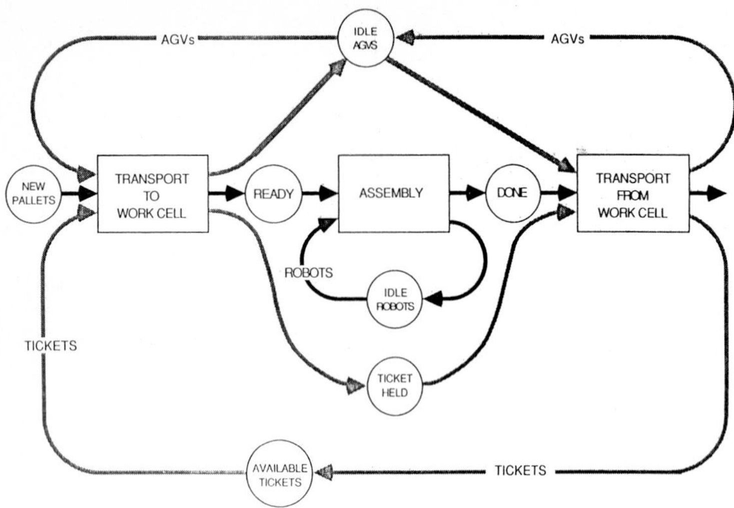

Fig. 15.3 Typical arrangement of activities and queues in an assembly system with transporters.

its LOCATION attribute, to the IDLE AGVS queue. The cell model contains the same number of tickets and robots. The importance of the ticket is apparent; it represents an empty pallet space in the work cell and is not returned to the AVAILABLE TICKETS queue until the TRANSPORT FROM WORK CELL activity occurs.

The ECSL description of TRANSPORT TO WORK CELL is as follows:

```
BEGIN TRANSPORT _ TO _ WORK _ CELL
FIND FIRST TICKET A   FROM AVAILABLE _ TICKETS
FIND FIRST PALLET B   FROM NEW _ PALLETS
FIND FIRST AGV C      FROM IDLE _ AGVS
DURATION = FETCH _ TIME(LOCATION OF AGV C) + MOVE _ TIME
LOCATION OF AGV C = NEW _ LOCATION
TICKET A FROM AVAILABLE _ TICKETS   TO TICKET _ HELD
  AFTER DURATION
PALLET B FROM NEW _ PALLETS          TO READY
  AFTER DURATION
AGV C     FROM IDLE _ AGVS            TO IDLE _ AGVS
  AFTER DURATION
REPEAT
```

The activity description begins with a series of FIND statements, which are tests to determine if the necessary entities are in their required queues. If any entities are not found, the activity cannot be started and the activity scanner skips ahead to the next activity description. If the entities are found, execution of the activity proceeds.

The duration is computed based on the AGV's current location, and the AGV's new LOCATION is specified as being that of the cell to which it will move. Here, FETCH _ TIME is a function defined by the user that computes the time required to fetch an AGV given its current LOCATION attribute. This time is based on the performance characteristics of the vehicles and the physical layout of the factory floor. The activity then executes a series of FROM/TO statements which specify the flow and event times for each of the entities. Finally, the REPEAT statement tells the activity scanner to start this activity as many times as possible during each scan.

This implementation of the TRANSPORT TO WORK CELL activity chooses rather indiscriminately among the AGVs in the IDLE AGVS queue. A more interesting activity description, which models a different operational strategy for the system, would use the MIN function as follows:

```
FIND AGV C FROM IDLE_AGVS WITH MIN
  FETCH_TIME(LOCATION OF AGV C)
```

In this case, the activity scanner selects the AGV that results in the minimum value of FETCH_TIME. This latter implementation models a dispatching strategy where the nearest AGV is always chosen for a transport activity. This strategy was used in the example simulation under "Results of a Simulation Run," below.

The other activities in the system can be described similarly. The ASSEMBLY activity requires a pallet from the READY queue and a robot from the IDLE ROBOT queue. The TRANSPORT FROM WORK CELL activity requires a pallet from the DONE queue, an AGV from the IDLE AGVS queue, and a ticket from the TICKET HELD queue. The TRANSPORT FROM WORK CELL activity doesn't really need this ticket except to return it to the AVAILABLE TICKETS queue. By the nature of the preceding activities, there will be a ticket in the TICKET HELD queue whenever there is a pallet in the DONE queue. It is left to the reader to formulate the ECSL code for these activities. Note that all of the transport activities draw AGVs from the same queue and thus are in competition with each other. The nature of the activity scanning approach gives priority to those activities listed first in the activity description block. For a system such as this one, with global competition for resources and an intertwined network of tickets, activity priority must be carefully considered.

Running the simulation

In this example, only the steady-state operation of the system is of concern; the characteristics of the system during start-up are not important. However, since the exact nature of the steady-state operation is unknown, the system must be started up "cold" and allowed to reach an equilibrium. The simulation will be started with no activities in progress and all entities in an idle or available state. Data will not be recorded until pallets, the primary flow entities, begin recirculating. The run will simulate 2 hr of production time.

The goals of the simulation require that the following information be recorded and computed:

1. The utilization of all work cell resources
2. The average AGV fetching time
3. The steady-state production rate
4. The number of pallets in use during steady state
5. The number and location distribution of available AGVs at periodic intervals throughout the simulation

All of this information must be recorded by writing specific statements into the ECSL program. Resource utilization is computed as the fraction of available time that a resource entity is engaged in a productive activity. The AGV fetching times are recorded every time an AGV is taken from the IDLE AGVS queue, then averaged after the simulation run has terminated. The steady-state production rate can be determined from the number of pallets processed during the period of steady-state operation. The number of pallets in use can be determined by counting the number of pallets sitting idle in an empty pallet queue at every time step. Finally, the number and distribution of available AGVs can be recorded by examining the contents of the IDLE AGVS queue at periodic intervals.

Two approaches can be used to determine the number of AGVs necessary. One approach is to run the simulation repeatedly, varying the number of AGVs in the system, and noting the effect on production rate. The other approach is to run the simulation once with an excess number of AGVs and examine the number that sit idle. The latter approach must be used cautiously because the effect of distribution is important. Clearly, it is advantageous to maintain several idle AGVs scattered throughout the system to minimize fetch times.

Results of a simulation run

The work cell resources in this system have been sized for a theoretical maximum production rate of 85 pallets per hour. Figure 15.4 shows an output report from a simulation of the system shown in Fig. 15.2 run with 25 AGVs. The system throughput for this run is 78 pallets per hour, slightly less than the theoretical maximum. At most times, there are several idle AGVs, but there are times at which all are occupied. Thus, it is expected that the throughput might increase with more AGVs.

In addition to these quantitative results of a single run, modeling and simulation of this system reveals several other performance characteristics which can lead to improvement of the design. Among them are:

1. Once the system reaches steady state, a pattern of AGV behavior is established. AGVs tend to be dispatched within the groups of parallel work cells. When a vehicle delivers a pallet, it most likely will be dispatched to pick up another pallet within the same group of parallel stations. This is a consequence of the condition that, in steady state, pallets must arrive and depart from the group at the same rate.
2. Given this pattern of operation, it is not necessary to allow global dispatching of AGVs; thus the floor layout of AGV paths may be simplified.
3. Also given this pattern of operation, attention should be given to the order in which the cells within a group are fed to equalize the dis-

E.C.S.L.SYSTEM 25/ 2/87 PROGRAM-AUTOSIM26A DATE-12/ 5/87 PAGE- 1

ECSL SIMULATION OF CSDL ALTERNATIVE SYSTEM 2.6A

TIME	PALLET BUFFERS					UNLOADED AGVS		
	KITTING	AUTO 1	MANUAL	F-KIT	AUTO 2	AUTO 1	MANUAL	AUTO 2
0	42	0	0	0	0	0	0	0
300	34	0	0	0	0	2	0	0
600	27	0	0	0	0	2	2	0
900	20	0	1	0	0	1	0	0
1200	13	0	0	0	0	1	1	2
1500	5	0	0	1	0	0	1	1
1800	4	0	2	0	1	0	0	2
2100	3	0	0	0	2	0	1	0
2400	3	0	0	1	1	1	0	1
2700	2	0	4	0	2	2	0	1
3000	2	0	2	2	2	1	2	1
3300	2	0	2	1	1	1	0	2
3600	0	0	6	0	3	0	0	0
3900	0	0	3	2	3	0	2	0
4200	0	0	3	1	1	0	0	1
4500	0	0	7	0	3	1	0	2
4800	0	0	3	2	3	0	2	1
5100	0	0	4	2	2	0	0	0
5400	0	0	6	0	4	0	1	0
5700	0	0	2	1	4	1	2	0
6000	0	0	2	2	4	1	0	1
6300	0	0	4	0	4	0	0	2
6600	0	0	2	1	4	0	2	1
6900	0	0	0	2	4	0	0	0
7200	0	0	1	1	5	0	2	1

Fig. 15.4 Simulation program output for layout in Fig. 15.2.

```
E.C.S.L.SYSTEM  25/ 2/87              PROGRAM-AUTOSIM26A           DATE-12/ 5/87      PAGE-  2

 RETP   WAS STARTED          125 TIMES
 UNLOAD WAS STARTED          126 TIMES
 MOVBU  WAS STARTED          128 TIMES
 AUTOB  WAS STARTED          135 TIMES
 MOVCB  WAS STARTED          140 TIMES
 FKIT   WAS STARTED          141 TIMES
 MOVMC  WAS STARTED          144 TIMES
 MANUAL WAS STARTED          154 TIMES
 MOVAM  WAS STARTED          157 TIMES
 AUTOA  WAS STARTED          161 TIMES
 MOVLA  WAS STARTED          161 TIMES
 LOADP  WAS STARTED          162 TIMES
 MOVKL  WAS STARTED          163 TIMES
 KIT    WAS STARTED          164 TIMES
 MOVQK  WAS STARTED          164 TIMES
 RAGVG  WAS STARTED            3 TIMES
 RAGVI  WAS STARTED            8 TIMES
 RAGVM  WAS STARTED            6 TIMES

 FIRST UNIT OUT AT TIME =        1407
 AVERAGE STATION ENTRY TIMES
    AUTO 1; TIME =           25
    MANUAL; TIME =           22
    AUTO 2; TIME =           21
 AVERAGE AGV FETCH TIMES
    AUTO 1; TIME =           22
    MANUAL; TIME =           25
    AUTO 2; TIME =           28

 UTILIZATION OF KROBOT         .9440
 UTILIZATION OF LROBOT         .9501
 UTILIZATION OF AUTO 1         .9135
 UTILIZATION OF MANUAL         .9990
 UTILIZATION OF FKIT           .7181
 UTILIZATION OF AUTO 2         .9992
 UTILIZATION OF UROBOT         .9093

 PRODUCTION RATE =           78. UNITS/HOUR
```

Fig. 15.4 *(Continued)*

patch times and thus equalize the utilization of the parallel cells. This is effective only if station times are constant and can be synchronized.

4. Finally, longer station times allow more efficient use of the AGV system and higher work cell utilization because the time lost while waiting for AGVs can be apportioned over a larger amount of productive time. This is made particularly evident by simulating variants of the system with different task allocations between the work cell groups. Of course, other issues, such as tool and equipment costs and tool change time, must be considered when designing the work cells and evaluating the total system cost and performance.

While many of these qualitative results can be predicted without the use of simulation, the modeling and simulation process provides much of the necessary insight and serves to validate and quantify the predictions.

Summary

Discrete event simulation is a valuable tool in the design and specification of manufacturing systems. It is not, however, a substitute for analytical methods. It is useful when a system is complex or subject to random behavior and as a means of verifying results obtained by an analysis based on unproven assumptions. A rough analysis is always a prerequisite for formulating a simulation model.

Many software packages are commercially available for performing discrete event simulations. They differ greatly in their capabilities and in their modeling methods. The suitability of any particular modeling method depends on the details of the system under study. These packages vary from powerful, general-purpose discrete or continuous system simulation programming languages to specialized tools for certain classes of systems. In general, there is a trade-off between power and ease of use.

Simulation must be used prudently. The results can be only as good as the underlying system model, which must be limited in scope to be practical. Furthermore, the statistical validity of any results obtained from a simulation must be considered, particularly if the simulation contains random phenomena. The effectiveness of simulation to the system designer relies on proper interpretation of its results and on the concurrent use of other design tools such as economic modeling.

References

Banks, J., and J. S. Carson, II: *Discrete-Event System Simulation,* Prentice-Hall, Englewood Cliffs, NJ, 1984.

Buxton, J. N.: "Writing Simulations in CSL," *The Computer Journal,* vol. 9, 1966, pp. 137–143.

———, and J. G. Laski: "Control and Simulation Language," *The Computer Journal,* vol. 5, 1962, pp. 194–199.

Clementson, A. T.: "Extended Control and Simulation Language," *The Computer Journal,* vol. 9, 1966, pp. 215–220.

Fishman, G. S.: *Concepts and Methods in Discrete Event Simulation,* John Wiley, New York, 1973.

———: *Principles of Discrete Event Simulation,* John Wiley, New York, 1978.

Gordon, G.: *System Simulation,* 2d ed., Prentice-Hall, Englewood Cliffs, NJ, 1978.

Greenberg, S.: *GPSS Primer,* John Wiley, New York, 1972.

Hooper, J. W.: "Strategy-Related Characteristics of Discrete-Event Languages and Models," *Simulation,* vol. 46, no. 4, 1986, pp. 153–159.

Kiviat, P. J., et al.: *The SIMSCRIPT II Programming Language,* Prentice-Hall, Englewood Cliffs, NJ, 1969.

———: *The SIMSCRIPT II.5 Programming Language,* Consolidated Analysis Centers, Los Angeles, 1973.

Pritsker, A. A. B., and C. D. Pegden: *Introduction to Simulation and SLAM,* John Wiley, New York, 1979.

Reitman, J.: *Computer Simulation Applications,* John Wiley, New York, 1971.

University of Birmingham, *ECSL/CAPS: Detailed Reference Manual,* 1980.

Chapter

16

Case Studies

In this chapter we present details of two actual case studies we have conducted on clients' products. These are an air conditioning module and an independent suspension rear axle. The narratives that follow are lengthy and detailed because that is the nature of true design and especially of concurrent design.

Automobile Air Conditioning Module

Introduction

Many modern automobiles have integrated passenger heating and cooling devices. Defrost, heat, air conditioning, and combinations thereof are to be produced by a single electromechanical device. The module is physically constrained by the available space that has been assigned by the car designers. The unit must contain a heater core (to warm air), an evaporator (to cool air), a blower (to circulate air), and various actuators and valves (to regulate where the air can flow and also the temperature combinations that can occur). The device must also permit in-car servicing and in-shop repair.

The goal of this study was to determine the feasibility of automating the assembly of such an air conditioning module (ACM). There is significant experience with mostly manual assembly of prior products; such systems will always be the basis for comparison of the cost effectiveness of any automated systems.

Original product design

As originally designed, this product has some difficult assembly tasks; they can be performed manually but are virtually impossible to do with automation. The original ACM case (see Fig. 16.1) has a remov-

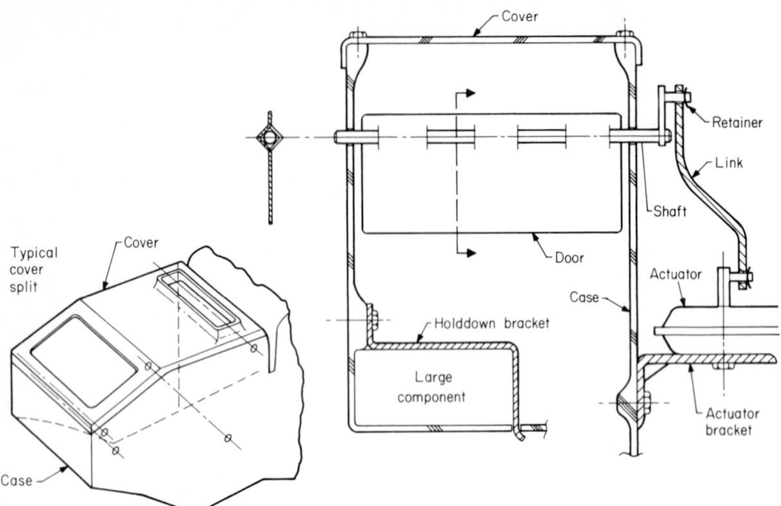

Fig. 16.1 Old design of ACM case. Note fasteners and brackets required to mount actuator plus separate shaft and door requiring assembly within the case to make a valve. Note location of split line between case and cover.

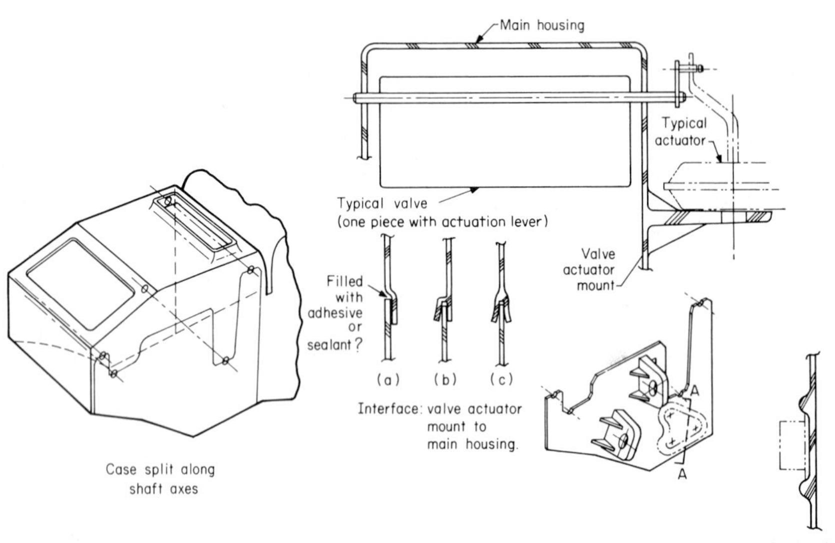

Fig. 16.2 Redesign of ACM case for comparison with Fig. 16.1. Note new location of cover-case split line permitting insertion of one-piece molded valves. Also note snap-on actuators and molded-on actuator bracket.

able cover (oriented up at assembly but down in the car). Large components are held in place with brackets and screws. Valves have two pieces (a door and a shaft) and are assembled manually by holding the door in place with one hand while sliding the shaft through one case wall, then through the door (with a slight interference fit), and finally through the second case wall. Actuators are mounted to brackets with screws, which are in turn attached to the case with screws. Links from actuators to valves are carefully positioned while the retainers are installed. There is a piping gasket as well which is rather difficult to assemble.

New product design

In general, the goal of redesign was to combine as many functions as possible into each final component (i.e., minimize the number of parts). The number of assembly directions and complex assembly motion requirements were to be minimized. Figure 16.2 exhibits the main new concepts employed. A one-piece valve and connecting link which can be dropped into the assembled position are shown along with some simplified case joints and locating features, especially those for mounting actuators. An idea for simultaneously assembling an actuator and connecting the linkage joint is shown in Fig. 16.3. Variations of these ideas were used in the final product.

Figure 16.4 shows an exploded view of the final assembly. The new case (part 1 and subassembly 3) is designed with interpart boundaries that are different from the old design. These boundaries create splits which greatly facilitate assembly. Subassembly 3 contains the air deflector valves, linkage, and actuators; all were designed to snap into place. This subcase is also split in a new way so that the valves (now one piece each) merely drop into position and the cover entraps them. The concept is demonstrated by the way part 11 is trapped between parts 2 and 1. Some clever component design was necessary to prevent air leaks. Snap-on actuators were possible only when the supplier agreed to redesign them; this was a welcome (and necessary) step by a company that had previously stated to the ACM producer, "This is the standard part that we make, take it or leave it." The newly established cooperation certainly made life much happier for everyone.

The net result of the redesign is that the components can be almost "thrown" together at assembly. This may have important ramifications for the assembly system's requirements. While many snap fits for various components occur, there is still a need for some screws to allow service and/or repair.

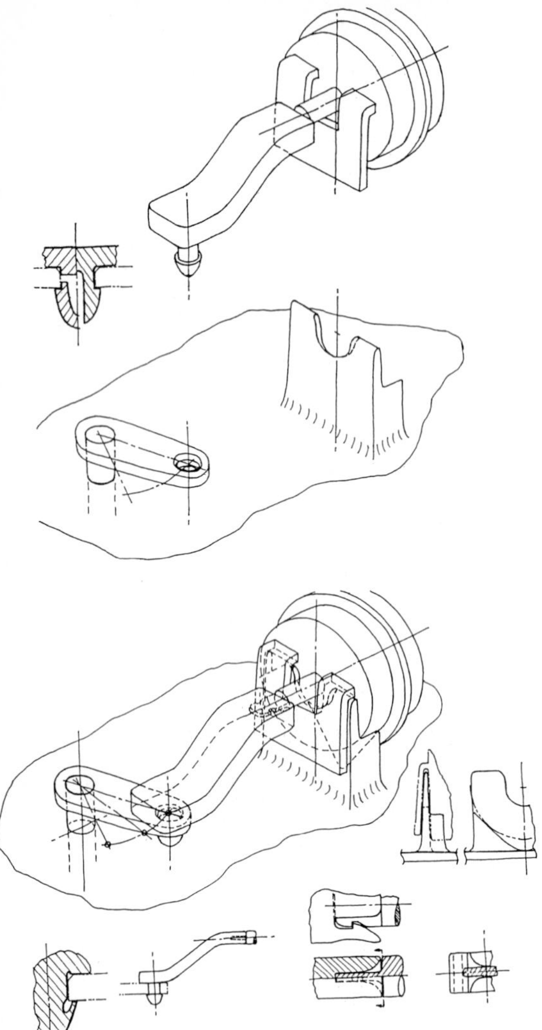

Fig. 16.3 New method for assembling actuator and linkage with snaps—no screws.

Design of the assembly system

An assembly sequence was chosen mostly based on the experience of producing similar products. Figure 16.5 exhibits the assembly planning data used; note the comments about freedom of motion at various points in the assembly process. While various directions for assembly are necessary, the required motions in each of those directions are not particularly complex. Some tasks (3, 4, 7, 11, 16, 17, 23, and 24) re-

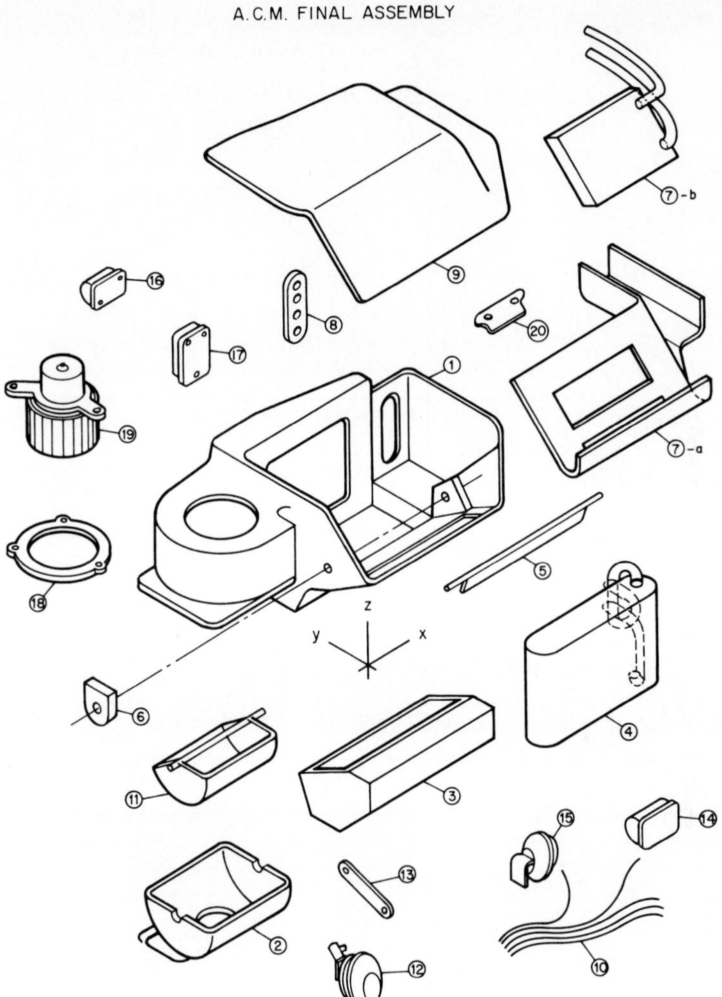

Fig. 16.4 Final concept design for ACM. Subassembly 3 and part 1 comprise the case shown in Fig. 16.2.

quire spatial motion, i.e., motion along arbitrary curves in space. Note that task 9 is to be an automated inspection regardless of the rest of the system components actually used and that placement of both the air inlet assembly (AI) and the mode valve housing assembly (MVH) in the pallet comprises the first task.

Once the tasks were established, the applicable technology was determined as shown in Fig. 16.6. Working days, shifts, and average loaded labor rate (wages plus benefits) were specified. Company economic criteria were transformed to the needs of the system synthesis

ASSEMBLY PLANNING CHART

SKETCH OF ASSEMBLY:

See

Figure 4

NAME: ACM FINAL ASSEMBLY

DATE: 10 July 198_

PREPARED BY: REG

SHEET 1 OF 2

TASK	SEQUENCE	TYPE OF TASK	BASIC ORIENTATION	MOTION(S) REQUIRED	JIGGING/TOOLING REQUIRED	DEGREE OF DIFFICULTY OF TASK	INSPECTION REQUIRED	CYCLE TIME (s)	COMMENTS
Get AI Case Sub-Assy. (2)									
Place in Pallet	1	P	X,Y	-Z	Y	1		~	
Assemble AI Vacuum element, (12)									
valve (11) and link (13).	2	P,A	X,Y,Z	-Z,-X	Y	3	C	15	Must move freely
Get MVH Sub-Assy. (3)									
Place in Pallet.	1	P	X,Y	-Z	Y	1		~	
Get Solenoid (14) & Vacuum Element (15)									
Connect sub assembly	3	P,I	X,Y,Z	X,Y,Z	Y	2		15.7	
Attach Harness (10) to Unit	4	P,I	X,Y,Z	X,Y,Z		3		13.6	Check actuation
Get Evaporator Case (1)									
Position & Snap Fit to AI & MVH.	5	A,I	X,Y	-Z	Y	3		15	
Get Solenoid Assy. (16)									
Position & Drive 2 screws.	6	T	X,Z	-Y		2	B	14.3	
Get Temperature Valve (5)									
Assemble into unit.	7	A,I	X,Z	X,Z, θY	Y	3	C	16.4	Moves freely, seats properly
Get Temp. Valve Actuator (6)									
Attach to unit with 2 screws	8	A,T	Y,Z	X		2	B	14.3	
Automatic Inspection	9	M	–	–		2	All		Check all functions
Get Resistor Assy. (17)									
Align to case, drive 3 Screws	10	A,T	X,Z	-Y		2	B	15.7	

ABBREVIATIONS USED:

TASK TYPE

- P – PLACE, ORIENT
- T – TIGHTEN BOLTS, NUT, etc.
- I – INSERT PARTS
- M – MEASURE
- S – SHAPE MODIFY
- A – ALIGN

INSPECTION

- B – BOLT TORQUE
- G – GAUGE DIMENSION
- C – COMPARISON

(a)

Fig. 16.5 Assembly planning chart for ACM. Numbers in circles refer to part numbers in Fig. 16.4.

ASSEMBLY PLANNING CHART

SKETCH OF ASSEMBLY: See Figure 4

NAME: ACM FINAL ASSEMBLY

DATE: 10 July 198_

PREPARED BY: REG

SHEET 2 OF 2

TASK	SEQUENCE	TYPE OF TASK	BASIC ORIENTATION	MOTION(S) REQUIRED	JIGGING/TOOLING REQUIRED	DEGREE OF DIFFICULTY OF TASK	INSPECTION REQUIRED	CYCLE TIME (s)	COMMENTS
Apply Case Seal	11	S	X,Y,Z	X,Y,Z		2		~	
Assemble Isolator (18) to Motor & Fan (19)									
Place in Case	12	A	X,Y	+Z	Y	3		16.4	
Assemble with 3 washers & 3 screws	13	P,T	X,Y	-Z	Y	2	B	~	
Get Evaporator Core Sub-Assy. (4)									
Position in case, drive 3 screws	14	A,T	X,Y,Z	Y,Z	Y	2	B	14.3	
Get core shroud (7)-a									
Assemble to unit with 2 screws	15	A,T	X,Y,Z	-Z	Y	3	B	11.6	
Get Heater Core (7)-b									
Position in case, clamp (20), drive 3 screws	16	A,T	X,Y,Z	X,Y,Z	Y	3	B	16.4	
Dispense case seal on shroud.	17	S	X,Y,Z	X,Y,Z		2		16.4	
Assemble cover (9) to unit.	18	P	X,Y	-Z		1		~	
Drive 4 cover screws	19	T	X,Y	-Z		1	B	15.7	
Drive 3 cover screws	20	T	X,Y	-Z		1	B	13.6	
Assemble Pipe Seal (8)	21	A	X,Z	-Y	Y	4			
Peel & assemble 3 Stud Seals	22	P	X,Z	-Y		2		15.0	
Final Inspect	23	M	X,Y,Z	X,Y,Z		2		16.4	
Pack	24	P	X,Y,Z	X,Y,Z		1		~	

ABBREVIATIONS USED:

TASK TYPE
- P – PLACE, ORIENT
- T – TIGHTEN BOLTS, NUT, etc.
- I – INSERT PARTS
- M – MEASURE
- S – SHAPE MODIFY
- A – ALIGN

INSPECTION
- B – BOLT TORQUE
- G – GAUGE DIMENSION
- C – COMPARISON

(b)

Fig. 16.5 (*Continued*)

APPLICABLE TECHNOLOGY CHART

TITLE ACM FINAL ASSEMBLY DATE 2 Aug. 198_

240 WORKING DAYS PER YEAR .3546 ANNUALIZED COST FACTOR

3 SHIFTS AVAILABLE 19 AVERAGE LOADED LABOR RATE ($/h)

5 s STATION-TO-STATION MOVE TIME

RESOURCE DATA SET NAME: ACMRES TASK DATA SET NAME: ACMTSK

FOR EACH RESOURCE:

- C HARDWARE COST ($)
- ρ INSTALLED COST/HARDWARE COST
- ϵ UP-TIME EXPECTED (%)
- v OPERATING/MAINTENANCE RATE ($/h)
- t_c SECONDS TOOL CHANGE TIME
- m_s MAXIMUM STATIONS PER WORKER

WHEN A RESOURCE CAN BE USED ON A TASK: OPERATION TIME (s) | TOOL NUMBER / HARDWARE COST ($)

TASK NUMBER \ RESOURCE	MNL (C: 1; ρ: 1.1; ϵ: 87.5; v: .5; t_c: 1; m_s: .83)			PS1 (C: 40000; ρ: 2.6; ϵ: 85; v: .8; t_c: 4; m_s: 5)			PAØ (C: 30000; ρ: 2.5; ϵ: 86; v: .8; t_c: 4; m_s: 5)			FXD (C: 0; ρ: 1.5; ϵ: 90; v: .8; t_c: 0; m_s: 4)		
	Time	Tool	Cost	Time	Tool	Cost	Time	Tool	Cost	Time	Tool	Cost
1. AI Case (2), MVH Case (3)	10	101	100	8	201	10000	X			4	401	60000
2. Vacuum Element (12), AI Valve (11), Link (13)	10	102	1000	10	202	8000	8	301	8000	5	402	80000
3. Solenoid (14), Vacuum Element (15)	6	103	100	6	203	2000	6	302	2000	2	403	30000
4. Harness (10)	12	104	500	15	203	2000	X			X		
5. Evaporator Case (1)	10	101	100	8	201	10000	X			5	404	60000
6. Solenoid Assy. (16), 2 Screws	12	105	2500	10	204	5000	10	303	5000	3	405	25000
7. Temperature Valve (5)	8	106	1000	7	202	8000	7	304	8000	X		
8. Temp. Valve Actuator (6), 2 Screws	12	105	2500	10	204	5000	10	303	5000	4	406	30000
9. Automatic Inspection	X			X			X			14	407	100000
10. Resistor Assy. (17), 3 Screws	12	105	2500	10	204	5000	10	303	5000	4	408	25000

	UNITS	DAYS
PRODUCTION	250000	240
BATCH	400000	240
DATA	750000	240

Sheet 1 of 3

(a)

Fig. 16.6 Applicable technology chart for ACM. Numbers in circles refer to part numbers in Fig. 16.4.

programs (see Chap. 14). Four resource types were identified: MNL (manual), PS1 (programmable device S1), PA0 (programmable device A0), and FXD (fixed automation station). The two programmable resources have similar operating characteristics; PA0 costs less but can only perform a few tasks. Note in Fig. 16.6 that some resources cannot perform some of the tasks; this is a common occurrence. On the other hand, some resources (especially PS1 and PA0) can use the same tool to do several tasks in a row. This suggests some natural groupings for

APPLICABLE TECHNOLOGY CHART

TITLE ACM FINAL ASSEMBLY DATE 2 Aug. 198_

______ WORKING DAYS PER YEAR ______ ANNUALIZED COST FACTOR

______ SHIFTS AVAILABLE ______ AVERAGE LOADED LABOR RATE ($/h)

______ s STATION-TO-STATION MOVE TIME

RESOURCE DATA SET NAME: ACMRES TASK DATA SET NAME: ACMTSK

FOR EACH RESOURCE:

- C HARDWARE COST ($)
- ρ INSTALLED COST/HARDWARE COST
- ϵ UP-TIME EXPECTED (%)
- v OPERATING/MAINTENANCE RATE ($/h)
- t_c SECONDS TOOL CHANGE TIME
- m_s MAXIMUM STATIONS PER WORKER

WHEN A RESOURCE CAN BE USED ON A TASK: OPERATION TIME (s) | TOOL NUMBER / HARDWARE COST ($)

RESOURCE / TASK NUMBER	MNL C: ρ: ε: v: t_c: m_s:	PS1 C: ρ: ε: v: t_c: m_s:	PAØ C: ρ: ε: v: t_c: m_s:	FXD C: ρ: ε: v: t_c: m_s:
11. Case Sealant	10 | 107 2000	8 | 205 5000	8 | 305 5000	X
12. Isolator (18) Motor & Fan (19)	12 | 108 3000	12 | 206 10000	12 | 306 10000	8 | 409 100000
13. 3 Washers 3 Screws	12 | 109 2000	9 | 207 5000	9 | 307 5000	3 | 410 25000
14. Evaporator Core (4) 3 Screws	12 | 110 2000	10 | 208 10000	10 | 308 10000	X
15. Core shroud (7)-a 2 Screws	10 | 110 2000	8 | 208 10000	8 | 308 10000	X
16. Heater Core (7)-b, Clamp (20), 3 screws	12 | 110 2000	10 | 208 10000	10 | 308 10000	X
17. Case sealant	12 | 107 2000	10 | 205 5000	10 | 305 5000	X
18. Cover (9)	10 | 101 100	8 | 201 10000	X	4 | 411 30000
19. 4 Screws	12 | 109 2000	8 | 207 5000	8 | 307 5000	3 | 412 40000
20. 3 Screws	9 | 109 2000	6 | 207 5000	6 | 307 5000	2 | 412 40000

	UNITS	DAYS
PRODUCTION		
BATCH		
DATA		

Sheet 2 of 3

(b)

Fig. 16.6 *(Continued)*

task assignment, assuming time is available. Larger groups can of course be made if tool changes are taken into account. The program compares available time to required time and determines whether these technical groups make economic sense.

We shall look at some general results shortly. First we will look at the conditions for a nominal yearly production requirement of 250,000 units. A direct comparison between an almost completely manual assembly system (the base) and a totally automated assembly system (the alternative) will be made. Figure 16.7 displays a schematic layout

APPLICABLE TECHNOLOGY CHART

TITLE ACM FINAL ASSEMBLY DATE 2 Aug. 198_

_____ WORKING DAYS PER YEAR _____ ANNUALIZED COST FACTOR

_____ SHIFTS AVAILABLE _____ AVERAGE LOADED LABOR RATE ($/h)

_____ s STATION-TO-STATION MOVE TIME

RESOURCE DATA SET NAME: ACMRES TASK DATA SET NAME: ACMTSK

FOR EACH RESOURCE:

C HARDWARE COST ($)
ρ INSTALLED COST/HARDWARE COST
ϵ UP-TIME EXPECTED (%)
v OPERATING/MAINTENANCE RATE ($/h)
t_c SECONDS TOOL CHANGE TIME
m_s MAXIMUM STATIONS PER WORKER

WHEN A RESOURCE CAN BE USED ON A TASK: OPERATION TIME (s) | TOOL NUMBER / HARDWARE COST ($)

TASK NUMBER \ RESOURCE	MNL (C: ρ: ε: v: t_c: m_s:)	PS1 (C: ρ: ε: v: t_c: m_s:)	PAØ (C: ρ: ε: v: t_c: m_s:)	FXD (C: ρ: ε: v: t_c: m_s:)
21. Pipe Seal (8)	12 | 111 1000	8 | 209 6000	X	3 | 413 100000
22. 3 Stud Seals	12 | 112 1000	9 | 210 3000	9 | 309 3000	3 | 413 100000
23. Final Inspect	15 | 113 5000	X	X	12 | 414 50000
24. Pack	12 | 114 100	10 | 201 10000	X	X

	UNITS	DAYS
PRODUCTION		
BATCH		
DATA		

Sheet 3 of 3

(c)

Fig. 16.6 *(Continued)*

of the base system; all stations are manual except for task 9 which was specified to be an automatic inspection machine for checking all functions (see Fig. 16.5). Note that the work is as well balanced as possible between the manual workers. Unit assembly cost is $2.783.

The most cost-effective automated system (Fig. 16.8) contains three PS1 robots, three PA0 robots, and two FXD stations (including the tester at task 9). This system would cost $1,005,000. The work is far from equal at the various stations but that is of little consequence here since there are no direct workers. Figure 16.9 shows the exact first-year unit costs: From Fig. 16.9(*a*) the variable cost is $0.809; from Fig. 16.9(*b*), at 18 percent IRoR, the total unit cost is $2.433.

A.C.M. FINAL ASSY. (250k 3yr Base)

```
              61.71 seconds  USABLE CYCLE TIME
87.5 %  BOTTLENECK UP-TIME          58.33  UNITS/HR EXPECTED
        336000 units  ACTUAL CAPACITY OF THIS SYSTEM

     180807 ($)   TOTAL INVESTMENT,  RHO FACTOR =  1.41
            7.48 WORKERS AT  19.00 $/hr REQUIRED
        3.80 $/hr   SYSTEM OPERATING/MAINTENANCE RATE

       0.744 YEAR REQUIRED FOR 3.0 SHIFT OPERATION
        240 DAYS REQUIRED FOR 2.23 SHIFT OPERATION
```

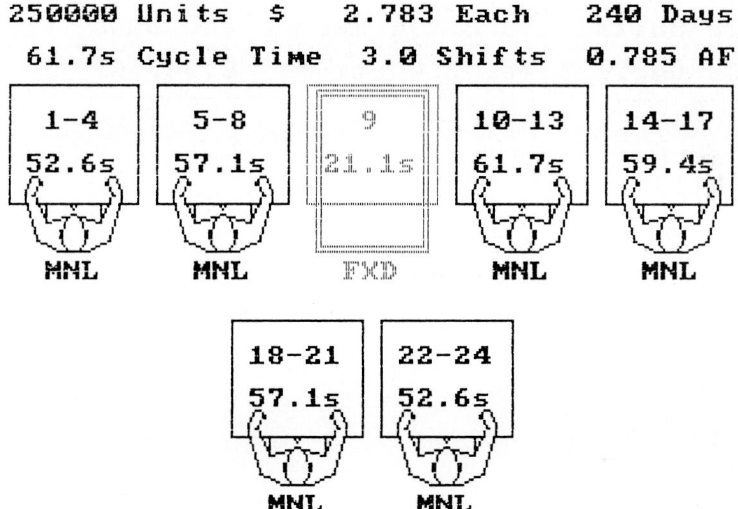

Fig. 16.7 Base assembly system. This represents how the new design would be assembled using manual techniques.

Note that each station has been charged for the cycle time (see Chap. 14) and not for only the actual time required to perform the task(s) at the station. All times shown in Figs. 16.7 and 16.8 correspond to expected throughput; theoretical time has been de-rated by the expected uptime of the resource type (see Chap. 14).

We must now do an economic comparison using the methods of Chap. 12. From Figs. 16.7 (the base) and 16.8 (the alternative), we obtain the actual cost and performance characteristics for the two systems. General results of the comparison are in Fig. 16.9; in this case, we assume a 3-year capital recovery period and constant material cost conditions since our goal is to compare only the assembly systems. The graph in Fig. 16.9(*b*) reveals that the alternative system provides unit cost improvement for each of the 3 years of the model. We have particular interest in the case in which the allowable investment equals the cost ($1,005,000) of the alternative automated system. While Fig.

A.C.M. FINAL ASSY. (250k 3yr)

75.29 seconds USABLE CYCLE TIME
85.0 % BOTTLENECK UP-TIME 47.81 UNITS/HR EXPECTED
275400 units ACTUAL CAPACITY OF THIS SYSTEM

1005000 ($) TOTAL INVESTMENT, RHO FACTOR = 2.18
1.70 WORKERS AT 19.00 $/hr REQUIRED
6.40 $/hr SYSTEM OPERATING/MAINTENANCE RATE

0.908 YEAR REQUIRED FOR 3.0 SHIFT OPERATION
240 DAYS REQUIRED FOR 2.72 SHIFT OPERATION

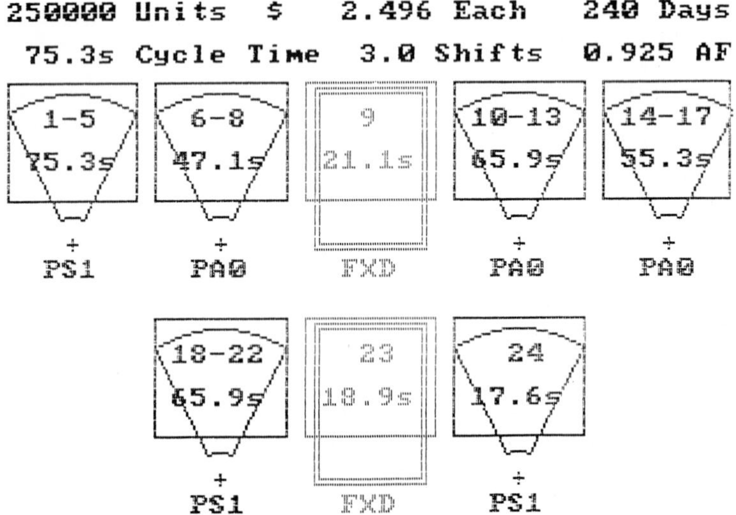

Fig. 16.8 Alternative assembly system for comparison with Fig. 16.7. This system was synthesized using optimal choices for each station.

16.9(*b*) allows an approximation, the precise expected cash flow behavior (see Fig. 16.10) shows that the actual internal rate of return would be 18.02 percent, which must be compared to the minimum acceptable return specified by the company.

If these conditions were the only ones to be evaluated, we could stop here. There can be significant value, however, in investigating a variety of production and economic requirements so that rational strategic decisions can be made. Using the method described above, we can assume different economic and production volume scenarios and define new base and alternative systems. The comparison between each pair of systems may be economically interesting to the company. For present purposes, we shall equate capital recovery years and the investment horizon (see Chap. 14) to establish the corresponding cost-effective systems. It is well known that the

A.C.M. FINAL ASSY. (250k 3yr)

MANUFACTURING COSTS 12-31-1987

240 WORKING DAYS PER YEAR
3.0 SHIFTS AVAILABLE
0.0 % ANNUAL INCREASE IN PRODUCTION
5.0 % ANNUAL COST INCREASE
3 YEAR RECOVERY OF CAPITAL EXPENSES
34.0 % TAX RATE IN YEAR 0 FOR EXPENSED INVESTMENT

45.9 % OF TOTAL COST IS DEPRECIABLE

COMPETING SYSTEM SPECIFICATIONS

	BASE	ALTERNATIVE
WORKERS REQUIRED PER SHIFT	7.48	1.70
AVERAGE LOADED LABOR RATE ($/HR)	19.00	19.00
OPERATING/MAINTENANCE RATE ($/HR)	3.80	6.40
IDEAL SYSTEM CYCLE TIME (SEC)	61.7	75.3
EXPECTED UP-TIME	100.0%	100.0%
MATERIAL COST ($/UNIT)	0.00	0.00
EXPECTED MATERIAL REJECT RATE	0.0%	0.0%
YEARLY SPACE ALLOCATION COST ($)	0	0
TOTAL SYSTEM COST ($)	180807	?
YEAR 1 VARIABLE COST ($/UNIT)	2.501	0.809
MATERIAL COST ($/UNIT)	0.000	0.000
TOTAL	2.501	0.809
YEAR 2 VARIABLE COST ($/UNIT)	2.626	0.850
MATERIAL COST ($/UNIT)	0.000	0.000
TOTAL	2.626	0.850
YEAR 3 VARIABLE COST ($/UNIT)	2.758	0.892
MATERIAL COST ($/UNIT)	0.000	0.000
TOTAL	2.758	0.892

1 YEAR NET COST SAVINGS REQUIRED

CASH FLOW PARAMETERS

YEAR	UNITS	SAVINGS	DEPRECIATION	TAX RATE	TAX CREDIT
1	250000	422986	14.29%	34.0%	0.0%
2	250000	444135	24.49%	34.0%	
3	250000	466342	17.49%	34.0%	
3*	SALVAGE VALUE		43.73%		

(a)

Fig. 16.9 Rate of return and allowable investment comparison between Figs. 16.7 and 16.8.

RATE of RETURN	ALLOWABLE INVESTMENT	APPROX. PAYBACK	ANNUAL COST	ALTERNATIVE SYSTEM - UNIT COST YEAR 1 250000	YEAR 2 250000	YEAR 3 250000
10%	1226697	3.04	418882	2.485	2.525	2.568
12%	1163472	2.90	415200	2.470	2.511	2.553
14%	1106010	2.78	411849	2.457	2.497	2.540
16%	1053575	2.66	408786	2.445	2.485	2.527
18%	1005548	2.56	405975	2.433	2.474	2.516
20%	961409	2.46	403388	2.423	2.463	2.506
22%	920714	2.37	400999	2.413	2.454	2.496
24%	883085	2.29	398785	2.405	2.445	2.487
26%	848197	2.21	396729	2.396	2.437	2.479
28%	815769	2.13	394815	2.389	2.429	2.472
30%	785555	2.06	393028	2.381	2.422	2.464
32%	757343	2.00	391356	2.375	2.415	2.458
34%	730945	1.94	389788	2.369	2.409	2.451
36%	706197	1.88	388316	2.363	2.403	2.446
38%	682954	1.82	386930	2.357	2.398	2.440
40%	661085	1.77	385624	2.352	2.392	2.435
42%	640477	1.72	384390	2.347	2.387	2.430
44%	621026	1.67	383223	2.342	2.383	2.425

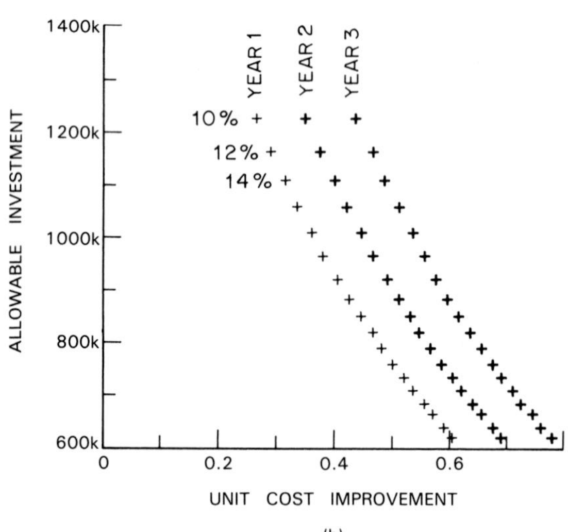

(b)

Fig. 16.9 *(Continued)*

A.C.M. FINAL ASSY. (250k 3yr)

ZERO PRESENT WORTH CASH FLOW ANALYSIS 01-04-1988

7 YEARS OF ECONOMIC LIFE, SALVAGE VALUE 0 % OF COST

	EXPENSE FORECAST			INCOME FORECAST			
YEAR	RATIO	TAX RATE	DEPRECIABLE	SAVINGS	DEPRECIATION	TAX RATE	CREDIT
0	100.00%	34.0%	45.9%				
1				422.986	14.29%	34.0%	0.0%
2				444.135	24.49%	34.0%	
3				466.342	17.49%	34.0%	
3*				SALVAGE VALUE	43.73%		

TOTAL INVESTMENT = 1005.000

DEPRECIABLE INVESTMENT = 461.295

INTERNAL RATE OF RETURN = 18.02%

PRO-FORMA CASH FLOW

YEAR	INCOME	DEPRECIATION	TAXES	CREDITS	NET	DISC. NET
0	-1005.000	0.000	-184.860	0.000	-820.140	-820.140
1	422.986	65.899	121.410	0.000	301.576	255.521
2	444.135	112.970	112.596	0.000	331.539	238.009
3	466.342	80.693	131.121	0.000	335.221	203.902
3*	201.733	0.000	0.000	0.000	201.733	122.706
INCOME TOTALS	1535.196	259.562	365.126	0.000	1170.070	820.138
NET TOTALS	530.196	259.562	180.267	0.000	349.929	-0.002

NOMINAL CAPITAL RECOVERY = 405.944

PAYBACK IN APPROXIMATELY 2.56 YEARS

Fig. 16.10 Zero present worth cash flow analysis of the system in Fig. 16.8 showing IRoR of 18 percent.

shorter the investment horizon, the greater the difficulty in justifying investment in automation. The real question becomes one of establishing the production and time conditions which meet the largest number of economic requirements.

Tables 16.1 through 16.6 exhibit least-cost systems for various production requirements and investment horizons. When plotted as Fig. 16.11, we can see the general behavior for numerous production volume possibilities. Note that the 3-year point on the 250,000/yr curve exhibits the 18 percent IRoR described earlier. Although the data for any particular production volume appears to be continuous, it generally is not. The specific points shown usually represent different sys-

TABLE 16.1 Comparison of Assembly Systems for 175,000 Units/Year

	BASE SYSTEM			ALTERNATIVE SYSTEM			ALTERNATIVE vs. BASE		
Investment Horizon	Components	Total Investment	Unit Cost *	Components	Total Investment	Unit Cost *	Variable Unit Cost Savings	Internal Rate of Return	Pay Back
1 year	3-MNL 1-FXD	$178k	$3.06	3-MNL 1-FXD	$178k	$3.06		N/A	
2 years	3-MNL 1-FXD	$178k	$2.92	3-MNL 1-FXD	$178k	$2.92		N/A	
3 years	3-MNL 1-FXD	$178k	$2.85	1-MNL 2-PA0 2-PS1 1-FXD	$767k	$3.05	$1.24 $1.30 $1.37	3.6%	3.6yr
4 years	3-MNL 1-FXD	$178k	$2.80	1-MNL 2-PA0 2-PS1 1-FXD	$767k	$2.60	$1.24 $1.30 $1.37 $1.43	10.1%	3.6yr

* Fixed cost assumed to be recovered at 20% MARR.

TABLE 16.2 Comparison of Assembly Systems for 250,000 Units/Year

Investment Horizon	BASE SYSTEM Components	BASE SYSTEM Total Investment	BASE SYSTEM Unit Cost *	ALTERNATIVE SYSTEM Components	ALTERNATIVE SYSTEM Total Investment	ALTERNATIVE SYSTEM Unit Cost *	ALTERNATIVE vs. BASE Variable Unit Cost Savings	ALTERNATIVE vs. BASE Internal Rate of Return	ALTERNATIVE vs. BASE Pay Back
1 year	6-MNL 1-FXD	$181k	$2.93	4-MNL 2-PA0 1-FXD	$399k	$3.18	$0.52	<18.0%>	N/A
2 years	6-MNL 1-FXD	$181k	$2.83	1-MNL 2-PA0 2-PSI 1-FXD	$740k	$2.64	$1.42 $1.49	12.5%	2.3 yr
3 years	6-MNL 1-FXD	$181k	$2.78	3-PA0 3-PSI 2-FXD	$1005k	$2.50	$1.69 $1.78 $1.87	18.0%	2.6 yr
4 years	6-MNL 1-FXD	$181k	$2.75	3-PA0 3-PSI 2-FXD	$1005k	$2.26	$1.69 $1.78 $1.87 $1.96	25.3%	2.6 yr

* Fixed cost recovered at assumed 20% rate-of-return.

TABLE 16.3 Comparison of Assembly Systems for 325,000 Units/Year

	BASE SYSTEM			ALTERNATIVE SYSTEM			ALTERNATIVE vs. BASE		
Investment Horizon	Components	Total Investment	Unit Cost *	Components	Total Investment	Unit Cost *	Variable Unit Cost Savings	Internal Rate of Return	Pay Back
1 year	6-MNL 1-FXD	$181k	$2.83	5-MNL 2-PA0 1-FXD	$424k	$3.23	$0.24	<28.0%>	N/A
2 years	6-MNL 1-FXD	$181k	$2.77	1-MNL 2-PA0 4-PS1 1-FXD	$978k	$2.56	$1.54 $1.62	15.4%	2.2 yr
3 years	6-MNL 1-FXD	$181k	$2.74	3-PA0 5-PSI 2-FXD	$1168k	$2.25	$1.77 $1.85 $1.95	25.3%	2.2yr
4 years	6-MNL 1-FXD	$181k	$2.72	3-PA0 5-PSI 2-FXD	$1168k	$2.03	$1.77 $1.85 $1.95 $2.04	32.7%	2.2yr

* Fixed cost recovered at assumed 20% rate-of-return.

TABLE 16.4 Comparison of Assembly Systems for 400,000 Units/Year

	BASE SYSTEM			ALTERNATIVE SYSTEM			ALTERNATIVE vs. BASE		
Investment Horizon	Components	Total Investment	Unit Cost *	Components	Total Investment	Unit Cost *	Variable Unit Cost Savings	Internal Rate of Return	Pay Back
1 year	9-MNL 1-FXD	$186k	$3.09	7-MNL 1-PAO 1-FXD	$312k	$2.86	$0.48	10.3 %	2.0yr
2 years	9-MNL 1-FXD	$186k	$3.03	3-PAO 5-PS1 2-FXD	$1260k	$2.36	$2.12 $2.23	30.8%	1.7yr
3 years	9-MNL 1-FXD	$186k	$3.00	3-PAO 5-PS1 2-FXD	$1260k	$2.02	$2.12 $2.23 $2.34	43.4%	1.7yr
4 years	9-MNL 1-FXD	$186k	$2.98	3-PAO 5-PS1 2-FXD	$1260k	$1.82	$2.12 $2.23 $2.34 $2.46	50.8%	1.7yr

* Fixed cost recovered at assumed 20% rate-of-return.

TABLE 16.5 Comparison of Assembly Systems for 550,000 Units/Year

	BASE SYSTEM			ALTERNATIVE SYSTEM			ALTERNATIVE vs. BASE		
Investment Horizon	Components	Total Investment	Unit Cost *	Components	Total Investment	Unit Cost *	Variable Unit Cost Savings	Internal Rate of Return	Pay Back
1 year	13-MNL 1-FXD	$188k	$3.15	4-MNL 3-PAO 1-PSI 6-FXD	$937k	$2.80	$1.41	22.6%	1.5yr
2 years	13-MNL 1-FXD	$188k	$3.11	5-PAO 6-PS1 2-FXD	$1543k	$2.13	$2.31 $2.43	44.7%	1.4yr
3 years	13-MNL 1-FXD	$188k	$3.09	5-PAO 6-PSI 2-FXD	$1543k	$1.82	$2.31 $2.43 $2.55	57.8%	1.4 yr
4 years	13-MNL 1-FXD	$188k	$3.08	5-PAO 6-PSI 2-FXD	$1543k	$1.65	$2.31 $2.43 $2.55 $2.68	65.1%	1.4 yr

* Fixed cost recovered at assumed 20% rate-of-return.

TABLE 16.6 Comparison of Assembly Systems for 750,000 Units/Year

	BASE SYSTEM			ALTERNATIVE SYSTEM			ALTERNATIVE vs. BASE		
Investment Horizon	Components	Total Investment	Unit Cost *	Components	Total Investment	Unit Cost *	Variable Unit Cost Savings	Internal Rate of Return	Pay Back
1 year	24-MNL 2-FXD	$346k	$3.34	10-MNL 2-PA0 9-FXD	$927k	$2.65	$1.24	40.5%	1.3yr
2 years	24-MNL 2-FXD	$346k	$3.27	7-PA0 2-PS1 7-FXD	$1705k	$2.01	$2.21 $2.32	57.9%	1.2yr
3 years	24-MNL 2-FXD	$346k	$3.23	9-PA0 3-PS1 7-FXD	$1780k	$1.78	$2.27 $2.38 $2.50	69.2%	1.2yr
4 years	24-MNL 2-FXD	$346k	$3.20	9-PA0 3-PS1 7-FXD	$1780k	$1.64	$2.27 $2.38 $2.50 $2.63	76.0%	1.2yr

* Fixed cost assumed to be recovered at 20% MARR.

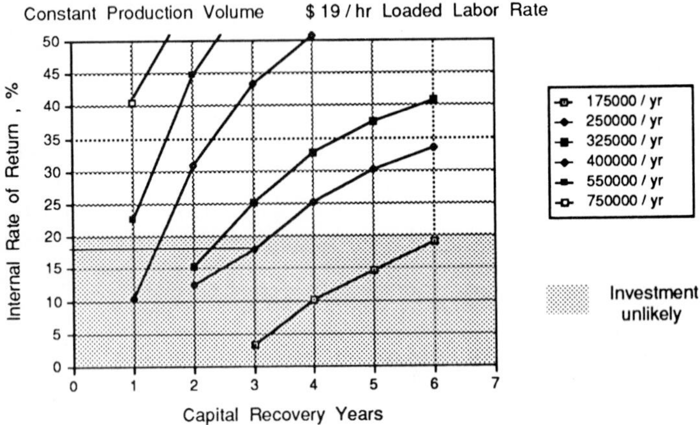

Fig. 16.11 Summary comparison of IRoR versus capital recovery years and annual production volume alternatives for ACM final assembly systems synthesized by computer.

tems (for both the base and the alternative) as shown in Tables 16.1 through 16.6. What Fig. 16.11 shows is this:

- Systems that include automation for producing 175,000 units do not meet the established (20 percent minimum) investment guideline.
- Any automated system that produces more than about 500,000 units per year can be economically justified.
- For 400,000 units per year production, at least 1½ years capital recovery are required. For 325,000 units per year, 2½ years are necessary.
- For capital recovery, 3⅓ years are required when the production volume is 250,000 units per year.

Summary

The air conditioning module is a fine example of concurrent design. Product design accounted for as many manufacturing considerations as possible while still providing all the required functions. The result was a product very easily assembled by people or by automation. Data exhibited in this section allowed the company to make rational choices for assembly systems for various production volumes and economic criteria. A general conclusion is that the larger the production volume and/or the longer the capital recovery period, the greater the number of automated stations that can be economically justified.

Robot Assembly of Automobile Rear Axles

Introduction and general approach

This section summarizes a study of automobile rear-drive independent suspension rear axles made to determine the feasibility of automating all or part of their final assembly.[1] The axle is illustrated in Fig. 16.12. The project involved all aspects of assembly, both technical and economic, including:

- Assembly operations
- Assembly system design and floor layout

[1] This section is actually a composite of several actual studies.

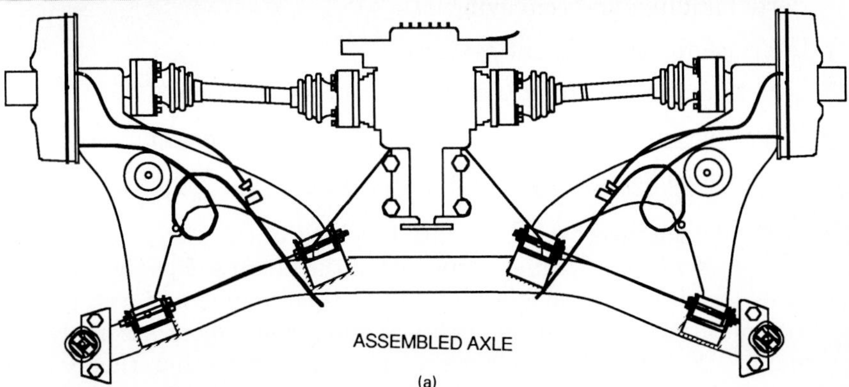

(a)

Fig. 16.12(a) Independent rear suspension rear axle, shown in the "upside down" orientation (compared to its orientation in the car).

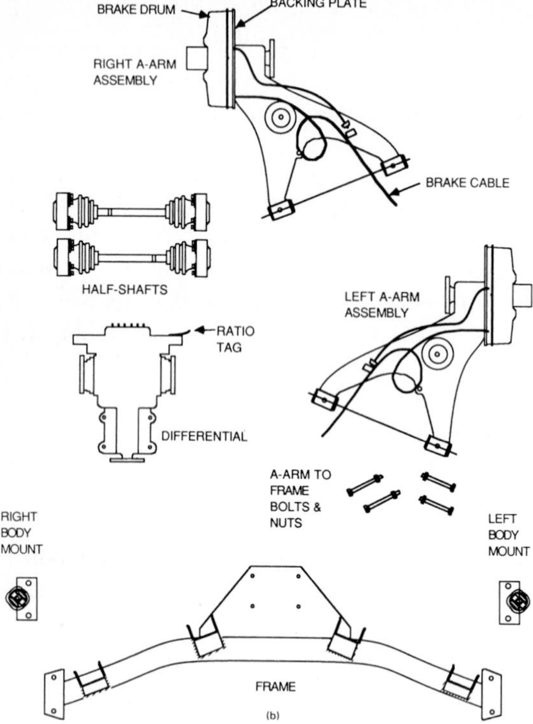

Fig. 16.12(b) Parts of the rear axle.

- Material flow timing and workstation timing
- Robots, tooling, and controls
- Parts handling and conveying
- Interface to management systems
- Investment cost estimates and financial justifications
- Computer simulations, transport studies, and throughput studies
- Suggestions for redesigns to improve ability to automate

The client's engineers were heavily involved in the study.

The project began with a statement of the client's objectives for the product, dealing with model mix, production volume and cost projections, quality issues, and the desire to learn more about assembly automation. Engineering analyses based on part-mating theory (see Chap. 5) were used to predict difficult mates, which often arise from close clearances and tolerance stack-ups, including robot, jig, and gripper errors. Several alternative assembly sequences were considered, since these alternatives affect final system layout, cost, tolerances, jig and grip surfaces, deployment of people where necessary, and so on. Several redesigns and robot lab experiments were suggested to reduce assembly risk, obtain timing data, or make several operations feasible for automatic assembly.

Candidate assembly sequences were then paired with possible assembly technologies, including fixed automation, robots, and people, using the algorithms in Chap. 14. These were analyzed by computer simulation and economic justification programs to determine good candidate systems for presentation to the client. Vendors were consulted concerning feasibility and cost for various robots, tools, and transport options. A final list of options was presented, along with our recommendations.

In the description of the study that follows, the reader will often encounter conclusions before they are justified by analysis. The reason for this is that the design process is iterative—some of the decisions depend on each other. The focus of this iteration is the choice of transport method, and the iteration will be explicitly noted at that point. Elsewhere the reader will merely find decisions whose explanations are promised later.

Characteristics of the rear axle

The axle is made in several models but the differences are internal to the differential and the brake systems. These comprise different gear ratios and, possibly, disk rather than drum brakes. In the future the client may want the option to assemble other models on the proposed assembly system. These models would be geometrically similar and have the same part identity and count but would be larger by perhaps 5 to 10 percent. Production volumes are currently projected to be in the range of 250,000 to 300,000 per year, with future models adding about 20 percent.

This is a mature product, well tested in the field. Only minor redesigns were considered acceptable. These deal with part mates that are presently deemed difficult or unsuitable for robots or automatic machines: attachment of the "A-arms" to the frame and insertion and coiling of the emergency brake cables. Solutions require increased attention to tolerances on a welded assembly or cooperation with vendors.

Two other aspects of the product affect the feasibility of automation, namely the accuracy of part fabrication and the method of presenting parts to the assembly system. In some instances, the probability of unsuccessful part mating is increased by parts that mate with tight tolerances and do not always have the generous chamfers shown on the drawings. As is typical in such situations, assembly workers have learned to overcome these problems, but automated systems are not yet that smart. The tooling and part-mating recommendations were aimed at overcoming these problems, but it is generally advisable to correct them where they occur.

Because redesign was not a major feature of this study, the emphasis fell on tooling and assembly system design. A major study point concerned options for material transport, kitting, and part provisioning. Provision of parts on kits was compared to more conventional feeding directly to the production line on conveyors and racks. Automated guided vehicles (AGVs) were compared to inverted monorails technically and economically, including counting how many vehicles were needed for carrying either a pallet fixture or a pallet plus parts kit(s). The interface between fabrication and assembly, which occurs at the kitting or conveyor loading area, was also examined carefully to determine feasible alternatives. These include structured dunnage ("dunnage" refers to either disposable or reused parts carriers, baskets, boxes, etc.), simple vision systems, and better parts handling in the fabrication areas.

We took as a starting point a preliminary system design and floor layout created by the client. This design was refined as to task definitions and times, using the client's standard time data, for comparison to designs the authors generated. All these designs used the same database of candidate task times and equipment costs, even though different assembly sequences and equipment choices were tried.

The candidate systems were similar in most respects to systems we are aware of around the world, although the most ambitious ones undoubtedly were preceded by thorough redesign of the product. The public literature includes information on VW's Hall 54 for automated final car assembly and engine dressing, FIAT's Termoli, Italy, engine assembly plant, and recent GM developments on engine assembly and dashboard installation. At various points, these systems include heavy workpieces, AGVs, vision systems, tool changing robots, two or three robots at one station, robot-borne cluster-head nut runners, a mix of people and automation in the same system, and so on. Completely unattended assembly is a goal in some cases. This is not readily attained without extensive redesign. The added cost of redesigned parts, if any, must be compared to the expected savings in reliability of the system, product quality, cost growth control, and so on.

Part-mating issues

Every part mate involved in axle final assembly was studied. Two involve risky mates, affect possible assembly sequences, or have other impacts on the final assembly system. These include attaching A-arms to the frame and mating half shafts to the A-arms and the differential. Each operation will be discussed in turn.

Major parts

The major parts are the frame, the differential (with its four mounting bolts, nuts, and washers), two body mounts (with two bolts and nuts each), two A-arms (with wheels, brake cables, and brake drums already installed, plus their two hinge bolts and nuts), and two half shafts (with six bolts and three bridge washers at each end of each shaft). Each of these bolted joints is of critical safety importance and the torque must be measured and certified to be within specifications.

It is assumed that the frame is to be attached to a fixture on which it will ride throughout assembly. However, it may not be the first part placed in the fixture. The approximate sizes and weights of the parts are as follows:

Frame	48 in (1.2 m); 22 lb (10 kg)
Body mounts	4 in (10 cm); 2.2 lb (1 kg) each
Differential	20 in (50 cm); 44 lb (20 kg)
A-arm assembly	32 in (80 cm); 33 lb (15 kg) each
Half shaft	16 in (40 cm); 11 lb (5 kg) each

The assembly operations are:

1. Mate body mounts to frame using bolts and nuts
2. Mate A-arms to frame using hinge bolts and nuts
3. Mate half shafts to A-arms using bolts
4. Mate half shafts to differential using bolts
5. Mate differential to frame using bolts and nuts

Assembly of A-arms to the frame involves heavy parts. Two locations on the arm must pass between ends of brackets that are welded to the frame and then must be positioned so that hinge bolts may be passed through and fastened with nuts. The lateral clearance available to fit the arm ends into the brackets ranges from 0.008 to 0.120 in (0.2 to 3 mm). Bolt-to-hole clearances range from 0 to 0.004 in (0.1 mm). Assembly is aided by the fact that A-arm ends contain rubber grommets that mate to the frame brackets. However, the large chamfers at the open ends of the brackets that appear on the drawings are almost nonexistent on real parts. Widening these chamfers is essential to successful mechanical assembly. The alternative would be to greatly tighten the tolerances on the widths of all the mating parts as well as tolerances on location of the brackets. However, the brackets are welded to the frame, so their location and final dimensions are bound to be somewhat uncertain. Furthermore, tightening tolerances is expensive as well as unnecessary. Another recommendation was to provide tapered tips on the hinge bolts. These recommendations were accepted (see Fig. 16.13).

The differential is also heavy, but its mate to the frame is simple. Its mate to the half shafts is not simple, however, and must be considered when assembly of shafts to A-arms and of A-arms to frame are considered. We suggested further simplifying the fastening of the differential to the frame by making the nuts captive to the frame in some way. While not accepted immediately, this suggestion was later included in a major redesign of the frame in which the nuts were replaced by threaded holes in the differential itself.

Mating of half shafts to differential and A-arms involves several steps. People currently make a subassembly offline consisting of a half shaft and an A-arm. The loose end of the shaft has the bolts and bridge washers already installed. [The rubber boots around the constant velocity (CV) joints keep the bolts from falling out.] Because of the action of the CV joint, the length of a shaft can be changed over a range of 1.25 in (3.175 cm) with considerable manual effort. The differential is added to the frame first. Then the shaft-arm subassembly is added. The assemblers compress the shaft to minimum length, support both the arm and the shaft in two hands, drop the arm ends into the frame, and push the shaft's cone end into the differential flange's cup. Attachment of the bolts involves rotating the shaft (or the brake drum) while pushing on the bolts until the holes align and the bolts drop in, then driving the bolts. This is an involved and dexterous procedure which we wished to avoid or simplify in mechanized assembly by

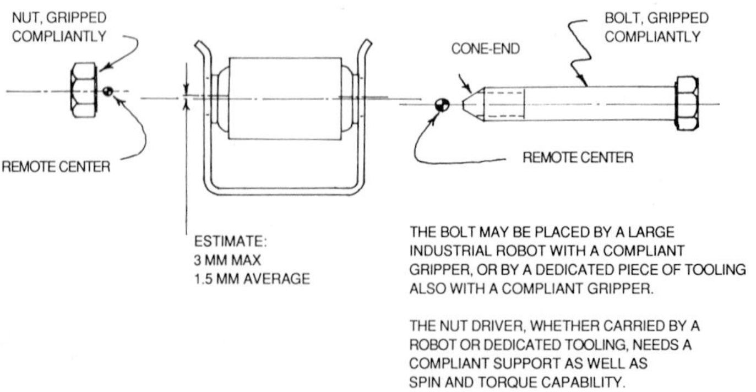

Fig. 16.13 Design improvements to aid mating of A-arms to frame.

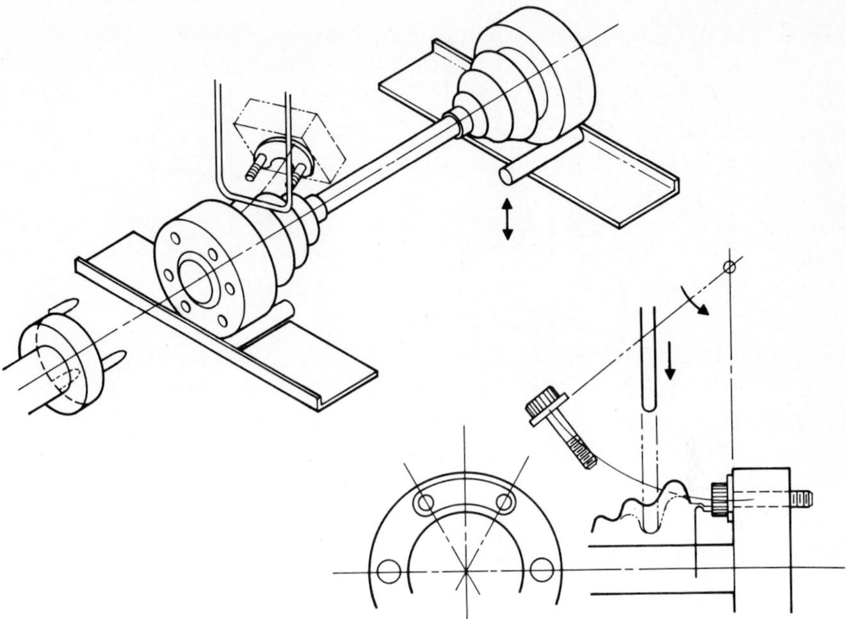

Fig. 16.14 Tooling concept for tightening shaft bolts.

changing the assembly sequence or method. Figure 16.14 shows a possible concept for tightening the bolts automatically.

Assembly of body mounts is simple in principle, involving only part placement and installation of bolts and nuts. However, the mounts install "underneath" (from the opposite side with respect to the differential), so they cannot merely be set in place on the frame and then secured. We inquired about a design change to allow the mounts to be added from the "top" but were told that safety was an issue; in the current design, if the frame-to-mount bolts drop out, the car will still be supported because the axle frame is trapped between the mount and the body itself. In our redesign, loss of the bolts would result in the frame falling to the ground. Figure 16.15 shows a tooling concept for attaching the body mounts to the frame from "underneath."

Brake cables present serious assembly difficulties that rippled through the entire study. They are awkward, and both ends must be dealt with at different times during assembly. The drum must be put on after one end of the cable is installed in the backing plate and before the other end is wrapped temporarily around the A-arm (see Chap. 9, Fig. 9.3, for a similar arrangement). The last operation seems unavoidably manual, forcing one of two alternatives: If brake drum installation were automated, a person would still be needed atthe end

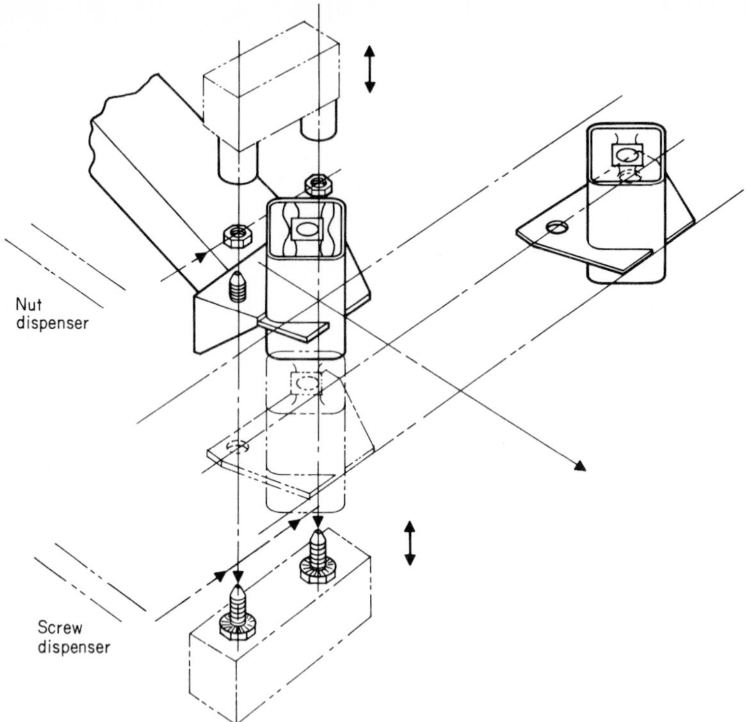

Fig. 16.15 Tooling concept for attaching body mounts to frame from "underneath."

of the line just to wrap cables around the A-arm, or brake drum installation could be manual and the person who installed them would also wrap the cables.

In this case, the client did not have sufficient space for an integrated final assembly system including assembly of the A-arms and chose to build A-arms manually as subassemblies. At final axle assembly, the brake cables must be unwrapped from the A-arms and threaded through holes in the frame. This awkward task will still be manual until extensive redesign is undertaken.

The ratio tag is an awkward part, hard to feed, easy to lose. We recommended that it be replaced with some other marking method, such as bar codes. The bar code could include model and date and time information and could be used by the production control system to coordinate launching of kits or matching model-specific parts to each axle.

Other parts and tasks

In general, other parts do not present great difficulties. Nuts can be fed down chutes to nut runners. Robotic pickup of kitted or conveyor-fed shafts, frames, and A-arms can be aided by attention to kit tolerances and gripper design. Simple vision systems above pallets or on grippers might be needed to take out gripping uncertainty, or grippers could be designed with wide enough throw and attention to closure motions so that parts are gripped correctly even if they are a bit off location in the kit. Such methods might eventually allow automatic kitting, depending on how much it costs to obtain good structured dunnage.

Part fabrication

It was noted above that some parts are not made as specified by the prints. The differences may not affect axle performance but could cause problems for assembly machine design and operation. We recommended that the parts be made to print or else a set of "as built" prints be prepared for issue to the vendors. This will help ensure that tools, grippers, and fixtures are designed to as accurate specifications as possible, reducing the risk of rework and delay in getting the assembly system operating at full capacity.

From a management point of view, one should strive for the level of quality that the product or the assembly system needs. The assembly system will "inspect" the parts and probably jam on ones that are too far out of tolerance. From an economic point of view, one must remember that the parts probably account for about 93 percent of an axle's in-plant cost, and final assembly accounts for only about 7 percent. Efforts to improve part quality just to facilitate assembly could cost too much.

Assembly sequences

The assembly of this product is fairly straightforward and there are not very many assembly sequence options. An informal analysis quickly revealed the choices, and a full liaison sequence analysis was not needed. One may build the axle "right side up" or "up side down." If right side up is used, the A-arms and differential are underneath the frame while the body mounts are on top of it. These relationships are reversed if the axle is built upside down [refer to Fig. 16.12(*a*)]. In addition, there is one important subassembly option, namely that of adding half shafts to A-arms before assembling either to the frame.

Either right side up or up side down assembly sequences present problems with respect to the nuts and bolts which are used to fasten most of the parts together. Referring to upside down, the differential is fastened with bolts inserted from above while the body mounts are fastened with bolts inserted from below.

Another subassembly option is to add the body mounts to the frame before putting the frame on the main assembly line. This option removes the associated fastening problem from the main line so that all bolts on the line enter from above, with the nuts inserted from below. The mounts are light and could be installed and bolted by simple fixed automation equipment.

Although the subassemblies remain an option, it was decided to pursue only upside down assembly. This orientation is better for ease of installing the A-arms to the frames.

Tooling, jigs, fixtures, and workstations

This section covers design of pallets, kits, and robot workstations. These designs required a decision as to how many axles to put on a pallet. Economic and system timing considerations (see below) showed that, depending on the speed of the pallet transport system, either one or four axles per pallet might be economically preferable.

Pallet design must conform to access needs of people, robots, and kits. For economy, one pallet design was used for all axle models. A suitable design for four axles per pallet places them on about 27-in centers, leaving about 16 in for a walk-in space to help a person attach the half shafts to the differential, if that were to remain a manual task (see Fig. 16.16). If longer pallets were used to create more space for people between axles, rotational-type robots would have difficulty reaching four axles. (Typical robots in this class include the Cincinnati Milacron T^3 767 or the GMF S 360R, each with about a 100-in reach and 150-lb payload. KUKA, ASEA, and Toshiba make similar robots.) If longer pallets are necessary, the robot's reach could be extended by mounting it on a linear axis along side the pallet at an extra cost of \$20 to \$30K and about 3 s per move. Alternatively, the pallet could make two stops near a fixed-base robot.

Robot access difficulties arise because of the unusable space around its center (see Fig. 16.17). This space has typically a 36- to 45-in radius. The unusable space problem is not solved by mounting the robot upside down. It is eased, however, by using the powered linear axis parallel to the pallet.

An alternative to rotational robots is gantries. Their reach is essentially unlimited. However, they are typically about twice as expensive as rotational robots. They were recommended only where their reach is essential.

We recommended that all reach estimates be confirmed by full-scale three-dimensional CAD simulations or actual mockups. The above studies used scale two-dimensional CAD based on manufacturers' drawings of reachable regions in their literature. Such regions may shrink when different wrist axis position combinations are used. Only the Cincinnati Milacron "3 roll wrist" may be immune to such prob-

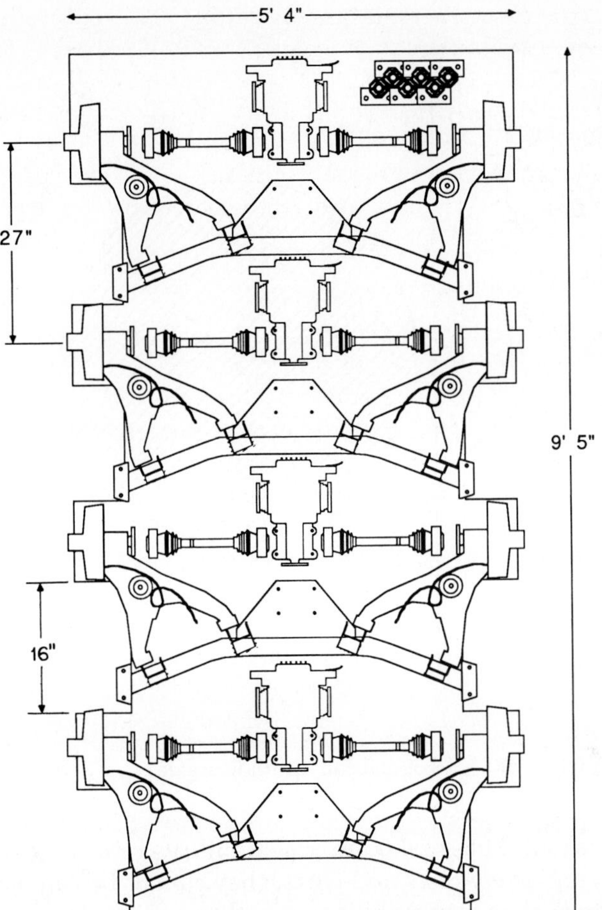

Fig. 16.16 Assembly pallet with four axles on it. All the parts are shown to demonstrate that they can be kitted onto the pallet or to show that there is space to move them in for assembly purposes if they are fed from the side of the line at each assembly station.

lems. Figure 16.17 shows a typical robot reach analysis, of which about 25 were done for this study.

The speed and repeatability of suitable rotational robots appear adequate for the axle's tasks. We assumed cycle times ranging from 10 to 35 s, depending on the task, plus about 3 s to reach from one axle to the next on the pallet. A 10-s tool change time allowance is probably more than enough, especially if tools are centrally located near the pallet. Experiments to verify task times were recommended because so much of the system design depends on timing and line balance.

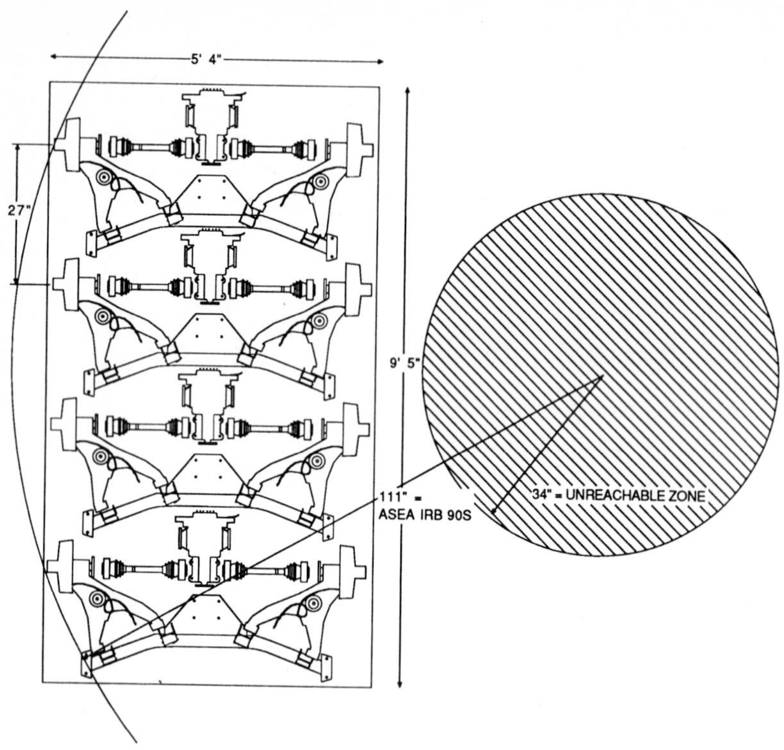

Fig. 16.17 Reach analysis for an ASEA robot and pallet with four axles.

These robots have about 0.02- to 0.05-in repeatability. To avoid oscillations when carrying heavy tools and parts, they cannot be run at full speed. To compensate for repeatability and other errors (jigging, part fabrication, gripping), chamfers were recommended on grippers, grip surfaces of parts, and the entry faces of mating parts. The width of these chamfers must sum to dimensions larger than the largest contemplated errors. Chapter 11 shows how these calculations are performed. To reduce contact forces during mating in the presence of error, it was recommended that tools contain engineered compliances such as remote center compliances (see Chap. 7).

If kitting were chosen, a parts kit would contain the half shafts, A-arms, and differential for one axle assembly. Kits would be approximately 5.5 ft long by 2 ft wide and would go on the pallet before the frame. We noted, however, that kits of the required size would crowd the space needed for assembly unless either a separate kit pallet (and transport vehicle) was provided or as few as one or two axles rode a pallet. Extra vehicles would be costly and geometrically awkward. Kitting would thus rule out four axles per pallet.

Assembly system design

Assembly system design has six main aspects: capacity planning, equipment choice, assignment of tasks to equipment, transport choice, floor layout, and kitting. These interact heavily, and there are many alternatives. We identified several cases worth studying deeply. Computer synthesis, analysis, and simulation tools played a large role in the design. Table 16.7 lists the alternatives studied.

Capacity planning

Capacity is influenced by several factors:

- The speed of individual workstations
- Time lost while robots change tools
- Time lost while people or robots shift attention from one axle on a pallet to the next (unit-unit time)
- Time lost shifting from one pallet to another or waiting while transport takes a pallet away and brings another (station-station time)

Robot tool changing is needed only if a robot is given more than one task and different tools are needed for some of them. Shifting from one axle to another arises if several axles are on a pallet versus only one. Finally, time is lost shifting pallets between stations because of their size; lost time can be reduced by double-buffering pallets at stations,

TABLE 16.7 Assembly System Options Studied

PRODUCTION VOLUME	# UNITS PER PALLET	UNIT-UNIT TIME	STATION-STATION TIME	TOOL CHANGE TIME	REMARKS
300000 PER YEAR	1	3 SEC	5 SEC	5 SEC	INVERTED MONORAIL CONVEYOR
↓	2	3 SEC	5 SEC	5 SEC	↓
↓	4	3 SEC	5 SEC	5 SEC	↓
↓	1	3 SEC	15 SEC	5 SEC	AUTOMATED GUIDED VEHICLES
↓	2	3 SEC	15 SEC	5 SEC	↓
↓	4	3 SEC	15 SEC	5 SEC	↓

although this requires the purchase of additional pallets. Transport type also affects station-station time, with AGVs assumed to be slower than conveyors unless double buffering is used. (Double buffering involves providing two work locations for a robot; the robot works at one while transport brings a new pallet to the other. This technique works well for stations with one robot but is almost impossible to arrange at stations with one robot on each side of a work area or with fixed automation equipment. Two robots might be used for cooperative work to mate half shafts, the differential, and the frame, for example.)

Two basic system configuration options are possible, serial and parallel. Serial systems represent the extreme in division of labor and efficiency. Each workstation does one task before passing the work to the next station. A system for assembling a high-volume product with 10 assembly steps might have 10 workstations in series. The parallel configuration gives several jobs to one station. Such a station could have one or more people or one or more robots. The multiple jobs could be in the form of several steps on one product unit, several product units within reach at once, or both. The time penalties cited above apply: tool change and shifting from job to job. For the high-volume product cited above, a parallel system might contain 10 identical stations, each of which performs an entire assembly. Alternatively it could contain five identical stations each doing the first five steps, followed by five more stations that each do the last five steps. Naturally, such stations must be capable of doing several tasks; usually this means that they are either manual or robotic.

Long ago it was shown at Ford that the most productive manual assembly line has maximum division of labor and a moving conveyor that brings work to the employees. The moving line turned out to be about 2.5 times more productive at the time (1913) than the team assembly approach it replaced. However, there are large benefits to be gained from giving several jobs to one person, including pride of workmanship. Thus the team method has reappeared in recent years.

Automated systems can also benefit from having several jobs at one station. A system with several parallel stations is on average likely to be more resistant to breakdowns, since production can continue on other duplicate stations when one station is down. A serial line with one job per station is quite vulnerable to breakdowns unless there are buffers between stations. Since station times are short in assembly systems, buffers large enough to provide significant breakdown protection (say 30 min of work) would be very large, especially for large products like axles.

Another advantage of parallel automated systems is that their capacity can be increased incrementally by adding identical stations one at a time. By contrast, serial systems' capacity can be increased only by duplicating the entire system. In this regard, parallel systems are more flexible.

An important disadvantage of parallel systems appears when some of the stations are expensive. Because parallel systems require several copies of each station to be purchased, the cost can rise rapidly with the number of duplications.

In the present case, the economics favored a system with several fixed automation stations, severely limiting the opportunities for a parallel arrangement. The reasons for this conclusion are discussed in the next section.

A second choice related to the above discussion concerns the number of axles per pallet. We considered quantities from one to four. Several axles per pallet has the beneficial effect of spreading over several axles the lost time caused by tool changes and shifting pallets in and out of the station. More than four per pallet could cause robot reach problems.

On the other hand, four axles per pallet can cause problems if only one person is assigned to a station. To install the body mounts on several axles on a pallet, for example, the person would have to walk around to the other side of the pallet to do half the task. This wastes a lot of time. At higher production volumes, several people would be needed to do the work and it would be natural to assign some of them to each side of the pallet. However, as discussed in the next section, at this product's production volume, manual stations contained only one person.

Furthermore, system synthesis studies showed that there was a cost penalty associated with fixed automation equipment that was designed to be large enough to deal with four axles. This cost was not offset by the time saving associated with sharing station-station move time over four axles except in the case where AGVs were used (15-s station-station time). This conclusion, too, emerged from the studies discussed in the next section.

Equipment choice and task assignment

These two aspects of system design are discussed together because the algorithms described in Chap. 14 do both at once in an optimal way that meets the required production volume while minimizing annualized cost per axle. The issue of serial versus parallel stations and number of axles per pallet can also be resolved economically at the same time. The number and type of transport vehicles can be decided as well if one iterates between system syntheses and scale floor layouts of the system.

Equipment choice required preparation of a database containing candidate "equipment" (people, robots, or fixed automation) that gave purchase cost, operating cost, operating speed, need for human supervision, and other economic data. For each assembly step, candidates were listed, including estimated task time. Engineering judgment is required when deciding which equipment types are suitable candidates for each task and when estimating task times. The relevant data for the axle appear in Table 16.8.

This table indicates that four assembly resource types were considered: manual (MAN), fixed automation (FXD), a small robot of the SCARA type (RBS), and a large jointed robot (RBB). All resource types were deemed adequate for all assembly tasks except that RBS was suitable only for tasks 2 and 3 because of its small size and load capacity, and task 7 was deemed manual. To account for the cost of monorails or AGVs, a transport resource (TRN) was also provided.

The computer calculated the attainable production rate while allowing for necessary tool changes and dead time while pallets are shifted in and out. Each type of resource was assigned an uptime factor (ranging from 80 percent for people to 99 percent for transport) to allow for personal time or failures.

In this study, 5 s were allowed for a tool change (10 s for a large robot). Station-station move time for an AGV was set at 15 s. An inverted monorail conveyor was given 5 s. Choosing four axles per pallet greatly reduced the effects of these time differences.

Table 16.9 shows the results of these analyses. This table shows that the best (i.e., lowest unit cost) combination is given by one unit per pallet and 5-s station-station time, meaning use of monorail conveyors rather than AGVs. If AGVs are desired for other reasons, the recommendation is to use four axles per pallet. Single-shift operation results in the opportunity to choose a parallel station layout because of the large number of human resources needed. However, the unit cost penalty is evident.

As a result of these studies, a serial system layout consisting of three people, three fixed automation stations, and one each of the robot types was selected. It is shown schematically in Fig. 16.18. The system synthesis algorithm does not consider enough geometric information and constraints to permit a detailed station layout to be designed entirely by computer. Thus the engineers improved this design by doing the following:

1. Reversing the sequence of tasks 1 and 2, putting the body mounts on the frames while the frames are in the feeder track before they are put on the pallet, thus employing the fastener-motivated subassembly discussed above
2. Using the large robot for part of its cycle to obtain and hold the

TABLE 16.8 Applicable Technology Chart for the Rear Axle

APPLICABLE TECHNOLOGY CHART

TITLE IRS Rear Axle DATE 6/4/88

235 WORKING DAYS PER YEAR — 0.2395 ANNUALIZED COST FACTOR

2 SHIFTS AVAILABLE — $24 AVERAGE LOADED LABOR RATE ($/h)

5 or 15 s STATION-TO-STATION MOVE TIME — PREPARED BY: [illegible]

RESOURCE DATA SET NAME: IRSDAT — TASK DATA SET NAME: IRSTSK

	UNITS	DAYS
PRODUCTION BATCH DATA	200,000	
	250,000	
	300,000	
	600,000	

FOR EACH RESOURCE:

- C HARDWARE COST ($)
- ρ INSTALLED COST / HARDWARE COST
- ϵ UP-TIME EXPECTED (%)
- V OPERATING / MAINTENANCE RATE ($/hr)
- t_c Seconds TOOL CHANGE TIME
- m_s MAXIMUM STATIONS PER WORKER

WHEN A RESOURCE CAN BE USED ON A TASK: OPERATION TIME (s) | TOOL NUMBER / HARDWARE COST ($)

TASK NUMBER \ RESOURCE	MAN C: 2000 ρ: 1.5 ϵ: 80 v: 4.00 t_c: 5 m_s: 0.83	FXD C: 0 ρ: 1.5 ϵ: 95 v: 6.00 t_c: 5 m_s: 4	RBS C: 40000 ρ: 2.5 ϵ: 90 v: 6.00 t_c: 5 m_s: 4	RBB C: 80000 ρ: 2.5 ϵ: 90 v: 6.00 t_c: 10 m_s: 4	TRN C: ρ: ϵ: v: t_c: m_s:
1. PUT FRAME ON PALLET	15 | 101 15000	10 | 201 75000	X	10 | 401 10 000	X
2. ATTACH BODY MOUNTS TO FRAME	25 | 102 5000	15 | 202 100 000	15 | 302 20000	15 | 402 20 000	X
3. SUBASSEMBLE SHAFTS TO A-ARMS	60 | 103 30 000	15 | 203 300 000	25 | 303 40 000	25 | 403 50 000	X
4. ATTACH A-ARMS TO FRAME	30 | 104 2000	15 | 204 300 000	X	20 | 404 40 000	X
5. PLACE DIFF ON FRAME	15 | 105 15000	10 | 205 150 000	X	8 | 405 20 000	X
6. MATE DIFF, SHAFTS, & FRAME	75 | 106 15000	20 | 206 250 000	X	35 | 406 50 000	X
7. ARRANGE BRAKE CABLES, ATTACH TO FRAME	40 | 107 2000	X	X	X	X
8. Transport: CONVEYOR OR AGV'S	X	X	X	X	5 | 508 258000
				OR:	963300

A-arm so that the small robot can maneuver the axle shaft onto it and drive the bolts

3. Using station 3 simply for manually placing the differential on the frame a few inches to the left of its final location and aligning the half shafts to the differential laterally and rotationally in anticipa-

TABLE 16.9 Results of System Synthesis Analyses

Each solution is based on providing 300,000 units per year. Some designs have reserve capacity above this level.

# UNITS PER PALLET	UNIT-UNIT TIME	STATION-STATION TIME	TOOL CHANGE TIME	# SHIFTS	UNIT COST	SOLUTION I J K M N
1	3 SEC	5 SEC	5 SEC	2	$3.32	3 3 1 1 1*
1	3 SEC	5 SEC	5 SEC	1	$3.93	10 4 0 0 1
4	3 SEC	5 SEC	5 SEC	2	$3.62	3 2 1 1 1
1	3 SEC	15 SEC	5 SEC	2	$4.71	4 2 1 1 1
4	3 SEC	15 SEC	5 SEC	2	$4.47	3 2 1 1 1

*NOTE: SOLUTION TYPE "IJKMN" MEANS THAT THE RECOMMENDED SYSTEM CONTAINS I MANUAL WORKERS, J FIXED AUTOMATION STATIONS, K SMALL ROBOTS, M LARGE ROBOTS, AND N TRANSPORT RESOURCES. N IS ALWAYS 1.

tion that final mating of differential, half shafts, and frame will occur at the next station

4. Providing that station with sliding action under the pallet to maneuver the differential and half shafts into their mated positions

This design is reasonable in that it gives fixed automation some straightforward assembly actions, reserving for a person or robot those tasks which require maneuvering in several degrees of freedom at once or a possible search for correct mating and alignment. Figure 16.19 shows the major assembly operations arranged in four stations for the case of one axle per pallet.

A review of the floor layout in scale as shown by this figure indicates that the actions performed by the SCARA and jointed robots at station 2 might better be carried out by a SCARA and a gantry or by two gantries that share a common set of rails arranged parallel to the direction of pallet motion. This decision awaits detailed design of the line, which is beyond the scope of this chapter.

Choice of transport method

Two types of transport were investigated, AGVs and inverted monorails. The cost of these was included in the system synthesis studies. An iterative approach was required because the cost of transport

```
IRS REAR AXLE-300K-CONV-1 AX/PALLET

              33.33 seconds  Usable Cycle Time
     90.0 %  Bottleneck up-time      108.00  Units/hr expected
          406080 units  Actual Capacity of this System

      1433000 ($)   Total Investment,   rho Factor =  1.58
             5.06 Workers at  24.00 $/hr required
         46.00 $/hr  System Operating/Maintenance Rate

           0.739 Year required for 2.0 Shift Operation
            235 Days required for 1.48 Shift Operation
```

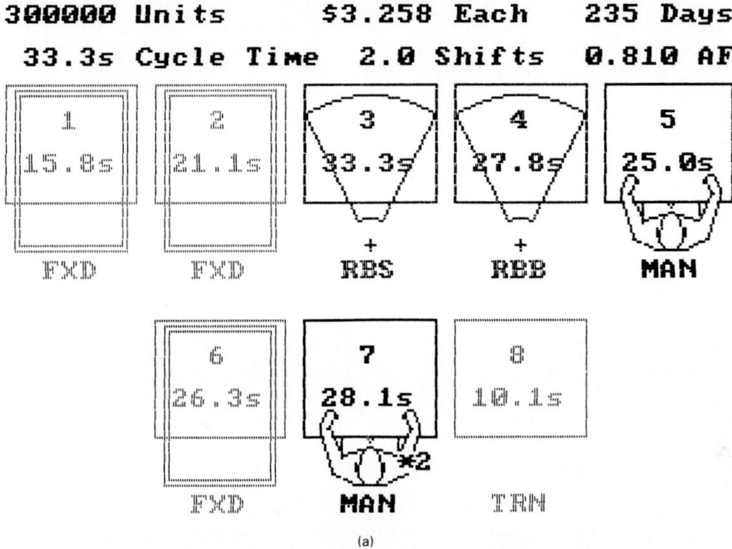

(a)

Fig. 16.18 System synthesis output showing schematic design of assembly system.

method depends on floor layout and number of stations to be served, which depends on equipment selection and task assignment, which depends on cost of transport, among other factors. The analysis method consisted of using system synthesis to obtain the required number of stations, making a rough floor layout, determining the length of transport track needed and approximate number of vehicles, then determining a cost for an inverted monorail system and an AGV system, and finally rerunning system synthesis with TRN resources representing these costs.

AGVs and inverted monorails are each capable of switching pallets between destinations, converging several routes to one, electronic control, and rip out and rerouting with substantial salvage of existing

IRS REAR AXLE-300K-CONV-1 AX/PALLET

300000 units in Production Batch

Unused Resource Available Time Scale Factor 0.810

190.4 Days for 2.0 Shifts; 235 Days for 1.62 Shifts

Resources

	*	MAN	FXD	RBS	RBB	TRN
Avltime	*	24.2	29.7	27.9	27.9	31.2
Nsta	*	7.0	4.0	2.0	5.0	1.0
Wrkr	*	8.4	1.0	0.5	1.3	0.2
Vrate	*	0.0091	0.0033	0.0033	0.0033	0.0024
Esttime	*	41.43	18.33	22.50	23.00	5.00
Vrstlty	*	1.0	1.0	1.0	1.0	1.0

Synthesized System

Task	Resource used	Resource Cost	Variable Cost	Operation Time	Tool Change	Tool Number	Station Cost	
1	FXD- 1	0	10526	10.0	0.0	201	39982	
2	FXD- 2	0	15789	15.0	0.0	1202	53309	
3	RBS- 1	37069	27778	25.0	0.0	303	37069	
4	RBB- 1	74138	22222	20.0	0.0	404	37069	
5	MAN- 1	1066	51431	15.0	0.0	105	7996	
6	FXD- 3	0	21053	20.0	0.0	2206	133272	
7	MAN- 3	2132	137149	40.0	0.0	2107	2132	* 2
8	TRN- 1	0	3704	5.0	0.0	508	86758	

Apparent System Cost = $866534

Resource	Total Cost	Number used	Time used	Unit Cost Fixed	Unit Cost Variable	Number of Tasks	Number of Tools	Number of Workers
MAN	287624	3	28.1	0.044	0.914	2	2	3.61
FXD	326562	3	26.3	0.755	0.333	3	3	0.75
RBS	107471	1	33.3	0.247	0.111	1	1	0.25
RBB	144540	1	27.8	0.371	0.111	1	1	0.25
TRN	111202	1	10.1	0.289	0.081	1	1	0.20

108.00 Units per Hour
33.3 seconds Cycle Time Expected
90.00 % Bottleneck Station Up-time Expected
406080 units Production Capacity of this System
46.00 $/hr System Operating/Maintenance Rate

977400 Cost ($) to produce 300000 units, with Unit Cost ($) 3.258
1433000 ($) Total Investment required
908000 ($) for required Hardware

(b)

Fig. 16.18 *(Continued)*

equipment. Each has about the same top speed, and each can carry a pallet of four axles.

The cost structures of these types of transport are quite different. The cost of inverted monorails for axle assembly was estimated to be 90 to 95 percent in the conveyor rails themselves, based on a cost figure (1987 prices) given us by an experienced vendor ($600 to $800 per running foot). Vehicles are so inexpensive ($2000 for power-free and $5000 for self-powered ones) that doubling their number to support buffering would not seriously affect the system's final cost. Tracks appear to be modular and can be reused as long as they are not placed

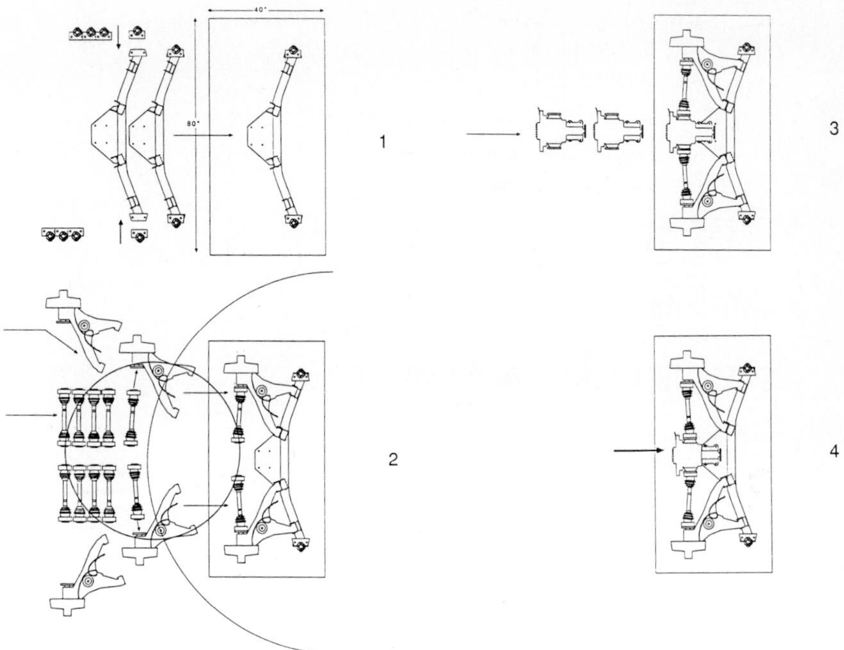

Fig. 16.19 Arrangement of assembly operations into four stations.

below the main floor level. Reuse would be especially easy if self-powered vehicles were used since there would be no drive chain to resize and restring.

On the other hand, the cost of an AGV system for axles would be dominated by the vehicles, at 70 percent, versus route-related costs of software, system integration, and guideway at about 25 percent (based on a 1987 estimate provided by another vendor, using the same floor plan as the conveyor vendor used). The vehicles could be reused if the route were changed, but the route costs would have to be paid again. A cost estimate of $79,000 per vehicle and $75 per foot of track was used. Figure 16.20 shows the scale floor layout used to estimate the number of vehicles and track length, based on the four-station scheme evolved using system synthesis.

On a cost basis, inverted monorails looked better even after a complete route change. AGVs have the advantage that they leave the factory floor clear. An inverted monorail could be set below the floor but this would substantially raise its cost as well as the cost of rerouting.

If AGVs were chosen, two issues would emerge: how to charge their batteries and how to dispatch them to pallets that need transport. AGVs originally found use in warehouses and flexible machining systems (FMSs). In both of these environments, the station times are

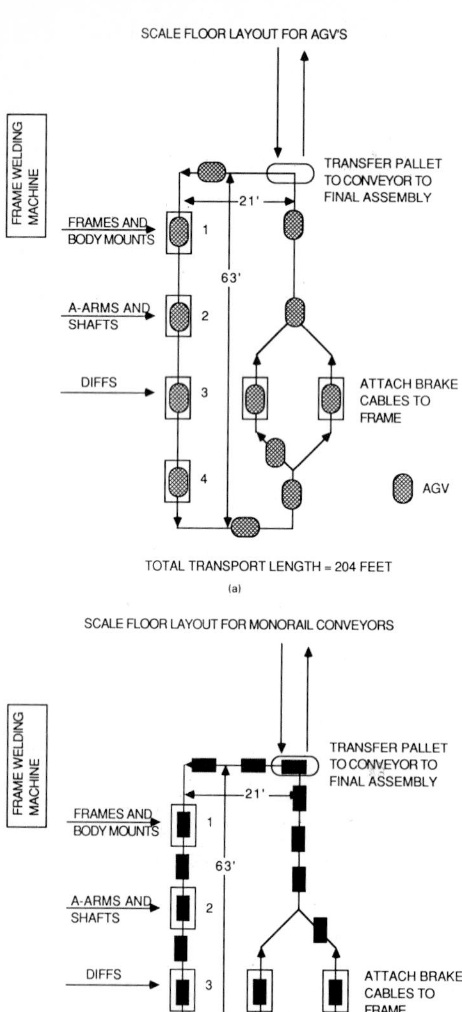

Fig. 16.20 Scale drawing of assembly system for transport analysis purposes. (*a*) Arrangement for 12 AGVs based on placing 1 AGV at each station and approximately equally spacing others along the rest of the track; (*b*) arrangement for 21 monorail conveyor vehicles based on placing 1 at each station, 1 between each assembly station, and equally spacing the rest. Total cost for AGVs = (\$79,000 × 12) + (\$75 × 204) = \$963,300. Total cost for monorail conveyors = (\$5000 × 21) + (\$750 × 204) = \$258,000. These costs were used for resource TRN in separate system syntheses.

long, sometimes an hour. Vehicles often have time to wait at one spot, where charging contacts could be located. This is called "opportunity charging" and permits AGVs to go many hours before a full charge is needed. Usually, however, even AGVs with opportunity charging will need a lengthy charge after 8 hr. In addition, charging usually takes longer than 8 hr, and a long cooling period is also needed. Thus multishift AGV operation presents several operational problems.

Long station times also permit the AGV to leave the pallet and go elsewhere and pick up another one. This is called the "taxi mode" of dispatching. Taxi mode is advantageous because fewer AGVs are needed, saving large amounts of money.

If station times are about the same length as or shorter than the time needed to travel from one station to another, fewer AGVs will be needed if AGVs are assigned to pallets; this is called "dedicated mode." Furthermore, if station times are short, there is not much time for opportunity charging.

Putting all this together, we found that short station times lead to two disadvantages for AGVs: lack of opportunity charging and need for more AGVs. If AGVs were selected, there would be an additional reason to use a parallel system structure, putting many jobs at one station and increasing station times. However, this option is not really available for these axles because of the low production volume and the small amount of work and bulky equipment needed to assemble them.

The alternative to charging is to change batteries. Extra batteries must be purchased, but they are relatively inexpensive and changing time is only about 5 min. This appears to be the way to solve the charging problem. Physical storage space would be needed for battery packs, and some people would be needed to manage changing, battery storage, and charging.

Simulations were performed to determine if the taxi mode could be used and to find out how many vehicles would be needed. Typically, taxi mode needs 8 percent fewer AGVs for a serial system (station times are short) and 35 percent fewer for the parallel systems we studied, compared to dedicated mode.

In the final analysis, because of the simple nature of this system and the economy of the serial arrangement, it was decided to use inverted monorails.

Floor layout

Floor layout is affected by the assembly sequence, serial or parallel structure of the system, size of pallets and equipment, safety zones, and the need to recirculate pallets, transport vehicles, and kit dunnage. If the taxi mode is used for AGVs, the efficiency of dispatching and the speed with which a vehicle can respond are increased if extra pathways are provided.

All the floor layouts we made were laid out in scale via CAD. Robot reach areas were taken from manufacturers' literature. Each layout avoided material transport pathways that cross. The scale models were used to determine travel times for AGVs and conveyors for use in the system synthesis analyses and dynamic simulations. Figure 16.20 shows a typical layout.

At the entry of the system is a transfer hoist. This hoist takes in axles from storage racks that buffer the output of the frame welding machines and puts them on a step conveyor. Along this conveyor is a station where body mounts are installed. Axles are then automatically loaded onto pallets.

The pallet goes through a series of stations that add the A-arms, half shafts, and differential and mate them all together. The pallet then is switched to one of two parallel manual stations where the brake cables are unwrapped from the A-arms and threaded through the frame. After this, the axles are transferred automatically to the transporter which takes them to the final car assembly. Empty pallets return to the beginning of the line.

If the system were parallel, the above pattern would be different in that a pallet would be directed to one of several parallel robot stations at the beginning of the line. The manual region at the end of the system would always be parallel.

This layout does not include kitting, which was finally ruled out by the awkward shapes of the parts and the increased pallet size needed to carry kits and provide assembly space.

Economic analysis

Economic analyses were carried out on several of the candidate assembly system designs to determine their rates of return. The current manual system was analyzed to obtain a reference variable assembly cost of $4.47 per axle. System synthesis was used for this analysis, using resources MAN and TRN conveyor and the same data as in Table 16.8.

Method

The economic analysis recognized three cost elements: labor, assembly system equipment, and transport system equipment. Each kind of equipment has allocated to it a purchase cost and an operating rate, and within the operating rate are some labor costs for supervision and maintenance. The cost of pallets is also included in equipment cost estimates. The rate of return is calculated by calculating a stream of savings in comparison to the current manual system and using those savings to pay back the equipment investment.

Labor cost is assumed to be $24 per hour, including fringe benefits. This is typical of the U.S. auto industry *circa* 1987. Current Internal

Revenue Service rules concerning tax rates and depreciation schedules are used (1986 law: 34 percent tax rate and 7-year MACRS).

Results

Table 16.10 shows the results of this analysis. The total investment of $1,433,000 is taken from Fig. 16.18. The savings stream is obtained as the difference between the manual baseline system's variable unit cost of $4.478 and the proposed automated system's variable unit cost of $1.55 multiplied by the annual volume of 300,000 for a first-year savings of $878,400. The analysis shows a rapid payback slightly under 2 years with an internal rate of return of nearly 43 percent. There is an adequate cushion in these results for errors in estimating costs

TABLE 16.10 Result of Cash Flow Analysis to Determine Rate of Return on Proposed Automated Assembly System

IRS REAR AXLE—300K—CONV—1 AX/PALLET

ZERO PRESENT WORTH CASH FLOW ANALYSIS 06-21-1988

7 YEARS OF ECONOMIC LIFE, SALVAGE VALUE 0 % OF COST

	EXPENSE FORECAST			INCOME FORECAST			
YEAR	RATIO	TAX RATE	DEPRECIABLE	SAVINGS	DEPRECIATION	TAX RATE	CREDIT
0	100.00%	34.0%	60.0%				
1				878.400	14.29%	34.0%	0.0%
2				922.320	24.49%	34.0%	
3				968.436	17.49%	34.0%	
4				1016.858	12.49%	34.0%	
4*				SALVAGE VALUE	31.24%		

TOTAL INVESTMENT = 1433.000

DEPRECIABLE INVESTMENT = 859.800

INTERNAL RATE OF RETURN = 42.93%

PRO-FORMA CASH FLOW

YEAR	INCOME	DEPRECIATION	TAXES	CREDITS	NET	DISC. NET
0	-1433.000	0.000	-194.888	0.000	-1238.112	-1238.112
1	878.400	122.828	256.894	0.000	621.506	434.823
2	922.320	210.563	241.997	0.000	680.323	333.004
3	968.436	150.402	278.131	0.000	690.304	236.398
4	1016.858	107.430	309.205	0.000	707.652	169.547
4*	268.576	0.000	0.000	0.000	268.576	64.348
INCOME TOTALS	4054.589	591.224	1086.228	0.000	2968.361	1238.120
NET TOTALS	2621.589	591.224	891.340	0.000	1730.249	0.008

NOMINAL CAPITAL RECOVERY = 772.746

PAYBACK IN APPROXIMATELY 1.91 YEARS

and times. In addition, the system as designed has a two-shift production capacity of over 400,000, allowing some excess for market growth.

Conclusions and recommendations

The study concluded that automation of axle assembly appeared feasible. Without redesign, some operations would remain manual, and for some operations involving brake cables it is possible that no redesign would ever make automation possible. The recommended systems were mixes of people, fixed automation, and tool changing robots.

Automation was also determined to be economically attractive, exceeding the minimum required 21 percent internal rate of return, based on cost estimates for robots, tools, fixed automation, transport systems, and engineering.

The client's original system assumed AGVs. We found that, on a cost basis, inverted monorail conveyors were clearly less expensive, even after including a complete rip out and rerouting (assuming AGVs, monorail vehicles, and most of the monorail track could be salvaged, and assuming that the monorails were placed on rather than below the floor).

Summary

These two case studies only scratch the surface, and space does not permit us to include more detail or other studies. Our experience, however, is that each problem contains unique elements within an overall frame that is similar to that of other problems. Thus each problem can be effectively attacked by the procedures illustrated in this chapter and described elsewhere in the book. The unique elements may involve materials, fastening, inspection, material handling, cleanliness, or other aspects of product function or manufacturing. Consultant-specialists are called in frequently. Altogether we find that the concurrent design paradigm is robust in practice and is able to improve the design and manufacture of many products.

Chapter 17
Summary

In this book we have tried to present the reader with several things:

- An appreciation for the complexity and intellectual challenges of manufacturing
- A systematic approach to addressing these challenges
- Acknowledgment of the gaps in that approach for which additional research and engineering are needed
- A sense for what has been achieved by some of the best practitioners and how they achieved it

One may identify two different emphases in manufacturing, which we might call "execution oriented" and "planning oriented." Execution orientation emphasizes technology, control, supervision, inspection of incoming parts, scheduling, sensors, feedback, and the like. Planning orientation, by contrast, emphasizes design, autonomy, simplicity, modularity, quality guarantees by vendors, worker involvement, and so on. Emphasis on execution implies an assumption that manufacturing is so complex that everything must be watched, surprises are everywhere, each task or situation is different, and planning is futile. Emphasis on planning implies an assumption that enough thought will reveal a simple way to do things that is inherently robust or can rely on underlying similarities and repeating patterns. Neither approach is sufficient by itself and neither assumption is totally true.

Nevertheless, many of the advances in manufacturing in recent years, such as just-in-time, modular shipbuilding, and design for assembly, fall into the planning category. While both planning and execution are required for manufacturing, the evidence portrayed in Fig. 1.1 indicates that an emphasis on planning will be highly rewarding.

For this reason, most of this book focuses on the planning aspects of manufacturing.

We showed that manufacturing is an essential link in a company's ability to analyze and fill a market need. The way a product is designed and made must fit the way it will be sold and used. Coordination of marketing, design, and production will become increasingly important as products become more complex, integrated, precise, and specialized to shifting market niches. Thus a central theme of the book is the importance of this coordination and the development of methods and analytical techniques for supporting it.

A review of the history of manufacturing indicated that the basic problems of design, manufacturing strategy, flexibility, efficiency, accuracy, technological change, and worker involvement have arisen and been addressed many times in the past and that past solutions have repeatedly been overturned by new technology, methods, materials, technical and economic analysis methods, and changing external conditions. Long-held assumptions about what is best, cheapest, most reliable or most likely to sell are regularly wiped out.

Assembly was shown to be a focal area of new manufacturing methods for several reasons. Assembly is the latest activity to be automated, and attempts to automate it have been full of surprises that revealed how little we knew about it as a process, as an institutional activity, and as an indicator for the behavior of the manufacturing enterprise as a whole. Its physics are inherently interesting and amenable to analysis, but beyond the physics lies a wide range of institutional issues it highlights. The inability of technology alone to automate what human assemblers do, including culling bad parts, dealing with lack of structure, and compensating for poor design, has reinforced and ratified the shift in emphasis toward planning and design in manufacturing.

Thus, beyond assembly as an interesting day-to-day manufacturing activity is the growing appreciation of assembly as an integrative factor in promoting concurrent design of products and processes. This appreciation is quite new and as yet concurrent design is only starting to gather the necessary design and decision support tools needed to make it a truly competitive force.

The focus of such design tools must be an array of processes that are well understood. This understanding is necessary regardless of whether the processes will be automated or not. Understanding provides the ability to predict behavior, and this is necessary for design. Perhaps, as in the case of rigid part mating, the understanding can be so complete that even high-precision assembly can become routine. On the other hand, understanding may be limited theoretically or economically to a statistical range of possible outcomes, as in welding. In this case, the premium is on experiment, robust designs, disciplined factory operations, and careful process monitoring.

We further considered assembly not just of isolated pairs of parts but of entire products or subassemblies. A good assembly sequence was shown to influence product design, part tolerances, manufacturing, quality control, factory floor layout, and assembly cost. For this reason, we emphasized the value of designing the assembly sequence as part of designing the product and described an algorithm for generating assembly sequences and choosing among them.

The design of assembly systems sharply focuses another main theme of the book, namely the need to integrate technical and economic decision making during the design process. System design consists of the wise choice among many competing alternatives. We emphasized economic bases for choice with the firm warning that all economically relevant issues must be considered. Reliance on past cost accounting methods that include only direct labor costs can be disastrously misleading. Data and theory for a new economic analysis technique have yet to emerge. In the meantime we must augment existing methods with good sense. This approach is no different than for other areas of manufacturing, such as system reliability or employee attitudes, where judgment is the dominant method and theory is weak or absent.

With the above reservations in mind, we showed how to make systematic choices of workstation and system design using computer synthesis and analysis tools. These tools are simple enough to use that they can be easily incorporated into early product design where the knowledge they provide can do the most good.

Finally, the techniques were illustrated with case studies from our own experience. While these focussed on automotive examples, we have applied the methods described in the book to over two dozen products in a wide range of industries, technologies, sizes, production volumes, and economic environments. While the emphasis is different in each case, the questions that must be answered remain remarkably similar:

- Is the product ready for manufacture? Are the processes understood?
- Do we understand the product's function so that we can make meaningful suggestions for simplification and redesign?
- Do we understand the structure of the costs for making the product so that we know the leverage points for improving the economics?
- Do we know the relationships between design intent, manufactur-

ing capability, and anticipated use so that the inevitable trade-offs can be resolved?

- Can the product be made and assembled for a reasonable cost with the desired levels of quality, flexibility, safety, and risk?

While a large part of the methods for answering these questions relies on information and techniques that are unique to the product or product family, another large portion appears to be generic and applicable to many kinds of products. The focus of this book is on those generic methods.

Index

ABOUT THE EDITORS AND AUTHORS

James L. Nevins, Daniel E. Whitney, Thomas L. De Fazio, Alexander C. Edsall, Richard E. Gustavson, and Richard W. Metzinger are on the staff of the Charles Stark Draper Laboratory. William A. Dvorak is on the staff of Ingersoll Engineers.